A HANDBOOK OF
HOSPITAL PSYCHIATRY

A Handbook of Hospital Psychiatry

A Practical Guide to Therapy

by Louis Linn, M.D.

Assistant Attending Psychiatrist
Mount Sinai Hospital, New York City

INTERNATIONAL UNIVERSITIES PRESS, INC.

New York   *New York*

To Miriam
for her courage and devotion

The difficult is that which can be done immediately; the impossible that which takes a little longer.

—*Santayana*

CONTENTS

ACKNOWLEDGMENTS . . . . **xv**

INTRODUCTION . . . . **xvii**

Part One—THE TREATMENT PROGRAM

I. *Individual Psychotherapy* **3**

Its place in the hospital (3). Formulating a case (4). Objectives or goals, supportive psychotherapy (5). Insight therapy (8). Transference and countertransference (9). Initial interviews (11). Taking notes (11). The art of listening (12). The role of dreams in psychotherapy (13). Psychotherapy and reality (14). The working-through process, the end of treatment (15). Case history (15). Research (22). Selected references (23).

II. *Group Psychotherapy* **24**

Its growth (24). The psychoanalytic theory of group formation (24). The special meaning of group life for the mentally ill (26). The group as a therapeutic instrument (26). Types of therapeutic group activities in mental hospitals (27). Supportive vs. insight therapy (28). Outpatient group psychotherapy with psychoneurotics (29). Group psychotherapy with hospitalized schizophrenics (32). Contraindications (35). Research (36). Selected references (36).

III. *Somatotherapy* **39**

Psychodynamics and physical methods of treatment (39). Convulsive therapy (41). Indications for ECT (41). Outpatient ECT (43). Curare-like agents (43). Intravenous barbiturates in ECT (43). Varieties of electrical stimuli (44). A.P.A. standards for ECT (44). Insulin coma therapy (ICT) (47). Technique of ICT (47). Complications of ICT (48). Modifications of ICT (49). Psychosurgery (49). The future of psychosurgery (51). Other somatic treatments (51). Theory of somatotherapy (52). The effect of somatotherapy on psychotherapy (58). Selected references (58).

IV. *Recreational Therapy* **60**

Regression in the service of the ego (60). Theory of play (60). Prescribing recreational therapy (62). Integrating recreational therapy into the total treatment program (63). A recreational program on every ward (64). The use of volunteers (65). Keeping records (65). Movies (66). Television (66). Dance (67). Bibliotherapy (68). Swimming (71). The beauty parlor and barber shop (72). Selected references (72).

V. *Occupational and Vocational Therapy* . . .   74

Theory of work (74). Work history (76). Place of vocational rehabilitation in the treatment plan (77). Occupational therapy: a bridge between recreation and work (78). Specific characteristics of O.T. (79). Functions of O.T. (80). Prescribing O.T. (81). O.T. on every ward (82). Keeping records (83). The transition to a genuine work program (83). Specific aptitudes vs. general employability: the role of motivation (84). Patients as employees (84). The transition to extramural work: governmental assistance (86). Vocational rehabilition services (86). The vocational counselor as therapist (87). The social worker and vocational rehabilition (88). Sheltered work situations (89). Role of industry and unions (90). Selected references (91).

VI. *Food as Therapy*   93

The role of early feeding experiences in emotional development (93). The psychopathology of eating (95). Food as therapy (96). The technique of feeding mental hospital patients (97). The dietitian as a member of the treatment team (99). Nutritional requirements (100). Selected references (101).

VII. *Special Ward Procedures*   102

The "release" effect of sodium amytal (102). Technique of eliciting the "release" effect (104). The sodium amytal test for organic brain disease (106). The face-hand test (107). The mecholyl prognostic test (109). Selected references (110).

Part Two—THE TREATMENT TEAM

VIII. *The Social Worker*   113

Definition (113). Intake (115). Reception (115). Taking a social service history (117). The period of active treatment (119). The preconvalescent period (121). Aftercare (122). Family care and sheltered homes (123). The economics of good social work (124). Research (125). The social worker and community relations (126). Qualifications (126). Training program (126). Selected references (127).

IX. *The Psychologist*   130

Psychological testing as an aid in planning treatment (130). Requesting psychological studies (130). Structured vs. unstructured test situations (132). Description of tests (133). Psychological testing by the psychiatrist (137).

Which patients should be tested? (139). The psychologist's report (139). Utilization of the report (140). Research (141). The psychologist as a therapist (141). Selected references (142).

X. *The Attendant*   143

The major dilemma (143). Recruiting new attendants (143). Screening candidates for training (144). What should be taught? (145). How should it be taught? (153). The role of anxiety in ward work (154). The role of transference in the attendant's relationship to the physician (154). Group therapy with attendants (155). Selected references (156).

XI. *The Nurse*   158

Duties of the mental hospital nurse (158). Requirements for psychiatric nursing (159). The shortage of psychiatric nurses (160). Federal funds for psychiatric nurses training (161). Toward a new program of education for psychiatric nursing (161). Relationship to the attendant (163). Selected references (163).

XII. *The Chaplain*   165

The psychology of religious feelings (165). Pastoral psychiatry in a mental hospital setting (166). A training program (167). Manifestations of anxiety in the chaplain (168). The separation between psychiatry and religion (169). The special power of religion (170). The importance of religious services (171). Work with individual patients (173). Other duties (173). Selected references (174).

XIII. *The Volunteer Worker*   175

His specific contributions (175). Varieties of volunteer activities (177). The hospital must want a volunteer program (178). The hospital's responsibilities to the volunteer worker (179). Initiating the program (180). Recruiting (180). Selection and screening (180). Training (183). Work on the wards (183). College students as volunteer workers (185). Selected references (185).

Part Three—THE PATIENTS

XIV. *The "Chronic" Patient*   189

The psychology of schizophrenia (189). The schizophrenic's needs and the realities of the hospital (190). The social psychology of deterioration (191). Practical aspects of treating the chronic schizophrenic (193). Psychotherapy with schizophrenics (196). Countertransference

(197). Somatotherapy (197). The results of treating
chronic schizophrenics (197). Chronic patients and research (199). Selected references (200).

XV. *The Aged and the Aging*   201

Statistics (201). The reasons for the problem (201). The
psychopathology of the "senile" disorders (203). Prevention (206). Treatment (207). A geriatric unit (208). Physical methods of treatment (209). Psychotherapy (211).
Extramural care (212). Research (213). Selected references (214).

XVI. *Children and Adolescents*   216

The emotional development of the child (216). Preventive psychiatry (220). Outpatient psychotherapy (222). Inpatient treatment (224). The intake problem (225). The
treatment program (226). Control of the disturbed child
(229). Preparation for discharge (229). The reformatory
(230). Juvenile narcotic addiction (230). Training for
child psychiatry (231). Research (232). Selected References (232).

XVII. *The Alcoholic*   235

Alcoholism as a disease (236). Acute alcoholic state (238).
Treatment of the immediate state (239). Long-term treatment (240). Alcoholics Anonymous (240). The conditioned aversion technique (241). Psychotherapy (244).
Miscellaneous considerations (245). Selected references
(247).

XVIII. *The Addict*   249

Definition (249). Popular misconceptions (249). Psychological factors (251). Tolerance and physical dependence
(253). The addicting drugs (253). The opiate abstinence
syndrome (255). Diagnosis of opiate addiction (255).
Treatment of the opiate abstinence syndrome (257). The
habituating drugs (259). Long-term treatment (260).
Selected references (261).

XIX. *The Mental Defective*   262

Definition (263). Diagnosis and classification (263). Somatic factors (266). Outpatient treatment (268). The role
of social service (271). Institutional care (272). Somatotherapy (273). Sterilization of mental defectives (273).
Prevention by other means (274). Training and research
(274). Medicolegal aspects (275). Selected references (275).

XX. *The Epilpetic*   278

What is epilepsy? (279). Classification (280). Diagnosis (282). Treatment (282). Some psychiatric aspects of treating epileptics (284). Institutional care (286). Epilepsy and other psychiatric disorders (287). Heredity (288). Medicolegal aspects (289). Selected references (290).

XXI. *The Pregnant Patient*   292

Psychological aspects of pregnancy (292). Therapeutic abortion on psychiatric grounds (294). Treatment of the pregnant patient in a mental hospital (296). Prevention of conception (297). Disposition of the baby (298). Selected references (299).

XXII. *The Veteran*   300

His rights (300). The value of the history of military service (302). How to obtain the military history (303). What to ask for (303). Outpatient facilities (304). Special problems in psychotherapy (304). Liaison between V.A. and other mental hospitals (305). The role of psychiatry in selective service (305). Selected references (306).

XXIII. *The Sex Deviate*   308

Dread of deviant sexuality (308). Theory of deviant sexuality (309). Clinical observations (310). Classification (312). Sociological classification (314). Examination (315). The integration of legal processes and medical science (317). Treatment (320). Selected references (321).

XXIV. *The Criminal*   323

Psychosis and criminal behavior (323). Sociological aspects (324). The problem of legal responsibility (324). Examination (328). Theory of criminal behavior (329). Psychotherapy (331). Parole (332). Criminal acts by patients on trial visit (333). Selected references (334).

XXV. *Caring for the Physically Ill*   336

Tuberculosis (337). The patients' infirmary (341). Other medical services (343). Accidents in mental hospitals (344). Physical illness and the patient's family (345). Notifying the coroner (345). Selected references (346).

Part Four—THE HOSPITAL

XXVI. *Architecture as Therapy*   349

Security vs. therapy (349). Location (350). Size (351). Relation to treatment program (352). Building arrangement (356). Total medical care (356). Aesthetic considerations (357). Training and research (357). Miscellaneous considerations (357). Selected references (358).

XXVII. *Administrative Psychiatry* 359
Definition (359). Group psychotherapy as an administrative technique (361). Basic principles of administration (362). The clinical staff conference (363). The hospital administrator and his relationship with patients (365). The administrator in the research and training program (370). The lay board (371). The medical executive committee (372). Public relations (372). The budget (372). Training in administrative psychiatry (373). Research (374). Selected references (374).

XXVIII. *Statistical Problems in Psychiatry* 376
The importance of statistics (376). Mental hospitals are "big business" (377). Asking the right questions (378). Special difficulties in mental hospital statistics (380). The new nomenclature (382). A simple reporting system (384). Outpatient psychiatric clinics (387). Compiling the data (387). Selected references (387).

XXIX. *Educating the Staff* 389
Background for psychiatric training (390). Board certification (391). Psychological problems of a psychiatric residency (398). Psychoanalysis and psychiatric training (399). Training for the senior staff (400). Lectures vs. seminars (402). The use of motion pictures (402). Additional areas for study (402). Teaching the rest of the staff (403). Administrative aspects of the training program (403). Training opportunities under the national mental health act (404). Training grants to institutions (404). Traineeships (405). Who is eligible? (405). Specific requirements and traineeship levels (405). How traineeships are administered (407). Responsibilities of traineeship recipients (407). Training under the Grants-to-States program (408). Selected references (408).

XXX. *Research* 410
Who can do research? (410). Special difficulties of psychiatric research (411). What projects are important? (413). Research opportunities under the National Mental Health Act (414). Research grants (415). Research fellowships (417). Selected references (418).

XXXI. *Forensic Psychiatry* 420
Mental illness and loss of personal liberty (420). Commitment proceedings (422). The patient and legal transactions (423). The psychiatrist as witness (424). Mail (425). Writ of habeas corpus (425). Insanity as a basis for divorce (426). Personal injury as a cause of mental illness (426). Malpractice suit (426). Competence of a witness

(427). Credibility of testimony (428). Medicolegal problems in psychosurgery (429). Privileged communications (429). Selected references (430).

XXXII. *Utilizing the Hospital Laboratory*   432
Needs vs. available facilities (432). Pathology (432). Electrocardiography (436). X-ray (437). Electroencephalography (437). Selected references (440).

XXXIII. *A Psychiatric Service in a General Hospital* . .   441
Hospitalization: therapy or trauma (441). A general hospital should include psychiatry (441). The advantages of a psychiatric service in a general hospital (443). The organization of a psychiatric department in a general hospital (447). Selected references (449).

Part Five—THE COMMUNITY

XXXIV. *The Relatives of Patients*   453
The hostile psychiatrist (453). The patient and his family: a unit (453). Families have anxieties (454). Families have guilt feelings (455). Psychological defenses employed by families (455). The psychological defenses of the physician (455). Relations with the average family (456). Do's and don't's for families (457). A positive program for families (458). Treatment of the "hostile" family (460). Selected references (461).

XXXV. *Outpatient Care*   463
Its importance (463). The National Mental Health Act and other sources of funds (464). Organizing a clinic (465). Referral of patients (467). Fees (467). Children and adolescents (467). Night clinics (468). Traveling clinics (468). The aftercare clinic (469). The day hospital (472). The Netherlands' plan (475). Outpatient electroconvulsive therapy (476). Statistical problems (477). Selected references (482).

XXXVI. *Family Care*   484
Its role (484). The Gheel colony (484). The growth of family care elsewhere (486). Types of family care (486). Selection of foster families (487). Instructions to foster families (488). Therapeutic advantages (489). Results (490). Patient returns from foster families (490). Popular misconceptions (491). The transition to unsupervised care (492). Selected references (492).

XXXVII. *Educating the Public*   493
The mechanism of denial (493). What should be taught? (494). Who should be taught? (495). Who should teach?

(496). How should the educational program be conducted? (497). The National Association for Mental
Health (500). The National Mental Health Act (503). A
visitors' check list (506). Selected references (506).

XXXVIII. *The Mental Hospital and Civil Emergencies* .   .   508
Are psychiatric casualties inevitable? (508). General prophylactic principles (508). The role of motivation (509).
Specific prophylactic principles (509). The emotional
needs of children during civil emergencies (510). The
initial reaction to disaster (511). Pathological reaction
types (511). Prevention (512). Treatment (513). Countertransference (514). Administrative aspects of disaster control (514). The mental hospital in civil emergencies (514).
Selected references (514).

                              APPENDICES

A. *Preliminary Psychiatric Formulation*   519

B. *Reading Materials Used in Group Bibliotherapy Program*   520

C. *Characterologic Inventory—A Check List*   525

D. *A Home Training Program for Retarded Children*   .   .   527

E. *Classification of Mental Disorders*   531

INDEX   543

ACKNOWLEDGMENTS

It is a pleasure for me to express a debt of gratitude to Dr. Newton Bigelow, former Commissioner of the Department of Mental Hygiene of the State of New York. The seminars out of which much of this book developed were held under his auspices. Special thanks are due to my chief, Dr. M. Ralph Kaufman, Director of Psychiatry of the Mount Sinai Hospital in New York, for his guidance and encouragement, to Dr. Israel S. Wechsler for his psychiatric and literary advice, and to my wife for the major editorial responsibility which she assumed in preparing the manuscript.

So many have generously put valuable information at my disposal that it is almost invidious to single out only a few for thanks: Mrs. Alice Adler, Dr. Herbert Bernstein, Miss Grace Caley, Dr. Hiland L. Flowers, Dr. Paul Haun, Mrs. Eva R. Hawkins and Mrs. Nancy Wilson Levy, of the National Health Library, Dr. Robert L. Kahn, Miss Lena V. Ovesen, Mr. Robert Rossberg, Dr. Paul H. Brauer, Dr. Aaron Stein, Dr. Leo A. Spiegel, Mrs. Ruth Schwarz, Dr. E. Gordon Yudashkin, Dr. Mortimer Ostow, Miss Louise Hamilton, Mr. Edward Linzer, Mr. Paul Harris, Mr. Harry Milt.

I want to thank the following publishers and organizations for permission to quote from their publications: The American Medical Association for permission to reprint material from the *Diagnostic and Statistical Manual: Mental Disorders;* the American Psychiatric Association for permission to quote from the *Proceedings of the Mental Hospital Institutes* and *Psychiatry and Medical Education;* Florence Boochever, Editor of *The Bookmark,* New York State Library, for permission to reprint the list of reading materials by R. C. Chaney and G. A. Ingalls used in the group bibliotherapy program of the Northport V.A. Hospital; Drs. M. J. Giannini and L. B. Slobody of the Pediatrics Department of the New York Medical College and Dr. C. D. May, Editor of *Pediatrics,* for permission to reprint the *Home Training Program for Retarded Children;* The National Association for Mental Health for permission to quote from their many valuable publications, with special thanks to Mrs. Marjorie Frank and Mr. Jack Neher; the New York State Department of

Mental Hygiene State Hospitals Press for permission to quote from H. M. Pollock's *Family Care;* W. W. Norton for permission to quote from W. A. Bryan's *Administrative Psychiatry;* M. S. Stewart, Editor of public affairs pamphlets for permission to quote from Katherine Doyle's pamphlet *When Mental Illness Strikes.*

Finally, I wish to express appreciation to my good friend, Leo W. Schwarz, for his invaluable assistance.

L. LINN

New York City
January, 1955

INTRODUCTION

In recent years I conducted a series of psychiatric seminars at various state hospitals under the auspices of the New York State Department of Mental Hygiene.[1] This experience awakened memories of my own career as a resident physician at the State Hospital in Trenton, New Jersey, fifteen years earlier, and as an officer in charge of psychiatric wards in the Medical Corps of the Army of the United States in World War II. The magnitude of the medical and social problems posed by patients in mental hospitals refocused my attention on the numerous professional responsibilities of the whole hospital staff, especially the psychiatrist. In addition to knowing how to diagnose and treat the most difficult of all mental disorders, the psychiatrist must be prepared to inaugurate a group therapy program in the hospital, pass upon the mental capacity of an individual to stand trial for a crime, manage an outpatient clinic for adults and another one for children, administer specific treatment to paretics, alcoholics or severe epileptics, address parent-teacher associations, establish a working relationship with local Alcoholics Anonymous chapters, deal with emotionally upset or at times paranoid relatives, or representatives of the press, advise a chaplain on his role in the treatment program, or deal with special problems of war veterans. There are a host of other problems, and one need merely allude to the medical, surgical and laboratory procedures requiring daily attention. What impressed me, too, was the paradox that the most complicated of all psychiatric tasks and the greatest responsibilities are often placed on the shoulders of the physician who has only recently entered the field of psychiatry, and is as yet unprepared for the burdens he is to carry. The original intention of the book was to meet his needs, but it soon became apparent that a great many others could profit from it.

While it is something of a commonplace to speak of the medical staff of a mental hospital as a "treatment team," the term has become a cliché in many quarters. That the ideal of co-ordinated effort is not

[1] Participating with me in these seminars were Paul Goolker, M.D., Fred Brown, Ph.D., and Robert L. Kahn, Ph.D. of the Mount Sinai Hospital in New York City.

always achieved does not alter the fact that the attendant, the social worker, the psychologist, the nurse, the chaplain, the volunteer worker, the recreational and occupational therapist, the dietitian, the architect, the foster families, and the outpatient services are all involved in the common goal of returning the mentally disordered patient to society. Although the primary responsibility for organizing these separate activities devolves upon the psychiatrist, each individual member of the team will do a better job if he knows his task and how he fits into the total treatment program.

The family doctor is often the first person to whom a patient or his family turns when psychological problems arise and defenses begin to crumble. Upon him rests the primary responsibility for meeting the psychiatric problems and for placing a patient in competent psychiatric hands or even having him admitted to the nearest mental hospital. If the family physician is informed of the hospital treatment program he may be more prompt in placing the patient where urgently needed therapy is available, and perhaps forestall a preventable suicide or early deterioration. In addition, he will be in a better position to act as guide or consultant to the family. It is hoped that the information contained in this book will increase his appreciation of the importance of his own continued interest in the patient after admission to the hospital and his participation in the aftercare upon return to the community.

The minister, too, may have to be consulted. His understanding of the mental hospital will make him a better guide and counselor for those who seek his help because of mental illness in the family. He will be better prepared to extend his spiritual comfort to the patient in the hospital in the form of letters and occasional visits, and to help mobilize the patient's inner resources to their fullest extent when he is returned to the community. Lawyers are sometimes consulted by paranoid persons to institute litigations which are based on delusions. As a respected adviser, the lawyer's understanding of the mental hospital may play a useful and sometimes crucial role in the matter of hospitalization.

Mental health is or should be the concern of everyone. There are comparatively few families today who have not had some member treated or hospitalized for mental illness. This book may help some of them to play a more constructive role in the rehabilitation of a loved one. Others may be inspired to lend their help in whatever way they can to improve the lot of the hospitalized mentally ill.

I began with the assumption that the physician to whom this book is addressed has been exposed to a regular program of medical school psychiatry and that he has learned the classification of mental illness and the elements of dynamic psychiatry. I attempted to identify myself with the new mental hospital psychiatrist or resident and the other members of the treatment team, and to face with them the many special situations that will confront them early in their mental hospital careers. The plan is to provide them with the basic information for each of those situations and to provide them with at least a working knowledge of the subject. This book aims in the main to furnish practical answers to many of the questions which arise in mental hospital work.

But while the aim of the book is practical, the emphasis throughout is on the relationship of theory to practice. In addition, the material is organized about the conception of the mental hospital as a "Therapeutic Community." Viewed against this double background the work of the mental hospital psychiatrist can become inspiring. The sickest of all mental patients, it seems to me, hold the clue to the future of psychiatry. The major psychiatric syndromes represent extreme and often seemingly final forms of emotional maladaptation. By studying them in the mental hospital one may learn much about the general problem of emotional adaptation in health and disease. From the lessons which these patients can teach us we may learn how to help them more effectively and how to prevent others from breaking under strain.

Each year the roster of the American Psychiatric Association is swelled by hundreds of new members. At the same time the number of hospitalized mental patients grows at a rate which unfortunately makes the available corps of psychiatrists inadequate. Since the likelihood of closing this gap in the foreseeable future is not great, it would appear that any therapeutic program which is based primarily on getting an increased number of psychiatrists to do more of what is already being done is not likely to succeed. What is urgently called for is a fresh approach, a different conception of the utilization of trained personnel and institutional resources, and a change in therapeutic concepts. The new point of view is to be found in what Maxwell Jones, the distinguished British psychiatrist, has called the "Therapeutic Community." One is sometimes tempted to think of treatment as that which takes place during the fraction of a second when a current flows from an electroshock apparatus or during the somewhat longer time involved in other therapies. During the longer intervals the patient is regarded as being "between" treatments. In the therapeutic community the whole of the time which the patient spends in the hospital is thought of as treatment time and everything that happens to the patient is, or should be, so regarded. Thus, the therapeutic community is to be found ultimately in an attitude which endeavors to integrate every detail of mental hospital life into a continuous program of treatment. Viewed thus, the appearance of the grounds, the structure of the buildings, the arrangement of the wards, the decorations on the walls, the way the food is served, are all part of a program. All personnel from the guard at the outer gate to the medical administrator in the main office are part of the program. All activities, recreational and occupational, are organized with regard to maximal therapeutic effectiveness. The relationship between patients is part of the plan. The emotional problems which arise among personnel are important factors in the therapeutic community. In addition to psychological factors, physiological and other organic factors obviously occupy a place of importance.

The psychiatrist plays a special role in the therapeutic community. His is the task of organizing and unifying the different activities of the treatment team. This requires that he have a clear conception of the contribution to the therapeutic community which each worker is capable of making. He will have to instruct each worker concerning the common therapeutic goals as well as the individual needs of patients. A major task will center about the most effective utilization of the psychiatrist's own time. This will involve the organization of a training program that includes all the members of the treatment team so as to make it possible for him to delegate authority to people who are fairly well grounded in theory and practice. The all-pervasive nature of his responsibilities makes it difficult to detail the psychiatrist's role in brief. In a fundamental sense, every chapter is about him and, therefore, no single chapter is devoted to him. However, special aspects of his training are taken up in Chapter XXIX.

The therapeutic community and the community outside of the mental hospital constitute a continuum. The emotional conflict which the patient was unable to resolve initially took place in the community proper, in contact with family, friends, workers and all else that men live by. It is in this setting, too, that he must resume his life when hospital treatment is terminated. Treatment taking place in the hospital may be regarded as an emergency measure which is called into play as a last resort, when all therapeutic resources in the community have been exhausted; and it is brought to a close as soon as the patient can be returned to the community for further care. In this sense the most important phase of treatment is that which takes place outside the hospital. Thus, outpatient treatment facilities are regarded as vital adjuncts of the mental hospital. A realistic treatment program, then, takes into account the environment to which the hospitalized patient will return. This calls for close liaison with the patient's family, foster home placement facilities, and utilization of all available community resources for living arrangements as well as for social and vocational rehabilitation.

If one can speak comparatively concerning the importance of scientific theory, it may be said that the need for theoretical orientation is particularly great in psychiatry where so much remains to be learned and where mankind's practical needs are so urgent. Even though lip service is generally paid to the proposition that there can be no scientific medical practice without scientific theory, in practice this is not always adhered to. Modern psychiatric theory does not always satisfy the needs of mental hospital psychiatrists. Often the theoretical formulations that one reads have no obvious applicability to the day-to-day mental hospital work. At times they are incomprehensible because couched in obscure terminology. In some instances the psychiatrist may fail to give a theory a fair hearing because of emotional bias. As a result the mental hospital psychiatrist is more apt to apply procedures empirically, perhaps even uncritically, and is less likely to relate his clinical experiences within a theoretical frame of reference. It is axiomatic that gross neglect of theory is a factor which retards progress in mental hospital psychiatry as it does in other fields of medicine.

The particular theory that the psychiatrist uses may be second in importance to the imperative that he employ some theory. What is important is that he know his theory well, apply it consistently in his work on the wards, and that he have the intellectual and emotional resources to modify or abandon his theory when it is not supported by the facts. For example, a psychiatrist treating a patient with a postpartum psychosis may theorize that the psychosis is due to an endocrine imbalance. If so, he will collect evidence of that imbalance, seek to define the details of that chemical imbalance as precisely as he can, and to correct it by hormones that are rationally selected on the basis of his findings. Then he must evaluate his results with proper regard for the use of controls. Finally, he must re-evaluate his theory on the basis of this experience and accordingly modify his treatment of similar cases. Or he may theorize that the psychosis is due entirely to psychological factors. If so, he will proceed in exactly the same way. That is to say, he will formulate and document the specific constellation of emotional problems to which the patient was unable to adapt and to alter it by appropriate means. Again, he must evaluate his results with proper regard for the use of controls. Thus, in two such widely divergent theoretical approaches to a given problem, the scientific method is equally applicable.

Without ignoring other important theoretical approaches I shall, in the main, utilize the psychoanalytic theory of human behavior and thought. Admittedly this theory like any other has certain limitations, but in my opinion psychoanalytic theory provides at present the frame of reference which appears to me most useful in describing the therapeutic community and in planning its program. Various aspects of the theory will be taken up as they are relevant to topics under discussion.

While I have tried to bring together the best current knowledge about mental hospital psychiatry, I cannot claim completeness. Our understanding of mental illness continues to deepen with the acquisition of new knowledge and experience. We are, in a real sense, at the very threshold of our understanding of psychopathology and psychiatric treatment. Completeness will only come with time and application. The idea behind this book is that medical science and psychiatry can provide sound treatment to the hospitalized mentally ill and restore many to health. It is, I believe, a hopeful and, in one sense, a cheerful book.

Part One

THE TREATMENT PROGRAM

Chapter I

INDIVIDUAL PSYCHOTHERAPY

Its Place in the Hospital

To a man struggling with a case load of many hundreds, discussions about intensive psychotherapy with individual patients must seem irrelevant. Pious advice concerning the value of psychoanalysis in the treatment of the psychoses must seem to him as unrealistic from a practical point of view as the delusions he is trying to treat. This frustrating dichotomy between the realities of the analytic method on the one hand, and the realities of state hospital psychiatry on the other, must generate much of the anti-analytic feeling which is encountered so often in state hospitals. And yet, granting this dichotomy and the indubitable impracticalities of the psychoanalytic method within the state hospital system, let us beware lest we throw out the baby with the bath. Psychoanalysis provides what I believe is the most effective theoretical frame of reference for understanding the meaning of the symptoms of mental illness, for bringing law and order into an otherwise chaotic situation. Psychoanalytic insights have made it possible to translate into meaningful human terms what was previously the incoherent gibberish of the insane. By thus translating the words and actions of the mentally ill, we have come upon the core of humanity which continues to exist within each patient, no matter how disturbed he may be. It becomes vouchsafed to us to understand his fears and longings. Armed with such understanding, we are in better position to allay some of his fears and more effectively meet his other needs. It becomes possible for the psychiatrist to increase his effectiveness in every phase of his hospital work—in his group therapy, in his supervision of the work of the nurses and attendants, and in organizing the various activity programs within the hospital. This is the justification for spending so much time with one or two patients when the psychiatrist counts his case load in the many hundreds.

3

Formulating a Case

When a therapist approaches a patient from a dynamic, developmental point of view, the questions he asks himself are these: What was the patient striving for when he became ill? What were the conscious aspirations that characteristically dominated his life, and what were the contemporary realities that frustrated them? In short, we want to know when precisely did his illness begin and what combination of circumstances elicited his maladaptive pattern of behavior. Has he suffered the loss of a loved one, financial reverses or physical illness? Has he undergone some important change of status such as becoming a parent, or receiving a promotion in his work? Such information calls for a careful history from the patient as well as his family. The latter information is usually obtained with the help of the social worker. Sometimes there may seem to be no precipitating factor of sufficient magnitude to account for the onset of the illness. In some cases the explanation of the patient's disturbance is to be found in the unconscious meanings with which he has invested seemingly minor details of his contemporary world. In all events the conscious aspirations of the patient are always mingled with longings from his early childhood which, although long since forgotten (or "repressed," as this forgetting process is designated psychoanalytically), continue to influence his adult thoughts and actions. Unconscious components in his adult thinking are deduced as tentative hypotheses from a detailed consideration of the patient's life history. The latter is best obtained by following a standard outline. Psychological tests are particularly valuable in providing insights concerning the unconscious meanings in the patient's clinical picture. Our understanding of the patient's longings should include not only those which we know as historical facts concerning his conscious life but also those which we deduce tentatively concerning persistent infantile aspirations (which we refer to as his unconscious wishes). Similarly our understanding of his contemporary external world includes not only the facts as they are apparent to objective observers but also the unconscious meanings with which he seems to have invested some of these facts. Armed with these data, it becomes possible to draw up a hypothesis concerning the nature of the patient's problem. This hypothesis is called the "tentative formulation of the case" (see Appendix A). If this hypothesis is valid it should be possible to demonstrate similar combinations of circumstances in his past which resulted in corresponding patterns of maladaptive behavior. And finally, it should be possible to trace back to the primordial circumstances in early childhood which started the maladaptive pattern in the first place. Within this formulation will be recognized certain misconceptions that the patient has about himself and his environment, misconceptions that represent a continuation of infantile attitudes into adult life.

All analytically oriented psychotherapy begins with this preliminary formulation. As the patient talks, the psychiatrist listens with this preliminary hypothesis in mind. If the patient's productions fit in, they lend, naturally, to the credibility of the hypothesis. The psychiatrist endeavors to predict what the patient's reactions will be in various situations as he first discusses them. If he errs, he makes the necessary corrections in his formulation. The relationship is a reciprocal one. The formulation helps to increase the patient's self-understanding; increased understanding of the patient helps to improve the formulation. The understanding of each grows side by side.

Objectives or Goals of Treatment: Supportive Psychotherapy

Ideally, psychoanalytically oriented psychotherapy endeavors to make the patient conscious of his unconsciously rooted misconceptions and, through a process of re-education in a setting which places a premium on reality testing, seeks to correct them. However, it is not always feasible to achieve this ideal, because of practical and material considerations. In other instances it is not possible or even desirable to make the patient conscious of his unconscious wishes because of purely clinical considerations. Sometimes it is not practical to strive for a basic reorganization of the patient's character in the previously mentioned process of re-education. In fact, complete restitution to an ideal "normal" is rarely possible in psychotherapy. In many instances it is necessary to view the patient as a person with a permanent emotional disability for whom a modestly circumscribed level is all that can be hoped for.

Many psychiatric clinics become "cluttered up" with chronic complainers, hypochondriacal patients, who parade an endless series of symptoms for which no physical reason can be found. Often we alternate between spending more and more hospital money on fruitlessly repeated laboratory studies on the one hand and railing against them punitively on the other. In a recent study at the Mount Sinai Hospital in New York City, Victor Rosen and his co-workers confirmed the fact that this hypochondriacal reaction represents a form of adaptation which in many instances is the best that can be hoped for. If this mode of adaptation is undermined, a potentially malignant psychotic reaction may emerge, which is an infinitely less effective form of adaptation. In the content of the psychosis which emerges under such circumstances, the analytically

oriented psychiatrist can recognize deeply rooted passive dependent attitudes often associated with unconscious homosexual wishes. No attempt
is made to impart these insights to the patient. To do so would be ineffectual at the very least and, potentially, harmful. Instead, the psychiatrist accepts the patient's emotional disability in the same way that an
internist accepts another patient's cardiac weakness. He helps to stabilize
him as comfortably as he can within his hypochondriacal framework. He
sees him briefly at long intervals; he gives him placebo medication; he
assures the patient that he can consult him at other times if his anxieties
get out of hand. If it is a male patient who has chosen to remain at home
to do the housework while his wife goes out to work, he is not reproached
for this since it represents for him a tolerable outlet for his feminine
longings. To deprive him of this is to make him liable to a more
malignant psychiatric disturbance.

The problem of the objective of therapy is related to the important
question as to what constitutes "cure" or "improvement." The mere fact
that a patient is not well is not an adequate reason for keeping him in an
institution. If he is able to adjust in a protected environment on the
outside, it may be the better part of wisdom to let him live there with
his delusions and hallucinations.

A forty-year-old married woman with a lifelong history of hypochondriasis was hospitalized for an involutional psychosis characterized
by agitated depression and paranoid delusions which developed gradually
over three or four months prior to admission. The precipitating factor
seemed to be the marriage of her only child, a son. An extremely tense
and unhappy marital relationship which had been maintained precariously over a period of years as a result of her devotion to her child became
intolerable to her thereafter. She developed the delusion that her husband was poisoning her. Sexual relationships which had been infrequent
up to this time because of her hypochondriacal complaints ceased entirely. A point of interest is the fact that she had a postpartum psychosis,
following the birth of this son twenty-five years earlier. Although less
severe, that illness too was characterized by agitated depression and paranoid delusions. Thus, what was called an involutional psychosis was
really to be considered the recurrence of a postpartum psychosis. This is
not a rare sequence of events—a postpartum psychosis, a one-child marriage based on a fear of subsequent pregnancies, with frigidity and infrequent sexual relations, a rejection of the child during the psychosis
followed by an overintense attachment to the child when the psychosis
subsides, and finally a recurrence of psychosis when the child grows up
and leaves home.

This patient remained psychotic for several years. During long intervals she was kept in seclusion because she was assaultive and denuded
herself. Then, unaccountably, she improved. She became quiet, orderly
and co-operative and very quickly thereafter was sent out on a trial visit.

She refused to return to her husband, blaming him for all her misfortunes. She worked as a housekeeper for years, carrying out her responsibilities with superb efficiency. She had a small group of acquaintances with whom she maintained a rather superficial social life. She visited quite frequently with her son. She maintained this adjustment in the community for many years. No one in the community regarded her behavior as abnormal in any way—no one, that is, except her psychiatrist who saw her from time to time and was able to confirm the fact that the delusional system concerning her husband remained as intense as on the day she entered the hospital. What factors produced the change in the hospital are not known. She was discharged from the hospital as "cured" because she succeeded in giving the correct answers to the staff of doctors who "paroled" her. What if she had admitted to the continued existence of her delusions? She might have remained hospitalized to this day. This patient, with intuitive wisdom, changed her environment, reorganized her way of life and has supported herself in the community for many years with satisfactions she would never have had as a patient in the hospital.

Here there was certainly no question of attempting to make the patient conscious of her unconscious wishes. There was reason to conclude, for example, that she had an unconscious homosexual attachment to her mother which she was able to sublimate in an acceptable manner in her relationship with the woman for whom she worked as a housekeeper and that it was this unconscious attitude which blighted her relationship with her husband and contributed to her paranoid delusion concerning him. However, knowing these facts made it possible for the psychiatrist to encourage her to hold fast to this limited solution of her problem in spite of proddings by well-meaning relatives and friends to return to her husband.

Therapy which does not seek to make the patient conscious of his unconscious motivations nor to make basic alteration in his character is referred to as supportive therapy. The foregoing examples point up the fact that a psychoanalytic understanding of the patient's problems can be invaluable even in the superficial approach to their solution. An elderly patient's infantile wish to be fed by a kindly mother may be adequately gratified by a mild tonic prescribed on the occasion of a brief consultation once a month. To tell the patient that he needs no medication is to fail to provide urgently needed emotional support, and as a result more serious psychiatric changes may ensue.

A patient who is hostile and offensive in his manner may be warding off a potentially suicidal depression. Permitting him to express this sarcasm or anger, without danger of retaliation may be a lifesaving measure for him. Another patient in a deep depression may reproach himself ceaselessly for one shortcoming or another. Such a guilt-ridden patient may crave and require more than anything a stern punitive attitude from the therapist, rather than the reassuring and comforting behavior which common sense would seem to dictate.

In all of these instances analytic insights are a guide to therapy even though no attempt is made to bring them into the patient's conscious awareness.

Insight Therapy

When we make a patient conscious of his unconscious wishes and seek to modify his attitude toward them, we are employing insight therapy. In psychoanalysis as the term is properly used this occupies the full extent of the therapist's efforts. Analytically oriented psychotherapy on the other hand is usually a mixture of supportive therapy and insight therapy.

A catatonic schizophrenic girl (in remission) came to a clinic over a period of years. Each week she would rail against her psychiatrist with fearfully sharp invective. She would accuse him of being an ignoramus, a swindler, or both. Each time she paid her fee, which was a very modest one, she would ask how the clinic had the heart to take money from a hard-working girl and give her nothing in return. Each week, too, she would ask meticulously for a written receipt. In spite of these complaints she kept her appointment religiously. No weather was too inclement to keep her away.

The plan up to this point had been to let her vent her rage in a permissive atmosphere and to provide her with a secondary "home" that she could visit to relieve her of her lonely existence in a women's residence. One day, in a maneuver calculated to promote reality testing, her psychiatrist said to her, "Since you are so dissatisfied with me, why don't you let me send you to a different doctor?" She stared for a moment in bewildered disbelief, then burst into tears and wailed that he was "the same as all the rest of them." On inquiry, "the rest of them" turned out to be her brothers and her "no good father." For the first time she ventilated her dissatisfactions with them and it became possible to show her that her disappointment in her psychiatrist was really an expression of her disappointment in them. The ways in which she had been disappointed by them both in reality and in her fantasies were explored. One day shortly before Christmas she described a dream which she had had on the previous night. In the dream she was walking in a beautiful starlit night. Suddenly a rain of lovely little dolls came floating down on her from heaven. She ran delightedly from one to another trying to catch them. In her discussion of the dream she recalled her unhappy childhood, how rarely she had received loving attention from her father let alone actual presents. He was an alcoholic and a ne'er-do-well. She spoke of her frustration in connection with the clinic, that she wanted some concrete evidence of the doctor's interest in her welfare and that the written receipt which she clutched in her hand when she left after each visit seemed a kind of present which she had wrung from the doctor.

Slowly it became possible for her to differentiate her psychiatrist from other members of her family and her realistic wishes from those which were obviously unattainable. In a slow process of re-education, she was able to change in a healthier direction her attitude toward her doctor and toward many other people in her environment.

In her visits to the clinic she sought to gratify frustrated wishes from her childhood. In that sense it was inevitable that she should feel so deeply disappointed in her therapist since he could never make up to her that which she was denied as a little child. Nevertheless, her attachment to the therapist had positive and deeply emotional aspects which also mirrored her childhood feelings toward her father. When she achieved a more realistic attitude toward her psychiatrist, she became less insistently demanding. Along with this came a willingness to seek her fulfillments in more realistic social relationships, so that she began going out on dates again after six years of seclusiveness. However, following any disappointment or frustration she would tend to resume her previously querulous behavior pattern. During such acute periods of distress the psychiatrist would permit her to vent her rage on him. Awareness of the unconscious determinants of this patient's behavior made it possible to understand her changing clinical picture and to intervene appropriately in her behalf.

Transference and Countertransference

The unconscious tendency of the patient to regard the psychiatrist as if he were a figure from childhood, rather than in terms of contemporary reality, is called *transference*. The phenomenon of transference is a powerful tool in psychotherapy and it develops inevitably in every therapeutic relationship. The psychiatrist may wish at times to use it in his influence on the patient through reassurance, suggestion, guidance, that is to say, supportively. In other therapeutic situations he may prefer to point out the unrealities in the patient's behavior, and to relate these unrealities to their origins in childhood experiences, in this way to help the patient give up his nonadaptive rigid reactions based on "ancient history," and finally to help him substitute in their place more flexibly adaptive reactions based on contemporary realities.

The foregoing case history exemplifies transference phenomena quite well. The patient's attitude toward the psychiatrist was based not on the contemporary realities of the clinic experience but on childhood disappointments in her relationship with her father. By making her conscious of this fact and helping her to adopt a more realistic attitude toward the clinic, she was helped to mature emotionally.

A self-searching attitude on the part of the therapist is as important in analytically oriented psychotherapy as is such an attitude toward the patient. The psychiatrist too has neurotic reactions based on his own past history. When these affect his relationship with the patient, we call it *countertransference.*

It will be recalled in that case history that the psychiatrist offered to send the patient to another doctor as part of a reality-testing maneuver presented deliberately as part of a plan. The psychiatrist was prepared to understand the material that came out subsequently, and to use it for the patient's welfare. Unfortunately, a genuinely rejecting attitude can at times be displayed by the psychiatrist. In response to a personal neurotic need he may be unable to tolerate an unfriendly rejecting attitude from a patient. In the foregoing case, a hostile attitude on the part of the therapist would have compelled the patient to conclude that contemporary father figures are no more reliable than the ne'er-do-well father of her childhood. It is obvious that this might have introduced hopeless complications into the therapeutic relationship.

A young male therapist was readily moved to hostility by elderly female patients as a result of a pathologically hostile attitude toward his own mother. A passive dependent therapist was unable to accept his properly dominant role in relationships with elderly male patients who reminded him of his domineering father.

Countertransference is a major source of error in psychotherapy with patients. For this reason, a personal psychoanalysis ought to be part of the basic training of every psychiatrist. This is a more practical goal than the hope of treating all hospitalized schizophrenics with psychoanalysis. Where a personal analysis of the psychiatrist is not possible, supervision of his work by an analytically trained psychiatrist represents the next best solution. This would require that at least one person on the staff of each institution should have analytic training including a personal psychoanalysis, and that his services be available in a supervisory capacity to those on the staff who are conducting intensive psychotherapy with their patients.

Initial Interviews

Psychotherapy with the individual patient begins during the initial contact with him. The therapist sees the patient as soon after admission as possible. He is warm in his manner and gives evidence of personal concern about the patient's welfare. Patients who are sick enough to require admission to a mental hospital are without exception regressed to an emotional state of helpless infantile dependency. In this state a patient is less accessible to verbal approaches but more accessible to actions expressive of love and interest in his well-being. If the psychiatrist brings nourishment to the patient from the ward kitchen and even feeds him, it may give rise to a deep emotional bond which will be invaluable in subsequent psychotherapeutic relationships. Even if the patient seems out of contact, the psychiatrist should explain as many of the realities of the situation as he can. If the medical director has a routine letter of welcome to the patients, it is well to present it to him during this initial contact. During the first few interviews the psychiatrist endeavors to get a history from the patient if he is communicative. One cannot depend on the family history alone. Give the patient an opportunity to tell his story. If he is unable to talk, try to explore with him the reasons for this inhibition. The reasons will involve fears or resentments of one kind or another. In addition to the contents of the accepted outlines for taking a psychiatric history, one asks the patient for his earliest memories. These earliest memories frequently contain some theme of central importance in the psychological development of the individual. Thus, every new admission should be approached as if he were a candidate for individual psychotherapy. This is not only good treatment in terms of the over-all needs of the therapeutic community but also because an unfortunate initial experience may complicate the outcome of all future psychotherapeutic endeavors.

Taking Notes

After the history has been obtained it is well to avoid taking notes. There are many reasons for this. A proper listening technique is most difficult. The psychiatrist should meet the patient's productions with active scanning thoughts of his own concerning the meaning of what the patient is saying and doing. For most people it is not possible to do justice to this task and to act as a stenographer at the same time. This is not to minimize the importance of written records. I like to record the opening sentence of each session. In a manner reminiscent of the remark about earliest memories, this opening sentence frequently contains a theme that will be of central importance during a given session. A brief summary of the session that can be referred to at the beginning of the next session will often reveal a continuity in the patient's thinking which might otherwise be missed, particularly if one's case load is large and the intervals between sessions long. Even when there is a lapse of several days between sessions, it is often possible to establish a continuity in the material by means of such notes.

But to return to the disadvantages of note taking, some patients develop paranoid suspicions about the fate of these notes. It is well to anticipate such fears and to reassure the patient that his confidences are respected (and then be sure that those confidences *are* respected). Patients will observe the note taking carefully and at times will draw some erroneous conclusions. For example, they may feel that their important utterances are recorded and not their unimportant ones. So, if the psychiatrist is not writing, the patient may feel crushed at what he believes is evidence of the worthlessness of his productions, even though the therapist may have stopped writing because of fatigue or a desire to listen more carefully. It is sometimes said that one should record dreams. This procedure may give the patient an erroneous conception concerning the importance of dreams and in response to what he feels is a special interest, he may regale his physician with nothing but dreams for hours on end. Finally, note taking acts as a barrier between patient and doctor, introducing an element of impersonality into the proceedings at a time when the patient may be in need of a closer, more human relationship.

The Art of Listening

It was said that the psychiatrist should meet the patient's productions with active scanning thoughts of his own concerning the meaning of what the patient is saying. This implies that not all forms of listening are equally useful. In addition to the foregoing active process of listening, which is a therapeutically constructive process, it is also possible to listen passively, that is to say, to hear the patient, to understand the literal meaning of his words and even to be intensely interested in what he is saying and yet be totally inactive in grappling with the hidden meanings in the patient's productions. In another aspect of passive listening, the patient's productions may touch off daydreams in the therapist which may carry him far afield from the therapeutic realities involving the patient. Sometimes this tendency will not yield to the psychiatrist's efforts at self-discipline but will require the resolution of certain of his passive tendencies through a personal psychoanalysis.

The Role of Dreams in Psychotherapy

While dreams have been called "the royal road to the unconscious," more often a preoccupation with dreams can be destructive to progress in psychotherapy. As has already been mentioned, if the patient detects a special interest in dreams he may bring dreams in profusion, in which case therapeutic sessions may degenerate into recitations of dreams on the part of the patient and idle speculation about them on the part of the doctor. It is well to begin a discussion of the role of dreams in psychoanalysis with a strong caution against the common error of drawing unwarranted conclusions from a dream. Dream interpretation is difficult, requiring analytic training ideally, and in any case direction by an analytically trained supervisor.

With the foregoing words of caution, a summary of some of the salient facts about the role of dreams in psychoanalysis will be presented.

Dreams that are brought spontaneously early in the therapy are apt to be particularly valuable. These dreams are characteristically simple and relatively transparent as to their hidden meanings. Important insights concerning the nature of patients' problems can often be deduced from them. Dreams which are brought later in the course of treatment are rarely as simple and as clear as the dreams first submitted by the patient. The therapist studies these first dreams as he would study the production of a patient on a psychological test and uses them in his preliminary formulation of the case. It is rarely useful to confront the patient early in his psychotherapy with conclusions drawn from these first dreams.

The following remarks are not calculated to instruct the reader how to interpret dreams but rather to emphasize the difficulties of this process and to underscore the importance of avoiding a less scientific approach in the utilization of dreams in psychotherapy.

Psychoanalytic studies have shown that dreams are compounded of many wish-fulfillments drawn from different phases in the development of the individual. These are wishes, the existence of which we cannot acknowledge to ourselves in the fully wakened state for a number of reasons, wishes relating primarily to infantile impulses which are repugnant by normal adult standards. Such repressed wishes achieve hallucinatory fulfillment in our dreams. Thus, dreams afford an opportunity to glimpse into the hidden recesses of the mind and to gain insight into the unconscious factors which play a role in the total mental functioning of the individual. The problem unfortunately is complicated by the fact that these unconscious wishes are repugnant even during the clouded state of consciousness which exists during dreaming. As a result, these wishes are disguised in order to make them more palatable to the dreamer. This disguising process is called the "dream work." If the disguise is inadequate, it may have a terrifying effect on the dreamer and what results is a nightmare. To understand the unconscious wishes that are expressed in the "manifest dream," it is necessary to undo the dream work. This process of uncovering the hidden or so-called "latent content" of the dream is called "dream interpretation." To interpret a dream one must know the contemporary reality situation which contributed to the formation of the dream (the "day residue"). Thus, one cannot try to interpret just any dream. One must know when the dream occurred, what incidents occurred on the day preceding the dream, what memories are brought to mind by the details of the dream (the "associations"), and, finally, we must have some general knowledge of the patient's problems from previous contacts with him, as well as the specific problems which concern him most urgently at the time of the dream. Only if one is armed with such a body of information is one justified in attempting the interpretation of a dream, never without it. The proper interpretation of a dream, almost by definition, is one which furthers the therapy of the patient. Not only is it necessary to expose the repressed wishes which the dream seeks to fulfill, but also to show how these repressed wishes impinge upon the patient's reality problems. Unless the past is clearly linked to the present, the dream is not interpreted.

Psychotherapy and Reality

Contemporary reality remains at all times the main concern in treatment. The therapist strives constantly to bring the patient's thoughts and actions more appropriately into contact with his environment. The content of his unconscious concerns us only to the extent that it distorts his comprehension of reality.

A common error in psychotherapy is to become so interested in the patient's past that his current problems are neglected. To avoid such an error Freud once recommended that we should think of the patient's past problems when he speaks of current events and of his current problems when he speaks of his past. At all times we should seek to link past with present and present with past. In this linking process insight therapy proceeds.

The Working-Through Process and the End of Treatment

It is the experience of every therapist that merely making the patient conscious of the way in which he distorts reality is not enough. He must be confronted with these insights repeatedly, in many different situations over a period of weeks, months and often years before he is able to abdicate his previously pathological rigidity in favor of a more mature capacity to adapt flexibly to his emotional needs and the demands of reality. This phase of psychotherapy, called "working through," is the longest and hardest part of the treatment and contrasts strikingly with the magical expectations for a quick cure which the patient usually has, and is sometimes entertained by the doctor as well. As a matter of fact, we never really cure patients with psychotherapy in the sense that a surgeon cures an acute appendicitis. What we do for our patient is to give him a new way of thinking which will become steadily more useful as he applies it over a period of years with increasing efficiency. In other words, we believe that the therapeutic process continues after the formal relationship with the therapist has come to an end, so that a patient whom we discharge may be better a year later than he was on the day he left treatment. As a result of this fact, we can never discharge a patient in the sense that we close a door on him permanently. We must leave with him a feeling of our continued concern about his welfare and our readiness to see him any time he gets into trouble. He may never come back, but the knowledge that he can come back has psychotherapeutic importance.

Case History

A fifty-five-year-old childless married woman was referred to a psychiatrist in a state of severe agitated depression. The case seemed in all respects to be typical. She displayed uncontrollable weeping, sleeplessness, loss of appetite with considerable loss of weight, obsessive thoughts about flinging herself from a window (a suicidal desire which was nevertheless associated with so much fear that she might act on this desire that she would never remain alone); she complained of a "dead feeling" in both legs, constipation, pain in the left side of her abdomen associated with the fear that this was a cancer blocking her bowels, thereby making her constipated. In addition, she feared that she had irrevocably lost her mind and that she had ruined herself by loss of self-control in dieting excessively.

The foregoing catalogue of complaints will not seem the least bit unusual to anyone familiar with this type of depression. Yet, as we shall see subsequently, each of these symptoms had a specific meaning for her, the elucidation of which contributed to her rehabilitation.

This was the second attack in her life; the first, having occurred eight years previously, lasting about seven months and then subsiding without special treatment. She seemed perfectly well until three months before. Her depression began insidiously and grew gradually worse until it reached its present intensity.

When her husband was asked whether there was any reason why she should have become depressed then, he answered that on the contrary it should have been a period of great joy. He had just told her that he was taking her to Europe, for her the fulfillment of a lifelong ambition. He had given her *carte blanche* to equip herself with a new wardrobe for the occasion. Before beginning her shopping, she decided to go on a diet so that she could show off her new clothes to best advantage. She was a person of considerable vanity. She had been a model prior to her marriage thirty years previously, and with great fastidiousness she had retained much of her good looks. It was after she had taken off a few pounds that the depression began.

A question immediately presents itself. Here is a woman during a period of fulfillment, and she reacts not with the anticipated joy but with a suicidal depression. Some might conclude that the depression is not related to external factors but is rather an example of a true endogenous depression. However, Freud described the syndrome of those who are destroyed by success and accounted for it on purely psychological grounds. It is not uncommonly encountered in ordinary clinical purview. Such people are able to adapt more successfully in life roles characterized by inferiority and dependency. They develop guilt of intolerable proportions when placed in a position of leadership or success. For this reason, they assiduously avoid the responsibilities of a mature adult life.

She was seen every day for an hour at a time. The anticipated guilt feelings came pouring out. She spoke of her great love for her mother and four older sisters, and of her many sacrifices in their behalf. She asked, in self-reproach, "Why should I have such good fortune when they are condemned to stay at home because of their less fortunate financial circumstances?" However, as she was encouraged to speak freely she admitted having great feelings of bitterness toward them. They had many things in life she didn't have. Most of all they had children. She complained that she had to buy their friendship all her life, earlier with her earnings as a model, later through gifts and other kindnesses made possible by her husband. They in return gave her nothing and were quick to withdraw to their own family interests when attentions from her came to an end. Out of this resentment came a secret satisfaction at her good fortune, but also a fear of their jealousy and retaliation.

Then she spoke guiltily about her husband. "Why am I doing this to him? I'll ruin this trip for him." She commented that however eager she had been for the trip, his eagerness was even greater, that as a matter of fact he planned the trip his own way, with little or no reference to her desires in the matter. She spoke at great length and with many expressions of gratitude of his generosity in most matters. Gradually, however, and with a considerable display of anxiety, she acknowledged that this concern for her needs did not extend to all matters, that as a matter of fact she had been quite frustrated sexually, not only with respect to their childlessness which she blamed on him but also in the sexual act, during which, in a manner reminiscent of the way he planned the trip, he seemed utterly unconcerned about her feelings and wishes. As a matter of fact she had permitted herself romantic daydreams about adventures in Europe with a more considerate lover, and that these daydreams had played an important role in her dieting and shopping. She hastened to emphasize that these were only daydreams, that she considered herself incapable of any such unladylike behavior. Nevertheless, the daydreams were there, and at the very moment, no less, when she was so richly the beneficiary of her husband's generosity. The intensity of her guilt feelings about this could be well imagined.

She then revealed that behind the guilt about her imaginary adventures was even more guilt, about a real occurrence. Following a disappointment in love prior to her marriage she had become involved in a very brief sexual liaison with an older man. This was done as an act of spite, and she could never recall it without mortification. Having found that she could expose this without outraging her doctor, she was encouraged to tell what she felt was the darkest secret of all. When she was eight years old she was seduced by the doorman of the apartment house in which she lived. He took her into the basement, exposed himself, held her on his lap and masturbated her. She was sure that whatever pleasure she experienced was more than overshadowed by her guilt and terror. This took place on several occasions because she was afraid to refuse him. Finally, when she threatened to tell her mother, the doorman left her alone.

It is striking to observe how complicated are the determinants of this single symptom—a feeling of guilt, combining as it does hostile and erotic impulses from the present and from various phases of her development in the past. As will be seen later, the foregoing by no means exhausts all the determinants of this symptom. Her experience as an eight-year-old impinges on another question of interest to the state hospital psychiatrist, and that is, what is the psychological impact of the adult sexual offender on his childish victim. It was quite evident, as the patient told the story, that her own willing role in this adventure was not to be minimized. The seduction by the adult was met by a readiness to be seduced, or even an active counterseductive attitude on the part of the child. This point is taken up in Chapter XXIII. Precocious sexual interest and a consequent susceptibility to seduction is often the product of insecurity feelings and a state of emotional deprivation in the child. The experience of our patient was a sign that she was already then having difficulties in emotional adaptation. She used a sexually seductive attitude in response to infantile feelings of loneliness and anxiety as a means of compelling attention from an otherwise indifferent adult. This was quite evident in her seductive behavior in the psychiatrist's office. It was very reassuring to her to learn that this behavior was not a sign of moral depravity but rather an attempt by an immature ego to master its loneliness.

All this material came out in daily sessions over a period of several weeks. One might ask at this point what was the effect of all of these revelations on her clinical picture? The effect, alas, was to make her worse! It was said earlier in this chapter that making the patient conscious of repressed memories and wishes is not in itself curative. We can add at this point that it can also be harmful. An important question to be considered in psychotherapy is what has been referred to as "dosage." It is not simply a question of what is revealed but the rate at which it is revealed. Is the quantity of anxiety which is aroused by this material overwhelming to the patient?

For example, a woman of fifty-eight developed a fear that the Negro postman who delivered mail to her office had sexual designs on her. A psychiatrist told her bluntly that these fears were the product of her own sexual desires for this man. She was plunged almost at once into a severe agitated depression which did not subside until she had had a course of electroshock therapy.

Because of the intensity of the patient's suffering, it was decided to give her a course of electroshock therapy (ECT). She was given four treatments, after which she got so much worse that it became necessary to hospitalize her. The question could be asked, why did this patient get worse whereas the latter patient in an apparently similar circumstance was helped by ECT? This is considered in Chapter III. Our patient was admitted to a nearby sanitarium where the psychiatrist was able to continue seeing her every day. Interestingly enough, she was very eager to resume their talks. This was an indication that she was working through some of the material which had come up, and from the safe vantage point of her hospital room, at least, the forces motivating her to continue her explorations were stronger than the fears which impelled her to hang back. This is the way all psychotherapy proceeds. The impulse to get well is countered by an impulse to cling to the status quo, however miserable that may be. The latter impulse is referred to as "resistance." A major part of the psychotherapist's efforts is directed to the resistance, endeavoring to understand it, diminish it or eliminate it.

While in the hospital, the patient started talking about her father for the first time. She spoke of her father's death from cancer which had been associated with left-sided abdominal pain and constipation, symptoms identical with her own. She added, "Whenever I get abdominal spasms I think of the way he suffered." This indicated rather clearly that thoughts about her father were somehow involved in her problem. Therefore, the psychiatrist employed a device first suggested by the psychoanalyst, Charles Fisher. He said to her, "Tonight I want you to have a dream about your father. Remember it and tell me about it when I see you tomorrow." In response to this suggestion the patient blushed, said it was nonsense to suppose one could dream at will (she had reported no dreams up to this point) and asked if he were trying to hypnotize her. Up to this time, she had been sleeping poorly, even with sedation. That night she slept not at all. The next morning she met her psychiatrist with red-rimmed eyes and announced wearily but triumphantly that she did not dream. She was told that she was afraid of what she might dream about and that is why she was up all night. She was assured that it was safe for her to dream and the suggestion to dream about her father was repeated. The next morning she reported the following dream: "I was playing cards with John T. [her family doctor and close friend]. I tried to make out if John's wife was there—I think she was absent." She then added, "What in the world made me dream about John? You told me to dream about my father." Suddenly a look of dawning recognition appeared on her face and she exclaimed, "Now don't tell me that John is my father! I'll admit that they were both lousy card players."

When a patient says, "Don't tell me that so and so is true"—or some equivalent, this negative statement is a common way of admitting a repressed idea into consciousness. Freud called it "negation." It represents a way of sidling up to an idea that may be intolerable on full impact. For example, a patient may announce with satisfaction, "I haven't had a headache in many weeks" as a signal to himself that he is about to have another one.

The patient then recalled that her depression eight years previously occurred when John developed a wasting illness for which he had to be hospitalized. She thought her family doctor was going to die of cancer like her father. Actually, he recovered. As he improved, her depression lifted.

The act of playing a game in a dream often symbolizes masturbation. Although no mention of this was made to the patient, she herself brought the problem up. She related how her father played with his genitals during his final illness. The patient was fourteen at the time. Her mother expressed considerable disgust and disapproval over this and told her that her father was always an "oversexed" person. She warned the patient at that time against indulging in masturbation—"It destroys your brain, it produces insanity and can cause all kinds of debilitating illnesses." She wondered at the time if her father had hastened his own death by masturbating. She recalled occasions as a youngster when her mother came into her bedroom at night and caught her fingering her genitals and reproached her in disgust. Thus, one could hypothesize that the urge to masturbate had been awakened with great intensity during the excitement of preparing for the European trip with its overt sexual fantasies, and that as a result she identified with her father. She developed the same abdominal complaints, the pain and the fear that cancer would plug her intestines and kill her.

The patient was reassured concerning masturbation, and for the next few nights she slept very soundly, an unprecedented event since the onset of her depression. Then one morning her psychiatrist received a panic-stricken phone call from her. Once again she had spent a sleepless night and wanted to see him at once. This is the story she told when he got there: The night nurse had come in and said, "I can't let you sleep with your windows open because you are such a restless sleeper. You kick all your covers off." When she was asked what this recalled to her she spoke again of her mother's nocturnal visits to her bedroom as a child, her expressions of disgust and warnings concerning the evidences of masturbatory play. In short, the patient reacted to the nurse's innocent remark as if the nurse were her mother reproaching her all over again for masturbating. The sleepless night once again represented a vigil that she maintained over her own masturbatory impulses. She went further and recalled a dream that she had one year ago, before she knew of her European trip and before her present illness began. She had been working at that time as a volunteer in a hospital. In a tour through the child guidance clinic she had been shown playrooms with one-way screens through which adults can watch the children without being seen. She thought at that time with great uneasiness that these children might even masturbate in full view of the grown-ups without realizing that they were being seen. That night she dreamed that the doctor in the child guidance clinic was telling her. "You will have to go to the hospital and be put into a strait jacket." The memory of the child guidance clinic brought up many thoughts about exposing one's self and seeing forbidden sights, the contact with the doorman at the age of eight, looking at her father's genitals, seeing evidences of wet dreams in her husband's bed and wondering if he too masturbated.

She recalled a childhood occasion when she walked into her parents' bedroom and saw them in a sexual embrace. At that time, she beat a horrified retreat and felt terribly disappointed that they did such things. "They had clay feet" was the way she put it—a favorite expression of hers in referring to her disappointment in various parent figures to whom she had turned for help, including her doctors. She then recalled that she used to masturbate as a child by pressing her legs together (a not un-common way for girls to masturbate). She now recognized the "dead feel-ing" in both legs as an expression of the fact that she too had clay feet. However, the symptom represented not only a punishment, and a dis-appointment in herself for losing self-control in the past, but also a defense against masturbation at this time, since she couldn't press her "dead" legs together. It became apparent that when she reproached her-self for loss of self-control in her diet, it was loss of control of her mas-turbation that concerned her most. When she first developed her ab-dominal symptoms, she kept them a secret from everyone, including her family doctor. Since she felt that these symptoms were evidences of masturbation, it becomes understandable that she chose to hide them.

She was told that the excitement concerning the forthcoming trip had impinged upon a group of "forbidden pleasures," starting with her wish to make herself more sexually attractive for the trip, and extending into the past to the problem of masturbation with all its childhood ramifica-tions. The psychiatrist went back to her dream of playing cards with her family doctor and reminded her how this had opened up the whole problem of masturbation and that the dream referred not simply to masturbation as a solitary experience but as a sexual adventure between her and a father figure, very much like that which took place with the doorman so many years ago. He reminded her also of the fact that the mother figure (John's wife) was excluded by her, as if the patient knew that she would disapprove of such goings on. Thus, he interpreted the dream as an oedipal dream; i.e., that masturbation aroused so much guilt in her because it involved fantasies of her father and that fulfilling these wishes (which were involved in her fantasies about a secret lover on her trip to Europe) would arouse her mother's disapproval (hence her guilt-ridden concern about her mother which was referred to at the beginning of this case history).

The next morning she told her doctor, "I had a dream about you." She blushed and continued, "If your wife ever knew she'd slap my face!" He connected this with their discussion of the previous day, i.e., that there was an expectation of punishment by her mother for sexual designs on her father. In other words, what appeared manifestly in the dream as a sexual interest in her doctor was really the persistence from childhood of an overly intense attachment to her father. During the next few days her depression lifted entirely. She now complained of a backache. She be-came very unfriendly. She complained to her family doctor that all this chatter was getting her nowhere, that what she really had was a neuralgia for which she wanted the help of a neurologist. In effect she dismissed the psychiatrist from the case. She was seen by a neurological consultant who reassured her, and gave her a mild analgesic. She left the hospital three days later, without complaints and has remained well over a period of years since that time.

The termination of the case in this way is most interesting. She appar-ently understood enough to help her master symptoms and then chose to re-repress all of it, so that she left treatment no longer depressed, yet apparently without insight. The hysterical symptom (the backache) provided her with a face-saving maneuver. In addition, it provided a means for belittling the father figure. It will be recalled in her association to the card-playing dream that her father and her family doctor were both "lousy" bridge players. Also she wondered if her husband were a masturbator and she had expressed dissatisfaction with him as a lover and as the man who had failed to give her a child. She dismissed her psychiatrist with the complaint that his idle chatter was doing nothing for her. In other words, throughout her relationships runs a tendency to disparage the selfsame father figure to whom she is deeply attached—they all have clay feet, they all masturbate just as she does, and what is more they do not give her babies. In a younger person we would certainly have wanted to explore these ideas further. In a patient with a so-called "late life" depression, setting a modest goal is more practical. The entire period of psychotherapy lasted only two months and cannot in any sense be compared with a thorough psychoanalysis. One might anticipate, for example, that future circumstances may touch off these symptoms again. If that happens I think she can be helped again with psychotherapy. On the other hand, it is also possible that she will not develop an incapacitating depression ever again.

Research in Individual Psychotherapy

For many years it was felt that the psychotic patients who made up the largest part of our mental hospital populations were not suitable for the methods of individual psychotherapy. Here and there enterprising individuals attempted to work with these patients psychotherapeutically, but for the most part an attitude of extreme pessimism prevailed. In recent years a group of pioneers have shown the way to establish contact with psychotic patients in psychotherapy. Drs. Frieda Fromm-Reichmann and John Rosen in this country, and Madame M. A. Sechehaye in Switzerland, have been particularly successful in inspiring others to work with psychotic patients. Fired by their example, many psychiatrists have been emboldened to try psychotherapy on psychotic patients whom they would have considered unapproachable a decade ago. The pooled psychotherapeutic experiences of mental hospital psychiatrists will contribute much to improve the techniques of psychotherapy of the psychoses as well as our understanding of the basic psychological mechanisms to be found in these patients. The latter is a point of particular importance in improving the general scientific level of the work of all other departments in the mental hospital.

SELECTED REFERENCES

ALEXANDER, F.; FRENCH, T. M.; et al.: *Psychoanalytic Therapy. Principles and Application.* New York: Ronald Press, 1946.
This is a textbook of psychotherapy based on psychoanalytic principles. A well-organized theoretical section is followed by a rich collection of clinical cases. The beginner will gain from it a useful and systematic approach to brief psychotherapy.

BRODY, E. B.; REDLICH, F. C.; eds.: *Psychotherapy with Schizophrenics.* New York: International Universities Press, 1952.
Based on the Conference on Psychotherapy with Schizophrenic Patients held at Yale University in 1950. Brilliant contributions and discussions make this an invaluable text.

FISHER, C.: Studies on the Nature of Suggestion. Parts I, II. *J. Am. Psychoanal. Assoc.,* 1:222; 1:406, 1953.
This paper contains a description of the phenomenon of the "suggested dream."

FREUD, S.: *General Introduction to Psychoanalysis.* New York: Permabooks, 1953.
A series of lectures, which first appeared in 1920, setting forth in simple language the basic principles of psychoanalysis.

FROMM-REICHMANN, F.: *Principles of Intensive Psychotherapy.* Chicago: University of Chicago Press, 1950.
A distillate of Fromm-Reichmann's unique and extensive experiences with the psychotherapy of schizophrenic patients.

GILL, M.; NEWMAN, R.; REDLICH, F. C.: *The Initial Interview in Psychiatric Practice.* With 3 long-playing phonograph records. New York: International Universities Press, 1954.
This book summarizes the various approaches to the initial interview and outlines the technique of dynamic interviewing. Contains verbatim records with technical discussions, which together with the actual recordings are invaluable for teaching.

Journal of the American Psychoanalytic Association, Vol. II, No. 4, 1954.
This entire number is devoted to a discussion of the relationship of psychoanalysis and psychotherapy.

LEVINE, M.: *Psychotherapy in Medical Practice.* New York: Macmillan, 1947.
This book provides a practical summary of the various forms of psychotherapy in simple, readable language.

MENNINGER, K. A.: *A Manual for Psychiatric Case Study.* New York: Grune & Stratton, 1953.
A detailed outline of all areas to be investigated.

ROSEN, J. N.: *Direct Analysis: Selected Papers.* New York: Grune & Stratton, 1953.
Rosen's highly provocative and controversial methods are presented in this collection of papers. They will stimulate the reader to thought and experimentation.

SCHWING, G.:*A Way to the Soul of the Mentally Ill.* New York: International Universities Press, 1954.
Demonstrates a sensitive approach for establishing contact with severely regressed schizophrenics. Particularly recommended for psychiatric nurses and attendants.

SULLIVAN, H. S.: *The Psychiatric Interview.* New York: Norton, 1954.
A dynamic approach to interviewing, based on the interpersonal theory of psychiatry.

WOLBERG, L. R.: *The Technique of Psychotherapy.* New York: Grune & Stratton, 1954.
An encyclopedic presentation of the subject. Its usefulness is enhanced by verbatim material from actual interviews to illustrate various psychotherapeutic methods.

Chapter II

GROUP PSYCHOTHERAPY

The Growth of Group Psychotherapy

Although group psychotherapy has been studied sporadically for the past fifty years, it has become the object of systematic and widespread study only since World War II. At that time, considerable pressure was brought to bear upon psychiatrists in the Service to return men to duty. Heavy case loads precluded the possibility of intensive psychotherapy on an individual basis, and as a result many psychiatrists began working with patients in groups. It soon became apparent that patients in such groups were deriving psychotherapeutic benefits from their relationship with each other as well as from their relationship with the doctor. Initiated reluctantly with the expectation that a watered-down form of individual psychotherapy would result, group psychotherapy turned out unexpectedly to have special properties and a therapeutic effectiveness all its own. Patients who were not responding to individual psychotherapy were often referred to group psychotherapy as a final resort. Time and again such patients improved. Ultimately group psychotherapy achieved status in its own right. It was utilized not as an expediency or an act of desperation but as the treatment of choice in specific diagnostic categories. These categories included withdrawn borderline psychotic adolescents, severe psychosomatic disorders and other patients not ordinarily responsive to the techniques of individual psychotherapy.

The Psychoanalytic Theory of Group Formation

To understand the specific therapeutic effects which can be generated within a group it is necessary to consider first what a group is. People can sit in close proximity and still not constitute a group in the psychological sense of the word. A psychological bond must develop uniting them into a group which is a new entity with properties of its own not to be found entirely in the qualities of the individuals who constitute the group. Freud developed the hypothesis that for group formation to take place there must be, first of all, a leader. The bond which welds a collection of individuals into a group is to be found in their common emotional attachment to the leader. The group unites in making the leader's standards its standards, his judgments of right and wrong its judgments. They become equal to each other because they are recipients in common of his love and guidance. He, however, is superior to all of them. What is involved in group formation is the surrendering of one's own standards and ideals, and substituting in their place those of the leader, which now become collectively the "group ideal." The group ideal does not necessarily have to differ from the ideals of the individual. In fact, the more closely they coincide the more readily will individuals accept a given leader.

The other factor which determines the readiness with which group formation takes place is to be found in the need for leadership which exists among the separate members. The greater the feeling of uncertainty and insecurity which each individual experiences, the greater will be his readiness to surrender his own individuality and accept a leader. Under such circumstances the individual may stray far indeed from his own ideals in accepting the leader's standards, as for example during times of socioeconomic crisis when people are more prone to accept the leadership of a despot.

The patient who is overwhelmed by mental illness is very much in a state of uncertainty and insecurity. For a sick person the doctor radiates a quality of special strength. If the doctor happens to work in a military hospital, his status as an officer enhances his prestige even further in the eyes of the anxiety-ridden patient. Thus, patients in hospitals tend to form groups readily, with the doctors as their natural leaders. Their common plight as patients provides an additional basis for identification of one with another, and hence for an intensification of the group bond.

Freud compared the relationship of the individual members to the group leader with that existing between a group of siblings and a parent. The parallelism of the group-leader relationship to the child-parent relationship explains why certain special phenomena arise in a group which are referred to collectively as transference (see Chapter I). Transference is characterized by a rigid, prejudiced set of expectations in each member of the group which are based on family experiences in early childhood rather than on contemporary reality. These prejudiced expectations relate not only to the leader of the group as the substitute parent but to the other members of the group who may assume the role of substitute siblings. These expectations include positive friendly feelings as well as hostile fearful ones.

The Special Meaning of Group Life for the Mentally Ill

Characteristically, the psychotic patient has suffered a disturbance in group life from early childhood, beginning with the first experiences in the family. He may have suffered the loss of parental love, or imagined that he did, as a result of his uncontrollable impulses to gratify childhood pleasures, or because of similarly uncontrollable expressions of hatred toward various rivals within the family group, siblings and parents alike. Such experiences may have given rise to fear, guilt and hatred in quantities too great for the youngster to master. As a result he may have sought relief by withdrawing from the human relationships within the family which were giving rise to his suffering. When the child then went on to school, these dysphoric emotions may have continued with sufficient intensity to cause further withdrawal from his fellows, a pattern which may have persisted until some particularly stressful life experience caused a more precipitate break with his fellows and a full-blown psychosis erupted.

The poverty and superficiality of group experiences in the past history of schizophrenic patients is most impressive. For example, in experiments in patient self-government in mental hospitals it is found that virtually none of the schizophrenic patients have ever belonged to a club, lodge, fraternal organization or other body which was group-structured for concerted social action.

As a result of this characteristic impairment in group living, it would seem logical to include a program of corrective group living in the treatment of these patients. However, the selfsame fears, guilts and hatreds which disrupted group living in the past tend to recur and to disrupt group living in the hospital when the psychiatrist attempts to organize it along therapeutically meaningful lines.

The Group as a Therapeutic Instrument

In spite of the pathological influences which run counter to group formation in the mental hospital, the group itself tends to generate certain therapeutically constructive impulses which stabilize it.

Patients tend to identify with one another. Their common plight in mental illness and the fact of being hospitalized exert a binding influence. To the extent that they share hopes for help from the group leader, or the need to protect themselves against him, they are further drawn to each other.

The realization that other people have similar morbid ideas, anxieties or impulses acts as a potent therapeutic agent which is particularly effective in relieving anxiety and guilt. The fact that others suffer makes the sufferings of each more tolerable. That others seem to have shown weakness of character tends to make each patient more tolerant of his own weaknesses.

The opportunities to see ourselves as others see us are great in group psychotherapy. Not only are patients able to see and discuss abnormalities in other members of the group, but they are also more willing to accept these judgments from each other than they are from the therapist directly. In addition, the therapist has the opportunity to point out that insights concerning another patient are often projections of similar mental mechanisms in the patient who made the observation.

In the exchanges between patients, ideas are pooled, and as a result significant material is brought up which the patient in individual psychotherapy might not have uncovered for a much longer period of time. In addition, rivalries develop between patients which facilitate the working through of pathological sibling rivalries. In competing with each other for the leader's favor, they strive to please him. In the process they are motivated to work well in the group session and to behave more normally.

The group exerts a powerful force in the direction of reality. The general tendency is to recognize and reject the irrational in each other and to move in the direction of the common denominator of reality which is shared by the group.

The group members tend to protect each other. If a patient experiences an excess of anxiety as a result of a possibly incorrect intervention by the leader, the group will rally around the injured one and take up the blow, as it were, thereby diminishing the effect on the patient. This also corrects the therapist in his relationship with the patient.

The group will awaken the therapist to neurotic impulses in himself which are interfering with the effectiveness of treatment, thereby opening the way to mastery of these impulses. (Such neurotic impulses in the therapist are referred to as countertransference. See Chapter I.)

Types of Therapeutic Group Activities in the Mental Hospital

It will be seen in subsequent chapters that there is no detail of hospital life that does not contain within it therapeutic possibilities. The way patients are received into the hospital, the admission procedure on the ward, the way he is fed, the recreational and vocational therapy programs, the religious services—each of these situations provide opportunities for corrective group living. The ways in which they can be utilized to the best therapeutic advantage are discussed in the appropriate chapters, and they are properly to be regarded as forms of group therapy.

There are many other ways in which group experiences within the mental hospital can be structured to achieve a therapeutic effect. For example, some therapists conduct classes in mental hygiene for their patients with formal lectures, readings and quizzes. One man organized rallies attended by as many as 500 patients where he would strive to create a state of pleasurable excitement reminiscent of a revival meeting. Alcoholics Anonymous has organized its program around a religious philosophy, in which members dedicate themselves to a program of mutual assistance. In psychodrama patients are provided with a stage, a cast of accessory characters and the opportunity to act out personal problems in spontaneous dramatizations. Patient self-government creates self-reliance and a sense of social responsibility. Some administrators meet with patients for "gripe sessions," that is, to consider realistic problems as they concern living conditions within the hospital. Such meetings serve a psychotherapeutic effect in their own right as well as facilitate other group-psychotherapeutic approaches with the same patients.

Each of these devices has merit. Their use is determined by the individual training and inclination of the therapist as well as by the accessibility of a patient to a given approach, a matter not easy to decide on purely theoretical grounds.

Supportive Therapy versus Insight Therapy

In Chapter I it was pointed out that the psychiatrist does not always seek to communicate to the patient the motivations (or psycho-dynamics) which enter into the formation of his symptoms. He may utilize this understanding, however, in helping the patient to fulfill certain previously frustrated emotional needs. Therapeutic procedures of this sort which do not increase the patient's self-understanding in the process of helping him are called supportive measures. Supportive group psychotherapy is in this category.

Psychoanalytically oriented, or insight group psychotherapy, seeks to make him conscious of his automatic, prejudiced and inflexible patterns of behavior, to trace the origin of these patterns to experiences in early childhood, and finally to replace them with more realistic and flexibly adaptive patterns.

Most modern group psychotherapy consists of a mixture of both techniques. Which approach predominates depends on the type of patients making up the group and the goals of therapy. For example, young clinic patients with psychoneurotic reactions of moderate severity would be treated by a predominantly psychoanalytic approach, and the goal would be to increase the emotional development of the individual to reasonably normal adult levels. On the other hand, we would use an almost exclusively supportive approach in treating a group of senile patients, and we would be satisfied if we could decrease their anxieties enough so that they could get along with their families or in a nursing home.

Outpatient Group Psychotherapy with Psychoneurotics

Formation of the group. The crowded conditions in state hospitals and outpatient clinics make group psychotherapy particularly appealing, since this technique seems to provide formal psychological help to larger numbers of patients. Although this is doubtless an advantage of group therapy, one must guard against the impulse to help too many patients at one time, since the therapeutic effectiveness of the group is reduced if it is made too large. Most reports indicate that a group of psychoneurotic patients ranging in size from six to ten members represents the ideal for group psychotherapy.

Age, intelligence and clinical diagnosis are not factors of primary importance in determining whether a group of psychoneurotic patients will function satisfactorily as a therapeutic unit. Of greater importance is the problem of aggression. How aggressive or competitive is a patient in relationships with his equals? How well can he absorb punishment if he becomes the object of the verbal aggressions of others? How free is he in exposing his weaknesses before others? Although these factors can only be approximated by present methods of clinical and psychological examination, the attempt should be made to "mix" and "balance" personality types so that the group does not become top-heavy with excessively passive or excessively agressive patients. The therapeutic skill of the doctor in dealing with aggression determines to some extent how important this problem of balance will be. If he is sufficiently ingenious and unthreatened by his patients, he can be somewhat less concerned.

Early meetings. A certain amount of confusion inevitably develops during the first few sessions, and patients will express feelings of frustration. If the group leader expects this, it provides him with a splendid opportunity to observe the patterns of behavior which characterize each individual in the group when subjected to stress.

The therapist encourages the patients to speak freely about anything that comes to their minds. He indicates to them that their spontaneous productions form the basis for the group discussions. Some patients may show a tendency to reveal painful material impetuously, before the group is ready to support them. If a burst of self-revelation elicits only silence from the group, the patient may feel embarrassed or otherwise overwhelmed emotionally, and as a result he may break off treatment. Similarly, if the doctor is too eager to have patients examine their attitudes toward one another, he may frighten some patients off. At the same time that the therapist keeps in mind his specific role in the group as its leader, it is useful to think of himself, in addition, as a member of the group in order to heighten his empathy.

Later stages in the development of the group. As material begins to flow, the therapist endeavors to associate the personal problems of the individual with problems common to other members of the group. Tension rises in a group when an individual patient feels isolated, and falls when the group comes to understand the way in which it shares in the patient's problems.

Silences represent a common complication of group therapy. Their greatest importance probably centers about the amount of anxiety generated in the therapist. Frequently the therapist feels deeply threatened by silences. They may arouse in him a sense of failure and a quantity of discomfort out of all proportion to their significance. Patients also react to silences with anxiety, particularly if the therapist's suffering is great. An increased capacity to tolerate silences by the therapist and the individual members of the group is a definite sign of progress for all parties concerned. Although silences are often the result of hostility toward the therapist, this is not invariably the case. It may be the result of a "thinking through" process after some particularly affect-laden material has been brought forth. In general, the therapeutic potentialities seem to be greater when the doctor waits for the patients to speak rather than when he breaks the silence. If the silence is inordinately protracted, the therapist may speculate before the group concerning the reasons for the silence. If he senses that some individual patient has a particularly strong need to speak, he may address his speculations to that patient. Group silences are most disturbing to the inexperienced therapist. In work with psychoneurotic patients they seldom present a major problem.

Monopoly of attention is a symptom not infrequently encountered among individuals in a group. A patient may talk compulsively and exclude all other patients from group participation. The group should be encouraged to examine this symptom and to assume some responsibility for its control. If monopolizing tactics appear intermittently, an attempt should be made to get the patients to see the circumstances which tend to elicit this symptom. It may be necessary to see such patients individually until they have gotten enough understanding of this symptom to control it. It may be necessary at times to drop the patient entirely.

Hostility to the therapist appears inevitably in analytically oriented group therapy. This should be given free opportunity for expression. This phenomenon may try the emotional stability of the therapist to the utmost. If he tries to placate, appease, retaliate or do anything besides accepting the hostility of the patient as a transference phenomenon, it will disrupt the orderly progress of treatment. The hostility of individual members of the group is usually easily resolved in group discussions. If the entire group becomes united in a hostile attitude toward the therapist, this may be the result of some error on the part of the therapist and may be more difficult to resolve.

Hostility between patients must be similarly examined. A lack of anxiety about this in the therapist will exert a steadying influence. At all times the goal held up to the group is the understanding of this hostility in terms of transference. This understanding is most effectively achieved in most instances by directed group work.

Introduction of a new member into a group always arouses anxiety. This should be taken up in the group prior to the actual appearance of the new member. It is better to introduce new members relatively early in the group's development (before the twentieth session). When the group is well stabilized, a new admission tends to exert a predominantly disruptive effect on the therapeutic process.

The replacement of the psychiatrist by a new therapist elicits important material concerning dependency needs and the struggle for independence. It is well to accomplish the transition to the new therapist in a few sessions during which both therapists are present. In general the group transfers its allegiance to the new therapist rather quickly, a fact which emphasizes the predominantly transference nature of this allegiance.

The relationship between individual psychotherapy and group psychotherapy. It is not at all uncommon for patients treated in groups to be treated simultaneously in individual psychotherapy. This may be accomplished by a single therapist or through the use of two separate therapists. There are advantages and disadvantages to these procedures, and no one procedure is of proven superiority. Material from individual sessions should be introduced cautiously into group sessions to avoid incurring jealousies or creating feelings in patients that confidences have been breached. If material comes up in an individual session which could be of value to the group the patient should be encouraged to bring this up himself.

Neurotic tendencies in the therapist, previously referred to as counter-transference, constitute a major source of error in the therapist's interventions in the group. As a result, personal psychoanalysis constitutes the ideal preparation for conducting group psychotherapy. Since this is usually not feasible, opportunities for discussing group proceedings with more experienced colleagues constitute the next best solution. Frequent clinical staff conferences in which all group therapists participate afford an opportunity for emotional maturation of each therapist as well as improvement in his technique. The use of an "observer" in each group who records the proceedings introduces a note of objectivity into the data, thus fostering the solution of countertransference problems. Such observers are also afforded an opportunity to learn from the experiences of the therapist, thereby providing a means of training further group leaders.

Group Psychotherapy with Hospitalized Schizophrenics

The unusually rich experiences of Powdermaker and Frank in this area will be drawn upon in the material to follow.

Formation of the group. It has been found that groups of fourteen or fifteen psychotic patients work together more satisfactorily than the smaller groups ordinarily employed in the group psychotherapy with psychoneurotics. It was found that male schizophrenics could discuss their homosexual problems with fewer disrupting emotional outbursts when the group therapist was a woman. A female therapist also mobilized more discussion and acting out of heterosexual drives, so that in the early stages of therapy with a given male group, female therapists seemed to fare more easily. However, after the first few sessions the sex of the therapist becomes less significant.

The wider the range of clinical pictures presented by the individuals in the group the more satisfactorily did group therapy proceed. Thus, the various subtypes of schizophrenia should be represented in a given group, as well as all stages of illness, acute and chronic. By and large, the relatively acute or subacute cases were more accessible, more voluble and more coherent. Prolonged silences and obscure communications were less frequently encountered with them. They engaged more readily in rivalry for group status and in close friendships. As a result their presence facilitated the therapy of the chronic patients.

Female groups were more verbal than groups of men and relied less on bodily or postural expressions of feeling. They were inclined to greater extremes of feeling (ambivalence) in a given session. Male patients tended to vie with each other for the position of leadership in the group. In female groups the doctor's leadership was not questioned. He was accepted as the leader, and it was always expected, and even demanded that he maintain this role. The question of mixing the sexes of psychotic patients in a group is one that calls for research. The tendency to act out could conceivably result in undesired pregnancies. However, the likelihood of this in the controlled environment of a mental hospital is relatively small. On the other hand, the diversity of reaction patterns displayed by male and female groups suggests that a therapeutically constructive interaction might take place if they were combined into a single group.

In forming a group it is well to try to include at least one patient who expresses his feelings freely, intensely and directly, especially with regard to sexual fantasies and aggressive impulses. Another type of patient who exerts a favorable influence on the psychotherapeutic group is the patient who responds compliantly when the therapist talks to him. Through such a patient the psychiatrist may succeed in resolving periods of silence and in raising issues involving withdrawn patients. Any patient who displays a characteristic and readily identifiable reaction to stress provides opportunities to enlighten the group about the meaning of symptoms.

Early stages in the development of group feeling. A central problem in the treatment of schizophrenic patients is that of fostering a positive relationship between the patients and the therapist. The emotional maturity of the therapist is a matter of considerable importance in this regard. His lack of anxiety in the face of the emotional storms of the patient is his most valuable asset. If he is consistent in his relationships and forthright in his manner, these qualities will foster positive feelings for him in his patients. In work with schizophrenic patients one often employs techniques reminiscent of those used with children. Gifts and refreshments may be provided as bribes. At times patients ask for the loan of valuable objects. In those instances where the therapist took the chance and lent the requested object (for example, a watch or a pen), it was invariably returned intact and with evidences that the loan had been requested as a test of the therapist's regard for the patient. The therapist of the psychotic group expresses praise and approval with complete freedom, unlike the more detached technique employed with psychoneurotic patients. At times he will deliberately foster rivalries and jealousies between patients to motivate them to more intensive therapeutic efforts.

If a patient expresses hostility on one day, it is important to let him know on subsequent occasions that the therapist harbors no retaliatory hostile feelings. The therapist may accomplish this by borrowing a cigarette, for example, from the very patient who attacked him on the previous day. At the same time that such familiarities can be helpful, they must be employed judiciously, since too friendly an attitude may arouse intolerable anxiety in a psychotic patient.

Needless to say, patients should be treated with respect. The patient's phraseology should be employed at every opportunity in making a point before the group. The patients must be encouraged to assume responsibility for their predicament as patients and for their future. If a patient is being attacked verbally or otherwise, the therapist should support and protect him.

In work with schizophrenics it is particularly important to avoid premature interpretations. If a patient expresses some fear or frustration, the therapist should never minimize his problem with automatic reassurances. Such reassurance will not help the patient. On the contrary, it will only make him feel that the therapist does not understand the gravity of his problem.

To foster relationships between patients the therapist seeks to generalize from the problems of the individual to the problems of the group. He emphasizes the similarities between the problems, experiences, and emotions of two or more patients. He uses one patient's statements to clarify another patient's problem. He asks one patient to comment on the problem of another. He emphasizes the continuity in the group process by reviewing the events of the previous meeting at the opening of each new session.

Silences are sometimes more difficult to overcome in a schizophrenic group than they are in work with psychoneurotics. As usual the therapist's first task is to try to understand the reason for the silence. Their silence may be a retaliatory hostility for some real or imagined aggression on the part of the therapist. He may try to overcome the silence by voicing tentative formulations as to its meaning. Sometimes taking up a seat alongside a silent patient will encourage that patient to talk even though nothing else is said or done. Talking directly to a patient who seems to have some urgent need to speak is sometimes effective. The presence of a compliantly verbal patient is useful on such occasions, as already mentioned. The therapist may comment on a remark which a patient made in a previous session and ask that patient to amplify on it. It is very gratifying to a patient to discover that the therapist pays attention to him as an individual and remembers what he said. In appreciation he may break the silence. The therapist may ask one patient to comment on the silence of another patient. The therapist may sense that the silence of the group is an expression of a need to be "fed" by him, and he may gratify this need by talking to them at some length. Finally, the therapist endeavors to hold before the group the fact that theirs is the responsibility for bringing material into the sessions for their mutual benefit.

Hostility toward the therapist appears with particularly great intensity in schizophrenic groups. This phenomenon above all others will test the therapist's emotional resources. All expressions of hostility must be accepted with tranquility and with the consistent attitude that the transference meaning of the hostility must be uncovered. With schizophrenic patients it is necessary to return over and over again to this theme, since they relinquish their pathological hostility with great difficulty.

Overt sexual activity is not uncommon in schizophrenic groups. This takes the form of masturbation and exposure in particular. It becomes a major problem for the group only if it is seriously disconcerting to the therapist. Such actions usually occur as expressions of anxiety. If the therapist is rejecting in his attitude then the anxiety is intensified and a vicious circle is set up. The therapist's interventions should be directed at the source of the patient's anxiety and should be reassuring in its effect. One encounters, for example, a fear of loss of masculinity as the basis for such behavior. Assuring a patient that he is not in danger of losing his masculinity may bring such behavior to an end.

Contraindications to Group Psychotherapy

Patients given to considerable acting out may exert a destructive influence on group psychotherapy. The disruptive effect of an aggressive psychopathic personality on the psychotherapy of a group of neurotic patients, for example, is well known. Suicidal patients may react to group material with an intensification of suicidal drives which may be overlooked by the therapist in the group situation. However, the close supervision possible in a mental hospital mitigates this danger. Individual patients may have a disruptive effect on one group yet make satisfactory progress in another group in which their special personality problems may be more effectively counteracted.

Research in Group Psychotherapy

Few areas in psychiatry provide investigative opportunities as rich as those to be found in group psychotherapy. An excellent example of this is the recent study by Abrahams and Varon of a collection of schizophrenic girls and their mothers treated as a single group. It was possible to verify by direct observation the intensely pathological mother-daughter relationships in this group. In the elucidation of the role of this relationship in the psychopathology of schizophrenia they made a contribution of great theoretical importance. They were able to show the regular occurrence of an ego weakness in the mother which antedated the illness of the daughter. The mother fostered and compelled a state of even greater ego weakness in the daughter in an attempt to maintain her own self-esteem. As a corollary of this finding it followed that the mother's ego weakness had to be treated so that she could permit her daughter's recovery. Abrahams and Varon were able to accomplish this in their group to a certain degree. Thus, their finding has practical therapeutic importance as well as theoretical significance.

Similar studies should be carried out with male schizophrenics and with fathers too. The group treatment of relatives of psychotic patients is in its beginnings. The utilization of motion pictures, television, music and readings as adjuncts to group psychotherapy deserves systematic investigation. The value of two therapists of opposite sex working jointly is becoming increasingly apparent. The male therapist plays a firm disciplinary role while the female therapist remains permissive and protective. By such a combined approach otherwise inaccessible patients become amenable to treatment. A striking example of this was reported by M. E. Linden in the treatment of a group of senile patients. This principle was also employed very successfully by Stevenson and Fisher in the vocational rehabilitation of a group of chronic "unemployable" psychoneurotics, although they did not use group psychotherapy in the process.

SELECTED REFERENCES

ABRAHAMS, J.; VARON, E.: *Maternal Dependency and Schizophrenia. Mothers and Daughters in a Therapeutic Group. A Group-Analytic Study.* New York: International Universities Press, 1953.

BURCHARD, E.; et al.: Criteria for the Evaluation of Group Therapy. *Psychosom. Med.,* 10:257, 1948.
    An excellent review article.

CRUVANT, B. A.: The Function of the "Administrative Group" in a Mental Hospital Group Therapy Program, *Am. J. Psychiat.,* 110:342, 1953.

FOULKES, S. H.: On Group Analysis. *Int. J. Psycho-Anal.*, 27:46, 1946.
—— *Introduction to Group-Analytic Psychotherapy: Studies in the Social Integration of Individuals and Groups.* New York: Grune & Stratton, 1949.
Written with great clarity, it provides an excellent introduction to the theory and technique of psychoanalytically oriented group psychotherapy. The text contains many informative clinical examples.

HYDE, R. W.; SOLOMON, H. C.: Patient Government: New Form of Group Therapy. *Digest Neurol. & Psychiat.*, 18:207, 1950.

International Journal of Group Psychotherapy, current volumes. New York: International Universities Press.
Excellent presentations of current practice of and research in various types of group psychotherapy.

JONES, M.: *The Therapeutic Community: A New Treatment Method in Psychiatry.* New York: Basic Books, 1953.
The classic text which develops the thesis that there are psychotherapeutic possibilities in the group life of every mental hospital.

KLAPMAN, J. W.: *Group Psychotherapy: Theory and Practice.* New York: Grune & Stratton, 1946.
This volume contains a comprehensive bibliography of group psychotherapy literature.

KURLAND, A. A.: An Evaluation of Drama Therapy. *Psychiat. Quart. Supplement*, 26:210, 1952.

LINDEN, M. E.: The Significance of Dual Leadership in Gerontologic Group Psychotherapy: Studies in Gerontologic Human Relations. *Int. J. Group Psychotherapy*, 4:262, 1954.

MC CARTHY, R. G.: Group Therapy in Outpatient Clinic for Treatment of Alcoholism. *Quart. J. Studies on Alcohol.*, 7:98, 1946.

PECK, H. B.; RABINOVITCH, R. D.; CRAMER, J. B.: A Treatment Program for Parents of Schizophrenic Children. *Am. J. Orthopsychiat.*, 19:592, 1948.

PFEFFER, A. S.; FRIENDLAND, P.; WORTIS, S. B.: Group Psychotherapy with Alcoholics; Preliminary Report. *Quart. J. Studies on Alcohol.*, 10:198, 1949.

POWDERMAKER, F. B.; FRANK, J. D.: *Group Psychotherapy: Methodology of Research and Therapy.* Cambridge: Harvard University Press, 1953.
This is a report of a Group Psychotherapy Research Project of the U. S. Veterans Administration. It describes experiences with outpatient groups consisting of neurotics and ambulatory schizophrenics as well as inpatient experiences with chronically ill hospitalized schizophrenics. Therapeutic situations are presented and analyzed in detail. Practical deductions from these analyses are then given. An important and somewhat unusual aspect is the frankness with which the personal problems of the doctors are discussed in relation to their therapeutic techniques, particular therapeutic situations and results. An invaluable text for any mental hospital wishing to investigate systematically the possibilities of group psychotherapy.

RANDALL, G. C.; ROGERS, W. C.: Group Psychotherapy for Epileptics. *Am. J. Psychiat.*, 105:383, 1948.

SILVER, A.: Group Psychotherapy with Senile Psychotic Patients. *Geriatrics*, 5:147, 1950.

SLAVSON, S. R.: *Introduction to Group Therapy* (6th ed.). New York: International Universities Press, 1954.
A classic text, rich case illustrations.

STANDISH, C. T.; GURSI, J.; SEMRAD, E. V.; DAY, M.: Some Difficulties in Group Psychotherapy with Psychotics. *Am. J. Psychiat.*, 109:283, 1952.

STEVENSON, I.; FISHER, T. M.: Techniques in the Vocational Rehabilitation of Chronically Unemployed Psychiatric Patients. *Am. J. Psychiat.*, 111:289, 1954.
The possibilities of dual leadership in psychotherapy are well developed in this paper.

STEWART, K. K.; AXELROD, R. L.: Group Therapy on Children's Psychiatric Ward: Experiment combining group therapy with individual therapy and resident treatment. *Am. J. Orthopsychiat.,* 17:312, 1947.
THOMAS, G. W.: Group Psychotherapy: A Review of the Recent Literature. *Psychosom. Med.,* 5:166, 1943.
    An excellent review article.
WENDER, L.: Group Psychotherapy—A Study of its Application. *Psychiat. Quart.,* 14:708, 1940.
    The concept is presented that every aspect of hospital life and activity can help in the patient's therapy if properly utilized by trained personnel.

Chapter III

SOMATOTHERAPY

Psychodynamics and Physical Methods of Treatment

The view presented in these pages is that mental disease is an expression of unsuccessful adaptation to acute or chronic emotional stress. To review briefly, a rational program of treatment is based on an accurate formulation of each patient's problem. That is to say, we are concerned with the central wishes which drive or motivate a patient and the frustrations which he encounters in striving to fulfill those wishes. We are interested in the extent to which his adult aspirations are contaminated by childhood wishes; the extent to which his frustrations exist as contemporary realities and the extent to which they exist only in the patient's mind because of unconscious symbolic values which he assigns to various details of his environment. By psychotherapeutic influences we attempt to free the patient of the rigid prejudiced expectations which he has concerning his environment, and to replace them with more flexibly adaptive ones. We endeavor to free him from the influence of immature attitudes. Where he is inclined to be excessively self-critical, we try to inculcate a less demanding attitude toward himself. Where his inner controls are underdeveloped, we try to instill in him ideals and values which he will cherish and which will constrain him. Where opposing motivations split him emotionally and intellectually, and reduce him to a state of psychological disorganization, the attempt is made to reconcile the warring elements within him. The aim is to accomplish these changes by means of corrective emotional experiences in the various activities programs and in all other aspects of mental hospital life, in group and individual psychotherapy, and by opening the way for corrective emotional experiences outside the hospital by means of social service modifications of his family environment, by family care placement, and vocational rehabilitation. All these matters are taken up in detail in their appropriate chapters.

To some people, the use of various organic devices, electrical, surgical and pharmacological, in the treatment of mental illness seems to be illogical and contradictory to the views and aims summarized in the preceding paragraph. These methods, which are collectively referred to in this chapter as somatotherapy, are nevertheless of proven clinical worth. The mental hospital psychiatrist sees many patients with incapacitating depressions who are withdrawn, anorexic, sleepless and suicidal, transformed into functioning human beings with a few shock treatments, able to leave the hospital and resume their life responsibilities. Often, this seems to be accomplished without any change in basic attitudes or home environment. Psychological studies may show that in a fundamental sense the patient is not much different when he is in remission than he was during the psychosis. The clinical remission may appear to be based on flimsy psychological devices such as denial, repression or paranoid mechanisms. Nevertheless, this apparently precarious balance may be maintained for years or even decades of successful living before it is disrupted again. The importance of this type of improvement, therefore, should not be dismissed too lightly. In spite of admitted limitations, somatotherapy is indispensible in the armamentarium of the modern psychiatrist.

Like any other method in medicine, these methods lend themselves to abuse. In an overcrowded mental hospital in particular, it is easy for the overworked psychiatrist to lapse into a mechanical approach to therapy. This is especially true when an over-all program of treatment is not already in operation, and the formidable task of instituting one devolves upon the shoulders of the mental hospital psychiatrist alone. In such circumstances, electrically induced convulsions and other organic interventions may represent all that is done for the patient in the positive sense of treating him and attempting to rehabilitate him. It is undoubtedly true, however, that many patients will be helped by such means alone.

For example, a twenty-four-year-old single woman suffered from panphobic symptoms of agonizing intensity. Because of the completeness of her withdrawal from human relationships, she was diagnosed as pseudo-neurotic schizophrenia. Four years of outpatient psychoanalytic therapy gave her no relief. A course of electroconvulsive therapy carried out in a mental hospital was of no avail. A topectomy, performed as a last resort, resulted in an immediate reduction in her suffering. She returned to the community, became self-supporting and involved herself in wholesome social activities. Altogether she functions more effectively and with more overt evidences of contentment than she has displayed over a period of years. This result has continued for over three years and was achieved without further formal efforts at rehabilitation.

However, this approach alone will result in lower recovery rates and wasted human resources. The integration of somatotherapy into a total rehabilitation program will salvage many patients who would not otherwise be able to leave the hospital. Ideally, somatotherapy is a detail in a larger plan of treatment.

Convulsive Therapy

Electroconvulsive therapy (ECT) is an outgrowth of pharmacologic convulsive therapy. On the theory that the induction of convulsions would benefit psychotic patients, Meduna induced convulsions with a variety of pharmacologic agents, of which metrazol proved to be the best. There were several disadvantages to this procedure. In the interval between the injection of the convulsant and the appearance of the seizure patients would experience what has been described as a feeling of impending doom and dissolution. This would commonly attain such terrifying proportions that many patients would refuse further treatment. Status epilepticus with fatal outcome was also seen from time to time. Orthopedic complications seemed to occur more often after metrazol than occurs currently with ECT. The difficulty of getting into a vein represented, at times, one more disadvantage of this method. It has been claimed that patients who do not respond to ECT will occasionally go into remission in response to metrazol. However, the over-all results with metrazol and ECT are not significantly different. The latter offered a number of major advantages over metrazol. It was simpler to administer, the intensity of the seizure was easier to regulate, and the terrifying preconvulsive anxiety was eliminated. As a result, ECT has superseded other devices for the induction of convulsions for therapeutic purposes.

Indications for ECT

The main indication for ECT is to relieve the symptom of depression. In involutional melancholia, the duration of the depression is shortened, the incidence of suicide is decreased, and the recovery rate is increased. In the depressed phase of manic-depressive psychosis, ECT shortens the attack and decreases the danger of suicide. Although ECT does not prevent subsequent attacks of depression or alter the frequency of recurrences, patients who tend to relapse can be maintained in a reasonable state of remission for extended intervals by means of ECT administered at monthly intervals on an outpatient basis. Depressions which are part of a psychoneurosis are best treated by psychotherapy. However, there are times when the danger of suicide or the degree of anguish is so great that the patient must be either hospitalized or given symptomatic relief on an outpatient basis. In these instances, the judicious application of ECT may spare a patient the necessity for entering a mental hospital and make continued psychological treatment in the community possible. Patients of advanced age often develop depressions. In spite of an outwardly frail appearance, patients in their eighth and even ninth decades can tolerate ECT very well. Contrary to expectations, the incidence of fractures is not higher among them than it is among younger patients. The restricted capacity to adapt to a new environment makes hospitalization particularly hazardous to elderly people. The outpatient administration of ECT to this group is not only good psychiatry but is even life-saving at times because of the rapid physical as well as mental decline which commonly occurs when these patients are hospitalized. Depressed patients with other forms of organic brain disease, including Parkinsonism, general paresis and multiple sclerosis, have also been helped by ECT.

Depression is treated in a purely symptomatic fashion. If the patient is extremely agitated, two or three treatments may be given at daily intervals. As the patient improves, treatments are given at longer intervals until remission occurs. The patient is then given one or two extra treatments after the depression has lifted.

Although ECT is primarily indicated in depression, it is often of value in other symptom complexes. In manic or catatonic excitement, ECT may play a life-saving role if the unremitting overactivity of the patient is dangerously exhausting. To interrupt such an overactive state it may be necessary to give three or even four treatments within the first twenty-four hours. After the acute excitement has subsided, treatments may be spaced at the usual intervals, three times, two times or once a week, depending on the reaction of the patient and the phase of treatment he is in.

Acute schizophrenic reactions usually respond very quickly to ECT. A common error in the treatment of schizophrenia is to stop treatment as soon as symptomatic improvement has occurred. In spite of continued improvement, it is felt that a course of at least twenty treatments should be carried out to achieve a sustained remission.

In a program of rehabilitating chronic schizophrenics, a trial of ECT is indicated if this has not been previously tried. In spite of the low remission rate in chronic cases, favorable results are occasionally seen. In overexcited schizophrenics, ECT can be employed symptomatically for its sedative effect.

Outpatient ECT

The most important phase of treatment of the mentally ill is that which takes place in the community. Hospitalization represents, in an important sense, an interruption of treatment which is called into play when all devices available on an outpatient basis have failed to increase the patient's capacity for emotional adaptation. Hospitalization, as an emergency procedure, is brought to an end as soon as treatment within the community can be resumed. In almost every case that is considered for hospitalization a trial of outpatient ECT is justified. For this reason a mental hospital should maintain suitable facilities for outpatient ECT. Along with these facilities it should maintain, as well, those departments necessary for the integration of ECT into a total program of treatment, including proper diagnostic evaluation, some form of psychotherapy and social service assistance for improving the environment.

In addition, outpatient ECT expedites discharge of the patient who is already in the hospital, since further treatments can be given, if necessary, on an outpatient basis. The usefulness of ECT given monthly, on an outpatient basis, to maintain remission in patients who tend to relapse frequently, has been mentioned earlier.

The Use of Curare-like Agents

Because of the relatively common occurrence of fractures as a complication of ECT, curare and agents with curare-like action have been employed to eliminate or to soften the muscular contractions during the convulsion. Although these agents do decrease the danger of orthopedic complications, they introduce a set of hazards all their own. Kalinowsky reports that his only fatality in a series of several thousand consecutively treated patients occurred following the use of curare. Kalinowsky and Hoch point out that good technique does not rule out curare fatalities since they occur even in the hands of those most expert in its use. Thus, the routine use of curare seems to introduce a greater hazard than that which it purports to prevent. When ECT is necessary for a patient with a recent fracture, curarization may be unavoidable. In that case it should be carried out by an anesthetist trained in its use as well as in emergency restorative techniques including tracheal catheterization for oxygen instillation.

The Use of Intravenous Barbiturates in ECT

Many psychiatrists routinely use sodium pentothal or amytal intravenously before administering ECT. This may be of value in the treatment of some apprehensive patients; although in general patients who fear the unconsciousness of ECT will have not much less dread of the unconsciousness produced by an intravenous barbiturate. Its main application is in the prevention of posttreatment excited states, a matter of greater concern if the treatments are given on an outpatient basis. If it is used, intravenous barbiturates should be given slowly, with full awareness that the hazard of respiratory failure after ECT increases with its use.

Varieties of Electrical Stimuli

It has been found that the patterns of response of patients to electrical stimulation of the brain can be modified by altering the nature of the electrical stimulus itself. For example, it has been noted that a unidirectional pulsating current produces a convulsion with much less postconvulsive confusion and fewer EEG changes than that which follows a regular alternating current stimulus. By systematically modifying the pulse intensity, pulse duration, pulse frequency and treatment duration of interrupted unidirectional stimuli, various other phenomena can be produced, including respiratory stimulation, salivary stimulation, and other autonomic manifestations. By continuing the flow of current after the convulsion is started, the muscular system can be maintained in a tonic state of contraction so that clonic convulsive movements are eliminated. By other current modifications, a subconvulsive state of unconsciousness can be sustained. Advantages have been claimed for each method. Up to the present moment, however, no definitive conclusions have emerged. Kalinowsky and Hoch state: "It is our impression that the various types of currents and their different ways of application, for the time being at least, have added little to the previous work with ECT. They have not contributed to our understanding of the mechanism of the treatment nor is there any evidence that therapeutic results have been changed. This must be stressed to avoid the increasing confusion among practicing psychiatrists regarding the claims made for the various modifications of ECT. The research worker will continue to be interested in new procedures, although it must be requested that no more claims be made without a scientifically reliable comparison between such newer methods and the standard technique."

A.P.A. Standards for ECT

In recent years, an increasing number of patients who sustained injuries following ECT have brought legal action against psychiatrists and have collected damages. As a result of the mounting incidence of adverse legal rulings, insurance companies have increased their rates for malpractice insurance for ECT, and in some states have refused to issue policies altogether. As a result, the Committee on Therapy of the American Psychiatric Association prepared a report which was approved by the Council of the A.P.A. in May, 1953. The opinion was expressed that previously published standards had been too elaborate and detailed and unfortunately conveyed the impression that if they were followed they would reliably protect against the occurrence of complications in ECT. It was found that these recommendations not only failed to diminish complications but served, on the contrary, to provide lawyers and plaintiffs with a long list of points for legal argument against the doctors.

That a careful consideration of the indications for treatment regularly precedes the actual application of ECT seems attested to by the fact that the indications or therapeutic reasons for ECT have not usually been argued in legal actions. Most malpractice suits have been based on allegations that the actual technique of application of the ECT was faulty. Nevertheless, it would seem that a conservative statement concerning the use of ECT ought to begin by reiterating that ECT should not be applied indiscriminately.

The complications of ECT which are most commonly a cause of concern consist of vertebral fractures and fractures of the long bones. These cannot be entirely prevented regardless of what techniques are used. Often a doctor who uses no restraint is blamed for failure to protect the patient. If he does use restraint, the opinion will be expressed that the use of restraint contributed to the fracture. The same applies to the use or nonuse of hyperextension. Our present knowledge of ECT-induced fractures shows that this complication is unpredictable in either sex, regardless of technique or type of current. For example, fractures occur with equal frequency with machines producing the so-called glissando stimulus, the unidirectional pulsating stimulus or the conventional alternating stimulus. It is also emphasized that the vertebral fractures which do occur heal without special treatment and without sequelae.

The following outline of standards is quoted from the report of the A.P.A. committee on Therapy:

1. Qualifications of operator. ECT should be administered only by a qualified psychiatrist who has undergone training for several months in the technique of ECT.

2. Apparatus. Many kinds of equipment are on the market and may be used if they are manufactured by a reliable firm. The unit

should be clearly marked with the manufacturer's name, serial number, and type. Home-made units or units made by persons inexperienced in this field should not be used.

3. Room facilities and Equipment.

a. The room where the treatment is given should be equipped with a bed or table on which the patient lies during treatment. No special way of constructing beds or tables has been discovered which would in itself prevent the occurrence of fractures.

b. If a gag is used, it should be made of a moderately resistant, unbreakable substance which cannot be swallowed.

c. Medical equipment should be available and in readiness, namely oxygen equipment, mechanical airway and tongue forceps, and necessary respiratory and cardiac stimulants.

4. Personnel. In addition to the person applying the treatment at least one other person should be present who is a trained attendant experienced in assisting in the application of ECT.

5. Standard procedures. Certain procedures have long been accepted as standard by physicians engaged in ECT.

a. The patient should not receive solid food for several hours prior to the application of treatment.

b. Patient's dentures and hairpins should be removed.

c. The bladder should be evacuated.

d. Extensive movements of the arms and legs should be prevented by having an attendant hold the patient's limbs gently in place. No force or mechanical restraint should be applied. (There is a considerable amount of literature as to what positions should be used or avoided without conclusive evidence of their value. There is, for example, no reliable evidence that patients who are hyperextended do not suffer fractures of the spine, or that the practice of putting pillows under the patient's back or knees is a safeguard against such fractures.)

6. Ambulatory patients.

a. A patient in good health may be treated as ambulatory, provided his mental condition permits.

b. Patients whose physical condition does not preclude the application of ECT but which will increase the hazards of treatment should be treated in a hospital. The same rule applies if the patient is too excited or suicidal to be treated as ambulatory.

c. In the case of patients who receive ECT outside of the hospital, special precautions should be used in applying intravenous sedation and in the use of muscle paralyzing drugs such as curare and the like.

d. The patient's family should be told of the hazards of ECT and a written statement consenting to the treatment should be obtained from the family. Specifically, attention should be called to the fact that fractures sometimes occur in this treatment which are not preventable irrespective of the skill and technique used.

Further, the patient's family should be instructed that many patients undergoing ECT develop a temporary memory impairment, and that ambulatory patients should be kept under constant surveillance during the course of treatment. If the family is unable to provide proper supervision, the patient should not be treated as ambulatory.

e. The ambulatory patient receiving ECT should be accompanied to and from the physician's office by a responsible person the first ten times. After that, if his reactions are known, he may come and leave the physician's office alone. The patient, however, should always remain in the physician's office until he has recovered from the treatment and can leave without untoward effects. If the patient should complain of pain or impairment of function, he should receive a physical examination, including X-ray, to ascertain whether he has suffered accidental damage.

Insulin Coma Therapy (ICT)

Many will recall the enthusiasm with which Sakel's ICT was greeted when first introduced into this country in 1938. Although ICT has not entirely fulfilled its initial expectations, results do justify its continued use. It is unfortunate therefore that the use of ICT has been sharply curtailed in most mental hospitals because of lack of personnel and funds. ICT is much more difficult from a technical point of view than is ECT. A much larger and more highly trained staff is necessary. However, the introduction of ICT into the total treatment program of the hospital results in actual dollar savings as well as in salvaged human minds, so that the elimination of ICT represents a false economy. Furthermore, a trial of ICT should precede more drastic psychosurgical procedures. Fifty to sixty comas (not treatment days) represent an adequate trial. Because of the aforementioned shortages, a really adequate trial of ICT preceding psychosurgery is rarely given nowadays.

The main indication for ICT is any case of schizophrenia which has not responded to intensive psychotherapy, if this is available, or to ECT.

Because so many special facilities are required, it has been recommended that certain hospitals be designated as ICT centers. For maximum economy of operation the service should be large enough to have at least twelve male and twelve female patients in active treatment all the time.

Technique of ICT

ICT is usually given in two phases. The preparatory phase is started with a ten to fifteen unit dose of insulin which is increased by ten to fifteen units each morning until signs of hypoglycemia are observed. This phase should not be excessively prolonged because insulin resistance tends to develop. When loss of consciousness occurs as part of the insulin reaction and the patient no longer responds to stimuli, then phase two has begun. When this occurs for the first time, the coma should be terminated after fifteen minutes. If no complications occur, this period of coma can be extended up to an hour in subsequent treatments. About four hours after the insulin has been injected the patient who has reached a coma level shows various dyskinesias and reflex changes suggestive of decerebrate rigidity. A grand mal seizure may occur at this time, in which case the coma is terminated. The coma reaction may deepen still further until a state of generalized hypotonia supervenes, which is interrupted by occasional tonic spasms. If this phase is reached, the coma should be terminated quickly. Phase two should be repeated until the patient's condition has improved maximally, or after fifty to sixty treatments if no improvement occurs. When treatments are stopped, the patient should be observed closely for at least four weeks. Most relapses will occur during this time. If this happens, ICT should be resumed with a dose of insulin which is twenty units less than the last dose and should be continued up to a total of 100 comas.

Coma is terminated by the administration of carbohydrates, by mouth if the patient can swallow or by stomach tube if the patient is in coma. In the latter instance, the position of the stomach tube should be checked by aspirating gastric contents or by listening with a stethescope for the sound of air entering the stomach when injected through the tube. Intravenous glucose is given only as an emergency measure when the patient does not respond to the orally administered glucose.

Complications of ICT

Because the physiological stresses imposed by ICT are so much greater than those of ECT, this treatment should be confined to younger patients. Its use in the presence of known heart disease or in the treatment of the paranoid reactions after the fifth decade is inadvisable. Pulmonary complications due to aspiration of secretions are sometimes seen. These can be avoided by and large by careful technique. The complication which is the greatest cause for concern is that of irreversible coma. It rarely occurs if coma is interrupted soon after generalized hypotonia sets in. If the patient does not respond to the usual termination of the hypoglycemia and does not wake up within ten to fifteen minutes after the intravenous injection of 20 cc. of 33 per cent glucose, then Kalinowsky and Hoch recommend that 100 cc. of 33 per cent glucose be given with 2 cc. of coramine. If there is no response the patient is given 500 cc. of 5 per cent glucose in saline with 2 to 4 cc. of coramine. Hot water bottles are applied as well as inhalations of 5 per cent carbon dioxide in oxygen. After an hour, if coma continues, 250 cc. of 33 per cent glucose are given, together with 500 cc. of saline in a slow intravenous drip; 500 cc. of 33 per cent glucose are instilled via stomach tube and 1/100 grain of atropine sulfate is given by hypodermic to facilitate absorption. The same procedure of intravenous glucose in saline and tube feedings should be repeated every three to four hours until the patient awakens. This may have to be continued for days. Several people have recommended a transfusion of 500 cc. of citrated blood in cases of irreversible coma.

Modifications of ICT

In the early experiences with ICT, the appearance of grand mal seizures during coma was regarded as an undesirable complication. However, it was found that this did not increase the hazards of ICT. Some deliberately induced grand mal seizures with ECT or metrazol during coma or as part of the treatment program between comas. It is not at all certain that this increases the incidence of remissions.

Polatin and others treated large groups of schizophrenic patients with insulin, confining the treatment to the preliminary phase of the insulin reaction. Although the over-all results were not as good as those with ICT, improvements were seen with sufficient frequency to warrant its use because of its simplicity compared to ICT. If changes in insulin sensitivity occur in subcoma insulin therapy, either in the direction of greater sensitivity or resistiveness, then the insulin dose is regulated accordingly. The patient is started on five units, and the dose is increased by five units each morning until weakness, drowsiness and generalized sweating occur. The patient is encouraged to be up and about and to participate in ward routines until this reaction sets in, at which time the patient may rest in bed or in a chair. The reaction is terminated with sugar water after one half hour.

Psychosurgery

Modern psychosurgery begins with the publication of a monograph by Moniz in 1936 on the results of bilateral frontal lobotomy in twenty psychotic patients. Moniz based his procedure on deductions from physiological and clinical observations. W. Freeman and J. Watts took up this work at once in the United States and promulgated the usefulness of lobotomy until it reached its present popularity. Because this procedure is so drastic and its effects so obviously irreversible, there was a widespread revulsion against it initially. However, it has stood the test of time as well as the test of carefully controlled observation. In a recent report by Jenkins and his associates in the Veterans Administration on patients with severe chronic schizophrenia it was found that "in a series of patients rigorously matched regarding general and specific severity of symptoms, lobotomized patients showed symptomatic improvement with a frequency reliably greater than that of the controls." Lobotomy has made possible the return to the community of a greater number of patients with chronic mental illness who have been sick for more than two years than has any other treatment procedure thus far available.

In addition to the classic bilateral lobotomy, a variety of other psychosurgical procedures are under investigation. Among these are transorbital lobotomy, unilateral lobotomy, medial lobotomy, precoronal lobotomy, topectomy and temporal lobe surgery. Spiegel and his associates in Philadelphia have employed a modification of the Horsley-Clark stereotaxic apparatus to produce lesions in selected thalamic nuclei, a procedure which they have called thalamotomy. Others have experimented with the therapeutic efficacy of electrical stimulation via electrodes implanted surgically in various parts of the brain.

Initially, psychosurgery, or lobotomy as it was then constituted, was used in the treatment of schizophrenia after all other methods had failed. Some of the more recent operations have a less disorganizing effect on the psychic functions and, because of this, they have been tried with some success in the treatment of well-preserved schizophrenics as well as in the more severe deteriorating cases. It has also been used in the treatment of patients with severe psychoneuroses and in an intermediate group that has been called by Hoch and Polatin "pseudoneurotic schizophrenia." All of these cases are characterized by a pan-anxiety of agonizing intensity. They are not deteriorated patients and have usually proven resistant to ECT or psychotherapy. In these cases, the newer, less extensive psychosurgical procedures have often resulted in dramatic clinical improvement at the same time that more serious personality changes were avoided. Kalinowsky and Hoch say of this group that they represent "the most gratifying chapter in work with psychosurgery."

The Future of Psychosurgery

As surgical techniques have improved, it has become possible to apply psychosurgery more freely and with less physical danger to the patient. With this there would seem to arise the danger that these procedures will be used with less discrimination. As a matter of fact, however, the number of psychosurgical procedures carried out in hospitals of all types has declined since 1949, so that this danger has not materialized. Continued careful selection of cases should be rigidly enforced. Every patient subjected to this drastic procedure should be studied systematically before and after surgery in the best scientific tradition. It has been predicted by many people that psychosurgery will be superseded in time to come by more rational methods which will not depend upon the destruction of brain tissue for their therapeutic effect. When such methods are found there is a strong likelihood that lessons from psychosurgery will have contributed to their discovery. However, this will occur only if all patients are studied with due regard for scientific method and with a deep sense of responsibility to the individual patient.

The necessity for integrating psychosurgical procedures into a total program of treatment has become increasingly apparent with time. It may be said with fairness that the future of psychosurgery depends on the extent to which we learn how to exploit the psychological changes which this procedure effects. Social service, in particular, plays a role in the rehabilitation of psychosurgical patients, which is no less important than that of the surgeon. The social worker can contribute information of great value in the selection of cases most likely to be benefited by psychosurgery. He assists also in the preparation of the patient for the operation and the family for the changes to follow. He helps to re-establish the patient in the community with his own family or in some other living arrangement if necessary. He helps the patient to maintain his vocational and social adjustment in the community thereafter. These matters are considered in more detail in Chapter VIII.

Other Somatic Treatments

Several pharmacologic agents have proven of limited value in psychiatric diagnosis and treatment. The use of amytal is described in Chapter VII. The application of antabuse in the treatment of alcoholism is described in Chapter XVII. Amphetamine and amphetamine-like substances have been used to elevate the mood of mildly depressed neurotics and to facilitate the verbal productions of emotionally inhibited patients in psychotherapy. Carbon dioxide inhalations produce vivid dream states associated with intense affective discharges, but the therapeutic usefulness of this procedure has not been convincingly demonstrated. A whole series of agents have had a brief vogue in recent years (histamine, acetylcholine, malononitrile, dibenamine, myanesin, methylguanidine, glutamic acid, lactic acid, ether, hormones, refrigeration, and many others). The judgment of clinical experience was in all those instances largely negative. New agents are constantly being brought out for clinical trial. Isoniazid, used primarily in the treatment of tuberculosis, produces some elevation of mood in depressed patients, although it is not effective enough in this regard to compete with ECT. Extracts of the root of Rauwolfia serpentina as well as its alkaloid reserpine are being tested, and a "tranquilizing" effect on anxiety is claimed for it. Chlorpromazine was recently introduced into this country from France under the trade name "Thorazine." It seems to be an unusually effective sedative in controlling hyperactive psychotic patients. Its apparent usefulness in treating impending delirium tremens is described in Chapter XVII. Thorazine has made it possible to control overactive psychotic states in the home or on the wards of a general hospital, thereby making possible continued treatment in the community for many patients that would have required admission to a mental hospital.

A fifty-six-year-old married man suffering from central nervous system lues developed a paranoid psychosis while awaiting antiluetic therapy on the neurology ward of the Mt. Sinai Hospital in New York City. He became overactive, noisy and abusive. He was given twenty-five milligrams of chlorpromazine intramuscularly. He tolerated this dose well and rested more quietly thereafter. With the repetition of this dose four to six times daily, he became completely co-operative for all subsequent therapeutic procedures. The improvement in his emotional state was not associated with a decrease in the psychological evidence of organic brain disease which was previously present (disorientation, memory defect and confabulation).

New agents should be studied in centers specifically organized for research or under the direction of expert research committees. In this way useless substances will be eliminated more quickly and the likelihood of arriving at truly useful agents will be enhanced.

Theory of Somatotherapy

The apparent lack of a logical relationship between somatotherapy and a dynamic psychological conception of mental illness was mentioned earlier. The undeniable usefulness of these procedures, however, necessitates an inquiry into their mechanism of action from a theoretical point of view, and the way in which this mechanism can be reconciled with our basic psychological conception of mental illness. Whenever knowledge is scanty, theories exist in profusion. As might be anticipated, many theories have been advanced concerning somatotherapy, and all of them remain for the most part unsubstantiated. The obligation to seek a satisfactory theory remains, nevertheless.

If the various forms of somatotherapy which have proved of value are studied for a common denominator, it will be found that a sustained alteration in consciousness is common to most of them. Above and beyond the paroxysmal loss of consciousness which occurs in ECT are more persistent changes which manifest themselves in disorientation lasting for an hour or more after ECT; in a positive face-hand test which is demonstrable for several hours, in abnormal amytal responses which may be demonstrable for several days (see Chapter VII); and in the well-known memory changes which may be conspicuous for weeks or even months. Although all of these manifestations tend to clear up, they last longer than is ordinarily realized by more superficial methods of examination. Similarly, the unconsciousness of ICT is followed by more subtle alterations in consciousness which may be demonstrable for days, weeks or months, depending largely on the number and depth of coma reactions. In unusually severe reactions a Korsakoff-like psychosis may be present for as long as six months. Here, too, as in the post-ECT reactions, these changes generally clear up rather quickly when ICT is terminated. Lobotomized patients show gross mental disorganization for variable periods of time up to many months postoperatively. Patients with more limited operations also show evidences of disturbed awareness, if these are carefully searched for. For example, a post-topectomy patient who was presented on one occasion as presumably free from psychological defect showed a positive face-hand test and paraphasic naming difficulties. Another such case was examined with intravenous sodium amytal and gave a response which was positive for organic brain disease, in spite of an apparent absence of clinical evidence of altered brain function.

Abnormal slowing of the electroencephalogram (EEG) is regularly demonstrable for several months after a course of ECT is terminated. Similar EEG abnormalities are less constantly demonstrable after ICT and psychosurgery, but are nevertheless commonly present. Most drugs which are capable of altering the mood or otherwise affecting mental function like isoniazid, cortisone, ACTH and Antabuse in high dosage also produce abnormal slowing of the EEG as evidence of a generalized disturbance in some aspect of brain function. Generalized slowing of the EEG is quite regularly found in deep-seated mid-line lesions in the region of the third ventricle. Such lesions are commonly associated with a clouding over of general awareness and other psychological alterations.

Patients who give evidence of a generalized abnormality in brain function, show characteristic alterations in the way in which they deal with anxiety. This was particularly well brought out by Weinstein and his co-workers in a series of studies on patients with organic brain disease. The fact of being sick is a source of great anxiety to these patients. Understandably, they are driven by a wish to be rid of the illness. In the fully conscious state this wish runs counter to observable fact. When the patient is asleep it is possible for him to achieve a hallucinatory fulfillment of the wish to be well in a dream; and to the extent that the dream is successful in fulfilling his wish, he is free from anxiety.

Patients with somatic illness who are given the suggestion to dream about their sickness typically have a dream in which physical well-being is the central theme. For example, paraplegic patients will dream that they are walking, enfeebled people will hark back in their dreams to a time when they were more vigorous.

If a brain-injured patient develops a sustained impairment of consciousness due to the progression of his disease, or as a result of neurosurgical intervention, or as a reaction to the radiotherapy of a brain tumor, or in response to ECT, he may develop a psychosis in the course of which he achieves in the waking state a hallucinatory fulfillment of his wish to be well. This may be compared quite accurately to a dream, even though the patient is awake. Depending on his premorbid personality and the degree to which his consciousness is impaired, he may show a complete denial of his organic disability. Or he may accept the main fact of his illness intellectually but deny its catastrophic significance in euphoric exhibitionistic displays. By means of such denials patients are often able to overcome anxieties which would otherwise occupy their thinking. Sometimes a patient achieves a partially successful denial in which he acknowledges that something is wrong with him but he angrily blames his discomfort on others. In other words, he develops a paranoid reaction. The following case exemplifies how the level of general awareness or consciousness influences the way in which the patient copes with the sources of his anxiety.

This patient was a fifty-two-year-old woman suffering from intractable pain as a result of a chronic adhesive arachnoiditis of the lumbosacral cord. At the height of her pain, she was deeply depressed. In an attempt to relieve her suffering, she was given an intensive course of ECT. At the height of the ECT-induced disturbance in brain function, the patient would display a manic reaction. At this time her denial was completely successful. She insisted that she had no pain, no paralysis, no illness, that she was not in a hospital at all but in the home of a friend, having a good time. At this time the face-hand test and the amytal test for organic brain disease were strongly positive. When ECT was stopped and brain function started to improve, the manic reaction gave way to a paranoid reaction. She acknowledged that she was sick but blamed enemies. When the effects of the ECT wore off further, she became fully oriented. Full awareness of the nature of her illness returned and at this time her former depression reappeared. Thus, as impairment in general awareness was greater, her capacity for denial was greater, and as brain function improved and her sensorium cleared, her capacity for denial grew weaker.

A particularly striking phenomenon was observed in the transitions from the manic to the paranoid reaction and from the paranoid to the depressed reaction. At these times, the patient was in a state of indescribable terror. She displayed a delirious reaction which was reminiscent of the catatonic excitement sometimes seen at the onset of a schizophrenic process. These transitional periods seemed to represent states of maximal anxiety resulting from the absence of any psychological means for coping with anxiety.

Thus, almost all the varieties of so-called organic reaction types could be seen in this one patient. The sequence described could be reproduced in this patient by repeated courses of ECT. She demonstrated quite dramatically how the general level of awareness helps determine the way in which psychological defense mechanisms pattern themselves. This case also brought home another fact which is not always appreciated: that depression can represent a way of dealing with anxiety and actually represents a state of relatively decreased suffering.

The denial which this patient used in dealing with her external sources of anxiety has its counterpart in another psychological mechanism of defense, namely repression, which is directed at the internal sources of anxiety to be found in the memory system of the patient. Thus, by lowering the level of general awareness psychologic mechanisms are mobilized which open up new adaptive possibilities for the patient. That there is a definite relationship between the denial of external reality and the repression of painful thoughts which are part of the patient's internal reality is seen in the reactions of postlobotomy patients. In them a denial that they were operated on is as common and as striking an aspect of the postoperative reaction as is, for example, an altered emotional reaction to their delusions.

If the newly mobilized psychological mechanisms serve a usefully adaptive function for the patient, they derive added stability from this fact and may survive long after the organic factors which brought them into being have subsided. Hence a remission after ECT can last for years even though the organic changes subside within a few months after treatment has ended. In other words, the patient utilizes the organic changes to reorganize his psychic life. If this reorganization fulfills the patient's emotional needs well enough, it continues to exist independently of the organic changes themselves.

It would seem then that the capacity to omit from conscious awareness certain psychological data is an important adaptive mechanism, and it probably comes as no surprise that there is a neurophysiological mechanism whereby this can be mediated. Over a period of years, H. W. Magoun and his co-workers have focused their researches on what they called the ascending reticular activating system in the brain stem. This system, which can be compared roughly to the volume dial on a radio, intensifies its activity when signals from the outside come in. This intensification of neuronal activity in the brain stem ascending reticular system results in an activation or an alerting of the cerebral cortex, as a result of which the general level of awareness is increased. The incoming information is scanned as to its meaning on a cortical level by the alerted cortex. If this information is emotionally meaningful to the individual, corticofugal impulses are fired to the activating system and the general level of awareness is further increased. If the data continue to be of special interest, activation of consciousness may occur still further until the percept in question is the object of maximal attention of the individual to the exclusion of everything else. On the other hand, a lesser degree of activation may take place, permitting attention to be shared with other percepts. Or the percept may have been without meaning to the individual, in which case no corticofugal stimulation of the activating system takes place and the percept consumes only an initial minimal quantum of attention.

On the other hand, a percept may arouse overwhelming anxiety—not some fear to which the alerted individual can respond with appropriate corrective behavior, but some inescapable fear, having its origin either in a potentially overwhelming environmental situation or internally from some psychopathological state. In that case, we can picture a flow of corticofugal impulses which decrease the general level of awareness, or "deactivate" the reticular system. Such a corticofugal stream could function as a barrier against stimuli of unbearable emotional intensity. If the total environment were threatening in catastrophic proportions, the resulting "deactivation" is so complete that consciousness is lost. In this way, one may visualize the mechanism whereby an individual faints in the face of some unbearable psychological situation. Lesser degrees of deactivation in such a situation may result not in outright fainting but in a clouded state of consciousness in which the experienced anguish is considerably mitigated. If the source of the anxiety involves not the entire environment but some circumscribed aspect of it, then a more circumscribed type of corticofugal deactivation might take place. The result could be an alteration limited to a specific traumatic perception and a diminution in the capacity of the latter to produce cortical arousal.

These activating neurophysiological mechanisms emphasize that stimuli have a twofold effect. First, they carry information to the cerebral cortex. This is mediated through the direct sensory pathways and relate to the purely intellectual informational aspect of the stimuli. Secondly, they have an emotional impact on the individual. This is mediated indirectly through the reticular activating system. If corticofugal impulses exert a sustained generalized "deactivating" effect on the activating system, this could be expressed on a psychological level as feelings of depersonalization or derealization. More circumscribed deactivating influences via thalamic pathways could be expressed on a psychological level as denial, repression and isolation.

Destructive lesions in the activating system in animals result in EEG-slow-wave activity like that seen in patients after ECT. One wonders whether the therapeutic effect may not depend on an ECT-induced diminution in the reactivity of the activating system, as a result of which previously traumatic experiences are no longer capable of eliciting disagreeably excessive arousal reactions. Sedative drugs or ECT need not act directly on the activating system. They might do so indirectly via corticofugal fibers. This is most likely the site where lobotomy exerts its effect. If the cortex has been firing a pathologically intense stream of "deactivating" impulses at the activating system, then interruption of corticofugal impulses makes possible a variety of release phenomena. With such a complicated interplay of forces it becomes understandable why it is not always possible to predict the new line of defense that the individual will take up when this system has been tampered with.

It has become apparent that the activating system is much more extensive than the ascending reticular system in the brain stem. It seems likely that parts of the temporal lobe and the so-called rhinencephalon are intrinsic parts of a larger activating system. Psychosurgical and pharmacologic explorations of this system may hold the clue to many somatotherapeutic contributions of the future.

The Effect of Somatotherapy on Psychotherapy

The question is often raised, is it possible to do psychoanalytically oriented psychotherapy on patients who have had some form of somatotherapy? This question comes up most frequently in patients who have been relieved of a depression by means of ECT and are then referred for psychotherapy.

Every patient who goes into psychotherapy brings with him his characteristic psychological defenses. In the course of analytically oriented therapy these defenses are systematically undermined. Part of the therapist's skill is to be found in the rate at which he undermines these defenses. If he does it too rapidly, he may harm the patient by the release of unsupportable quantities of anxiety.

In a patient who has had ECT, the psychotherapeutic problem is essentially the same, except possibly for the fact that a patient who was sick enough to require ECT will most likely require even more cautious dissolution of his defenses, and perhaps more active help in elaborating sublimations to take their place. The defenses which the patient brings into psychotherapy after ECT are probably the same as those which he would have elaborated spontaneously if the depression had subsided without special treatment, so that in this sense, too, the problem in psychotherapy is not altered by ECT. Naturally the persistence of organic changes may cause the therapist to assume a more actively supportive role until these changes have subsided.

The patient who has been helped by some form of somatotherapy always has need of psychotherapy in one form or another. Not to consolidate these gains by a total rational approach to the emotional needs of the patient is to incur unnecessary therapeutic failure.

SELECTED REFERENCES

JASPER, H.; et al.: Corticofugal Projections to the Brain Stem. *A.M.A. Arch. Neurol. & Psychiat.*, 67:155, 1952.

KALINOWSKY, L. B.; HOCH, P. H.: Shock Treatments, Psychosurgery and Other Somatic Treatments in Psychiatry (2nd ed.). New York: Grune & Stratton, 1952.
This well-known textbook has proven its value to the practicing psychiatrist over a period of years. Based on a vast personal experience and thorough coverage of the literature, it is a dependable and authoritative source of information.

LIBERSON, W. T.: Current Evaluation of Electric Convulsive Therapy. The Correlation of the Parameters of Electric Current with Physiologic and Psychologic Changes. In *Psychiatric Treatment* (Proceedings of the Association for Research in Nervous and Mental Disease, Vol. XXXI). Baltimore: Williams & Wilkins, 1953.

LINDSLEY, D. B.; et al.: Effect Upon the EEG of Acute Injury to the Brain Stem Activating System. *EEG Clin. Neurophysiol.*, 1:455, 1949.

LINN, L.: Psychological Implications of the "Activating System." *Am. J. Psychiat.*, 110:61, 1953.

MAGOUN, H. W.: An Ascending Reticular Activating System in the Brain Stem. *A.M.A. Arch. Neurol. & Psychiat.*, 67:145, 1952.

Proceedings of the Third (1951) Research Conference on Psychosurgery of the National Institute of Mental Health. Supt. of Documents, U.S. Government Printing Office, Washington, D. C.

    The contributions and discussion of a distinguished group of scientists. The social service contributions are particularly noteworthy.

SARGANT, W.; SLATER, E.: *An Introduction to Physical Methods of Treatment in Psychiatry* (3rd ed.) . Baltimore: Williams & Wilkins, 1954.

    This book is based on the vast personal experience of the authors. As such it is a recommended companion piece to the volume by Kalinowski and Hoch.

STEVENSON, G. H.; GEOGHEGAN, J. J.: Prophylactic Electroshock. *Am. J. Psychiat.*, 107:743, 1951.

    The technique and results of outpatient ECT used for maintenance purposes.

WEINSTEIN, E. A.; KAHN, R. L.: *Denial of Illness: Symbolic and Physiological Manifestations.* Springfield, Ill.: C. C. Thomas, in press.

    Based on the original researches of the authors, this monograph contains much data of theoretical and practical significance in the correlation of psychological phenomena with brain function.

Chapter IV

RECREATIONAL THERAPY

Regression in the Service of the Ego

One of the major propositions of modern psychiatry is that the psychological differences between so-called normality and mental disease are essentially quantitative ones. Infantile yearnings persist in the most mature of adults just as certainly as they do in patients. What is more, the normal adult obtains fulfillment of his childish wishes, too. It is the way in which he achieves this fulfillment that distinguishes him primarily from the patient. When a patient becomes passive, helpless and dependent, or when he gives direct expression to infantile impulses such as his masturbatory desires or his wish to play with feces, or when he chooses to indulge in endless daydreams of self-aggrandizement, we say that he has regressed. That is to say, he has resumed a mode of adaptation to his environment which was normal in early childhood but is an anachronism in the life of the adult. What makes this regressive behavior evidence of illness, however, is not only the form which it takes but also the fact that it is no longer under his control. The normal adult, on the other hand, is able to regress in a controlled fashion, for as long as he wants and to the degree that he wants in the process of discharging certain tensions which arise in his daily life from conflicts between childhood wishes and the demands of reality. Controlled regression which serves so important a role in the process of adaptation has been called "regression in the service of the ego" (Kris). Recreational activity in general represents an important example of this.

Theory of Play

What characterizes recreation is its quality of irresponsibility, spontaneity, enthusiasm, hilarity, and other relatively uncontrolled expressions of emotion. During play, the adult is permitted to become a "kid" again. This is not only socially approved, but the capacity to act childishly in a controlled setting is regarded as a distinct asset. In play it is permitted to vent aggressive feelings against one's opponent. It is possible even to urge out loud for some one to "kill the ump"—who may represent symbolically the bad parent who makes unfair decisions. In games it is permitted to triumph over parent figures, so that patients can play against attendants, for example, and be permitted the pleasure of beating them. A mounting peak of excitement culminating in a victorious climax in a card game may conceal forbidden sexual impulses. Repetitive motor discharge in games may evoke happy childhood memories associated with early experiments in motor mastery. The lonely competitive lives to which so many people are doomed find relief in the joint effort and team spirit of a Sunday baseball game. Even if one does not actually participate in the game, he may aggrandize himself vicariously by identifying with the hero on the ball field, the symbolic, strong, good father figure who can accomplish anything he chooses.

Standing guard over regression are the rules of the game, a spirit of fair play and the good sportsmanship which is part of adult recreation. These are the connections with reality which are never dropped and by means of which control is maintained over regressive impulses.

In sharing the emotional reactions of one's neighbors in rooting for the home team, by joining them in their joy, their rage, their fears and their sorrow, spectators are drawn more closely to each other, and to that extent loneliness is lessened. In these make-believe emotional experiences, neurotic anxieties are diminished, feelings of exhilaration and fulfillment are aroused, and as a result people return to work with new energy. It is in this sense that recreation has been properly called a process of re-creation. An ability to play is a necessary component in the psychological make-up of the normal adult. Where it is deficient a good program of psychotherapy requires that we inculcate it and encourage it.

The preferred channels for controlled regression in the service of the ego are highly personalized matters. It is not necessarily in the form of sports. Artistic interests of all kind fulfill this function too. Here, as in athletics, one may find fulfillment through an active role or in the form of audience participation. The essence of the aesthetic experience is to be found in the combination of infantile fulfillment on the one hand and the preservation of adult standards of aesthetic appreciation on the other. The emotionally mature spectator may lose himself in a movie or a play, yet never so completely that he ceases to evaluate the quality of the acting, the excellence of the production, or the musical score. If these adult functions are surrendered entirely, then the activity becomes more like childhood daydreaming than a genuine artistic experience.

Because of the primitive currents of feeling that are impinged upon in these controlled regressions, nonverbal means of expression are often employed. Bodily movements or musical sounds may substitute for verbalized ideas. Rhythm, color, design may be employed to convey an emotion. It has been said that a picture is worth a thousand words. The same may be said of a song, or a dance. In the regression which characterizes mental illness there is a tendency to retreat from the normal use of words and to rely again upon preverbal means of communication. In these instances, recreational activity affords a special opportunity with which to contact the patients, to learn about their fears and to give them reassurance on a level that they can accept.

Prescribing Recreational Therapy

It would follow from these theoretical considerations that one cannot "prescribe" recreational therapy in the sense that we order one form of it rather than another. All we can do is to search, painstakingly, for those channels of controlled regression which are preferred by a given patient. The ward personnel are often the ones most successful in eliciting from the patient his preferred recreational outlets. Social service may help us in this regard with information from the family. Armed with factual data of that kind we can then write an individualized prescription. Naturally, there will be some severely constricted individuals in whom natural inclinations will be more difficult to find, and in such instances we may have to improvise.

Once the prescription is written, as it were, the psychiatrist must implement it by every means at his disposal. This will be done most effectively if the psychiatrist keeps in mind the theory of play and the needs of each patient. Because of the symbolic meaning of play as a disguised fulfillment of infantile wishes, play often generates feelings of self-consciousness and guilt. The active participation of hospital personnel in these activities as well as the approving and encouraging presence of the psychiatrist will go far in overcoming these inhibitions. In the interest of spontaneity, ward play materials should not be kept locked up but should be made available for the patient's use as the whim strikes him. Ward personnel should be made to understand, too, that these play materials are expendable. That is to say, the use, not the preservation, of play materials is to be encouraged.

Integrating Recreational Therapy into the Total Treatment Program

In addition to the specific function of providing opportunities for controlled regression, recreational therapy also provides a setting for therapeutically useful human relationships. Pathologically dormant social feelings may be aroused in the group spirit of a ball team. Most important of all are the relationships which patients develop with the recreational therapists. In the informal recreational setting, the patient may communicate previously withheld personal matters. It is common, for example, for patients to speak to the recreational therapist of their loneliness. The therapist with understanding of the motivations and emotional needs of the mentally ill is more likely to utilize such communications constructively. The following case history is a good example of this.

A twenty-seven-year-old schizophrenic man had been on the disturbed ward of an Army general hospital for four months. For most of this time he was seclusive, uncommunicative, and given to impulsive destructive behavior. A recreational therapist began spending every afternoon on this ward, participating in games with small groups of patients. There was never any special attention paid to this patient, nor any pressure brought to bear upon him to join the group, only a smile and a nod in his direction when the recreational therapist entered and left the ward. After about two weeks the recreational therapist noted that the patient came over timidly and watched the games. This passive participation was accepted in a friendly manner. At the end of the third day of this behavior he timidly stopped the recreational therapist as she was leaving. He asked hesitantly if she knew if he would be allowed to have any visitors. An insensitive person might have said "yes" and let it go at that. Feeling, however, that this was his first reaching out toward some one, she said that this sounded like a very important question to her and she would make inquiry for him. Fifteen minutes later she returned to the ward with a member of the social service department who assured the patient that she would work on this problem. In a few days she was able to arrange for a relative to visit him, his first contact with his family after two years of separation. A favorable change in his clinical picture began at once. He became tidy, he ate and slept more normally, and he began to communicate freely for the first time since entering the hospital. The social worker engaged him in discussions of vocational planning and encouraged him to re-establish a relationship by mail with a girl to whom he had not written for a long time. Imbued with enthusiasm as a result of a letter from this girl, he became active in the occupational therapy shop and made a present for her. He was able to leave on a trial visit about one month after his initial approach to the recreational therapist.

The foregoing history represents a not uncommon experience. Other instances may be cited in which the first tentative contacts with reality were made through the recreational therapist, the occupational therapist or some other member of the treatment team. When this happens, the worker in question, if properly trained to expect it, will exploit this contact to its fullest therapeutic advantage.

A Recreational Program on Every Ward

The recreational program is so important that it should be constituted as a separate department with its own director and staff. The recreational director should attend the hospital staff meetings and be alerted to the place of his department in the total treatment program. No matter how large a staff the hospital permits him to have, it can never by itself be large enough to fulfill the hospital needs. As a result, he will have to involve as many extra people as his ingenuity can contrive. A most important part of his work will be to set up recreational programs on every ward of the hospital.

The teaching program for attendants should include at least two weeks of training in the recreational therapy department. The aim of this training is to equip every attendant to set up a recreational program on his own ward. This involves not only instructing him in the general principles of recreational therapy but exploring systematically the special skills and interests of each attendant as they impinge upon the program. It is advisable to collect this information by means of a questionnaire. Does he prefer group activities, or activities with individual patients? In groups, is he prepared to lead in some specific activity such as sports, music, art, reading or other cultural activities, a hobby club, for example? Or does he prefer to participate in informal groups, such as chatting, playing cards, joining patients in motion picture showings and television? By means of a systematic approach every attendant can be imbued with the feeling that he is making a specific contribution to the recreational program.

Patients enjoy playing with hospital personnel, not only in individual games but in teams. The formation of employee teams and patient teams which play against each other will arouse considerable interest among patients, particularly if properly publicized. For the proper integration of these activities into the hospital treatment program it is important to inculcate in the attendants some understanding of the theory of play and its role in psychiatric treatment.

The Use of Volunteers

The success of the recreational program depends to an important degree upon the help of volunteers. The recruiting of volunteers for hospital work is an important question in its own right and is taken up in Chapter XIII. However, the recreational director must make his needs known to those actively involved in work with volunteers. For example, he may ask for dance instructors, music teachers, dramatic coaches, swimming and other athletic instructors, beauty parlor technicians, donations of books, phonograph records, musical instruments, or sheet music. Not only will he concern himself with bringing volunteer recreational workers into the hospital, but—possibly of greater importance—he will seek volunteers to procure recreation for the patients outside of the hospital in the form of passes for ball games, circuses, theaters, concerts, and amusement parks. It is advisable to have hospital buses for the transportation of patients to and from such extramural activities. However, the community may provide extra transportation for special occasions. In some communities, women have had social evenings for patients in their own homes. These were usually arranged for patients ready for trial visit who benefited from such evenings as preparatory stages in returning to the community. Golf and tennis facilities in public parks can be utilized. Daily outdoor activities are to be provided for the largest possible percentage of patients. Nature walks and gardening are popular outdoor activities in some hospitals. An evening program should be available as well as one during the day and should be in operation seven days a week if possible. Such an ambitious program is not possible without the help of volunteers.

Keeping Records

Orderly records of the observations made by recreational therapists and their aides will facilitate the task of integrating this program with other therapies. Records should be simple, kept preferably on a separate mimeographed form headed "Observation Notes: Recreation." One entry should include the interests of the patient as learned from relatives and from the observations of personnel. It should be noted whether the patient participates actively, as an observer, or in some other passive role. His capacity for relationships with the patients as a group in teams and with individual patients and therapists should also be noted. Characteristic reactions under stress should be described, as well as psychological areas of particular vulnerability. Progress notes should include evidence of changes, in the direction of improvement or regression. Most im-

portant, there should be an entry for recommendations to other departments. It is through such recommendations that team work can be fostered.

Movies

Motion picture showings are provided in almost all state hospitals.
In addition to the showings in the hospital theater, there ought to be at
least one sixteen millimeter sound projector available for ward use for
patients who are unable to attend the general performances. Most movies
shown to patients are selected purely on the basis of their availability.
No attempt is made, by and large, to select movies on the basis of content. As a matter of fact, we do not have enough information to know
how to select movies for our patients from a psychotherapeutic point of
view. The reactions of psychotic patients to motion pictures has never
been systematically studied, a most important area for research. I have
seen patients spend restless nights and require sedation after movies portraying uncontrolled violence. We have to decide what we want our
movies to do for patients and then select our program accordingly. It
would seem senseless to stir up their anxieties unless this is done in small
groups under controlled conditions as part of a specific plan of group
therapy. It would seem as if movies portraying the beauty of life and the
satisfactions that come from positive values would be therapeutically
more helpful. If we studied the problem carefully we might decide, for
example, to show our patients nothing but comedies and musicals. Haphazard selections and indiscriminate showings are contrary to the whole
philosophy of a therapeutic community.

For the titles of movies which may be used in group therapy with
patients the motion picture catalogues listed at the end of Chapter XXIX
may be consulted.

Television

Television has introduced an instrument of incalculable potential
therapeutic value. When a television set is placed on a disturbed ward,
the number of "violent" episodes decreases at once. One can find objective
evidence of this fact in the diminished use of sedation. When it is recalled
that lobotomies are sometimes justified simply because they diminish the
number of violent outbursts on a ward, then television emerges as a more
gentle means of achieving the same result. Television exercises a curiously
intense hold on the individual's attention. That primitive emotional
mechanisms are involved is indicated by reports of parents that children

too young to comprehend what is going on will watch a television program with transfixed attention. It has even been reported that dogs will lie before the illuminated television screen similarly fascinated. This extraordinary attention-fixing capacity of television can be readily confirmed. Chronic agitated patients will sit quietly before a television set for hours on end. Curiously, even deteriorated schizophrenics are selective in their interests. They will watch some programs and turn their backs on others. Here, as in the movies, is a situation which calls for research. No one has studied what television means to these patients, what programs they prefer, and why. Out of the answers to these questions may well emerge a significant advance in group psychotherapy. If we knew what to present, psychotherapeutically potent material could be administered to patients thus transfixed to the television screen. The finest talent could be recruited for specially prepared films to be telecast to every state hospital ward in the land as part of a vast program of group psychotherapy.

Many times I have entered wards and seen the television set turned off and locked away for safekeeping while disturbed patients move about, idle and restless. Whereas patients will often attempt to destroy radios, I have never heard of a single instance where a patient injured a television set. This is perhaps another measure of the intensity of the pleasure which patients derive from television. In any event, television sets are so rarely the objects of destructive attacks by patients that it seems foolish to keep these therapeutically valuable instruments locked away for the largest part of the day. Inasmuch as it can be anticipated that television will play an increasingly important role on the wards of our mental hospitals, the installation of a master antenna should be included in the construction of all large mental hospital buildings.

Dance

Many workers have confirmed the importance of dancing as a psychotherapeutic procedure. Patients are sometimes attracted to modern expressive dancing. If given a genuine opportunity for self-expression, the productions which the patient brings in this way may be invaluable in understanding the psychodynamics of his illness. It has often been observed that patients who are verbally uncommunicative will express themselves quite freely in this more primitive fashion. Formal dancing, too, is of great value. The awkward, faltering beginnings of deteriorated schizophrenics gradually give way to more graceful performances in ball room dancing. Square dancing too has been used. In addition to the release of inner tensions, the opportunities for self-expression, and the feeling of personal accomplishment which occurs in dancing, there is an intensely socializing influence in formal dancing, too. Patients find themselves enjoying each other's company. The party setting in which the dancing takes place contributes to closer relationships between patients and those who take care of them. It has been observed that patients who are too shy to participate in dancing will do so if the psychiatrist attends the dance sessions. Such patients may dance to seek his approval or because his friendly presence diminishes guilt feelings aroused by the dancing.

Bibliotherapy

Many people turn to books for relief of mental suffering. Each year they buy thousands of books on psychology in their search for relief from their emotional woes. Although many of these books are written in sincerity by earnest and well-trained individuals, it is an unfortunate matter of record that solitary readings of such books rarely contribute significantly to the improvement of the mentally ill. An exception is to be found in the Bible which has been a source of comfort to troubled minds for many centuries.

A good book read in a group, on the other hand, is a powerful socializing force and therefore an agent capable of promoting mental health. The Great Books Foundation has demonstrated this fact in their nationwide reading and discussion program. In libraries and other community centers all over the country they have brought together groups of lay people, provided them with inexpensive sets of books and trained discussion leaders and launched them on the road to greater emotional maturity. Their program is based on the following premises:

That men and women are capable of thinking for themselves.

That there are certain basic problems which have confronted mankind in every era.

That some of mankind's best thinking on these problems is to be found in books written by the great thinkers and writers of the past.

That through reading these books and discussing them with their friends and neighbors, individuals can educate themselves and find better solutions to their daily problems.

That education is a continuing activity, not dependent upon school attendance.

J. W. Powell reported his experiences with this program as applied to several groups of patients in mental hospitals. He stated that an initially competitive attitude is characteristically replaced in time by a wish to learn from each other. In the discussions there is a growth of mutual respect, in which the discussion leader is viewed increasingly as one of the group rather than as a detached superior. The leader emphasizes the fact that the great authors are the teachers, for they are the ones who bring knowledge and originality to the discussion. The leaders themselves act as catalysts for the interaction of the minds of the group with each other and with the authors. These discussions provide a non-threatening situation which emphasizes reality. Groups consisting of approximately fifteen patients each meet once a week for one and a half to two hours. Each group begins by reading the Declaration of Independence, a brief social document with proven power to evoke the basic personal orientation toward life in the discussants. Other books included are Plutarch's *Lives of Alexander the Great and Julius Caesar,* selections from St. Augustine's *Confessions, Crime and Punishment,* and others. In each of these books the patients were quick to see basic human motivations in the lives of others which resembled their own. Powell also used tape recordings of the patients' discussions, playing them back to the patients and comparing them with recordings of discussions of those same books by "normal" groups. By such comparisons it was often possible to demonstrate to them the ways in which their reasoning coincided with that of discussion groups in the community, thereby emphasizing the intact or normal ego which exists in all patients, however psychotic they may be.

The use of the Great Books Discussion Program in mental hospitals is relatively untried. It represents an exciting approach to group therapy that is deserving of study.

A visit to the commissary of the average state hospital will reveal an extraordinary collection of paper-covered books for sale. Lurid covers advertise stories of violence and passion. It is inconceivable that such books are beneficial from a psychotherapeutic point of view. Books which emphasize wholesome values should be selected for mental hospital libraries (see Appendix B for suggested titles).

Every hospital should have a central library with an attractively furnished reading lounge where patients may be drawn closer to each other by their common interest in books. There should also be a book cart service available to those patients who are unable to leave the ward. Even where a formal Great Books Discussion Program cannot be organized, volunteers enjoy reading aloud to patients on the ward, and are often successful in organizing informal, flexible group readings and discussions which are of therapeutic value.

Music

Music is known to influence the receptivity of people to emotions and ideas. That is why it is used so extensively in churches, movies, theaters, and political rallies. In view of this fact it would seem logical to make use of music to increase the receptivity of the mentally ill to psychotherapeutically useful emotions and ideas.

Music has the capacity to compel certain automatic responses in people, at times with almost irresistible force. An impulse to beat time is an example of this, or the impulse to march, dance or hum a tune. By arousing an identical impulse in many separate people it promotes group feeling. Since so much of psychiatric treatment is aimed at socializing isolated individuals, this property of music is of therapeutic importance.

Along with these primarily rhythmic aspects of music is melody. Many familiar melodies are taught in early childhood and are known almost universally. For most people they hark back to a relatively untroubled time of life and hence call forth feelings of contentment. This is an added factor in music which makes for group feeling. A musical background is provided in some hospitals for patients as they emerge from shock treatment. It has been claimed, for example, that loud bright jazz music shortens the period of postconvulsive confusion in patients receiving ECT. Mentally defective children are less prone to episodes of disorganized behavior if they are involved in group musical activities.

In addition to its group effects, music elicits personalized psychological responses which are determined by the cultural and educational background of the individual as well as the memories which are aroused by a given piece of music. This quality of music has been used by some as a projective technique in a group setting, in which patients are asked to write or to say the thoughts that a particular piece of music calls forth. Material obtained in this way may be of diagnostic significance, may clarify the psychodynamics or motivations of a given patient, or may give rise to therapeutically fruitful group discussions.

Music appreciation may be a passive or an active experience. In its most extreme form passive appreciation consists of an autistic reverie induced by music. This property of music is undesirable from a psychotherapeutic point of view, particularly in the case of patients whose readiness to lapse into autistic reveries constitutes a major aspect of their mental illness. Accordingly, active forms of musical appreciation are to be encouraged. All listening is not necessarily passive. A person who listens critically and with technical appreciation can be said to listen actively.

The ideal form of active musical appreciation is the actual making of music, in the form of composing it, playing it and singing it.

The musical activities program in a mental hospital includes group singing, vocal instruction, rhythm band work, small instrumental ensembles, bands, orchestras, individual instruction in note reading and playing of instruments. Such a program calls for a sheet music library, a collection of instruments, and a staff of instructors and leaders. Music is employed as an accompaniment to dancing, marching, gymnastics and calisthenics. Theatricals and social activities may be provided by visiting talent or by the patients themselves. Music plays an important role in the religious program of the hospital.

With such varied application it is advisable to have a single director who is responsible for the music program and who endeavors to integrate the available facilities into the therapeutic needs of the hospital.

After mentioning the many ways in which music can serve it is well to recall that music can be overdone. Public address systems on the wards of a mental hospital which pour out an endless stream of music can be harassing as well. Therefore, recorded and broadcast musical presentations should be limited and preferably made available in a special room which patients can avoid as well as frequent voluntarily.

An interest in the psychology of musical enjoyment has grown in recent years, particularly as this applies to psychotherapy. It has been said that high register notes tend to increase tension, low register notes to decrease it. Tension tends to mount during certain portions of a piece and to fall away with the final resolution of a theme. In many persons musical pleasure seems to be associated with certain fixed expectations concerning melody, harmony, rhythm and resolution. What is familiar is pleasing and relaxing, what is not in line with their musical expectations is disturbing. Other people, on the other hand, derive their greatest pleasure in music from the unusual or unexpected. The appreciation of modern music may be an expression of the latter. The psychological implications of these differences and their application to psychotherapy are problems for research.

Swimming

There has been a trend in veterans hospitals to provide a pool which can be utilized for swimming as well as for hydrotherapy. Thus, the well-known relaxing effects of hydrotherapy in its traditional form can be combined and expanded into a whole program of aquatic activities, including instructions in swimming and diving, races and various games.

Massage to improve muscle tone and circulation, as well as ultraviolet therapy to improve skin color can be incorporated in the aquatic program.

The Beauty Parlor and Barber Shop

The importance of keeping patients well groomed to maintain their self-esteem is obvious. In some hospitals, a skilled beautician with the assistance of an attendant trains a corps of patients to maintain these services for other patients. In addition to the expected increase in self-respect, this program resulted in friendships between patients, improved family relations and in the vocational rehabilitation of some chronic patients. A broadcast musical program can liven the atmosphere of the beauty parlor.

These items by no means exhaust all the aspects of the recreational therapy program of a mental hospital. Ingenuity and an alert dedication to the idea of recreation as therapy will lead to more ideas. At all times, however, the theory of recreational therapy must serve as a guide, and the psychiatrist must be responsible for the integration of this program into the total treatment program.

SELECTED REFERENCES

A Guide for Leaders of "Great Books" Discussion Groups. Chicago: Great Books Foundation.

BLAIN, D.; VOSBURGH, P.: Recreational Trends in North American Mental Institutions. Washington, D.C.: American Psychiatric Assn. Mental Hospital Service.
    A short pamphlet which outlines the philosophy of recreational therapy, current trends and needs.

HANNIGAN, M. C.: Hospital-wide Group Bibliotherapy Program. The Bookmark, New York State Library, 1954.
    This article contains a list of books which have proved of value in this program. The titles are arranged according to the type of ward in which they have proved most useful. (See Appendix B.)

KRIS, E.: Psychoanalytic Explorations in Art. New York: International Universities Press, 1952.
    A collection of papers which illuminates the psychological mechanisms involved in creative artistic activity both in normal and psychopathological states.

MARTIN, D. W.; BEAVER, N.: A Preliminary Report on the Use of the Dance as an Adjuvant in the Therapy of Schizophrenics. Psychiat. Quart. Supplement, 25:176, 1951.

MCCONNELL, G. F.: The Doctor Prescribes Beauty: "Vanity Shop" is an important aid in the treatment of mental patients. Modern Hospital, 73:63, 1949.
    A detailed description of the organization of a beauty parlor operated by patients.

MILLER, A.: Growing with Music: A Program for the Mentally Retarded. Exceptional Children, 20:305, 1954.

PODOLSKY, E., ed.:*Music Therapy*. New York: Philosophical Library, 1954.
A collection of papers dealing with various uses of music as therapy. Contains illustrative clinical material.
POWELL, J. W.: Group Reading in Mental Hospitals. *Psychiatry,* 13:213, 1950.
A detailed study of the Great Books Program applied to a mental hospital.
ROSEN, E.: Dance as Therapy for the Mentally Ill. *Teachers College Record,* 55:215, 1954.
VAN DE WALL, W.: *Music in Hospitals*. New York: Russell Sage Foundation, 1946.
A useful and comprehensive summary of the place of music in mental hospitals.

Chapter V

OCCUPATIONAL AND VOCATIONAL THERAPY

Theory of Work

To some people the story of Adam and Eve in the garden of Eden is an account in allegorical form of the development of the individual from the innocence and carefree irresponsibility of childhood to the sometimes grim reality of adult life. A child has no occupation. Its right to freedom from the necessity of work is universally accepted, and in civilized countries this right is protected by law. But there comes a time in everyone's life to put childhood ways aside and the right of the child to idleness is replaced by a no less deeply rooted feeling about the importance of work for the grownup. The development of specific capacities or skills, which are of importance to the community, is intimately bound up with the process of psychological development. This process contributes in a fundamental way to the transition from the stage of helpless dependency characteristic of early childhood to the self-sufficiency and the capacity to give to others characteristic of emotional maturity.

To a considerable extent, the adult's conception of himself is given substance by his work. If you ask a child "what are you?" he is likely to answer "a boy" or "a girl" as the case may be. The same question addressed to an adult is more likely to result in, "a housewife," "an electrician," "a bookkeeper." If an adult has a definite occupation or profession, a certain basic strength of ego is necessarily present, whereas the absence of a definite occupation ordinarily bespeaks an enfeebled ego structure.

Work contributes to the self-esteem of the individual. The accomplishment of a specific task is associated with irreplaceable satisfactions. Pride of craftsmanship, and a feeling of certainty about one's powers, give direction and meaning to life. Work is associated with a product or a service which links an individual to his fellows and gives him a sense of social belonging. He develops a feeling of indispensability to his organization, to his family and at times to society at large which contributes to his self-respect. During the intensified production schedules of World War II, when more attention was paid to the problem of motivation in the worker, it was realized that a sense of pride in the product of his labor greatly intensified the efforts of the worker. To exploit this fact attempts were made to overcome the impersonality and detachment engendered by the conveyor systems of modern mass production and to develop in its place a sense of personal accomplishment with respect to the final product. If the worker was made to feel that this product was important to society, then the positive emotional aspects of his work were augmented still more. Social life tends to develop around one's work. People who work together will commonly choose to relax and play together. Their wives and children are drawn together by this fellowship. Many employers foster a family feeling among their workers, not only by sponsoring group recreational activities but also by providing insurance protection and other evidences of concern for the worker and his family in the event of illness or advancing age. Union membership also contributes to the emotional significance of work. The Union headquarters is usually a social center where workers congregate for leisure time activities or during periods of unemployment. The Union provides the worker with a greater sense of control over his destiny. He is usually protected by a Union insurance plan with medical care and hospitalization. Retired older workers too are drawn to the Union headquarters where the round of daily activities helps them pass the time in an environment which supports their self-respect.

In addition to these important spiritual factors, there are material rewards as well. The acquisition of money represents probably the major motivating force behind the incentive to work in our culture. Through the acquisition of the means to purchase what he values most, each person becomes the arbiter of his own final reward system. Extra pay as an incentive for overtime work is standard in our society. The amount of an individual's income becomes a conspicuous measure of the importance of his contribution to society. The capacity to purchase certain luxuries becomes a source of social prestige.

Work is an important means for sublimating instinctual drives. A man's tool as an unconscious symbol of his masculinity is an idea that has invaded consciousness in modern slang. The size of one's "bankroll" as an unconscious measure of potency has invaded consciousness via popular usage in the German language (vermögend—material means, potency). Tender feelings toward the product of one's labor, whether it is a woman who labors to have a child or an artist who labors to complete a picture, are well known. The sublimation of aggressive impulses is involved in almost all work. This, in fact, is one of the qualities of work, that it permits the channeling of destructive impulses into socially useful activities, whether it is a carpenter who drives in a nail or a surgeon who amputates an extremity. Work provides an outlet for ambitiousness and sibling rivalry. The idea of working is inculcated by parents as a duty. Sooner or later the child learns that he has to work, that he must contribute his share to the community of family living. Thus, idleness can give rise to guilt and conversely hard work can be an expiation of guilt feelings, a masochistic act of restitution. In adult life, an employee will tend to establish relationships with an employer which are based on childhood experiences with his own parents, whether in the form of acquiesence or rebellion. The need to win the approving love of a protective parent is often a powerful motivating force in the compulsively conscientious worker. The neurotic immutability of these needs is sometimes seen in psychoanalytic studies of people who have been accepted as partners or who have become owners in a business where they worked for many years as employees. The acquisition of the associated adult responsibilities, and the need to effect basic alterations in their relationships to others, may give rise to such quantities of anxiety and depression that the mechanisms for emotional adaptation break down.

That work can serve defensive functions is a familiar fact. "Work brings its own relief. He who most idle is has the most of grief." There are compulsive workers who apply themselves grimly and joylessly to their appointed tasks as a device to ward off feelings and impulses to which they are unable to adapt.

In view of the many human needs that work fulfills, it becomes understandable why many people are unable to tolerate idleness, and are overwhelmed with anxiety and depression every Sunday, holiday, summer vacation or other period of enforced idleness. It follows, too, that a program of treatment of the emotionally ill, which omits vocational rehabilitation is unthinkable.

Work History

Every psychiatric history should include a detailed work history. It has been suggested by Rennie and his co-workers that the following items be covered.

What did the patient do before he was hospitalized?

Did the patient's previous employment contribute to his breakdown?

If dissatisfaction is expressed concerning former employment, is this related to mechanical or routine features of the job, or with the human relations aspect?

Does the patient want to return to his former job, or does he want to get into a different type of work?

Is the patient worried about prospects of employment after being put on convalescent status?

Is the patient interested in special training which will equip him with a more definite skill?

In the case of young patients with little or no work experience, what do they think they would like to do? It is worth knowing their wishes even if they are unrealistic.

What are the patient's preferences and aversions with regard to work? These may be concerned with such factors as moving about or remaining in one place; gross movements or hand-finger dexterity; co-operation with many people, few people, work by himself; attitude toward noisy jobs; wish for variety or a definite and fixed routine; directing or supervising others; white-collar work or labor; opportunities to express initiative; capacity to take orders; attitude toward dirt and mess as part of job; use of sharp instruments; indoor or outdoor work; work with living things, on farm or elsewhere.

A work history should include a list of all the jobs that the patient has held, in so far as this is feasible. A history of frequent job changes is often an indication of the presence of a psychopathological process and may help date more accurately the onset of the patient's illness. Detailed inquiry concerning reasons for job changes may uncover early paranoid trends, phobic reactions, hypochondriasis, or alcoholism.

If the patient works for an organization that concerns itself with the welfare of its sick employees, it should be contacted, with the permission of the family, and further work history obtained. This should include a clarification of his status in the firm on recovery from his illness. Representatives from the firm should be invited to visit the patient. If he belongs to a Union, it should be similarly notified and its co-operation obtained as far as securing more data about the patient, protecting his Union status, writing him, visiting him and participating in his vocational rehabilitation.

Place of Vocational Rehabilitation in the Treatment Plan

By this time most of us have heard of the legendary patient in a mental hospital who was told by her psychiatrist, "You are cured. Now go out and find your niche in life." Needless to say, this patient quickly returned to the hospital because the only niche to which she was able to adapt was that which she had carved out for herself in the hospital, and because preparation for community living had been omitted in the hospital's treatment program. Maxwell Jones has said in his book on the *Therapeutic Community*:

> I have seen what appears to be a most sincere attempt to give the patient the best possible treatment, spoilt by a failure to distinguish between a hospital role and a normal community role. In these hospitals everything possible was done to make the patient's stay pleasant and interesting; even when the patient was nearing discharge, the planned day was designed to please him rather than to prepare him for his outside role. The result of this was that frequently the patient was unable to settle down when discharged to his home, and he soon found his way back to the hospital. [In the therapeutic community] we have tried to avoid this error and have stressed the ultimate job goal from the time of the patient's admission. The cultural pressure of the [therapeutic] community is directed towards his acceptance of a more useful social role, which may then appear desirable because of his growing identification with the group. This insistence on a work goal is much more unpleasant for both patients and staff than the more usual type of hospital environment but it is more realistic and probably yields better results in the long run.

Occupational Therapy: A Bridge Between Recreation and Work

In all hospitals a distinction is made between occupational and vocational therapy even though the two words have much in common from a semantic point of view. All too frequently occupational therapy seems to concern itself with the problem of occupying the patient's time. Its primary concern seems to be the elimination of idleness. It is sometimes contended that useful products should not be made in occupational therapy, but then it is added in the same breath that patients often enjoy making presents for their families. It goes without saying that occupational therapy has specific purposes which must be understood if it is to be utilized effectively.

Some of the confusion about occupational therapy derives from the fact that it constitutes a bridge between recreation and real work. The obligatory pressures brought to bear in real work situations do not exist in occupational therapy. A useful product does not have to result necessarily from occupational therapy, even though it usually does. There is much about occupational therapy that is playful, so that it is sometimes hard to designate a given activity as belonging to the category of work or of play. As a result, jurisdictional disputes may occur in state hospitals, and the psychiatrist must sometimes mediate between warring departments, which compete with each other for a given patient—a seeming absurdity but a fact nonetheless. As a general principle, a genuine work assignment within the hospital which fulfills the patient's therapeutic needs should take precedent over the occupational therapy shop (O.T.). When the patient is not yet ready for work because of mental illness, then occupational therapy is employed as a step in that direction. However, the potential contribution of occupational therapy goes far beyond simple preparation for work.

Specific Characteristics of Occupational Therapy

Unlike a true work situation the patient is permitted considerable latitude in the choice of his project, material, manner of work and in the disposition of the final product. It is easier for the patient to regulate the emotional distance between himself and other patients in O.T. than it is at a regular job. In his status as a patient his relationship to the occupational therapist is clearly defined. The therapist is trained to make professionally competent observations concerning the patient's verbal productions and behavior in O.T. The therapist's records provide data of importance to the psychiatrist in understanding the patient and in planning treatment.

O.T. provides opportunities for the expression of hostility in the controlled and permitted destruction of materials. Painstaking detail work may facilitate repression and motor control, thereby replacing psychotic activity with more normal behavior and ideation. In a setting where expectations and standards are minimal, opportunities for release of tension by regressive behavior and acting out are great. An insecure patient may obtain much needed approbation, or a feeling of being protected while receiving detailed instruction from the therapist. Competitive urges are given opportunity for expression. The pleasures of co-operative endeavor can also be fostered. Patients with a great fear of their own passivity can be relieved of paranoid tensions by means of opportunities to take control in O.T. projects. Inhibited patients can be encouraged to become more self-assertive in their use of tools and materials. A severely depressed patient may accept some monotonous drudgery as a psychologically necessary act of expiation for an imagined sin. Patients with difficulties that involve sexual identification can be given projects calculated to fortify healthy ego strivings.

Functions of Occupational Therapy

It has been said that a major function of O.T. is to prepare the patient for work. Specific skills may be inculcated in O.T. which are applicable elsewhere in genuine work assignments. For example, patients may learn to type, to paint signs and posters, and to repair clothing and furniture.

Diagnostically useful data can be obtained from the patient's behavior and verbalizations, from his choice of project, his selection of materials and his manner of working with them, and from his attitude toward the finished product. A patient may express great love for a member of his family and work on a present with considerable care only to spoil it before its completion, revealing in that act a previously undetected ambivalent attitude toward the loved one. Excessive praise of a patient's work may arouse anxiety because of the stimulation of unconscious homosexual tendencies or oedipal conflicts, and as a result of this anxiety the patient may destroy his work. On the other hand, an active reaching out for a positive relationship with another human being may be first expressed in the preparation of a gift. Weinroth of Mount Sinai Hospital in New York City demonstrated that patients making dolls in O.T. tend to make dolls in their own image, and express unconscious attitudes toward themselves in the way they treat the doll, whether destructively or solicitously, whether discarding it indifferently or giving it for safekeeping to an important mother figure. All such observations can be utilized in formulating a case diagnostically and in terms of the patient's motivations or psychodynamics.

O.T. plays a therapeutic role in many ways. Emotional needs which are recognized in the formulation of the case may be gratified by means of specifically selected O.T. projects, as indicated in the previous section of this chapter. In addition, O.T. provides a setting for therapeutically useful human relationships, with other patients and most of all with the occupational therapists. The therapists should address patients as Mr. or Mrs. and seek to enhance the patient's self-esteem by whatever means they can. The first reaching out toward other human beings may take place in O.T. rather than in the psychotherapeutic session with the psychiatrist. While working on a wood carving or a piece of leather a patient may speak of the fact that his parents have not visited him since his hospitalization, or of difficulties arising from living arrangements at home or at his job. Such information can be relayed to the psychiatrist, or the social worker. Used sensitively such data can become the turning point in the patient's treatment. (See case described in Chapter IV, for example.)

In all treatment situations "transference" develops (see Chapter I). Sometimes the patient will act toward the therapist in a manner which is understandable only if viewed as a repetition of a behavior pattern from the patient's past. In transference the patient acts in a rigid, prejudiced manner, as if the therapist were a parent or some other important figure from the patient's childhood. For example, a patient may be provocatively unruly in order to elicit a wrathful outburst from the therapist, a pattern which repeats his childhood relationship with his mother and which in a sense restores the ambivalently longed-for parent. The therapist should be instructed about this and his behavior toward the patient regulated accordingly.

In addition to transference, "countertransference" can occur. This is also described in Chapter I. The therapist may seek to gratify certain of his own emotional needs in the relationship with the patient. The resulting actions may not always coincide with the best interests of the patient. For example, a therapist may have a strong personal need to see results from his patients and may prohibit a patient from destroying what he has made even when this destructive act may be psychologically beneficial to him. Countertransference, as previously stated, is a great source of error in the treatment of the mentally ill, and occupational therapy is no exception to this rule. Frank exchanges in staff conferences can serve to diminish the effects of countertransference.

Prescribing O.T.

It is apparent from the foregoing analysis that O.T. cannot be employed haphazardly. The psychiatrist acquaints the therapist with the individual needs of each patient as well as he understands them, and the therapist endeavors to meet these needs with the means at his disposal. If his observation suggests that the psychiatrist's preliminary formulation of the patient's emotional needs is inaccurate, then the formulation and the plan of treatment are modified accordingly.

The therapist must be flexible in filling the psychiatrist's prescription.

For example, Fidler and Fidler describe a patient who was assigned to a leather-working project. The patient rejected the suggestion that he make something for himself. Instead he asked that he be allowed to make a pair of shoes for his baby. Furthermore, he chose to make it by following instructions in a book rather than by accepting the help of the therapist directly. He derived evident pleasure when he completed the project and was able to give the shoes to his wife. He acted as if he had atoned in some measure for neglecting his child. Then, as a similar act of restitution to his wife, he made a wallet for her. This act completed, he became more spontaneous with the occupational therapist in his speech and actions, and more willing to acknowledge his feelings of helplessness and his need for reassurance. Finally, he achieved sufficient freedom from guilt feelings so that he was willing to make something for himself. After that he was introduced to wood carving and carpentry which provided an outlet for aggressive impulses which were becoming more tolerable to this passive and inhibited patient. As his capacity to express aggression in a controlled and constructive manner increased, he displayed more adult masculine behavior in his relationship with the therapist. When this adult pattern clearly emerged, he was assigned to a hospital workshop. Subsequently, he improved enough to leave the hospital.

Although projects, materials and other necessities were provided by O.T., it is unlikely that anyone would have been wise enough to provide the suggestion that this patient start with a pair of shoes for his baby. The skillful occupational therapist, however, was able to exploit each lead as provided by the patient, and was able to carry him through a series of successive stages, characterized by diminishing guilt feelings, an increasing capacity to express aggression and growing psychosexual maturity until it became possible for the patient to handle a genuine work assignment in the hospital which culminated in his rehabilitation and discharge.

At times an incorrect O.T. assignment may affect the patient adversely. A case is described by J. E. Barrett of a banker in an agitated depression who was told to weave a basket in O.T. By enhancing a self-belittling feminine identification, this patient's depression deepened. He made a successful attempt at suicide immediately thereafter. Although such a drastic outcome is unusual, the possibility of its occurrence must be kept in mind, particularly since patients have been known to employ occupational therapy materials in self-destructive actions.

Occupational Therapy on Every Ward

As in the recreational program, the hospital goal should be to establish occupational therapy on every ward. This calls for the inclusion of occupational therapy training in the teaching program for attendants. The occupational therapist should prepare a questionnaire to canvass the attendants for specific skills. In addition, the services of volunteers are necessary to implement a full O.T. program in the hospital. With the help of volunteers, stamp clubs, photography and other hobbies can be fostered. Liaison with similar clubs in the community can be established and joint meetings arranged. (See Chapters IV and XIII for more data about the utilization of the services of volunteers.)

Keeping Records

O.T. data should be recorded on a special O.T. form. This should include an explanation for the selection of specific projects in terms of the formulation of the case. Verbal productions and behavior should be described, particularly as these involve relationships with other patients and the therapist. Characteristic reactions under stress should be noted as well as the situations most likely to elicit these reactions. Progress notes should include evidences of change, as well as recommendations to other departments.

The Transition to a Genuine Work Program

It was mentioned earlier that the goal of vocational rehabilitation should be stressed from the time the patient is admitted to the mental hospital. In some instances, it may be clear at the time of reception that vocational rehabilitation cannot be hoped for because of old age or physical infirmity. In other patients who have never been established vocationally it is clear that a period of vocational training will be necessary before any kind of job placement can be considered. Still other patients may require a period of retraining after prolonged absence from a skilled trade. Some patients may require training for a new job when it appears that the previous occupation contributed to the mental breakdown. In any case all members of the treatment team must become vocation-minded from the outset in planning a patient's treatment. This calls for a routine work history on every patient (see above). In addition, a vocational counselor should conduct a job survey of the hospital, listing all the vocational training opportunities available in hospital routines. An intramural employment service should be set up under the direction of a vocational counselor. Close liaison between the professional and non-professional services of the hospital is necessary to exploit these opportunities to the fullest. Volunteer workers should be recruited to conduct classes in cooking, sewing, tailoring, typing, stenography, beauty parlor operation, laboratory work, restaurant work, to mention a few.

Specific Aptitudes versus General Employability:
The Role of Motivation

There tends to be an overemphasis on the importance of specific aptitudes in vocational counseling today. Although the inclinations and
talents of the individual should by no means be omitted, it has been the
experience of many people that a properly motivated patient can adapt
successfully to a wide variety of jobs, whereas the unmotivated patient
will accomplish nothing in spite of specific skills.

This is well exemplified in a case described by Rennie and his associates. A young schizophrenic woman made a good social recovery after a
lobotomy but suffered some slowing up in her general responsiveness.
During the war she worked at a bench-assembly job of small parts for
submarine instruments. There was a very strong sense of urgency throughout the plant, for the commissioning of submarines was dependent on
the prompt supplying of these parts. All the workers felt a patriotic
responsibility to get on with the task as quickly as possible. The patient
caught this feeling and was so stimulated to overcome her slowness that
she was able to keep up with the others. After the war, when the plant
closed down, she got a job in a mechanical pencil factory. The physical
requirements of this job were entirely comparable to those in the war
factory. It was a bench-assembly job of small parts requiring no greater
dexterity or attention to detail than the previous one. However, the emotional climate was entirely different. The patriotic stimulus was lacking,
and her inherent slowness again appeared. She was entirely unable to
keep up with the work.

Such motivational factors are not easily recognized in the ordinary
investigative techniques of vocational counseling. Yet they represent the
bridge between the psychiatric treatment program and the ultimate goal
of vocational rehabilitation.

Patients as Employees

The need to work exists in chronic psychotic patients more frequently
than is ordinarily realized. This was demonstrated by R. A. Solow who
went on a "chronic" ward of a V.A. psychiatric hospital and asked for
volunteers for work details. He offered jobs in the laundry, the furniture
repair shop, and on the grounds. A surprising number of patients signed
up, each selecting the job of preference. Solow felt that he had to eliminate some of the more disorganized patients. On the job there was a mid-
morning and a mid-afternoon break for coffee and simple refreshments.

The patients not only enjoyed these snacks but voluntarily cleaned up the dishes. Most of the job details required co-operative endeavor rather than work in isolation, and the usefulness of the work to the hospital was made clearly evident to them. Solow's patients manifested pride and satisfaction in their ability to make a contribution to the welfare of the hospital. Many remarkable changes occurred. They struck up friendships, went to work together, chatted and ate together. Mute patients became communicative. All became more tidy personally and in their behavior on the wards. It was also observed that they utilized their leisure time constructively and socially rather than in autistic reveries as heretofore.

Most people work for money. They will put up with discomforts, hardships and even considerable physical danger if the financial rewards are adequate. Patients in mental hospitals are found not to differ in this regard from their "normal" fellows in the outside community. Some hospitals have arranged to turn over a considerable part of the operation of the hospital commissary to patient labor, including sales, general up-keep and bookkeeping. Profits from sales provide salaries for patients who work there. Surpluses are applied to ward improvements. By means of such rewards otherwise unmotivated patients can be involved in activities which will lead to their rehabilitation.

In some instances this principle has been carried to its logical conclusion and patients have been hired as hospital employees. S. T. Walkiewicz, a social worker, described such an experiment at Central Islip Hospital in Long Island during World War II. As a result of the the severe personnel shortage of that period, fifty-four patients were discharged to convalescent status and hired to work as ward attendants. They were listed on the payroll as "laborers" so that they would not have to take the civil service examinations that would otherwise have been required. Over seventy per cent did well, and either remained at work in the hospital or resigned to get jobs in the community. Only sixteen of the experimental workers had to be readmitted as patients. Walkiewicz observed that the experimental workers were treated no differently than the regular hospital workers. She expressed the opinion that if they had been provided with adequate social service supervision, in keeping with their status as convalescent patients, the success of this experiment would have been even greater.

A similar experiment was carried out more recently by P. A. Peffer of the Veterans Administration. A group of patients were selected to fill vacancies that would ordinarily be filled by regular employees. They were discharged to convalescent status, were given quarters and subsistence and were permitted to attend all the recreational functions of the hospital. They were provided with full medical and dental care. Their salaries ranged from $657.00 to $821.00 per year. Of twenty patients so assigned only three had to be readmitted on patient status.

Remarkable personal improvement resulted, and the experiment was regarded as a most successful and effective intermediate rehabilitation procedure. An additional outcome of this experiment was a financial saving to the government of approximately $69,379 per year in the operation of this one hospital!

The Transition to Extramural Work: Governmental Assistance

Since the First World War, the Federal and State governments have been engaged in vocational rehabilitation of the physically handicapped. In 1943 the Barden-LaFollette Amendment (Public Law 113) authorized the State rehabilitation bureaus to extend their services to the mentally handicapped and to provide remedial services as well as training and job placement for both the physically and mentally handicapped. State laws were amended to take advantage of the changes in the Federal law. This means that every psychiatrically handicapped individual is entitled to help in job finding, in vocational counseling and guidance and in vocational training, whether he be a veteran or not. The agency set up in each State to provide such services is called the State Rehabilitation Bureau. Until recently, the availability of these services was relatively unknown to professional people. However, they are being used increasingly and with growing effectiveness in the rehabilitation of the mentally ill. In addition, the Department of Labor in each state maintains an employment service which can be utilized for the placement of patients. Some states (New York, for example) maintain a "selective placement" service for the physically and mentally handicapped, where one can secure the help of specialists trained to understand the problems of the emotionally handicapped. A preliminary obligation of the treatment team in the mental hospital is to ascertain whether these vocational facilities are being used with maximal effectiveness.

Vocational Rehabilitation Services

Vocational rehabilitation usually comprises five interrelated services all of which are aimed at establishing and maintaining the client or patient at a job.

Vocational counseling. This includes evaluation of the client's abilities and interests.

Vocational training. This is accomplished through enrolling the client in a trade or professional school, or by arranging for on-the-job training.

The State Rehabilitation Bureau is not authorized to establish and maintain its own training facilities, but pays for tuition, textbooks, laboratory and other equipment as well as for the subsistence of the client during the training period.

Restoration services. By this is meant the payment for medical, surgical or other treatment which can reasonably be expected to eliminate or minimize a vocational handicap. The policy regarding restoration services as applied to the psychiatrically handicapped varies considerably from state to state. Payment for private psychiatric care is provided in some instances in which a short-term period of treatment is expected to suffice. Although this is commonly used for the treatment of psychoneurotics, it is conceivable that its application for ambulatory maintenance shock treatment of psychotics is equally feasible as a means of minimizing a vocational handicap.

Job finding and placement. Such services are more commonly provided by specific job finding agencies, particularly the State Department of Labor's agencies. In case these agencies do not provide selective placement service for the mentally handicapped as previously mentioned, the state rehabilitation service may undertake job placement too for this group of patients.

Personal counseling throughout the entire period of rehabilitation and follow-up until the occupational adjustment is complete. This follow-up should extend for at least six months, and a liberal policy should be maintained as far as reopening cases is concerned. Prompt attention during periods of emotional crisis may frequently ward off a psychiatric catastrophe necessitating readmission to a hospital.

The Vocational Counselor as Therapist

The vocational counselor inevitably becomes a member of the hospital's treatment team. He needs some preparation for his responsibilities in this regard. In the event that the available vocational counselors have not been trained to work with former mental hospital patients, the psychiatrist or someone else on the treatment team may have to correct exaggerated and erroneous expectations concerning the thinking and behavior to be encountered among this group of clients. The vocational counselor will be agreeably surprised at the capacity of the majority of these patients to co-operate. He may be even more surprised at the capacity for useful work which many of these patients will display. When untrained people first come into contact with the mentally ill, they tend to experience considerable anxiety. The vocational counselor may be inhibited by an undue fear of doing or saying the wrong thing, for example. Effective resolution of his anxieties will increase his usefulness to the hospital's treatment program. In some instances a patient may relate better to the vocational counselor than to anyone else on the treatment team, and this relationship may be the decisive factor in the recovery of the patient.

Because the fears of mental hospital patients are abnormally great, they are reluctant to go into unfamiliar surroundings and to meet with strange people. For this reason patients frequently fail to keep appointments at the Rehabilitation Bureau made for them prior to leaving the hospital for convalescent care. This experience emphasizes the need for having the counselor from the Rehabilitation Bureau see the patient in the hospital. An ideal arrangement is to have the counselor at the hospital one day a week during which he can see all the patients who have been referred for his help, as well as the psychiatrist, the social worker, the occupational therapist and any other member of the treatment team who has data that can contribute to the patient's vocational rehabilitation.

The Social Worker and Vocational Rehabilitation

The client's ability to handle a job is affected by his adjustment to other aspects of living. Family difficulties are probably the most frequent outside cause of work maladjustment. Rennie and his co-workers quote one counselor's opinion that in practically every instance of failure in vocational rehabilitation with psychiatric clients the cause was to be found in family misunderstanding and interference with the vocational objectives. The patient may have to be protected from the excessive ambitiousness of a parent or spouse, or he may have to be relieved of certain responsibilities in the home. This was the case with one patient whose responsibility for an aged, widowed, psychotic mother contributed to his breakdown initially and who had to face this same responsibility on leaving the hospital. Another patient may require assistance in obtaining legal separation in an untenable marital relationship. Allaying the excessive anxiety of other members of the family may relieve the anxiety of the patient. The social worker may help the patient to prepare for an employment interview. In some hospitals this has been done successfully by means of psychodrama in which the social worker takes the role of the interviewing employer.

In a recent study by I. Stevenson, psychiatrist, and T. M. Fisher, social worker, a technique is described in which the psychiatrist plays a depriving role, and the social worker a protective one. For example, the psychiatrist places a final date for the receipt of assistance from the Department of Public Welfare. This compels a previously inactive patient to go out and seek employment. The social worker assumes a "motherly" and supportive role during this period of transition. The social worker's relationship with the client is somewhat more intensive than that of the psychiatrist. She makes herself useful in various ways, assisting in job finding, or arranging for a patient to obtain necessary articles of clothing or equipment, the lack of which had ostensibly delayed employment. This combination of authoritative firmness and maternal support from two different therapists usually results in a striking alteration in the patient's attitude toward work. They were able to get twenty out of twenty-five severely neurotic patients to return to work for six months or longer after years of supposed unemployability. They were able to accomplish the result in an average of ten interviews prior to return to work.

Sheltered Work Situations

Ideally, the goal of unsupervised work in the community is arrived at in stages. Some hospitals permit patients to go off the grounds to work in the community by day and to return to the hospital in the evening. At Traverse City State Hospital in Michigan about eighty patients are permitted to live and work in the immediate vicinity of the hospital on convalescent status. They can still be seen at frequent intervals by the doctors or receive further help from the social service department in preparing for return to their own communities. The second 1953 Mental Hospital Award of the American Psychiatric Association went to the Modesto State Hospital in California with the following citation: "As recently as 1951 townspeople believed that all the patients were in restraint and were dangerous. Today more than 1,000 patients work in the town while living under hospital supervision with selected land-ladies in 'half-way houses'. . . Local organizations, the local press and the Chamber of Commerce help in publicizing job training and job finding for these rehabilitated patients."

Some states maintain sheltered workshops for the mentally handi-capped where vocational training and further psychiatric treatment may take place on an outpatient basis. For the most part such shops are utilized as temporary devices in the process of readying the patient for full vocational independence. However, in some instances, particularly where the picture is complicated by mental deficiency (see Chapter XIX), a sheltered workshop may be regarded as a permanent solution for the patient's needs.

Role of Industry and Unions

If a man has had a good work record, social service should contact his employer and endeavor to recruit his assistance in the rehabilitation of the patient. In placing patients at jobs in any circumstances it is well to emphasize to prospective employers the positive aspects of each worker's potential rather than the need for making allowances because of possible future deficiencies. Some companies have a particularly liberal policy toward employees who have required admission to a mental hospital. The Endicott-Johnson Company in Binghamton, New York, for example, will carry such employees on leave of absence, provide disability insurance for their families, and re-employ them when they have recovered enough to resume work. In addition they employ the services of a psychiatrist in their plant to give such people supportive help. In some instances management will send representatives to visit the patient in the hospital. The Consolidated Edison Company of New York carried out a particularly effective program in reducing alcoholism among its employees.

Labor unions have been slower in participating in the rehabilitation of the mentally sick worker. The United Auto Workers Union (CIO) in Detroit, Michigan, has pioneered in this regard. Their Health Institute started a Mental Hygiene Clinic in 1943. For the first nine years this clinic was under the direction of psychiatric social workers. However, in 1953 full-time medical coverage was provided by two psychiatrists. A psychiatrist sees all patients referred to the Mental Hygiene Clinic from other departments of the Health Institute. He sends a formal reply to the referring physician indicating the diagnosis and recommended disposition. He utilizes a treatment team of one psychologist and two psychiatric social workers in carrying out the therapy. In addition to these services, the Mental Hygiene Clinic provides supervised training in psychotherapy for the social workers as well as education in mental hygiene and child care through mailings of literature to the total population of the Health Institute.

A similar program was set up by L. L. Tureen for the A.F.L. Teamster's Union, local number 688 in St. Louis. The St. Louis Mental Hygiene Clinic gave supportive psychotherapy to the wives of union members who were admitted to mental hospitals. In addition they provided after-care for patients who had been hospitalized for psychotic episodes. Tureen reports his experience as follows: "Psychotic patients have been kept on their jobs for as long as two years (the length of time the clinic was in existence) while they remained ambulatory and could function in their particular jobs. This required tolerance from their fellow employees but more particularly from their supervisors. Sometimes a brief work interruption for electroshock therapy was granted. Fellow employees usually recognize the fact of the patient's illness and are inclined to be protective. The liaison established between the St. Louis Labor Health Institute and the employer similarly serves as a protective device. These dependent persons could thus be maintained at their jobs despite illness or periodic brief losses from work because of incapacity."

In one instance a schizophrenic boy whose father belonged to a union was accepted by the union for apprentice training. After he completed his training the patient was accepted as a member in his father's union and a regular job was secured for him. The union's co-operation played a crucial role in this young man's rehabilitation.

The opportunities for vocational rehabilitation afforded by direct co-operation with management and labor unions are great. Only now are we beginning to utilize this resource properly. Future developments along this line will be determined by the extent to which mental hospital personnel can instruct these organizations concerning their potential contribution.

SELECTED REFERENCES

Annual (1953) Report of the Mental Hygiene Clinic of the Health Institute of the UAW-CIO (7930 E. Jefferson Ave., Detroit 14, Mich.).

BARRETT, J. E.: Occupational and Recreational Therapy in Our State Mental Hospitals. *Virginia Med. Monthly,* 77:555, 1950.

FIDLER, G. S.; FIDLER, J. W.: *Introduction to Psychiatric Occupational Therapy.* New York: Macmillan, 1954.
> An unusually useful presentation of this subject. Theoretical material clearly presented. The range of applications of occupational therapy for the mentally ill is well explored. Rich in illustrative case material.

MEISLIN, J.: The Psychiatric Sheltered Workshop in Rehabilitation of the Mentally Ill. *Arch. Phys. Med. & Rehabilit.,* 35:224, 1954.

PEFFER, P. A.: Money: A Rehabilitation Incentive for Mental Patients. *Am. J. Psychiat.,* 110:298, 1954.

RACKOWER, L. W.: The Vocational Rehabilitation Act and the Mentally Ill in New York State. *Psychiat. Quart. Supplement,* 1:1, 1949.

RENNIE, T. A. C.; BURLING, T.; WOODWARD, L. I.: *Vocational Rehabilitation of Psychiatric Patients.* Cambridge: Harvard University Press, 1950.
> This book is based on a three State survey. It examines the vocational needs of posthospitalized psychiatric patients and explores the possibilities of obtaining professional help for them through the co-operation of State agencies for vocational rehabilitation and the financial assistance of the Federal government.

—— BOZEMAN, M. F.: *Vocational Services for Psychiatric Clinic Patients*. Cambridge: Harvard University Press, 1952.

    A companion to previous reference. An invaluable study pointing the way to a closer co-operation between outpatient psychiatric treatment facilities and vocational agencies.

Chapter VI

FOOD AS THERAPY

The Role of Early Feeding Experiences in
Emotional Development

From earliest infancy, mealtimes are occasions charged with great emotional significance. The mother concerns herself primarily with feeding problems during the first year of her infant's life. Is the child to be breast fed or bottle fed? Should it have a bottle when it cries, or should it be compelled to wait until the precise hour prescribed by the pediatrician? Is the diet properly balanced for nutritional needs and normal bowel function? Should the baby have a pacifier or be permitted to suck its thumb? These questions which are of such great concern to the mother have their impact on the baby too. The mother's tensions and indecisions give rise to awkward movements which can be deeply disturbing to the child, and which can cause it to refuse to nurse. The nursing infant's need for tender loving care is now well known. It is a clinically proven fact, for example, that without the gentle ministrations of a mother the child can lapse into a state of psychomotor retardation which is for all the world a deep depression, and in which the child may waste away and even die.

The imprint of the feeding experience during the first year has a lasting effect on the subsequent psychological make-up of the individual. The child must learn to tolerate hunger for a shorter or longer period of time while the mother is preparing its food. When teeth appear, the child must learn to control its biting impulses, particularly if it is breast fed. In the weaning process, it must learn to control its pleasurable sucking impulses. Because the child is not yet able to speak during this first year, it must rely on nonverbal bodily actions in its communications with the mother. The child utilizes the feeding situation to express its feelings. The mother, in turn, expresses her deepest feelings toward the

93

child when she gives it food. The manifest pleasure which the hungry child gets in being fed is matched by the intense pleasure which the mother gets in feeding it. The child soon learns of the mother's need to give food. Accepting food then becomes part of an attitude of compliance and rejecting food, by spitting, vomiting or shaking the head, an expression of defiance. Food thus becomes invested with extra meaning, and the attitude toward food becomes a symbol for the attitude toward mother. The child learns it can express one set of feelings by means of gentle sucking movements and quite an opposite set of feelings by biting. It learns some of these facts in experiments with its own body, particularly its hands. The child learns that it can satisfy some of its oral cravings by sucking its own hand. As a result of the immaturity of the psychic apparatus, particularly as regards the perceptual system, the hand can substitute for the breast in certain aspects of the feeding process, and the child tends to identify or confuse the mother's body with its own body. We describe this by saying that the child's "ego boundary" is not yet sharply defined. In a manner of speaking the umbilical cord has not yet been severed. Intimately associated with eating in infancy is sleep. During the first months the child spends most of its time either sleeping or eating. It wakes up when hungry and falls asleep again when its wishes to be fed are completely gratified. In this way, sleeping becomes linked associatively with eating to satiation, and the beginnings of sleep become a kind of symbol for blissful satisfaction. Feelings of helplessness, awareness of dependency upon the mother or some substitute for her and great preoccupation with eating, drinking and sleeping—all characterize this earliest phase of human development, which has been called the "oral phase." The foregoing patterns, when they appear later in life, are referred to by psychoanalysts in a kind of shorthand as "orality," thereby emphasizing the origins of these qualities during the earliest phase of emotional development.

These involved symbolic implications of the feeding process do not cease at the end of the first year, naturally, but continue throughout 'life, taking on added qualities as life becomes more complex. Mealtimes, for example, can be occasions for great happiness. They are occasions for reunion with parents whose absence caused loneliness or anxiety. All the loved ones are assembled about the table, painful separations are ended and a spirit of contentment or even gaiety prevails. It is no wonder that the foods which were associated with these early years remain the favorite foods throughout life, even though in actuality they were often quite simple and relatively tasteless. But food like mother used to make it, or food like that which was eaten in the "old country," has a specific capacity to gladden the heart.

The Psychopathology of Eating

Just as once upon a time the child did not clearly differentiate its own thumb from the mother's breast, similarly it may not clearly differentiate between the favorite dish which mother places on the table and her actual presence. When he is lonely for her he consoles himself with the food she has left for him. After awhile, any food may come to substitute for the absent mother; so that maternal deprivation gives rise associatively to a craving for food and may become a cause of obesity. And when the mother expresses her displeasure with him for overeating or for otherwise misbehaving, in his anger he may "bite" the food instead of biting her. In short he now overeats for two reasons, out of loving loneliness for her and out of hatred for her. We then say that his attitude toward food has become ambivalent, that is to say, compounded out of opposite feelings—love and hate. This ambivalence may give rise to great swings in food intake from overeating to starvation. A history of great variations in body weight may be a clue to the presence of a state of ambivalence of pathological intensity, and may be one of the earliest clinical signs of an impending mental illness.

The eating process becomes overlaid with further meanings. When the child becomes curious about pregnancy and childbirth, he is commonly told that the baby is in the mother's stomach. This usually means to the child that it got there because of something she ate. When the child learns that the father has something to do with it, it usually arrives at a fantasy that the father impregnated the mother through her mouth. Thus, a child may overeat because it wants to have a baby or refuse to eat because of guilt concerning this wish. Eating and drinking may become connected with homosexual fantasies in the boy who wishes to have a baby.

The psychiatrist who thinks of his clinical material as he reads the foregoing remarks will recognize their implications for psychopathology. Chronic schizophrenic patients often show sucking and chewing mannerisms that can be related to infantile oral wishes. Complete refusal of food, necessitating tube feedings or other devices to maintain nutrition are reminiscent of the battles that take place so often between mother and child at the dinner table.

A forty-year-old woman with recurrent episodes of depression was treated with psychoanalytically oriented psychotherapy. During depressions, she would stop eating and on several occasions was tube fed in mental hospitals. Much of her depression in adult life seemed to be a repetition of depression which she suffered as a child on enforced separation from her ailing mother. When the mother would return from the hospital, the patient would then stop eating. Fearful altercations with the mother concerning her refusal of food would ensue. The refusal of food as an adult, with the cajoling and finally stern compulsion to eat, reproduced in detail the periods of reunion with the ambivalently longed-for mother.

Psychotic patients are more apt to become disturbed at mealtime or at bedtime, much more placid after eating or after getting into bed, particularly if they have been given an evening snack. This pattern is certainly reminiscent of the crankiness of children when hungry and their restlessness at night unless prepared for sleep by some oral gratification. The expression that "a hungry man is an angry man" more often has its origins in infantile impatience for a feeding than in hypoglycemia, as is sometimes contended. Compulsive spitting in schizophrenics is at times a primitive oral way of casting out or defending against the poisoning influences of a "bad" mother. A schizophrenic fondling of self is a reversion to the time of poorly defined ego boundaries. The schizophrenic who leaps about kissing the wall or the floor will sometimes verbalize directly that this is a symbolic expression of the wish to get closer to mother. These and many other of the phenomena of schizophrenia are the result of an impairment in the ego boundary. Just as he was unable at one time to distinguish his own hand from the body of his mother, so he now has difficulty in distinguishing his own thoughts from the thoughts of others. A self-reproach, for example, becomes to him a critical voice from the outside, heard as a hallucination. Schizophrenics will often gorge themselves, if permitted to, in greedy eating patterns reminiscent of the uninhibited child. Pregnancy fantasies associated with eating are also quite common. Many mechanisms which are manifestly evidenced by psychotic patients in delusions and hallucinations are present in nonpsychotic people, too, in repressed form. They emerge in perfectly normal people in dreams, or in disguised form in some of the symptoms of psychoneurosis, as for example in cases of obesity or anorexia nervosa.

Food is Therapy

When the newly admitted patient is given a snack, the very heart of his emotional needs may be touched, even though the food is proferred naively, out of a simple sense of humanity. Preferably, this important act should not be carried out naively. When ward personnel are taught about the symbolic meaning of food, they are less likely to forget to feed the newly admitted patient. What is more important, if the proferred food is refused or angrily thrown to the floor, the nurse or the attendant will be in better position to understand that this is an expression of rejection or anger directed at people from the patient's past, and not at all a personal attack or expression of ingratitude. Thus informed, they will be better able to cope with such outbursts. A glass of warm milk at bedtime is often recommended as a sedative. There is nothing sedative about the milk itself, but milk as a symbol of a good mother and its use at bedtime to relieve oral tensions arising from emotional deprivation invests it at times with a very useful sedative action.

A recovered schizophrenic patient once remarked, "Anyone who thinks that chronic schizophrenics have no affect should visit the 'chronic' ward when the food cart appears at mealtime. He will see greed and ferocity of an intensity that may shock him." This observation highlights the fact that schizophrenics are capable of very intense feelings, traditional statements to the contrary notwithstanding. More important, it shows that food is a potent agent for getting to these feelings. Recently, when dietetics was placed in the administrative or business department of a hospital's table of organization, one doctor reminded his colleagues that dietetics represents an important treatment service of the hospital, and that this should not be forgotten just because the business department purchases its ham and eggs.

The Technique of Feeding Mental Hospital Patients

Most mental hospitals have come to accept the superiority of cafeteria service to other ways of feeding ambulatory patients. Light, airy, well-decorated dining rooms are more frequently seen. Sound-proofing devices for muffling the clatter of silverware and dishes add to the pleasantness of the setting. The use of partitioned trays makes the slopping together of several semiliquid courses on a single plate a thing of the past. The cafeteria technique ensures that the food will be hot when eaten.

An opportunity to select one's own food, one's table and one's dinner companions all contribute to the self-esteem of the patient, just as the lack of these opportunities is undermining. Patients should have napkins. One hospital had its patients make and dye gay-colored napkins using sewing room scraps for the purpose. Facilities should be ample so that patients may be leisurely at mealtime. The patient who cannot be trusted with a full set of silverware is far and away the exception. With a spoon as one's only utensil and a sleeve as the napkin, one can't help but act "regressed" and "deteriorated" while eating. Patients should be encouraged to wash, and tidy up before meals. They should be appropriately dressed for the out of doors if they must leave the building to eat.

Because patients are under greater tension before mealtime, careful scheduling to avoid long waiting in line is important. Otherwise episodes of disturbed behavior can be expected in increased numbers. This is particularly true before breakfast when oral tensions are at their peak after a night of not eating. A striking confirmation of the validity of this hypothesis is the fact that in most mental hospitals the accident rate associated with altercations between patients is at its peak before breakfast. A coffee urn on the ward with provisions for a small snack immediately on arising may be a useful device to ameliorate this period of maximal tension.

As important as the food itself is the necessity for enough personnel to be in attendance in the dining hall to help the patients with their needs and to make the mealtime as pleasant an occasion as possible. Patients should be encouraged to use good manners, to be controlled and considerate in their actions. Patients who are eating poorly should be helped. The psychiatrist should include frequent visits to the dining hall during mealtimes as part of his rounds. A display of concern about their welfare at this time will be most rewarding in establishing a sound therapeutic relationship, since in this way he provides direct evidence to the patient of his role as a "good" parent. As part of his visit to the dining hall the psychiatrist should inspect the table refuse as the most sensitive of all indicators concerning the quality of the food and the extent to which the patient's tastes are being met.

The patient who must eat on the ward should not be neglected either. If the food is served with dignity, then a force is brought to bear against the process of deterioration. The more unaesthetic the eating circumstances, the more the schizophrenic process is aided and abetted. Ideally, locked wards should be provided with a serving kitchen to provide facilities for the serving of food cooked in part in the main hospital kitchen and in part here. Heated carts distributing food to each ward are filled in the main hospital kitchen and their contents modified as necessary in the serving kitchen. All dishwashing for the floor should be carried out in the serving kitchen. Patients pick up a tray and cutlery and are served food that they themselves select from the heated food cart. The provision of proper eating facilities on the ward or immediate accessibility to it makes it unnecessary to "guard" groups of patients going to and from meals. At the same time it insures their proper control in an unobstrusive fashion, and permits most disturbed patients to eat with dignity.

Patients who refuse food present a special problem. Tube feedings tend to perpetuate the psychotic process. At times, one can see that the patient surrenders himself to the passage of the tube with manifest pleasure. Electroconvulsive therapy (ECT) usually interrupts a pattern of no eating. Certainly, during the mild confusional state which follows ECT most patients will take nourishment. Sometimes an injection of sodium amytal, given very slowly, intravenously, until the patient displays a change of affect will result in a receptive attitude toward food. If the doctor uses his special authority at such times with firm but gentle ministrations he may help the patient to overcome his block against eating. Most important of all is the need to try to understand the patient's refusal to eat.

A schizophrenic boy of fifteen revealed under intravenous sodium amytal that he couldn't eat because he believed that the food placed before him was made from the body of his deceased father. He was reassured that he did not kill his father, that his father loved him dearly and would certainly have wanted him to eat if he were alive. After that reassurance, the patient ate his first meal in several days and ate regularly thereafter.

The Dietitian as a Member of the Treatment Team

A trained dietitian understands the emotional aspects of eating. Hers should be the responsibility for inculcating all hospital personnel with the therapeutic possibilities of each feeding situation. She should also be involved in the family care program of the hospital (see Chapter XXXV), instructing foster families in the proper preparation of food for the patients under their care and supervising the general nutrition of these patients.

Patients are often assigned to work in some aspect of food handling. The dietitian has the opportunity of involving these patients in therapeutically meaningful human relationships, either directly or by properly instructing those who work in her department. The dietitian should also bear in mind that training which the patient receives on such assignments may be of importance in his vocational rehabilitation.

Another way in which the dietitian can be involved in therapy is by setting up cooking classes. One mental hospital got a local utilities company to install a "school" kitchen in which classes for patients could be conducted. They were provided with realistic experiences in meal-planning, cooking, baking, and cake-decorating. Classes would meet twice weekly for two-hour sessions. Encouraging psychotherapeutic results were obtained.

Nutritional Requirements

Although the emotional aspects of eating have been emphasized, the physiological nutritional aspects must not be neglected either. There are still cases of pellagra to be found in mental hospitals. Most elderly psychotic patients and alcoholics are severely malnourished on admission to the hospital. Avitaminosis and anemia may contribute significantly to a toxic state underlying a psychosis. In these instances, proper diet is a direct physiological attack on the disease process.

Carelessness in preparation can result in the contamination of food with insecticides and rodent poisons.

A patient with delusions that his food was being poisoned was actually severely affected one time by the accidental contamination of his food with bichloride of mercury. He was told of the accident with many expressions of guilt and apology by the one responsible for it. The patient was most friendly, and earnestly reassured the guilty one that he knew it was an accident.

This case is a cogent reminder that accidents can occur in the preparation of food in large institutions so that poisonous substances must be kept well out of reach. But it is even more strikingly a reminder of the symbolic meaning of food. What makes the food poisonous to the psychotic patient is his attitude toward the person giving that food. If the person represents a bad parent then the food is automatically poisoned by the giver. The approach to the delusion is not to give reassurance about the food but rather to help the patient to understand the error of confusing the attendant (for example) with the feared giver of food from long ago. In this case, the disarmingly frank confession by the hospital employee stamped her as a good, well-intentioned parent figure, and as such even bichloride of mercury became acceptable to him from her hands.

SELECTED REFERENCES

FENICHEL, O.: *The Psychoanalytic Theory of Neurosis.* New York: W. W. Norton, 1945. This encyclopedic summary of psychoanalytic psychology contains much interesting data concerning the unconscious meanings of eating.

HAUN, P.: Food Service in Psychiatric Hospitals of the Veterans Administration. *Modern Hospital,* 74:104, 1950. An inclusive study of the practical aspects of a mental hospital food service, including thirty sample menus.

—— *Psychiatric Sections in General Hospitals.* Garden City: Country Life Press, 1950. Some architectural considerations of a mental hospital food service on a closed ward are presented.

MILLER, V.: Role of the Dietetic Service in a Neuropsychiatric Hospital. *J. Am. Dietetic Assn.,* 30:465, 1954.

ROSEMEIER, M. R.: Cooking—A Therapy for the Mentally Ill. *J. Am. Dietetic Assn.,* 30:470, 1954.

Chapter VII

SPECIAL WARD PROCEDURES

In discussing the treatment program in previous chapters the goal of individualizing the care of each patient has been emphasized. Before proceeding to a more detailed consideration of the contribution of each member of the treatment team toward the achievement of this goal, a few special techniques will be described which are useful in planning treatment and which require the specific skills of the psychiatrist for their application.

The "Release" Effect of Sodium Amytal

Sodium amytal was initially used in mental hospitals as a sedative. With improved treatment methods its importance for this purpose has fallen off. However, certain other useful applications of the drug remain.

In 1931 Bleckwenn observed that one could interrupt a catatonic stupor by means of intravenous sodium amytal and bring about a period of normal responsiveness. Although this effect was transitory, it aroused considerable interest from a theoretical point of view as well as with regard to possible clinical applications. It was found, for example, that patients who required tube feeding would eat normally under the influence of the drug. This fact could be used at times to re-establish normal eating habits in psychotic patients. However, lasting improvements in psychotic behavior could rarely be achieved in this way. The phenomenon appeared also to have prognostic value in that the degree to which withdrawn, negativistic schizophrenic patients were "normalized" in their speech and actions measured the likelihood of a good result in response to insulin or electroconvulsive therapy. During the "release" effect of sodium amytal the patient may produce material of a personal nature which uncovers the source of emotional stress. Such revelations may increase the psychiatrist's understanding of the motivations (or psychodynamics) of the patient, thereby opening the way for more effective psychotherapy. In some instances previously undisclosed delusional material may emerge in response to sodium amytal and shed light on problems of diagnosis.

The way in which sodium amytal elicits this "release" effect is not known. However, a phenomenon described by Pavlov in his conditioned reflex studies may be relevant. If a conditioned reflex was established in a dog so that he salivated on the sound of a bell, Pavlov found that the amount of saliva which was secreted each time the bell was sounded was proportional to the loudness of the bell. When he plotted the quantity of the saliva against the intensity of the signal, he found that a maximal point was reached after which a further increase in the intensity of the stimulus resulted in an inhibition in salivary flow. He called this latter effect the "supermaximal" response. Reducing the intensity of the stimulus below the maximal level resulted in a reappearance of the previously excitatory effect of the stimulus.

In the theoretical discussion in Chapter III reference was made to the ascending reticular activating system of the brain stem. It was pointed out that incoming sensory stimuli alert the cerebral cortex to a heightened level of awareness and increased motor output via the reticular system. The phenomenon of increasing salivary secretion following an increase in the intensity of the conditional stimulus is most likely mediated through the reticular system. Similarly, it is probable that the supermaximal inhibitory effect is also mediated through the reticular system after its reactivity has been modified by corticofugal deactivating impulses. It was suggested in Chapter III that corticofugal deactivating impulses may serve a defensive function protecting the organism against unbearable arousal effects of stimuli of traumatic intensity.

By analogy, some schizophrenic reactions can be visualized as a state of chronic defensiveness in which the patient reacts to normally excitatory stimuli as if they were supermaximal in intensity. That is to say, the patient reacts to them with inhibition and withdrawal instead of excitation. Increasing the intensity with which we urge these schizophrenic patients to respond only increases the degree of their inhibition. This is the effect that we refer to clinically as negativism. The theory suggested now is that sodium amytal acts on these withdrawn negativistic schizophrenics to reduce the impact of stimuli so that these stimuli no longer exert a traumatic supermaximal effect, and as a result their normal excitatory effect is restored. This may be the outcome of direct action of the barbiturate on the reticular system or an indirect diminution of the intensity of corticofugal deactivating impulses.

It should be noted that this theoretical discussion does not take up at all the reasons why certain stimuli which are within excitatory limits for normal people have become traumatically supermaximal for these schizophrenic patients. This is doubtless the result of specific psychological experiences which have made the world seem more fearful and confusing to these patients as well as to a possibly pathological reactivity of the reticular system which is of a "constitutional" nature. That is to say, the foregoing theoretical formulation is entirely compatible with psychological theories concerning the pathogenesis and treatment of schizophrenia.

Technique of Eliciting the "Release" Effect

To elicit the foregoing release phenomena, it is important that the amytal be administered in accordance with specific rules. It should be injected intravenously at a rate of not more than one cubic centimeter per minute. As it is injected, the psychiatrist maintains contact with the patient with a few reassuring comments, avoiding direct questions or leading remarks. It is useful to observe the patient's features very carefully. If this is done the examiner will see a flush come over the patient's face in many instances and his expression become more animated, either in the direction of cheerfulness, sadness, or anger. When this point is reached, the psychiatrist, speaking in a gentle voice, asks a leading question such as, "Is there something you want to tell me?" or, "Is there something you want to ask me?" If the patient starts talking, he is allowed to go on uninterruptedly. At times the patient may launch into a long speech without any initiating remarks from the psychiatrist. The main aim is to elicit a spontaneous flow of material from the patient. When this emerges it is often associated with intense affect. A deeply emotional reaction is referred to as an abreaction. Patients who have been exposed to a particularly traumatic event, on the battlefield for example, may re-enact that experience with hallucinatory vividness and with complete reawakening of the terror which accompanied it initially. There may be expressions of deep guilt about sexual fantasies, or the patient may weep bitterly as he recalls his abandonment by a loved one. At times paranoid ideas may emerge with anger of sufficient intensity to interrupt the amytal interview. It is worth emphasizing that the mere release of material in this way is rarely in itself curative. Its main usefulness is as an aid in formulating the case as a guide to psychotherapy. The diagnostic and prognostic usefulness of these data has already been mentioned. The patient's remarks should be recorded, preferably by mechanical means if available, so that the full implications of these productions may be ascertained in subsequent study. Questioning the patient unnecessarily may interrupt the spontaneous flow. If he stops talking, he may be started again by the use of some general remark. If he has spoken about his mother, for example, he may be asked, "Is there anything more that you want to tell me about her?" or, "Is there any one else you want to tell me about?" The more ambiguously phrased the question is, the more likely is the psychiatrist to get at material which is most relevant to the patient's illness.

It is important not to press for material. Too often the psychiatrist, in his eagerness to obtain information, finds himself in the role of a cross-examiner, speaking loudly, insistently, and at times even angrily. Contrary to proper technique he may fire specific questions at the patient. One may compare the correct approach to that of a surgeon who opens an abscess. The surgeon merely touches the infected area with his scalpel, and the pus comes pouring out. The area from which this spontaneous outpouring takes place is determined by the pathological process itself. The surgeon cannot incise at any place he chooses. If a free flow of pus is not obtained, the surgeon does not press for material. If he did he would not help the patient. On the contrary he might spread the infection and harm him. Similarly, in a sodium amytal interview, the psychiatrist is interested in releasing the material which is under pressure. This he cannot do by active probing. This material must well up spontaneously from within the patient's mind. Direct questions plied in a loud voice and with clamoring insistence will usually inhibit the patient from communicating freely, or will switch him from presenting the material which he would want to discuss to that which the psychiatrist, for reasons of his own, wants to hear.

To produce the release effect it is rarely necessary to give more than three or four cubic centimeters of a ten per cent solution of sodium amytal, although more may be given during the interview to maintain the proper level of amytal effect. If the patient shows nystagmus and slurring of speech, or if his facial expression becomes ironed out and he looks as if he is about to fall asleep, the optimal release point has been passed. The patient's need to repress or withhold the material may be great enough to overcome the "release" effect of the sodium amytal, and as a result no spontaneous productions occur. In that case the patient's needs should be respected and the psychiatrist must accept this negative result without probing. In other words, not every amytal attempt must result in a dramatic abreaction.

The amytal is usually given to the patient with the explanation that the medication will relax him and make him feel better. If the patient asks if this is "truth serum," he should be reassured that he does not have to say anything he does not wish to say. If he actively resists taking the drug, it is usually advisable not to administer it. If the amytal is given against his will, the patient will feel that he has been attacked and overwhelmed, and he will carry away with him a justifiable distrust of his psychiatrist, which may seriously interfere with all other treatments. Furthermore, deeply hostile paranoid patients are usually able to maintain complete control over their productions in spite of the medication. So that nothing whatever is gained unless the patient can be prevailed upon to accept the fact that the procedure is being carried out for his own good.

Although one occasionally elicits disturbingly violent abreactions or even unanticipated psychotic outbursts in patients who had not previously been regarded as psychotic, lasting psychological harm rarely, if ever, results from amytal given in accordance with the foregoing instructions.

The Sodium Amytal Test for Organic Brain Disease

Another clinical application of sodium amytal which is of interest to the psychiatrist in the mental hospital is in the diagnosis of organic brain disease. If a patient is oriented for time, place and person, if he does not confabulate the events of the preceding evening, and if he discusses whatever physical disabilities he has in a realistic fashion, he will usually continue to give all this information correctly after intravenous sodium amytal, unless he happens to have organic brain disease. In the latter case, the patient may make persistent errors in the previously mentioned categories of information which he did not make prior to the administration of the amytal.

This technique is entirely different from that previously described for the "release" effect. Nystagmus, slurring of speech and drowsiness are deliberately induced, and are not avoided as in the previously described technique. Specific questions *are* directed at the patient in the information categories enumerated, even when this necessitates breaking in on his spontanous productions. Given in this way, Weinstein and his co-workers at the Mount Sinai Hospital in New York City found that fifty-seven of eighty-eight patients with known organic brain disease showed characteristic changes as indicated. These changes were not obtained in any of fifty control cases. Thus, a negative test is not of diagnostic importance, but a positive result is strong presumptive evidence of organic brain disease. In an acute psychotic reaction where organic brain disease is suspected of playing an etiologic role this procedure can be very useful.

Several cases were seen on the Neurologic Service of the Mount Sinai Hospital in New York City with a clinical picture which was indistinguishable initially from acute schizophrenia and which showed a positive amytal test on admission. These patients showed electroencephalographic abnormalities as well as spinal fluid and neurologic signs which confirmed the amytal test impression of organic brain disease. The amytal test made possible in these cases an early diagnosis of a schizophrenic reaction with organic brain disease (encephalitis). It also made it possible to predict correctly that the psychosis would subside as the organic brain disturbance subsided.

In one case the amytal test made possible the differential diagnosis of a brain tumor reaction from a functional hypomanic state.

A forty-nine-year-old unmarried traveling salesman was admitted to the Mount Sinai Hospital with the complaint of failing vision and headaches of three or four months' duration. For a year prior to admission he noted a diminution in his libido. He had had eye trouble since the age of six, including two operations for glaucoma. There was a history of consuming one to two quarts of whiskey per week.

On admission, the patient was elated. He showed pressure of speech, flight of ideas and some grandiosity about his past sexual adventures and his wealth. A hypomanic reaction was diagnosed, even though some contended that this amount of exuberance was within normal limits for a successful traveling salesman.

Prior to sodium amytal he was completely oriented in all spheres and gave all data concerning his illness correctly. When amytal was given to the point of nystagmus, he denied having anything wrong with him physically; he gave the date as September 20, 1920, his age as twenty-one and stated that he was on a furniture selling mission. Later he said he was in a hospital in Pittsburgh in order to have a baby. When the amytal effect wore off, he became correctly oriented again in all respects. On the basis of this amytal response a presumptive diagnosis of organic brain disease was made. This was confirmed by pneumoencephalography which revealed a large third ventricle tumor. This responded well to radiotherapy and he was discharged in a considerably improved state, showing no overt disturbances in behavior. Although he appeared clinically normal, when seen a year later, his amytal test was again strongly positive.

Control studies on psychotic patients without organic brain disease have shown negative amytal responses.

The Face-Hand Test

Over a period of years, Morris B. Bender and his co-workers have studied the reactions of patients presented simultaneously with two sensory stimuli (Double Simultaneous Stimulation, or DSS). It was found that there are circumstances in which an individual capable of perceiving all stimuli presented one at a time made errors of perception when two stimuli were presented simultaneously. For example, a patient with a temporal lobe lesion might show normal visual fields when the eyes were examined one at a time but would show a field defect if both eyes were exposed to light simultaneously. Some patients with intracranial or spinal cord lesions may perceive all cutaneous stimuli if applied one at a time, yet show a hemianesthesia when symmetrical points on the body are tested simultaneously. Thus, symmetrical simultaneous stimulation of the right and left halves of the body provides a simple but highly useful refinement in the neurological examination of the central nervous system.

Bender and his co-workers studied most intensively the responses of subjects to two cutaneous stimuli on DSS. If normal adults with eyes closed are touched on the face and any other part of the body, the face stimulus is almost invariably reported correctly. If any errors are made, it is the other stimulus which is not perceived at all (extinction) or incorrectly localized (displacement). As a result, the face is said to be most dominant on DSS. If the hand is touched simultaneously with any other part of the body and an error is made, then the hand is almost invariably the one to be reported incorrectly, again either as an extinction or a displacement. In accordance with the previous terminology, the hand is said to be least dominant on DSS. Because the face and the hand are extreme opposites in DSS responses, simultaneous face-hand stimulation gives the highest percentage of errors of all double cutaneous combinations. If the normal adult who has made an error on face-hand stimulation is tested repeatedly, he usually corrects himself spontaneously within three or four trials. If erroneous responses persist, then he is alerted to the possibility that he may be touched in more than one place. When this is done, almost all normal adults cease making errors. In children up to the age of four, errors on face-hand stimulation persist in spite of attempts to correct them. In older subjects with a diffuse disturbance in brain function due to organic brain disease of any type, errors persist similarly in spite of attempts to correct them. Bender and his associates suggested that this fact be used as a test of organic brain disease. The test is simply carried out and provides a useful routine device for screening out patients with organic brain disease from among the general admissions to a mental hospital. As in the sodium amytal test, a negative result is not diagnostic and a positive result is regarded only as presumptive evidence of organic brain disease. Patients who have apparently reacted fully from a general anesthetic will show a positive face-hand test for many hours after all other evidences of altered brain function have subsided. A patient with organic brain disease may show a positive test at one time and a negative test on another in response to a fluctuating state of consciousness.

Patients with schizophrenia often show an impaired capacity to correct errors as compared to normals, although not as markedly as do patients with organic brain disease. It is possible that some of the cases diagnosed as schizophrenia in the large mental hospital populations so tested had organic brain disease. In any event, the schizophrenic patients who tend to show a positive face-hand test should be investigated for points of difference from those schizophrenics whose face-hand test is immediately negative.

The Mecholyl Prognostic Test

Funkenstein and his co-workers have studied the autonomic responses of patients with mental disease. Out of this work came a clinically useful procedure. Intramuscularly injected mecholyl produces a fall in blood pressure. They found that the greater the depth of this fall and the longer the time it was sustained, the more likely was a mentally ill patient to respond to electroconvulsive therapy (ECT). If, in addition, the patient reacted to the intramuscular mecholyl with a chill, the prognosis was even better. These physiological indices had a higher correlation with the clinical outcome in ECT than did the diagnostic categories. For example, a patient with a depression whom one would expect to respond to ECT did not respond if he did not show the foregoing reactions to mecholyl. On the other hand, a schizophrenic patient in whom one might anticipate a poor response would react well to ECT if his mecholyl responses predicted it.

The procedure is carried out with the patient in a reclining position for at least thirty minutes before the test begins, and at least two hours after his last meal. His resting blood pressure is recorded and he is given 10 mg. of mecholyl chloride intramuscularly. Blood pressure readings are recorded and plotted on a graph every five minutes for twenty-five minutes. A high basal blood pressure (systolic over 130), a considerable fall after mecholyl, and a long time interval before the systolic value climbs back to the preinjection value correlated well with a good response to electroconvulsive therapy. A low basal blood pressure with a small fall after mecholyl and rapid return to the preinjection systolic level correlated with a poor clinical response to electroconvulsive therapy.

Although the theory of this test procedure is by no means elucidated, the authors have suggested tentatively that patients with a good prognosis secrete an excess quantity of an adrenaline-like substance which is neutralized by mecholyl, whereas patients with a poor prognosis secrete an excess of a noradrenaline-like substance which is not. Psychological studies of these patients have shown that autonomic responses with a poor prognosis are associated with impairment in so-called abstract thinking and with "looseness of association." In patients with autonomic responses indicative of good prognosis, on the other hand, the capacity for abstract thinking is well preserved, and logical thought processes show less disorganization.

Although the foregoing procedures do not represent all of the devices which can be utilized on the ward by the psychiatrist in the mental hospital, they have the virtue of simplicity and experience has proven their practical worth.

SELECTED REFERENCES

BENDER, M. B.: *Disorders of Perception*. Springfield, Ill.: C. C. Thomas, 1952.
This monograph describes the phenomena characteristic of double simultaneous stimulation and the basis of the face-hand test.

FUNKENSTEIN, D. H.; GREENBLATT, M.; SOLOMON, H. C.: An Autonomic Nervous System Test of Prognostic Significance in Relation to Electroshock Treatment. *Psychosom. Med.*, 14:347, 1952.
This article describes the mecholyl test and the data upon which it was statistically validated.

KALINOWSKY, L. B.; HOCH, P. H.: *Shock Treatments, Psychosurgery and Other Somatic Treatments in Psychiatry*. New York: Grune & Stratton, 1952.
The use of sodium amytal for eliciting data of diagnostic and prognostic importance are described in this volume.

WEINSTEIN, E. A.; KAHN, R. L.; SUGARMAN, L. A.; LINN, L.: The Diagnostic Use of Amobarbital Sodium (Amytal Sodium) in Brain Disease. *Am. J. Psychiat.*, 109:889, 1953.
The technique of the sodium amytal test for organic brain disease is described in this paper.

Part Two

THE TREATMENT TEAM

Chapter VIII

THE SOCIAL WORKER

Definition

The social worker, or social caseworker as he is usually called, has as his objective the improvement of the social adaptation or adjustment of the individual and his family. Sometimes he accomplishes this through modification of the environment; sometimes a change in attitude and behavior is necessary; generally he employs a combination of the two. The treatment approach depends on the extent to which the individual's problem stems from, or is augmented by, his external situation or his own inner tensions. The caseworker utilizes environmental manipulation and such techniques as psychological support, reassurance and clarification. In order to deal effectively with a wide range of social and personal problems he must have comprehensive knowledge and skill in the use of community resources. In addition he must have an understanding of the emotional needs of the people who seek his help.

The social worker may function in a great many settings. The *family caseworker,* for example, works with the members of a family individually and as a unit, helping them to work out a better adjustment to one another and to their situation in life. He helps them to develop more satisfactory patterns of family living and to deal more effectively with periods of crisis. If serious mental illness seems imminent, he secures psychiatric help and takes whatever other steps are possible to prevent a more serious breakdown.

The *child welfare worker* is equipped with a sound knowledge of child development in order to help children pass through periods of personal upset caused by loss of parental support or affection. He plays a role in obtaining satisfactory placement in foster homes or adoptive homes where substitute parents can provide the satisfactions and love that a child needs. He works with children suffering from behavior disorders, delinquency or other manifestations of emotional disturbance.

The social worker in the *public assistance agency* works with families whose financial security is threatened by illness or death of the breadwinner, or by other causes. In addition to the purely material problems involved in such crises are major emotional ones. Feelings of inadequacy, difficulties in asking for and accepting help, feelings of futility and depression are all part of the problem as dealt with by the public assistance worker.

The *medical social worker* deals with the emotional aspects of physical illness, particularly with respect to the chronically ill and the physically disabled and their families, giving them the psychological support necessary to adapt emotionally to the illness or handicap, to accept proper treatment, to achieve vocational rehabilitation and to learn to live successfully with the handicap.

The *parole and probation worker* deals with delinquent children and adults whose violations of society's laws indicate some problem of personal or social disorganization. His contribution to the rehabilitation of a person who has violated the law depends to a large extent on his understanding of the psychological motivations of the person involved and of the contributing factors in the environment.

The *school social worker* deals directly with children whose major difficulty centers about the problems of school. He has the opportunity to observe home conditions and to help bring about psychological and environmental changes which will prevent more serious emotional problems later on.

The *social group worker* utilizes his understanding of the emotional needs of groups and individuals to aid in achieving effective group action and satisfying communal experiences, as well as to further the social growth of the individual. He utilizes the group work process in recreational and educational centers in the community. He is in a particularly strategic position to observe early signs of deviant behavior in groups of children or adolescents, and to initiate appropriate preventive measures.

The social worker who functions in *community organization for social welfare* helps define the sociopsychological needs of the community and endeavors to mobilize public resources to meet those needs.

In all of these areas the social worker deals with the emotional tensions of individuals, and as such is never distant from psychiatry in his interests. However, there is a category of social worker who specializes in work with the mentally ill and who is specifically referred to as a *psychiatric social worker*. He may function in a mental hospital or in a psychiatric clinic for children and adults; as the resident member of a traveling clinic (see Chapter XXXV) ; in a specialized clinic for the treatment of alcoholism, or epilepsy. He may participate as a member of a research team investigating clinical, epidemiological or other research problems. The psychiatric social worker may also serve as a consultant in schools, industry, health departments and citizens' mental health associations; and as a special adviser to community welfare agencies and to local government units.

The social service department in a mental hospital is part of the total body of social work. Its activities can and should be integrated with those of agencies outside the hospital. If the mental hospital psychiatrist is acquainted with the full range of social work in all its ramifications, he will utilize his own social service department with greater effectiveness.

In the mental hospital the social worker is an important member of the treatment team. The character of his contributions depends on the phase of treatment that the patient is in. These will now be described in succession.

Intake

Many communities maintain psychiatric outpatient facilities in which a social worker may see patients and their families prior to hospitalization. Hospitalization itself is often necessary, not so much as a result of the severity of the symptom but because of the breakdown of the patient's particular social situation. This means the immediate environment can no longer tolerate his behavior because of a specific combination of circumstances. Occasionally the social worker may be able to work out some environmental rearrangement as a result of which an admission to a hospital can be averted. Where an admission is urgently indicated but resisted by a family out of fear or ignorance the social worker can help them to understand why the patient will be better off in the hospital. He can also allay some of the patient's terror by explanation and reassurance concerning what will happen to him in the hospital. If hospitalization results in serious family disruption, as when a wage earner is taken away or a mother is compelled to leave small children, the social worker can make whatever arrangements are necessary to maintain relatively normal family life. Most important of all, the social worker lays the groundwork, before the patient has even entered the hospital, for planning the return of the patient to an improved home environment.

Reception

The admission of a patient to a mental hospital is usually a psychological trauma of major proportions to patient and family alike. Due to widespread prejudice this incident may be associated with real and imagined loss of social status. Commitment procedures which resemble criminal actions in some states reinforce these feelings. Often families have been advised to resort to trickery to get a patient to enter the hospital, and they feel guilty about that. They may fear that their loved one will be beaten, starved or chained in a dungeon, or that once having placed him in the hospital they will never be able to get him out again. They may be burdened with deep guilt feelings about their role in the patient's breakdown. For these and other reasons the patient and the family need reassurance and other forms of psychological support at the time of admission. Accordingly, they should be received in a pleasant setting, in an unhurried manner, in order that they may be given some preliminary psychological help.

When the patient has been formally admitted and taken to the ward, the social worker turns his attention to the family. In his preliminary interviews with them he provides them with an outlet for their pent-up emotions. The relatives are given an opportunity to ask questions about the hospital and to air their doubts and fears. He gives them reassurance if they seem particularly guilt-ridden. He explains to them what a social service history is, its content, why it is taken, and how it helps the patient. He also explains what the social service department is prepared to do for the patient and the family. The hospital routines are explained and the legal aspects of hospitalization are discussed. A member of the family who seems most reliable is selected as an informant and an appointment is made for the social service history.

The social worker should be prepared with literature for the family which they can study in calmer moments at home, explaining the nature of mental illness, the role of the hospital in rehabilitating the mentally ill, and most of all the therapeutic importance of continued interest on the part of the family in the patient's welfare (see references to Chapter XXXIV for suggested titles). This is a good time to establish a clothing policy with the family. If they keep the patient properly equipped with clothing which he likes, it will contribute significantly to his self-esteem and hence to his rehabilitation.

It should be ascertained at this time if there have been previous social service contacts with agencies in the community. In the event that there have been such contacts, an attempt should be made to secure a summary of pertinent material on the patient and the family, utilizing the facilities of the Social Service Exchange.[1] Such information may save much time

1 The Social Service Exchange (S.S.E.) is a clearing house for social service information. It has offices in most of the leading cities of the United States. Organizations, in-

and effort in clarifying the diagnosis, the specific environmental stresses, the prognosis and the plans for future rehabilitation. Whenever possible, requests should be couched in the form of specific questions. Agencies which are geographically more accessible to the family may be called into the case from the very outset in helping the family to understand the patient's illness, and in effecting useful modifications in family attitudes and living arrangements. The social worker usually obtains written permission from the family to secure information from other sources. Written permission is also obtained at this time for the administration of all necessary treatments.

Taking a Social Service History

A source of data of vital importance for the formulation of a case by the psychiatrist (see Chapter I and Appendix A) is the social service history. The social service history should cover the following topics:

I. *Identifying information:* Name of patient, marital status, family composition, where patient makes his home, race, nationality, and religion.

II. *Sources of information:* List informants, their relationship to patient, length of time they knew patient, records consulted (Social Service Exchange, school, hospital, juvenile or other court).

III. *Precipitating situation,* or circumstances attending the onset of the illness.

IV. *Developmental history:* Give date and place of birth and any unusual influencing factors. Was there a birth injury? Did he walk and talk at an unusually early or late age? Note anything unusual in development, such as feeding difficulties, stuttering, nail biting, fainting spells or convulsions, nightmares, sleepwalking, bed wetting longer than usual, special fears, temper tantrums.

V. *Health and medical history:* Was the patient ever admitted to a hospital in the past for either a medical or mental condition? When? Reason? Secure details and a report from the doctor. Note any unusual use of tobacco, alcohol, or drugs.

VI. *Family history:* What appear to be the attitudes in the family group? How many brothers and sisters? Patient's relationship to parents? Are they divorced? Are parents foreign-born? Is this a source of

---

cluding mental hospitals, with properly accredited social service departments may become members. If the name of a new patient is submitted to the S.S.E. the organization will provide the member agency with a list of all previous social service contacts of this patient that are on the records of the Exchange. In this way a complete social history can be obtained with greater speed and economy. A properly run Exchange protects the interests of the patient by avoiding unauthorized disclosures and is usually directed by a committee of representatives of the agencies which belong to the Exchange.

conflict? If either parent is dead, what age was the patient at the time of death and how did he react to it? Were methods of child training oversevere or overindulgent? How did the patient get along with brothers and sisters? Was there an extreme attachment between the patient and any member of the family? Was there any mental illness, epilepsy or alcoholism in immediate family?

VII. *Personality:* What kind of a person is the patient. Did he play alone or in groups? Was he a leader, or was he shy and always the follower? Timid, overly modest, or a show-off? Did he have a sense of duty? Calm or high-strung? What were his interests and hobbies? Did he have pets? Was he cruel to animals? If so, at what age? Was he happy-go-lucky or responsible? Were there any marked changes in habits, interests, and attitudes during adolescence? Did he have any girl friends, older or younger, approved or disapproved socially? Did he have any strong attachment to boys? Describe any unusual interest in religion. What were his ambitions? (See Appendix C for more detailed outline of personality inventory.)

VIII. *Education:* How far did he go in school? Regularity of attendance and promotions? Reasons for leaving and age. How well did he do in his studies? Did he have any special interests or outstanding difficulties in school subjects? Were there any particular problems of behavior or of adjustments to teachers and fellow students?

IX. *Employment:* What kind of work has the patient done? Has he worked consistently at one type of work? Did he change jobs frequently and what were the reasons for changing? What kind of a workman was he considered by employers? (See Chapter V for further suggestions concerning work history.)

X. *Military history:* (see Chapter XXII).

XI. *Present home situation:* Describe home. With whom was the patient living before he entered hospital? If married, what does the relationship seem to be—congenial or unhappy? If the patient is divorced or separated, give date and reason. Are there any children? Give ages. Give any unusual facts about the health situation of the family. Describe how the relatives who furnished the information feel about the patient. Did they know about the patient's illness. What was the attitude toward the interview? Were they glad to give information or did they seek to hide unfavorable facts? What is their attitude toward the patient's return home?

The relatives should be approached in a friendly fashion, recognizing that they are inevitably tense and fearful. They may display suspiciousness and hostility. They may be highly provocative in their manner. All such reactions should be understood by the social worker as defenses against anxiety. The sources of anxiety should be searched for and reassurances should be directed at these sources. (See Chapter XXXIV for discussion of hostile relatives.) The approach to relatives should always be helpful, and guided by scientific understanding of human behavior. The success of the social worker in getting the family to accept sound mental hygiene goals for themselves and the patient at this time may be the critical factor in determining the outcome of the patient's treatment.

In the course of taking a social service history the informant is encouraged to speak freely and informally. The social worker has to take notes during the interview since all the factual data cannot be retained from memory. However, note taking should not be permitted to become a barrier or to give the impression of a formidable procedure. Every effort should be made to maintain the interview on a friendly and cooperative plane. Direct questions should be plied infrequently and then with due regard for the sensitivity of the informants. Above all, the history should not be elicited in a mechanical question-and-answer fashion, nor will it necessarily be completed in one interview. This not only yields less significant information, but it destroys the relationship with the family, which is the most important item of all.

The Period of Active Treatment

After the initial history is taken the social worker will provide supplementary historical data from subsequent contacts with the family, or indirectly through community agencies working with the family. These data will enlarge the knowledge concerning the patient, but most of all will record changes in family relationships and attitudes as they involve the patient and as they affect plans for his aftercare. During this time the social worker attends all conferences in which the patient is discussed. These include conferences with supervisors in the social service department, with the psychiatrist treating the patient, jointly with the "treatment team" consisting of members of other departments working with the patient, and the daily clinical staff conference.

An important part of his work involves direct interviews with the patient and his relatives. The timing of these interviews is determined by the patient's condition, increasing in frequency as the most acute phase of the illness subsides. While the diagnosis, formulation and plan of treatment are basically the responsibility of the physician, the social worker makes a fundamental contribution to the fulfillment of this responsibility. From the very beginning the caseworker makes observations concerning the social functioning of the patient. In addition he elicits, supports and builds ego strength. In so far as community resources, financial assistance and other services must be used the social worker will be involved to a greater or lesser extent.

The social worker focuses on the anxiety, the dependency and the defensive structure in helping the patient and his relatives adapt to his disability and the realities of the social situation. In the casework process the worker must be able to identify with the client, accept him as a person, analyze and clarify for him his reality situation, and help him to make the most of the inner and outer resources which are available to him.

Typically, the emotional disturbances uncovered among members of the family are not much less severe than those displayed by the patient, and these profoundly affect the treatment.

For example, a fifty-year-old married man with a suicidal reactive depression was not responding to treatment in a mental hospital. His wife was observed to be a domineering individual who had the capacity to mobilize great guilt feelings in him. One day while on a vacation in a summer camp, which had been arranged for by the caseworker, the wife saw two women dancing together. She reacted to this sight with expressions of indignation and growing agitation. In a short time she was in an acute paranoid schizophrenic state, characterized by strong homosexual delusional trends. Because of her disturbed psychotic behavior it was necessary to hospitalize her.

In retrospect it became clear that the wife was psychotic all along but had been able to control the gross manifestation of her mental illness in her conferences with the caseworker. The hitherto intractible reactive depression of the husband became more understandable to the therapists. With the wife in custody he improved rapidly and was able to return to the community in remission.

The more subtle but no less malignant psychopathological family reactions which are usually encountered provide the social worker with important opportunities for therapeutic modifications in family relationships and individual behavior by means of sustained and intensive casework techniques.

The social worker should check all legal documents which come to his attention. At times a large estate may be discovered as a result of which extramural care can be made possible. In one instance an insurance company was discovered paying out disability funds to a wife who had divorced the patient many years previously and had done nothing for his welfare in the interim. Another insurance company was found to be sending the patient's disability checks to his mother who had died in Sweden several years previously. In a third instance a family which was being supported by the patient's insurance funds refused to co-operate in his rehabilitation. In all these cases it was possible to reapply these funds more effectively to the patient's advantage.

The Preconvalescent Period

It has become increasingly apparent that the environment to which we return the patient is the point of central importance in the total treatment plan. We must estimate the patient's needs and the extent to which the home environment is capable of meeting them. For example, a patient who is only partially recovered may do well in an overprotective environment, whereas a patient who has achieved a desire and a capacity for personal independence might be destroyed by that same environment. Careful study of the patient's home situation with respect to his specific emotional needs is a necessity. The following outline for a social study for home visits is detailed by Sara F. Schroeder, Director of Social Service at St. Elizabeth's Hospital in Washington, D.C., and appears in the *Proceedings of the Third Research Conference on Psychosurgery*. This outline should be used as a flexible guide, keeping in mind that the essential interest is in the patient and not in a frame into which he must be fitted. It should be indicated that the study is a process worked out among those most concerned: the patient, his relatives, his physician and caseworker, and those others in the hospital who have contributed to his improvement.

> *Referral request by the psychiatrist:* This contains a detailed estimate by the psychiatrist concerning the patient's current condition; his ability to adjust socially; the responsibility he is able to assume for care of self and family, his capacity to work, and the amount of protection and supervision that he needs.
>
> *The patient:* This is a summary of the work that social service has done with the patient. It considers the patient's attitude toward his illness and hospitalization, the use he has made of the hospital facilities, his attitude and plans concerning leaving the hospital, his feelings about his home, his relatives, and his work, his relationship with the caseworker, and the way he has been helped.
>
> *The relatives:* This is a summary of the work with relatives. It contains a statement of the relationship of the relative to the patient, an impression of him as a person, and the length of his association with the patient. Also included are such points as his attitude to the patient, the relative's strengths and weaknesses, the member of the family who is most significant to the patient, the anticipated impact on the family of the patient's return, the attitude of the relative toward the caseworker. What modification, if any, has the relative been able to achieve in his attitude toward the patient and how this has been accomplished.
>
> *Social agencies:* Interviews with social workers in other community agencies go under this heading.

Living arrangements: This contains the address; a brief description of the home and neighborhood, including an estimate of the standard of living: the names of persons living in the home and their relationship to the patient; and the sleeping facilities for the patient.

Employment of the patient: Here is recorded factual information about job opportunities and placement.

Evaluation and recommendations by the Social Service Department: The evaluation is based on the factors brought out in the study, having to do broadly with the physical conditions and mental health aspects of the home as they relate to the needs of the patient. It can be analyzed as follows:

Needs of the patient: Adequate living conditions, protective care, interest and warmth of feeling, freedom to develop self-direction.

Ability and willingness of the family to meet these needs: Extent of financial and emotional security, interest in the patient, and understanding of his emotional needs.

Relationships to patient within the home: Such attitudes of positive value as warmth of feeling, acceptance, permissiveness, understanding, tolerance. Such attitudes to patient of negative value as indifference, rejection, hostility, rivalry, competiveness, jealousy.

Cultural factors, as they influence the situation.

The recommendation for the convalescent visit is based on a comparison of the positive and negative factors inherent in the patient's situation as brought out by the preconvalescent social study. The morbid features are weighed against the strengths in order to arrive at a prognosis for the trial visit. Calculations in terms of cold analysis alone yield few beneficial results unless accompanied by personal warmth on the part of the worker.

Aftercare

Despite the fact that the social worker has many duties to the patient and his family prior to release from the hospital, his most important functions relate to the patient's return to the community. Therefore his activities in the patient's behalf become more numerous when this is imminent. In addition to the preconvalescent measures already described, it is the social worker's responsibility to follow the patient into the community, to help him to adjust to his home environment, to give him further assistance in vocational rehabilitation and in finding social and recreational outlets. Such attentions are in themselves therapeutic and contribute significantly to the patient's well-being. In addition, however, the social worker will endeavor to secure further care for the patient in an outpatient clinic, in a community social agency, or privately if this can be arranged.

Social service aftercare takes several different forms. In the oldest type and still most frequently used, the social worker visits the patient in his home, makes observations, contributes what he can to the welfare of the patient and his family, addresses a lengthy report to the hospital psychiatrist, and makes further plans in a conference with him. This method is time-consuming, inefficient, involves considerable travel and very incomplete control of the situation by the psychiatrist. As a result, a further plan was evolved in which clinics were set up in the community and on a given day a team of workers from a specific mental hospital would see former patients who were able to get to the clinic on that day. If the patient experienced difficulty between appointments, he had no recourse for help. The most logical method is that which sets up independent outpatient facilities in the community to serve a given area. These are called "aftercare clinics." The hospital social worker sees to it that the aftercare clinic is apprised of the patient's return to the community and the personnel of this clinic assumes responsibility for the problem from then on. The goal of this plan is to provide psychiatric service on a regular and emergency basis to all patients in the area seven days a week on a twenty-four-hour basis. A full-time staff provides all the services of a psychiatric treatment team. This is discussed in detail in Chapter XXXV.

Family Care and Sheltered Homes

The placement of patients with families other than their own for care and further treatment is recognized as a major development in rehabilitating the mentally ill (see Chapter XXXVI). The social worker and psychiatrist will select those cases which seem most in need of such environmental reorganization on the basis of studies outlined in the preceding paragraphs. Many psychotic patients end up friendless and without families. For them, foster home placement represents the only way in which they can be restored to the community. The social worker's responsibilities in this program are primarily those of finding suitable homes and conducting studies of prospective foster homes to determine their capacity to meet the specific needs of the patient. He will interpret the patient and his needs to the foster family. He will help the patient accept the placement and will aid in all other aspects of his readjustment.

In addition to foster family arrangements, some communities have set up sheltered residences where patients may stay for one or two months. Homes such as these serve as a stepping stone between the controlled environment of the mental hospital and the freedom of the outside world. In some areas family care funds and facilities have been used to set up groups of fifteen to twenty young men or young women in properly appointed homes in the city under the supervision of house parents or a house mother.

Still another means for providing a gradual transition to the outside community are to be found in ex-patient social clubs.

Fountain House Foundation, Inc., organized in 1948 as a private club in New York City, is an example. It offers membership to persons who have been hospitalized because of mental illness. It purchased a home with facilities for its various programs and hired a staff under the direction of an executive director who is a psychiatric social worker. The director supervises the entire program and handles finances. A social group worker directs the activities program. In May 1950, the staff of Fountain House, in addition, consisted of a commercial subjects teacher, two part-time recreational leaders and a secretary. Rockland State Hospital assigned one of its occupational therapists to Fountain House to devote her time to patients on convalescent care from that hospital. Various organizations and agencies have offered their services to the club. As of July 1950, 363 persons were participating in the program. Voluntary contributions and Federal grants have made it possible for them to manage a $44,000 annual budget. The activities include a Saturday night dance, a glee club, a sketching class, a craft program, an occupational therapy course, and a work adjustment program providing courses in commercial subjects. The club publishes a newspaper called *Fountain House Speaks* which carries articles, stories and poems contributed by members. There seems to be no question that a service like this could be useful in enabling chronically ill and even "deteriorated" patients to adjust successfully in the community.

The Economics of Good Social Work

In 1945, Minna Field, who was then supervisor of social work on the insulin research unit of the Brooklyn State Hospital, reported on the effects of social service care on the outcome of insulin coma therapy. For this purpose 207 insulin-treated dementia praecox patients and their families were exposed to intensified social service care during the period of treatment in the hospital and during the aftercare period. Another group of 207 insulin-treated dementia praecox patients carefully matched with the experimental group received the ordinary, relatively inadequate social service care which obtained in the hospital at large. The patients receiving intensive psychiatric social service did substantially better than the control group. A significantly larger percentage of these patients were able to leave the hospital. The proportion needing rehospitalization following release was one half that in the control group. Returns to the hospital within a few days after release were completely eliminated in the special research group. During the period of study the research group patients spent an average of 61 days more at home and 40 days less in the hospital. The percentage of patients functioning at a level equal to or superior to that which they displayed prior to hospitalization was considerably higher in the experimental group. It was estimated that these superior results represented a direct saving to the hospital of over $15,000. In addition to this purely monetary advantage there were many others to be found in the mental hygiene improvements which were achieved within the family group.

The Social Worker and Research

In the foregoing research project the social service department played the central role. There are many other investigations in which social service help is necessary. Criteria for the selection of patients for psychosurgery seem to center increasingly on social data rather than on clinical psychiatric observations within the hospital. For example, what were the patient's psychosocial attainments before he became ill? What is the family situation to which he is to be returned? In no area in psychiatry is basic research more urgently needed than with respect to the fate of patients after they are discharged from mental hospitals. The proper investigation of this problem calls for a much larger corps of trained social workers to pursue follow-up studies than is currently available. Significant studies on the role of psychosocial factors in the epidemiology of mental illness which are currently in progress depend upon the help of social workers. Investigations of sociologic phenomena which take place within the mental hospital can be enriched by social service participation. No new treatment can be properly evaluated unless detailed follow-up studies by the social service department are part of the investigation. In recent years social workers have participated increasingly in group work with patients and relatives. This may consist of orienting talks to groups with common problems or participation in actual group therapy under the direction of a psychiatrist. These developments represent important areas for social service research. Thus, whether independently or collaboratively, the social service department plays an extremely important role in the research program of the mental hospital.

The Social Worker and Community Relations

An important part of the duties of the social worker in the mental hospital is in the field of community relations. He helps organize and direct mental health organizations in the community, including Alcoholics Anonymous, recruits people for the hospital volunteer program, speaks to various professional groups such as physicians, nurses, teachers, clergymen, lawyers, and judges. He also works with lay groups, and in conjunction with social service agencies in the community. These activities consist of teaching mental health principles, organizing new mental health resources in the community and educating groups in the role of social service so that they can make better use of available facilities when necessary.

The Qualifications of the Social Worker

Trained social workers in mental hospitals are usually classified into three categories. (1) The staff worker has two years of graduate professional training in a recognized school of social work leading to his Master's degree, with a major emphasis on psychiatric social work. (2) The casework supervisor has in addition a minimum of three years' work experience, at least one of which was in a responsible working relationship with a psychiatrist in a clinical setting. (3) The chief social worker or director of social service should have at least five years' experience, with at least two years in a supervisory capacity, and at least three years in a psychiatric setting, hospital or outpatient. It has been recommended by the Group for the Advancement of Psychiatry that there be at least one trained psychiatric social worker on a staff level to every eighty new admissions per year; and in addition at least one psychiatric social worker for each sixty patients receiving aftercare. Administrative and supervisory psychiatric social workers should be added in the ratio of one supervisor to every five staff case workers.[2]

A Training Program for Social Service

Ideally, every mental hospital should be affiliated with a school for social service, with a teaching staff and facilities for training students. It must be clear, however, to anyone who works in a mental hospital that

[2] Liberal scholarships for graduate training in social work are available under the provisions of the National Mental Health Act. (See H. B. Crutcher in "Selected References" at the end of this chapter; also Chapter XXIX.)

recommended professional standards are rarely met in actual practice. In addition to shortages in trained personnel to fill existing vacancies is the fact that almost one half of all the personnel currently providing social services in mental hospitals have had incomplete training or none at all. The likelihood of closing this gap in the foreseeable future is quite small. As a result it is necessary to utilize subprofessional groups to fulfill the hospital's needs.

The United States Armed Forces have approached the problem of shortages in trained social workers by setting up a category of so-called social worker technicians. Enlisted personnel without previous training in social work but possessing the interest and the qualifications of personality and intelligence are given special training. This consists of about three hundred hours of classroom instruction and an additional amount of time in supervised work. The student is taught the different forms and functions of social service work, the form and content of the social history, and techniques of interviewing, so that he can properly relate his work to the specific unit to which he is assigned. In addition psychiatric concepts, medical information, psychiatric nursing procedures, psychological evaluations and casework practice are taught to help the student appreciate the complexity of the human personality and the techniques of each discipline in helping the patient through the team approach. Case material illustrating interview techniques is studied, and the casework content is utilized to impress the student with his limitations while acquainting him with professional social casework practice. Psychological concepts of personality growth and development give the student a basis on which to evaluate basic personality differences and an understanding of elementary psychiatric concepts. This program, which has worked out so successfully in the Army, has application to civilian practices, too. It awaits only the initiative of individual mental hospitals and state mental hygiene programs. By developing a corps of trained technicians to work under the supervision of professional social workers the social service departments in civilian mental hospitals can be enlarged to meet the expanding needs.

SELECTED REFERENCES

BERKMAN, T. D.: *Practice of Social Workers in Psychiatric Hospitals and Clinics.* New York: American Association of Psychiatric Social Workers, 1953.
A research study describing current practices with recommendations for curriculum improvements and further research.
CRUTCHER, H. B.: The Function of the Psychiatric Social Worker in a Mental Hospital. *Newsletter, Am. Assn. Psychiat. Soc. Workers,* 12:3, 1947.
This article contains much valuable information concerning the provisions of the National Mental Health Act as they concern social service training and research.

DEWITT, H. B.: Family Care as the Focus for Social Casework in a State Mental Hospital. *Ment. Hyg.*, 28:602, 1944.
>   This article is directed primarily at the problems of training the new social worker. It is particularly rich in illustrative clinical material.
—— What Hospitalization Means to Mental Patient, Community and Hospital Social Worker. *Ment. Hyg.*, 31:266, 1947.
>   This deals primarily with problems of intake. Many useful case histories.
FRAIBERG, S. H.: *Psychoanalytic Principles in Casework with Children.* New York: Family Service Association of America, 1955. (192 Lexington Avenue, N. Y. C. 16.)
>   A lucid and highly practical presentation of dynamic case work principles. Invaluable guide in work with children.
GARRETT, A. M.: *Interviewing, Its Principles and Methods.* New York: Family Welfare Association of America, 1942.
>   Theoretical and practical considerations. Includes a group of clinical examples which are analyzed in detail.
GOODALE, E.: Intake Interviews with Relatives of Psychotic Patients. *Smith College Studies in Social Work,* 15:15, 1944.
>   A dynamic study of intake problems illustrated with twelve excellent case histories.
GROUP FOR THE ADVANCEMENT OF PSYCHIATRY: The Psychiatric Social Worker in the Psychiatric Hospital. G. A. P. Report No. 2, Jan. 1948.
>   An outline of the functions of the social worker in the mental hospital, and recommended standards of practice.
HAMILTON, G.: *Theory and Practice of Social Casework.* New York: Columbia University Press, 1949.
>   This has been rightly described as a classic text in social work.
HOLLIS, F.: *Women in Marital Conflict. A Casework Study.* New York: Family Service Association of America, 1949. (192 Lexington Avenue, N.Y.C. 16) .
>   An analysis of the factors which enter into marital conflict as these are elucidated by the case work process. The role of the social caseworker in the treatment of the disturbed family is presented with illustrative clinical material.
KASIUS, C. ed.: *Principles and Techniques in Social Work: Selected Articles 1940-1950.* New York: Family Service Association of America, 1950.
>   A collection of papers by authorities, reprinted from "The Family," "Journal of Social Casework" and "Social Casework." Covers theory, problems relating to teaching and supervision, and practical clinical considerations.
LOWRY, F., ed.: *Readings in Social Case Work, 1920-1938.* New York: Columbia University Press, 1939.
>   A collection of papers reprinted from the major social work journals and conference reports between 1918 and 1938. Covers basic theory, technique of interviewing, problem of diagnosis, treatment, relationships with other social service agencies and related professional fields.
MORAN, M. L.: Some Emotional Responses of Patients' Husbands to the Psychotherapeutic Course as Indicated in Interviews with the Psychiatric Caseworkers. *Am. J. Orthopsychiat.,* 24:317, 1954.
>   This paper takes up the fact that families need help after a patient has been changed by psychiatric treatment.
SCHROEDER, S. F.: *Social Service Aspects of the Research Conference Group on Psychosurgery.* Appendix I. Proceedings of the Third Research Conference on Psychosurgery. Public Health Service Publication No. 221, U.S. Gov. Printing Office, Washington, D.C.
>   An excellent presentation of the problem of selecting a suitable environment for the patient who is to be released from a mental hospital. Quoted in the text.
SCHWARTZ, C. G.: *Rehabilitation of Mental Hospital Patients. Review of the Literature.*

Public Health Monograph No. 17. Supt. of Documents, U.S. Gov. Printing Office, Washington, D.C.

A particularly useful review of aftercare techniques.

SEEFELDT, C. J.: Patients' Participation at the Staff Level. In: Role of the Psychiatric Social Worker in Mental Health Programs. A symposium. *J. Psychiat. Soc. Worker*, 23:142, 1954.

This article describes the role of social service in setting up a patient government program in a mental hospital. The entire symposium, of which this article is a part, is highly recommended.

Symposium on Military Social Work. Office of the Surgeon General, Dept. of the Army, Chief of Social Services Branch, Washington, D.C.

A particularly useful presentation of the training program for social service technicians and the way in which they can best be integrated into the hospital social service program.

WALKIEWICZ, S. T.: Convalescent Patients as Mental Hospital Employees. *Smith College Studies in Social Work*, 16:282, 1946.

The role of the social worker in setting up a work rehabilitation program.

WHITE, R. R.: The Social Services in the State Hospitals of Illinois. *Ment. Hyg.*, 27:554, 1943.

The fact that not all of the patients' irritations are delusional is illustrated with several clinical examples.

Chapter IX

THE PSYCHOLOGIST

Psychological Testing as an Aid in Planning Treatment

In 1896, when the first psychological clinic was established at the University of Pennsylvania, the psychologist's clinical function consisted primarily of administering tests designed to determine the presence or absence of mental deficiency. However, with the development of a more dynamic conception of the human mind, the importance of the emotional life of the individual came into focus. It became clear, for example, that a simple statement of a mental age gave no clue as to the use the patient made of his intelligence. A low score might be the result of a curable emotional or physical disturbance. A high score might be associated with a relatively incurable schizophrenia. The clinical problem of paramount importance in psychological testing today centers about the patient's emotional adaptation. What is the patient striving for? What are the factors within him and in the external environment which frustrate those strivings? How does he integrate or synthesize these opposing forces? In short, the questions we should like the psychologist to answer are those which concern every member of the therapeutic community. Whether in the occupational therapy shop, a ball game or a group therapy session, the patient brings with him his total personality, his fears, his characteristic ways of relating to other people and his typical reactions to frustration. These data contribute to the psychiatrist's over-all understanding of the problem. In this sense, the information contributed by the psychologist represents only one category, albeit a category of special importance, in a broader body of data which is used by the psychiatrist in formulating his working hypothesis concerning the patient's illness.

Requesting Psychological Studies

When the psychiatrist requests a psychological test, he should have specific questions in mind and make them known to the psychologist. For example, there may be a problem of diagnosis. Very often if the clinical picture is equivocal, the patient's performance in the psychological test situation is also equivocal. However, the psychologist can pick up unmistakable evidences of psychotic behavior, for example, which were not previously evident. The psychiatrist is always interested in the dynamics of the case. He will want to know the basic patterns of behavior with which the patient reacts to psychological emergencies; also what infantile trends exert a dominant unconscious influence on his adult behavior. The patient's conception of himself and his role in life are often clearly expressed in the psychological data. Thus, an adult may conceive of himself as a child. Confusion in sexual identification may be evident. The male patient may reveal a wish to be a woman and the female patient may express similar dissatisfaction with her role. The data may expose a conflict between aggressive impulses and passive, dependent impulses; between rebellion against authority and excessive acquiescence. The tests will often show how successfully the patient is reconciling these conflicting drives. For example, an actual or an imminent dissolution of the patient's integrative capacities may be expressed, in characteristic ways, on various tests. Under such circumstances, the patient will tend to see in general two concepts, often clearly at odds with each other, in situations where the more integrated mind will see only one.

The question of integrative capacity touches upon the prognostic function of psychological testing. Psychological data show the patient's potential as well as his actual performance. The psychologist can extrapolate from his findings and estimate what the patient's capabilities would be if he were untrammeled by a severe neurosis or an organic brain disorder. That is, the psychologist's data may help to quantitate the extent of deterioration that has taken place. Evidences of attempts at restitution in the psychological data are of prognostic importance. The patient with an acute schizophrenic process may show restitutive efforts to a considerable degree, the chronic unsuccessfully lobotomized schizophrenic may show them not at all. The psychologist may estimate from the evidences of active fantasy life the likelihood of success with a patient in individual or group psychotherapy, thereby providing a means of selecting patients for such therapeutic approaches.

Retesting a patient is a means of evaluating the results of treatment. By this means, the psychiatrist can verify directly how psychoanalytically oriented psychotherapy can, if successful, result in fundamental qualitative alterations in the patient's relationship to reality, and how the shock therapies and psychosurgery, by contrast, alter certain quantitative factors, yet leave the core of the approach to reality relatively untouched.

Patients are sometimes admitted to the hospital with a schizophrenic syndrome associated with acute encephalitis. In these cases, one can demonstrate improvement quite strikingly by improved scores on retesting.

Structured Versus Unstructured Test Situations

A test may be designed to measure a patient's capacity to do arithmetic. A series of arithmetic problems of increasing difficulty are devised, the test results are standardized and we have in effect a so-called structured test. This is a test which is designed to measure a specific mental capacity, in this case, the capacity to solve arithmetic problems. It concerns itself with little more than a quantitative statement about the subject's ability in this regard. However, suppose the subject bursts into tears or throws a temper tantrum when confronted with a task he cannot solve? Or suppose he solves the simplest problem and remains completely uncommunicative until confronted with the last and most difficult problem at which point he responds again and solves it at once. Under such circumstances, other factors besides a "simple" capacity to solve arithmetic problems would seem to be involved, such as motivation, the relationship to reality in general, and to the psychologist in particular, or the way in which the patient handles anxiety. Thus, there are certain aspects of the arithmetic test situation which have a common denominator with other life situations. To the extent that these common denominators exist, we say that the situation is unstructured.

It is quite clear that there is no conceivable situation involving a human being which is not to some extent unstructured. For this reason, we want the psychologist to include in his report a description of the patient's behavior in the psychologist's laboratory, as to whether he is suspicious, ingratiating or evasive. Just as important as the answer to a question is often the manner in which it is given. Inasmuch as the test situation itself is a highly stressful one for the patient, all of these represent legitimate facts upon which the psychologist may base his report. At the opposite pole from the arithmetic test are other tests designed specifically to elicit these common denominators, tests for which there is no right or wrong answer but which provide clues concerning the subject's behavior in general life situations. For example, a subject may be asked to complete a series of sentences such as "What I like best in life is—" This is an example of an unstructured test. Because the patient tends to project into the test situation his dominant personality traits, we refer to these designed unstructured situations as projective tests.

Description of Tests

A few of the tests which have been of particular value in my experience will be described briefly in the following paragraphs.

The Wechsler Bellevue Intelligence Scale. This test consists of eleven subtests, six of which are verbal (vocabulary, information, comprehension, arithmetic, similarities, and digit span), and five are performance (picture arrangement, picture completion, object assembly, block design, and digit symbol). Each of the subtests has been standardized separately as well as compositely at each age level, making possible a detailed comparison of the performances of a subject of a given age with standardized performances at that age. The patient emerges from the test with certain data called the raw scores on each subtest. The raw scores thus obtained are then converted into "weighted" scores and compared with the weighted scores of a standardized population of his own age. Out of this comparison one arrives at a quotient which measures his intelligence level as compared to persons of his own age. Thus, an obtained score at age twenty has a different significance for general intelligence than that same score at age sixty. The raw scores of each subtest are expressed as converted weighted scores by means of a table. This makes possible comparison of a subject's relative ability on the separate subtests. The scale was devised to furnish a general adult intelligence rating, and for this purpose it is probably unequalled. The basic intelligence rating will influence the psychiatrist concerning the type and goals of therapy and other clinical decisions. However, as must be abundantly clear at this time, much more can be gleaned from this test than a static score concerning intelligence.

Variations in the levels of performance within the subtests have diagnostic significance. It was found, for example, that certain subtest scores tend to hold up with age and others tend to fall off. Specifically, there is a characteristic relationship between subtest scores, the pattern of which varies with age. So that if one finds a test pattern in a young person which one expects to find in an older subject, one might interpret this as evidence of deterioration of function due to organic brain disease. Performance on the information test, comprehension and vocabulary, tends to remain high, whereas performance on digit span, especially digits recited backwards, block design and similarities, tends to fall off with age or generalized organic brain disease. Epileptics tend to have an over-all higher score on performance tests than they do on verbal tests. In general, the degree to which over-all intelligence scores are affected by organic brain disease is related to the extent of the brain damage. Patients with unilateral lesions tend to do more poorly on performance than on verbal tests. When a lesion affects the cerebrum bilaterally, verbal test impairment becomes more marked and frequently exceeds in degree the impairment on the performance scale. Subtest variability which is great but which does not follow any characteristic pattern may be a sign of schizophrenia.

In addition to the purely quantitative scoring aspects of this test, much can be learned from a qualitative study of the responses. In responses on vocabulary, information, comprehension and similarities, in particular, the patient may reveal delusional trends and other evidences of a psychotic alteration in his relationship with reality. Thus, one patient revealed a tendency to clang associations by saying that Marco Polo discovered the North Pole; another defined the function of the heart with the schizophrenic neologism that "it palpulates the blood." One well-educated patient revealed psychotically contaminated thinking by saying that George Washington's birthday is on the fourth of July. When one patient was asked why taxes are necessary, he answered, "It all began with the idea of taxation without representation." To this same question another patient answered, "In order to maintain equilibrium." One patient said that wood and alcohol are alike because "they consume themselves." Such answers are correct in a manner of speaking but are expressed obliquely or neologistically and as such may be subtle evidences of psychotic thinking. While all such atypical responses are particularly characteristic of schizophrenia, they are not by themselves pathognomonic. All the data must be taken into account in making a differential diagnosis. Mention has already been made of the fact that one can follow the improvement of a patient recovering from brain injury due to any cause by his improvement on retest performance. One young woman with encephalitis obtained a full-scale intelligence quotient of 75 during the period of acute illness. Tested again during her convalescence four months later, her I.Q. rose to 132. Thus, in the use of this so-called structured test of intelligence, we have traveled very far from the days when our concern was to determine simply the presence or absence of mental deficiency.

The Rorschach Test is usually described as the best of the projective tests. It consists of ten ink blots (five black and white, five in color) which are presented in sequence to the patient with the simple comment, "What might this be?" The patient's responses are recorded with minimal prompting from the examiner. After all ten cards have been seen, the examiner may direct questions to clarify certain responses. The responses are scored in a standardized manner, depending on whether the subject uses the whole blot for his response (W), a conspicuous part of it (D), or a relatively inconspicuous detail (d); whether the patient uses color in his response and whether his response is based primarily on the color or the form of the blot (FC, CF, C); whether the patient sees human movement (M), animal movement (FM), or the motion of inanimate objects in space (m); whether the response corresponds with reasonable realism to the actual appearance of the blot (F+), or whether the response seems to bear little obvious relationship to its actual appearance (F—). In addition, the psychologist scores the presence of three-dimensional or depth responses (FK, KF, K); surface texture responses (Fc); and several others. Some responses recur quite frequently when one tests many people, and these are called popular responses. Others occur quite rarely or uniquely and these are called original responses. If these unique responses are associated with poor form quality (F—), they are expressive of pathologically deviant thinking.

In addition to these purely formal aspects of the responses, the psychologist is also interested in content from a qualitative point of view. Card II has been called the childhood card because of its tendency to elicit responses relating to children's play. Card III tends to elicit evidence of confusion concerning one's sexual role because of some ambiguity in its outlines. Card IV has been called the father card because of its tendency to elicit images of a frightening father figure from early childhood. Card V has been called the reality card because of its clear form, and the small number of relatively stereotyped responses which it tends to elicit. An inability to give some response to the obvious outlines of this blot is usually expressive of psychopathology. Card VI tends to elicit evidence of sexual disturbance, and Card VII often elicits data concerning attitudes toward the mother. A patient may reveal an infantile dependent attitude by his preoccupation with food responses, or a guilt feeling by his preoccupation with religious symbols. The range of responses as far as content is concerned is practically limitless. It is in the area of content in particular that direct examination of the test protocol may be rewarding to the psychiatrist. Because of his generally broader knowledge of the patient's life history and of personal details which emerge during psychotherapy, he may appreciate the significance of certain responses that may elude the psychologist. Certain patients divide the card along its midline into two concepts which oppose each other, men or animals fighting each other, or more abstractly, good versus evil, or love versus hate. This is an expression of a splitting tendency in the ego that has become clinically manifest or is about to do so. Where most people are able to integrate the two halves of the card, or at least to ignore half of it, these patients thus project their inability to integrate their own warring impulses.

Although scoring of the Rorschach responses is not difficult, interpretation of the meaning of the total test result requires much experience and training. This test in many ways complements the Wechsler Bellevue Scale. Although one may make certain inferences concerning the general intelligence rating from the Rorschach, the test derives its main usefulness as a means of evaluating the patient from a general psychiatric point of view with respect to diagnosis, psychodynamics, and prognosis.

Thematic Apperception Test (T.A.T.) consists of a series of pictures portraying dramatic life situations. Some are to be presented to men, some only to women, and some to both. The patient is asked to make up a story based on each of these pictures. The theory upon which the test is based is that the main character of the patient's story is in reality the patient himself. From the fate and behavior of this character and the outcome of the story, one may draw certain inferences concerning the patient's conception about his role in life, about his longings and about his expectations from others. What we do in effect is to get the patient to daydream out loud. A certain theme may recur in each of his stories. When this occurs, it is a fact of particular significance in the formulation of the case. Although formal scoring of these stories has been suggested, the main usefulness of the test is a qualitative one. For this reason, the psychiatrist should himself study each of the patient's stories in addition to accepting the psychologist's conclusions about them. An example of the material obtained by this test is shown in the story given by a patient with conversion hysteria in response to picture 18 G.F. This picture shows two women, one holding on to the other.

The patient said at once, "I have two thoughts. One woman fell and the other is trying to help her to her feet. . . . Now it looks like she is trying to murder her! Her hands are around her throat. The other woman looks weak so I imagine the murder is carried out successfully. She looks sad while she is strangling her victim, as if she doesn't really want to do it. It couldn't be anything really terrible."

This story suggested primarily a stormy and ambivalent relationship to her mother, a finding which was confirmed clinically.

The Word Association Test is an old test devised by Jung. A list of words is read off to the patient with the instruction that he is to respond with the first word that comes to his mind. The list contains so-called neutral words and words with affective significance. A standard list of words may be used or a list may be designed by the psychiatrist to explore certain specific areas of the patient's thinking. The psychologist records the word with which the patient responds and his reaction time. A strange response word or an unusually long reaction time are clues that point to areas of psychological stress.

House-Tree-Person Test (the HTP). This test is particularly useful because of the simplicity of its administration as well as the wealth of projective material which it often provides. The patient is given a blank sheet of 8 by 10 inch paper and is asked to draw a house. He is then given a second sheet of paper and asked to draw a tree. On a third sheet he is asked to draw a person, and on a fourth he is asked to draw a person of the opposite sex to that which he drew on the third. He may then be asked questions about each of these figures or asked to tell a story about each of them. If he protests that he cannot draw, he should be reassured that the quality of the drawing is unimportant.

The theory of the test is that the patient projects himself into each of the drawings so that what he draws on each page is himself. Because both the house and the tree are more widely separated in the patient's mind from any conscious awareness of identification with himself, he is apt to project more deeply hidden aspects of his personality into these figures. For example, ego-splitting tendencies may be expressed in the drawing of a tree, a garage or an annex in addition to the main house, or the tree itself may be drawn as two separate trees. The normal subject draws a figure of his own sex on page three. If his first figure is of the opposite sex, this is usually an expression of confusion concerning his own sexual role. The way in which the person is drawn is revealing too —an adult may draw a picture of a child, the facial expression may be one of anger or sadness.

Although the psychiatrist will want to take these drawings to the psychologist for help in interpreting them, he can collect the basic data very readily by himself because of the ease with which the test can be administered. For this reason it is a test that should be given by the psychiatrist to all patients routinely on admission. Many deep insights will be more quickly arrived at in this way.

Psychological Testing by the Psychiatrist

The foregoing test descriptions are not intended to instruct the reader concerning the actual administration and interpretation of these procedures but rather to acquaint him in a general way with some of the more useful tests, so that he may not only raise specific clinical questions with the psychologist but possibly also request specific tests which he feels are most likely to provide the answers he is seeking. Although the administration and particularly the interpretation of the most useful psychological tests require the special skills and experiences of a clinical psychologist, many large hospitals are without such services, and where there is one, he is usually far too busy to fulfill all the demands that are made upon his time. What is the psychiatrist to do under such circumstances? What happens most often is that the psychiatrist does the best he can without the benefit of psychological data. This is unfortunate because it is precisely in the state hospital setting where the longer, more painstaking psychiatric approaches to the deeper levels of the patient's mind are most impractical that the psychologist's short-cut to the unconscious looms with particular importance. What makes the psychological test particularly useful in this regard is the fact that it gets at the hidden material through an indirect approach, and in that way by-passes the patient's defenses against self-revelation. It is for this reason that I feel justified in urging psychiatrists to learn some of these techniques more thoroughly, at least as far as the proper administration of the tests are concerned. The most effective utilization of the psychologist under these circumstances might well be in personal consultations with psychiatrists concerning the interpretation of psychological data which the psychiatrists themselves have collected. In time, the psychiatrist might learn enough in such consultations to do some of his own interpretation. While this is time-consuming and therefore uninviting to the overburdened psychiatrist, some relatively short procedure at least, like the HTP, should be part of his routine clinical psychiatric examination.

Psychotic patients who are in a precariously balanced state of emotional adaptation may occasionally become acutely disturbed during psychological testing if this is carried out by his or her own therapist.

A thirty-one-year-old unmarried girl was subject to recurrent acute episodes of paranoid schizophrenia. After a remission was produced by means of electroconvulsive therapy her psychiatrist treated her psychotherapeutically for one year on an outpatient basis. She had returned to work and, within the framework of her personality limitations, she was making an adequate adjustment. One day her therapist decided to do a Rorschach test on her without preliminary warning or explanation. When he showed her the first card she became hostile and suspicious, put the card down and refused to talk. When he then urged her to pick it up and continue, she leaped up and fled from his office. Within a matter of hours her family reported to the psychiatrist that she was acutely disturbed. It became necessary to admit her to a sanitarium as an emergency on that same day.

This is a rare complication of psychological testing and emphasizes the fact that the psychological test situation is an emotionally stressful one. In any event, every patient should be prepared for testing with some explanation of what is in store for him, and why it is being done. Where the therapeutic relationship is highly fragile, as in the foregoing case, it is inadvisable for the psychiatrist to do his own testing. When the one administering the test is not also the psychotherapist on the case, such stormy reactions are rarely if ever encountered.

Which Patients Should Be Tested?

Although it is theoretically desirable to obtain a full battery of tests on all patients, the shortage of clinical psychologists in mental hospitals makes this an impossibility. The psychiatrist must decide, therefore, which among his many patients he will refer for testing. In general, he will prefer to utilize the psychologist's limited time in the following situations:

When there is a problem of differential diagnosis.

When a patient is being considered for individual or group psychotherapy. The clinical psychologist can provide information concerning the extent to which the patient is suitable for such a therapeutic procedure. In addition he can supply information concerning the conflicts underlying the patient's illness. In this way a more accurate formulation of the patient's problem becomes possible, and the treatment can be planned more successfully.

In cases requiring a precise determination of the degree of mental retardation or defect.

In criminal cases, in which the psychiatrist is asked to determine if the patient's mental condition is such that he may be tried in a court of law; or to pass an opinion as to whether his mental condition at the time of an alleged crime was such that he could be held accountable for his actions.

As part of research projects. All candidates for psychosurgery should be tested as well as any other categories that are part of a planned study.

For didactic purposes. When a patient is being presented before a seminar, a conference or a class, psychological studies will make it possible, in many ways, to teach and learn more about the patient.

The Psychologist's Report

There is no all-purpose test in psychology. A detail of personality which emerges on one test may be missed completely on another. And there is no way of predicting what single test will be most useful in studying a given patient. As a result the psychologist must administer a battery of tests. While working with a patient, the psychologist should have clearly in mind the questions which motivated the psychiatrist to refer him, and he must scan the test results with reference to these questions. The psychologist should have access to the patient's chart, too, and should be free to weigh the significance of his data in the light of all the other clinical findings. He then proceeds to synthesize all the findings into a report which is aimed primarily at answering the psychiatrist's questions. The language of the report should be free of special terms, the meaning of which is not entirely clear to the psychiatrist for whom the report is prepared. To the greatest extent possible, the psychologist should document his reasoning with actual examples culled from the test protocols. Finally, the original protocols should be made available to the psychiatrist and he should be encouraged to go over them with the psychologist with particular reference to the psychodynamic significance of content as contrasted with questions of formal scoring.

Utilization of the Report

The main usefulness of the psychological report is in its application to the formulation of the problem. This was defined earlier as the elaboration of a working hypothesis concerning the patient's failure in emotional adaptation. Every plan of treatment should be based upon such a hypothesis, and the psychologist's findings are often vital in its construction. I have referred several times to the revelations concerning the patient's unconscious which are provided by the psychologist's data. The question is often asked, "Do we confront the patient with these revelations?" The answer is almost invariably, "No." Usually, the patient will have no more feeling of recognition when confronted by the products of his unconscious as they emerge in psychological data than he has when he encounters them in a dream. He will usually reject them because they make no sense to him. Sometimes such confrontations are deeply disturbing to the patient and may disrupt his emotional adaptation even further. An example of this was described in Chapter I. A patient may react to such revelations with an exacerbation of paranoid tendencies, feeling that he was tricked, as indeed he was by the psychological test procedure. Rarely if ever is it useful to confront patients with data secured by such circumventions of his defense mechanisms. Occasionally, however, we may want to do so in the treatment of schizophrenia by so-called direct analysis as described by John Rosen. For the most part, the psychiatrist uses these insights in his plan of treatment without ever making them known to the patient. Examples of this are to be found in the discussion of supportive therapy in Chapter I.

The Psychologist as a Research Worker

So far I have discussed the role of the hospital psychologist exclusively in terms of psychological testing. It must be abundantly clear that this is his major function and if his services in this regard are utilized to the fullest, it will leave him little time for anything else. However, by training and inclination he is often well equipped to participate in clinical research. He has been instructed in matters relating to experimental design. He knows something about statistics and the evaluation of data, and his test procedures are invaluable in a variety of research projects that can be conducted in a state hospital. For these reasons, the psychologist's help may be recruited in at least an advisory capacity in planning clinical research. And if he can budget his time so that he is able actually to participate in the research, he may be able to make a useful contribution.

The Psychologist as a Therapist

No one argues about the psychologist's role in testing or concerning his participation in research. When it comes to therapy, however, he has been the subject of considerable controversy. Many psychologists have been trained in psychotherapy and some have evidenced considerable talent in this field. The controversy centers not so much about whether psychologists should do psychotherapy as to whether they should ever be permitted to do it when unsupervised by a physician. The consensus among physicians is that it would be a backward step to separate out the mentally ill from those who suffer from other diseases, and that the diagnosis and unsupervised treatment of mental sickness by nonphysicians is as inadvisable as the diagnosis and unsupervised treatment of any other kind of sickness by nonphysicians. It is felt that psychiatry has grown in knowledge primarily as a medical discipline and that our knowledge is likely to grow further if we continue to see mental illness as a problem of adaptation of the total organism as a psychobiological unit. In any event, the problem is less pressing in a hospital setting where all therapy is under the direction of the psychiatrist and where automatically the psychologist's work as a therapist would come under the purview of a physician. The only question is whether this represents the most effective utilization of the psychologist's specific ability within the therapeutic community of a mental hospital. This is a question which the psychiatrists in each hospital have to answer for themselves. It has seemed to me that a dynamically oriented hospital with a rational program of therapy and an active research department is not able to spare its psychologist for treatment. I would make one exception to this: If the psychotherapy which the psychologist is conducting is part of a research program involving, for example, the individual psychotherapy of chronic deteriorated schizophrenics or some problem in group therapy, then there is a justification for his use in this manner. In that case his work should be conducted with rigorous regard for the high traditions of psychological research, and under the direct supervision of a psychiatrist.

SELECTED REFERENCES

ABT, L. E.; BELLAK, L.: *Projective Psychology*. New York: Knopf, 1950.
A number of brief but excellent chapters presenting the elements of the various projective techniques.
ANDERSON, H. H.; ANDERSON, G. L.: *An Introduction to Projective Techniques*. New York: Prentice-Hall, 1951.
Good theoretical discussion of general problems of projective testing.
BECK, S. J.: *Rorschach's Test*, Vols. I, II. New York: Grune & Stratton, 1944.
Useful for reference purposes and for a relatively advanced discussion of this test.
BOCHNER, R.; HALPERN, F.: *The Clinical Application of the Rorschach Test* (2nd ed.). New York: Grune & Stratton, 1945.
A manual of instruction for administering, scoring and interpreting the test. Useful to the beginner.
BROWN, F.: An Exploratory Study of Dynamic Factors in the Contents of the Rorschach Protocol. *J. Projective Techniques*, 17:251, 1953.
A psychoanalytically oriented discussion based on extensive clinical material.
SCHAFER, R.: *The Clinical Application of Psychological Tests*. New York: International Universities Press, 1948.
Concise presentation of test findings in psychiatric diseases, with illustrative clinical case material.
WECHSLER, D.: *The Measurement of Adult Intelligence* (3rd ed.). Baltimore: Williams & Wilkins, 1944.
The basic book on the administration, scoring and interpretation of the Wechsler Bellevue Intelligence Scale.

Chapter X

THE ATTENDANT

The Major Dilemma

Attendants are in many ways the most important members of the treatment team. In sheer numbers alone they constitute the largest personnel category. If one considers, in addition, the number of hours during which they maintain direct personal contact with patients, their significance looms even larger. If corrective emotional experiences in hospital group living constitute the most important factor in the rehabilitation of the mentally ill, then the attendant's responsibility is indeed a major one. Yet for a long time no individual in the mental hospital came to so great a responsibility with so little preparation. The attendant was relegated to a position of minimal prestige and respect by the other members of the treatment team, a position which was passively accepted and agreed to by him. In a setting where the wage scale is admittedly ungenerous, the attendant was often the lowest paid of all. When one adds to this the geographic isolation of most mental hospitals, the modest living quarters, the difficulties in maintaining a normal social life, particularly where young children are involved, one begins to understand why so many positions remain unfilled and why the employee turnover rate remains high. One begins to understand, too, the magnitude of the dilemma which faced the psychiatrist when he finally awakened to the need for a professionally sound corps of attendants.

Recruiting New Attendants

The first problem which had to be solved in meeting this need was that of attracting a group of potentially competent young people. In Saskatchewan this began with the formation of hospital employee unions through which the wage scale was raised to levels which far exceeded prewar values. General living conditions, too, were improved. The most

143

attractive feature of all was the offer of an intensive three-year training program under the direction of D. G. McKerracher, the Commissioner of Mental Services in Saskatchewan, Canada. Throughout the United States somewhat similar programs were set up. Some hospitals affiliated with nearby colleges and offered a training program which led to a full first year of college credit for those qualified to receive it. This academic opportunity was provided to the candidate not only tuition free but to a considerable extent on full pay during his work hours. On completion of the course, the candidate is usually given a diploma, greater responsibility, and an increased salary. The change in status is usually marked by a change in title so that the graduate attendant is designated as a "Psychiatric Aide," or a "Psychiatric Technician." In Saskatchewan, the graduate is called a "Psychiatric Nurse," (cf. Chapter XI) and is eligible for membership in the Saskatchewan Registered Psychiatric Nurse's Association, an organization with official legislative status. Such developments have considerably increased the prestige and morale of attendants as well as the quality and effectiveness of their services to patients.

As soon as mental hospitals offered professional training and benefits, the problem of recruiting candidates was greatly facilitated. In some areas a full-scale drive was instituted, utilizing the press, radio, television, vocational guidance bureaus, and the high schools to set forth the advantages of the training program. In Saskatchewan a candidate had to be eighteen years of age or more, with at least three years of high-school training. In an increasing number of hospitals in the United States, a high school diploma or its equivalent is required. In response to such campaigns the number of applicants exceeded the number of available places for the first time. It became possible to speak realistically of the problem of selecting the best candidates in contrast to the previous indiscriminate search for people to fill vacancies.

Screening Candidates for Training

Once it was felt that the prime qualification for an attendant's job was physical strength. If his appearance also commanded obedience and "respect," it was an additional advantage. When the preoccupation with security and custodial care was superseded by an emphasis on treatment, it was realized that new criteria for the selection of attendants had to be sought. Various psychological studies were carried out for tests which would predict with reliability which candidates would make the best attendants. By and large these tests have been unsuccessful. However, the results have been sufficiently suggestive to encourage further studies along these lines. N. S. Kline approached the problem statistically and found that applicants were more likely to succeed if they were less than thirty years of age, came from a small town, had a wholesome family background, and applied for the job because of the opportunities for educational and economic advancement. The successful applicant was either single or congenially married. On the other hand, the applicant who was less likely to succeed was usually unhappily married, separated or divorced, came from a broken home, and applied for the job because it offered him security. By and large, the clinical impression based on direct interview has remained the most reliable means for screening applicants for training.

What Should Be Taught?

Because of the chronic nursing shortage in mental hospitals, attendants are commonly called upon to administer general nursing care. For this reason a training program for attendants should include instruction in bedside nursing. It is not necessary to explore this subject in further detail in these pages. However, there is a fundamental body of psychiatric information which every attendant should learn.

The asylum versus the hospital. The attendant must be taught that the institution in which he works is not an asylum but a hospital. It is a place where sick people come for treatment, where they can get well and go home. His role is not that of a guard or a watchman but a member of the treatment team whose responsibility it is to make as many as possible of the patient's daily experiences therapeutically meaningful.

Prejudices. Attendants come to work with many prejudices. They share the common misconception that mental illness is a disgrace; that it is mysterious or uncanny; that it cannot be prevented or cured; that people who work in mental hospitals are queer or become so sooner or later; that all mental hospital patients are alike; that they are all potentially homicidal; that many of them are willful and require punishment or stern handling; that these patients are oversexed; that they became ill because of excessive masturbation; that mental patients do not appreciate ordinary human kindness; that many are malingerers or potential criminals; that they have tell-tale physical stigmata, particularly around the eyes; that all patients use foul and shocking language. This list of misconceptions could undoubtedly be expanded. They are more likely to occur in the uneducated applicants and in those of lower intelligence. Older attendants who have worked in the hospital for many years are prone to these prejudices. Because of the prestige that "experienced"

attendants command, they are apt to inculcate such notions in the newcomer and create in them a destructive cynicism and pessimism. For this
reason a program for establishing a constructive approach should include
the experienced attendant along with the new trainee.

The meaning of symptoms. The attendant should be taught that
every speech and action of patients which he observes has meaning, however bizarre and unintelligible they may seem to him initially. They
represent the patient's attempts to communicate his wishes and his
needs. He tries to protect himself against real and imagined hurts which
he suffers all day long. We do not always understand the patient's communications because his sick mind distorts and disguises the way in which
he expresses himself. When someone knows that these reaction patterns
have meaning, and meets them with an active attempt at deciphering
them, many new insights concerning the patient's problems are uncovered. Often the attendant will not be able to comprehend the personal
language of the psychotic patient while the psychiatrist may be able to
do so, not only because of his special training but because he has the
added benefit of observations reported by other members of the treatment
team. The attendant's observations will be very important to the psychiatrist in perfecting his understanding of the patient. For this reason
attendants must be taught not only the importance of observing, but how
to observe and how to record their data so that they will be most useful
to the psychiatrist.

The attendant should be taught the major diagnostic categories into
which mental illness can be classified. It is more important, however,
that he understand how each of these reaction types represents an attempt to cope with personal problems. Mental illness consists precisely
of the fact that these attempts were unsuccessful or maladaptive in the
outside community. Because reality had become intolerably painful for
them, these patients retreated into private worlds of fantasy in an attempt
to protect themselves from further hurt. This psychological retreat is
associated with groups of symptoms which characterize the various diagnostic categories. When these symptoms did not ease their suffering sufficiently or resulted in behavior that was excessively disturbing to the
community in which they lived, hospitalization became necessary. To
these tortured people the hospital often represents a refuge and a surcease from suffering. The relative simplicity of routine in a well-ordered
hospital and the constant presence of protecting people are often very
reassuring to these frightened human beings, and the therapeutic value
of this situation should not be underestimated. Some patients improve in
response to this environmental simplification alone.

The object of the treatment program is to get the patient to make contact with reality more frequently, and for longer periods of time. If reality as represented by the hospital environment becomes no less dreadful to the patient than that which he experienced on the outside, the patient is driven ever more deeply and more desperately into his own fantasy world. When that happens we say that the disease has progressed and the patient has regressed or "deteriorated."[1] If reality on the ward and elsewhere in the hospital can be made enticing enough, these patients will emerge from their dream worlds and tend to behave more normally. Conversely, transitory imperfections in the treatment program will cause transitory periods of "deterioration" or regressive behavior in the affected patients. Thus, an understanding of the meaning of the patient's symptoms automatically leads to a more rational treatment program.

The need for empathy. In their most deteriorated state psychotic patients display psychological processes and behavior patterns which are recognizably human. Indeed, psychotic patients always remain more human than otherwise. It should be emphasized to attendants that in many ways psychotic patients differ from normal people only in degree. They respond positively to friendliness, courtesy, tact, and affection. They are also sensitive to humiliations, rivalry situations, hunger and cold. If the attendant tries to identify with the patient he will often sense the appropriate course of action in a variety of ward situations.

The need for objectivity. This need to empathize with the patient must be balanced with a no less important need for objectivity. Although mental patients hunger deeply for a protective human relationship, they grow fearful if this relationship becomes too intimate and they may even defend themselves against excessive intimacy with hostile or violent behavior. The sensitive attendant will "feel" for the interpersonal distance which is appropriate with each patient. Patients are all equally deserving of our help. Favoritism may give rise to disturbing rivalries, although the psychiatrist may at times deliberately foster such rivalries as part of a therapeutic plan (see Chapter II). A policy of scientific detachment will help the attendant guard against feelings of disgust or condemnation. Such judgmental attitudes may reinforce psychotic mechanisms (see Chapter XIV). The attendant may sometimes be seduced by masochistic patients into angry attitudes or even be provoked to a point where he feels impelled to strike the patient. The realization that the patient induces these feelings in others in order to gratify pathological emotional

---

[1] If we mean by deterioration an irreversible destructive process, this term is a misnomer (see Chapter XIV).

needs may help the attendant control such impulses and replace them with therapeutically more effective actions.

A forty-eight-year-old single man was admitted to mental hospitals on many occasions because of episodes of panic which would descend upon him suddenly in public places. At such times he would fling himself to the ground, clutch desperately to the sidewalk and cry for help. He was also hospitalized on several occasions for alcoholism.

In the hospital he would make a conspicuous nuisance of himself by embroiling other patients and attendants in arguments with each other and with himself. Several times he was the victim of physical assault by other patients and once or twice he was struck by attendants. He rarely struck back and derived evident pleasure from his role as troublemaker and victim. The staff would "groan" each time he was readmitted and would discharge him as soon as they could "get rid of him." However, within one or two months he would be hospitalized again. This pattern went on for several years.

On the occasion of his most recent admission the ward psychiatrist met with his attendants and discussed the patient. He explained this patient's pathological need to "take a beating" and how each time they placed him in the role of a victim they were fortifying his abnormal mental processes. There were insufficient anamnestic data to arrive at an understanding of the meaning of this symptom in terms of his life history; however, unconscious homosexual impulses seemed to be involved. This formulation of the case was sufficient for guiding the attendants in a proper course of action. They understood his provocations as "seductions." Thereafter they would react by explaining to the patient that he was indulging in abnormal behavior and would urge him to control it. In about a week his provocations ceased. He became a cooperative worker and was discharged after three months of satisfactory adjustment in the hospital. He has remained in the community for over nine months, the longest time interval in several years.

The initial contact with patients on the ward is an event of critical importance. The attendant should be encouraged to visualize the intense anxiety which overwhelms them on their first glimpse of a mental hospital ward. Often the patient has gone through a period of mounting anguish which achieves its climax at this moment. The hospital, which is strange in so many ways in its own right, will seem stranger to the patient because of his delusions. There is probably no gentle way of divesting a patient of his clothing and personal possessions at such a time, but this should nevertheless be carried out with as much consideration as possible, leaving the patient with whatever is permitted by hospital rules, and reassuring him that scrupulous care will be taken of his other possessions. The attendant should then show him his bed and the place where he may keep his personal belongings. He should introduce him to his neighbors and, if possible, assign a co-operative patient to help him. He should show him the toilet and give him an opportunity to use it. The emotional needs of psychotic patients are better answered by deeds than words. Thus, feeding the newly admitted patient is an act of considerable therapeutic significance. This should not be omitted even if it is between meals. (Further details of the emotional significance to the patient of being fed are to be found in Chapter VI.) When he is fed the attendant can invite him to watch television, or provide him with reading matter, and explain to him some of the procedures he will undergo in the immediate future. Thus, the work of enticing the patient back to reality begins at the moment of admission.

Efficient ward management has a twofold therapeutic purpose. First of all, an attractive orderly looking ward is restful and therapeutic in itself. A dilapidated-looking ward makes for dilapidation in the patients who occupy it. The initiative of attendants should be encouraged in decorating wards with pictures, flowers, or curtains. Needless to say a compulsive quest for orderliness should not give rise to tension-creating restrictions in the patients' activities.

More free time from mechanical chores means additional hours to spend with patients. This is the second therapeutic advantage of efficient ward management. An "experienced" attendant was once heard instructing a beginner not to "fraternize" with patients because this might interfere with the work of the ward. Such a point of view is the antithesis of the true objective which is to provide the patient with as many therapeutically meaningful human relationships as possible. Direct contacts with patients should be increased to the utmost. Needless to say, the ward work itself provides the greatest opportunity of all for involving patients in constructive and co-operative activity of therapeutic importance.

The "violent" patient. Many of the attendant's fears come from his expectations of violence. Accordingly, it is necessary to teach him that only a few patients are ever violent or dangerous and that even very disturbed patients have adequate control most of the time. Disturbed behavior appears under characteristic circumstances. It is necessary to teach attendants what these circumstances are, and to strive to prevent violence rather than to deal with it after it has arisen. To accomplish this the attendant must know the patients on the ward, their basic problems, their interests and their characteristic ways of relating to other people. The attendant should observe the way in which specific patients react to him and how they in turn affect him. He should have opportunities to discuss these matters with those who are able to instruct him. He must seek to understand his patients as completely as he can.

In general, violent behavior occurs as an attempt to deal with an intolerable frustration. Although a patient may be extremely intelligent, emotionally he is quite immature. He reacts to change of any kind with anxiety and mounting tension. This is particularly true when patients are hungry (see Chapter VI). Bedtime is another period of maximal tension. After mealtimes, on the other hand, and after patients have been put to bed, tensions are at their lowest ebb and disturbed behavior is least likely to occur. The analogy with patterns of disturbed behavior in young children will be apparent to those who have experience in this field. At the same time that emotional immaturity is emphasized, the attendant should be cautioned against a condescending attitude, since in other respects patients may be quite mature. In any case, self-respect is more apt to grow within the patient if the attendant shows him the deference which is his due as an adult.

It has been observed that crowding increases disturbed behavior. Conversely, the more floor space per patient, the fewer the number of outbursts. Therefore, attendants should seek to utilize the space on the wards with maximal efficiency. For example, floor cleaning procedures should be carried out when the patients are away at meals. Abrupt movements and harsh tones may elicit defensive behavior. Hence activities should be conducted without haste. Patients should be addressed gently but firmly and never given arbitrary commands. In seeking a patient's co-operation all suggestions of physical coercion should be avoided. In particular, there should be no unnecessary physical contacts with patients. The attendant must not lose sight of the psychotic world in which patients live. Things may not have the same meaning for the patient as they have for the attendant. Taking away some bit of trash which the patient has collected may be regarded by the patient as an intolerable intrusion on his privacy. In the patient's delusional system nonconforming may represent literally a way of staying alive. He may believe that to obey is to lose his individuality or to suffer annihilation. Thus, what may seem at first glance to be willful antagonism is, more accurately, behavior motivated by fear. Needless to say, attempts to compel obedience by force will increase the patient's fears and inevitably result in violent acts of self-defense. If a request is made of a patient, the reason for the request should be explained. When possible the request should be presented in such a form that the patient feels it was his own idea. Gentleness blended with strength is what these patients need most. "Strength" includes strength of character too. Dishonesty, trickery, bribery have no place in the therapeutic milieu.

Patients who tend to become disturbed at bedtime may be soothed with a warm bath, a warm glass of milk, or a few extra attentions after the patient has been put to bed.

At the same time that the attendant is mindful of the delusional component in a patient's behavior, he must not lose sight of reality. A patient in seclusion may become more disturbed because adequate toilet facilities are not at his disposal. A patient in restraints may seethe with mounting fury because he is not relieved of his craving for a cigarette. Bath water that is too cold or too hot may arouse resistive behavior in a patient, as may unnecessary exposure of his body in the bath. In short, if the elementary physical needs of the patient are not provided for, he may become disturbed.

Attendants usually believe that the mute and resistive patient pays little attention to his surroundings. The detail in which recovered catatonic patients can recount the happenings on the ward during periods of stupor should be explained to attendants, so that they may appreciate the important therapeutic effects, positive and negative, which can result from remarks made in the presence of an apparently inattentive patient.

Patients need outlets for their energy. A full program of activities will do more than anything else to decrease the incidence of disturbed behavior. Various aspects of the activities program are taken up in the appropriate chapters. Proper training and co-operation on the part of the attendants is indispensable for the success of this program.

Patients who have to remain on the ward should not be omitted from the activities program. Patients often have a powerful creative urge which is an expression of their wish to be well. They have a craving to write things down, to draw pictures, to make designs. Such expressive activity is therapeutic in that it helps the patient relieve inner tensions. In addition, these data may clarify diagnostic problems and help the psychiatrist to understand the motivations (or psychodynamics) which underlie the patient's illness. Pencil and paper is all that is required for these productions. These materials should be available in ample quantities. Checkers, chess, ping pong, cards should all be available on the wards. Attendants should play with patients, not with each other. Books, magazines, daily papers, jig-saw puzzles, modeling wax, games, should also be maintained in adequate supply. The powerful effect of television in decreasing tension in patients is discussed in Chapter IV. A cigarette lighter chained to a table will permit patients to light their own smokes, and spare them the indignity of seeking out an attendant each time they need a light.

Emergency measures. It must be clear from the preceding paragraphs that the problem of preventing violence does not differ from that of running any psychiatric ward properly. In spite of the best efforts, however, a certain number of patients will become disturbed. It may then become necessary to employ emergency measures in order to protect the patient and those about him from physical harm. At no time should an attendant by himself endeavor to control an assaultive destructive patient by physical means. When psychological means have proven useless, then three or more attendants, depending on the strength of the patient, should act in concert, confronting the patient with overwhelming physical odds. The patient should still not be touched. Often this "show of force" alone is sufficient to quiet the patient and to secure his co-operation for further procedures. If this fails, the attendants should immobilize the patient in accordance with properly accepted techniques (calculated to protect both the patient and the attendants) and place him in a seclusion room. The ward should be instructed to notify the psychiatrist at once if this happens. The psychiatrist provides a final echelon of emergency treatment in the acute disturbance. Flanked by sufficient attendants to protect him, he sees the patient in the seclusion room as soon as possible and endeavors to ascertain the cause of the disturbance. Often he will be able to learn things that the attendants have not understood or have not dealt with adequately. When the patient quiets down, he should be given an opportunity to return to the ward at once. Ideally, sufficient attendants should be on duty for an immediate "show of force," if disturbed behavior recurs. Where routine ward work is efficiently organized, a maximal number of attendants will be available for dealing with such emergencies. This increases the safety of working with disturbed patients and expands the psychotherapeutic possibilities of dealing with them. More important than numbers of available attendants, however, is the readiness of those who are on duty to meet the patient's emotional needs with an activities program which will help him to re-establish and maintain his self-control.

Restraints. If a patient behaves wildly, the primitive impulse is to place him in mechanical restraints. This was the guiding principle of our untutored ancestors who, in their ignorance, put the mentally ill in shackles and chains. We all know the error of this, and we celebrate the memory of Pinel who liberated his patients from their chains in 1792. It became quickly apparent to careful observers that mechanical restraints usually increased the violence and overactivity which they were supposed to eliminate. This is the elementary fallacy of restraints. They produce aggression, resentment and hatred. If it is the goal to entice psychotic patients back to reality, nothing could be further from the mark than the effects of mechanical restraint. Its use generates a punitive atmosphere on the ward which in the psychotic mind becomes rapidly transformed into an atmosphere of terror. This is not only psychologically injurious, but may result in serious physical harm to the patient too, no matter how carefully employed. There is no greater fallacy than the belief that shortage in ward personnel justifies the use of restraints. Patients in restraint require more individualized care than ever, and its use only increases the help problem where a shortage already exists.

When psychological measures alone fail to control disturbed behavior, somatotherapeutic techniques may be employed (see Chapter III). A charted record should be kept of the number of emergency procedures for disturbed patients that take place on each ward. This record should be posted conspicuously in the nurses' station. An attempt should be made to analyze increases in disturbed behavior. The reasons will usually be found in disturbances in the relationships among personnel. These are best dealt with in group discussions in which attendants have an opportunity to air their problems (see below).

How Should the Attendant Be Taught?

Whatever the details of the training program in each hospital, it should be directed by a single individual who is the supervisor of staff training. Most training programs for attendants lean too heavily on classroom instruction, whether the course runs for only a week or two as in some hospitals or for as long as three years in others. In all instances where teaching experiences have been critically examined the major weakness in the course has been found in the gap that exists between classroom theory and ward practice. Candidates are taught one point of view in the classroom and they encounter a different one in the pessimistic and negativistic attitudes of all those who supervise their work on the wards. Confusion results, and in the process ineffective old techniques become further intrenched and staff demoralization ensues. The conviction has grown that the most valuable teaching is that which takes place on the wards with the daily practical problems of the attendants constituting the basic material for the instructors. For the most part teaching should take place in small groups on the wards, seminar fashion, with ample opportunity for each attendant to air his anxieties, misconceptions and grievances.

Formal lectures have their place for mass instruction. These can be rendered more effective with the liberal use of training films (see references to Chapter XXIX for catalogues listing psychiatric motion pictures suitable for training purposes). Trainees should be given copies of the various publications for attendants put out by the National Association for Mental Health and instruction should be based on these texts.

The Role of Anxiety in Ward Work

The trainee attendant experiences considerable anxiety when he first begins his work and study. The vast, strange institution to which he has come exerts an overpowering and at times demoralizing effect upon him. He brings to his work a variety of superstitions and prejudices which generate in him a feeling of dread in his relationships with patients. His work is unlike anything he has ever tried before. Often his responsibilities are great from the very outset. He may encounter cynical attitudes in older workers which confuse and depress him. He may become embroiled in antagonisms with other attendants and in emotional involvements with patients. All these factors combine to give rise to a quantity of anxiety which may seriously impair his efficiency as a student.

The Role of Transference in the Attendant's Relationship to the Physician

Doctors play a special role in their relationships with other people, even when the people involved are not their patients. The origin of this special role may be somewhat simply outlined as follows: The feelings of helplessness and dependency which exist in childhood are often and rather typically exaggerated during periods of illness. The child's fears at such times are frequently augmented by the fears of his parents which may be all too obvious to the sick youngster. Into this atmosphere of anxiety, if not panic, where even his parents have failed him, comes the doctor with his special knowledge, strange medical "smells" and instruments. He understands what is wrong and he knows what to do. Child and parents alike look to the doctor with expectation of magical cures and even supernatural powers. When the child recovers, intense gratitude naturally follows. The prestige of the doctor increases, and he emerges with the aura of a good and all-powerful parent. This is the attitude which persists more or less in all people. It recurs with renewed intensity during periods of illness or feelings of helplessness from whatever cause. At such times, the doctor is looked upon once again as the "good" parent, and previous magical expectations are reawakened. Persons with this reaction are said to display emotional regression. The new attendant, heavily laden with anxiety, inevitably tends to regress. He, too, turns automatically to the physician for support. This regressive type of relationship may occur even when the attendant is much older than the doctor. The psychiatrist who expects this attitude to develop will recognize its manifestations when they appear. To the extent that the psychiatrist is prepared to play the role of a good parent to these insecure people, he will reinforce the transference attitude and will have a powerful instrument for guiding them in their new work. For this reason psychiatrists should make clearly known to new employees their direct concern with their welfare.

It is well to have a planned routine for the reception of trainees or new employees. Experienced attendants who have been well indoctrinated and who are sensitive to the problems of the beginner should be assigned the task of orienting the new employee. These assignments should not be made haphazardly, since this initial contact may have a far-reaching effect on the attitude and receptivity of the beginner. A map of the hospital should be prepared for his use, since the vastness of most mental hospitals is a source of anxiety. In addition, he should be given a brochure which describes his privileges and what the hospital is prepared to do for his health, comfort and happiness. This should include information about the surrounding community and the recreational facilities which are available to him. He should be told something of the history of the hospital in a manner to arouse his *esprit de corps*. Finally, he should be invited to consult with a competent personnel counselor who is a member of the professional staff, perhaps a psychiatrist, if he feels he is in need of help.

If an employee resigns or is dismissed, his final pay envelope should be given by the personnel counselor in a setting where they can talk in confidence, in order to explore the reasons for the interruption of the employment. This is done not only in the constructive interest of the departing employee but as a means of learning from his dissatisfactions in order to smooth the path for others.

Group Therapy with Attendants

It has been said that the chief therapeutic instrument in the mental hospital is to be found in the corrective emotional experiences of hospital group life. In the light of this it would follow that the mental health of the attendants and all other members of the treatment team should be a matter of paramount importance in the treatment program. As a matter of fact, ward seminars which are organized ostensibly to improve the level of treatment regularly develop into group therapy sessions if permitted to do so (see Chapter II).

Conflicts between employees are quickly reflected in incidents on the ward. At times these conflicts are the result of provocative or seductive behavior on the part of patients, as in the example described earlier in this chapter. A common method is for the patient to ally himself in some respects with one attendant and in other respects with a second, and thus to engage the two in a conflict which projects into the outer world the struggle that rages within the patient's mind. Whether the product of specific provocation by patients or unrelated to it, evidences of conflict in the outer world intensify feelings of helplessness within the patient. When it is recalled that the illness itself is an expression and a result of irreconcilable conflict to start with, the malignant implications of personnel conflict becomes more clear. An increase in regressive behavior on a ward (see Chapter XIV) should suggest at once the need for intensified exploration for dissensions between employees. In a recent study by R. L. Kahn of Mount Sinai Hospital in New York City, a group of schizophrenic patients was asked, "If you had one wish, what would it be?" A surprising number answered, "Peace on earth. An end to the cold war." This unexpected answer reflected poignantly the longing for inner peace, and the feeling of discouragement engendered by evidences of lack of inner harmony among those who are presumably well and strong, and to whom they turn for help.

Conversely, an atmosphere that reflects unity of purpose among all the members of the treatment team is a therapeutic force which opposes and neutralizes the inner conflicts of the patient. Ward seminars which are also group therapy sessions provide the means for creating this atmosphere. New employees must feel free to voice critical attitudes toward their superiors, and older employees must be inculcated with a therapeutic attitude in which they feel less threatened by such criticism. Such procedures may quickly restore demoralized wards to therapeutic effectiveness and improve the level of treatment in the mental hospital at large.

SELECTED REFERENCES

BAER, W. H.: The Training of Attendants, Psychiatric Aides and Psychiatric Technicians. *Am. J. Psychiat.*, 109:291, 1952.
  A survey of training programs in the various states.
HALL, B. H.; et al.: *Psychiatric Aide Education* (Menninger Clinic Monograph Series No. 9). New York: Grune & Stratton, 1952.
  A report of an experimental training program. Rewarding reading as much for its report of errors as for its many positive ideas.
Handbook for Psychiatric Aides—Section One: A General Guide to Work in Mental Hospitals, 1946; Section Two: Care of the Overactive and Disturbed Patient, 1950. New York: National Association for Mental Health.
  These are basic texts for classroom instruction.

KLINE, N. S.: Characteristics and Screening of Unsatisfactory Psychiatric Attendants and Attendant-Applicants. *Am. J. Psychiat.*, 106:573, 1950.

    A report of a personal inventory test for selection of trainees.

MC KERRACHER, D. G.: A New Program in the Training and Employment of Ward Personnel. *Am. J. Psychiat.*, 106:259, 1949.

    An excellent description of what is probably the best of the current attendant training programs.

MIDDLETON, J.: Prejudices and Opinions of Mental Hospital Employees Regarding Mental Illness. *Am. J. Psychiat.*, 110:133, 1953.

STANTON, A. H.; SCHWARTZ, M. S.: *The Mental Hospital. A Study of Institutional Participation in Psychiatric Illness and Treatment.* New York: Basic Books, 1954.

    The outcome of several years of study of the emotional interactions which develop between patients and the personnel of a mental hospital. A major contribution to the literature of the mental hospital as a therapeutic community. The data relating acute psychotic disturbances to hidden staff disagreements are particularly relevant to the material of this chapter.

STERNE, E. M.: *The Attendants Guide.* New York: National Association for Mental Health, 1953.

    Written for the attendant. Highly practical and readable. Excellent text for classroom instruction.

Chapter XI

THE NURSE

Duties of the Mental Hospital Nurse

General Nursing: The average mental hospital is a community consisting of thousands of patients and hundreds of employees living in close quarters. All the public health problems of a congested city are to be found within its walls (see Chapter XXV). Accidents in mental hospitals are common, as well as surgical and medical emergencies from other sources. Many patients are chronically ill and disabled. Each of these situations calls for special nursing skills which the psychiatric nurse is expected to have.

The Physician's Immediate Assistant: In the absence of the psychiatrist the nurse is responsible for the management of the ward. Her observations and records concerning patient behavior have special weight because of her more exacting scientific background. She is an important member of the treatment team as far as formulating the patient's problem and carrying out the plan of treatment.

Ward Supervisor: The psychiatric nurse is responsible for developing and maintaining therapeutically effective relationships among patients and co-workers. It is her responsibility to create a secure, wholesome and free atmosphere in the highly specialized environment of a psychiatric ward. The nurse, along with the attendant, the volunteer and the others who work with her, assists patients individually and in groups to meet the ordinary demands of their everyday living.

Treatment: The nurse is responsible for carrying out the nursing instructions of the psychiatric team. She is expected to provide emergency support for patients in psychological crises. She assists in the administration of many forms of therapy, such as insulin and electroshock. She administers parenteral medications. She may assist in psychosurgical procedures and postoperative care. She supervises the work of attendants and volunteers, student nurses, and other personnel on the ward, scheduling and co-ordinating their activities for maximal therapeutic effect. She may supplement occupational and recreational activities in some instances. During visiting periods she contacts the family and contributes to the preparation of the home environment for the ultimate return of the patient. In many hospitals the nurse functions as a leader in group psychotherapy. At times she may lead a group by herself, under the direction of the psychiatrist. In other situations she may function as a dual therapist, taking the role of a permissive protecting mother figure as contrasted to the psychiatrist who plays a role symbolizing a more stern and disciplined reality (see Chapter II).

Teaching: In most mental hospitals the psychiatric nurse has a major educational function. Nurses in a supervisory or head nurse position assist in the training of all personnel who are to have any contact with the ward environment. The attendant, the volunteer, the collateral therapists, the psychiatric social worker, the psychologist and the student nurse all gain part of their clinical experience from the assistance of the psychiatric nurse.

Requirements for Psychiatric Nursing

It is quite clear from the list of duties catalogued in the preceding paragraphs that the generalized nursing program must be supplemented by special training. To a considerable extent the subject matter of this supplementary training is covered in Chapter X. However, because the nurse starts with a background of scientific training it is possible to present these topics to her in greater technical detail. Because an important part of her responsibility will center about supervisory duties and a capacity to co-ordinate the activities of groups, she will require special administrative training and some instruction in group psychology. And because of her important role as a teacher she will require instruction in educational techniques.

In some schools of nursing associated with universities the B.S. degree is awarded at the end of the generalized nursing program. In these universities specialization in psychiatry or in any other branch of nursing can occur only as part of a graduate program toward a Master's degree. The majority of schools, however, provide for specialized training even on an undergraduate level. Furthermore, a number of schools provide a program of specialized training in psychiatric nursing that can be completed in one year after the generalized nursing program is completed.

The Shortage of Psychiatric Nurses

Although there are shortages in almost all personnel categories in mental hospitals, the problem with respect to nurses is greatest of all. It has been estimated that between 50 to 58 per cent of all hospitalized patients are in psychiatric hospitals. This vast group, however, is serviced by only 3 to 5 per cent of all available graduate professional nurses. Many state hospitals are without a single registered nurse. Many more have so few that it is difficult to know how to utilize them properly. Typically, nurses in such institutions are so overwhelmed by administrative tasks that their actual nursing contribution is almost nil.

The explanation for this plight is not hard to find. We can pass over at once the hardships that are shared by most mental hospital workers —low salary, or physical isolation, and consider those problems indigenous to the field of nursing itself.

The psychiatric nurse as defined in the opening paragraphs of this chapter is, relatively speaking, a newcomer. In spite of great advances in all other branches, the field of psychiatric nursing has lagged far behind, so that the number who have actually received specialized training in psychiatric nursing with regard to modern dynamic principles is small. The Group for the Advancement of Psychiatry in its bulletin on the *Psychiatric Nurse in the Mental Hospital* states, "It should be borne in mind that there has been little or no experience with the skilled psychiatric nurse as an integral part of the therapeutic team."

Thus the graduate nurse who comes to work in a mental hospital is rarely equipped with specialized psychiatric training. What then is the psychiatric education which the nurse received as a student in her generalized nursing program? For many years the majority of the nursing schools had no affiliations for psychiatric training at all. In recent years, however, this has been remedied to the extent that over 90 per cent of the nursing schools now provide such affiliation. This usually takes the form of a twelve-week training program in a state psychiatric hospital. This affiliated training often suffers from the fact that the mental hospital nurses responsible for it are already overburdened with other duties. However, given even an ideal training program during this period of state hospital affiliation, it is universally agreed that twelve weeks are too short a time to achieve a proper degree of proficiency in psychiatric nursing.

If the nurse with this limited training accepts a position in a mental hospital she is usually put in charge of a group of wards at once, and is expected to organize the nursing care of patients, and the clinical supervision and teaching of students and attendants, without benefit of any guidance from more experienced nurses. One would not think of placing a newly graduated nurse in charge of several wards of a general hospital without supervision. Yet, if such an ill-advised step were taken the young nurse would have had at least some experience as a student with the problems she would encounter on the wards of a general hospital. In such a setting it is understandable that young nurses should be assailed with an overwhelming anxiety and decide to turn to simpler duties elsewhere.

Federal Funds for Psychiatric Nurses Training

The National Mental Health Act has made provisions to meet this problem. It provides funds to be paid out in monthly stipends to registered nurses who have been accepted by an accredited university to be applied to a course in psychiatric nursing. A total of $1,600 is paid out for one year of college work on an undergraduate level, and $2,000 if applied toward a Master's degree. Although some schools readily use all the stipends that are awarded to them, others have difficulty in finding enough students who are interested in education in the field of psychiatric nursing to use the available stipends. This is so in spite of the fact that the expenses of the student's education are to be paid without any commitments whatever on the student's part. It would seem as if there is need for a more effective program of publicizing these educational benefits to general duty nurses in the community (see Chapter XXIX for further details).

Toward a New Program of Education for Psychiatric Nursing

Psychiatric training for nurses has to undergo a revolutionary change like that which took place in the curriculum of the medical student. Not long ago the third and fourth year medical student was shown a few extreme examples of psychopathology culled from the back wards of the state hospital, he was taught the Kraepelinian classification of mental disease, and by and large that was the extent of his training. Now we regard psychiatry as a basic science. It is introduced into the curriculum in the first year. Its conceptions are dynamic and are integrated into all aspects of human function, normal and abnormal.

The student nurse must be taught similarly. She should learn about

normal emotional development and about problems of emotional adaptation. She should learn about regression (see Chapter VIII). Indeed, she
must become aware of the fact that physical illness is a frightening experience to many people, even to those who seem quite mature. Physical
disability reawakens feelings of helplessness and attitudes toward others
that existed in childhood. Thus, along with regression goes the phenomenon of transference (see Chapters I, II, X). For example, the helpless patient attributes to the nurse qualities and expectations which
characterized his relationship with his mother or some other important
parent figure from childhood. The nurse's uniform is a symbol. It represents to the patient knowledge and power which, because they are based
on actuality, reinforce transference attitudes. To understand the behavior
of an adult during periods of regression it is necessary to understand the
psychology of the child. More specifically, in order to understand fully the
reactions of an adult patient the nurse will want to know something
about his past history, particularly his childhood. In this way she will
learn to regard her patient not simply as a wound that must be dressed
or a back that must be rubbed, but as a total human being with a past as
well as a present, with a persistent core of childishness that exists in the
most grown-up of her charges.

In her work on medical and surgical wards she will see many transitory deliria from which she can learn much about the major psychoses.
In the emotional reactions of patients to mutilating surgery and permanent incapacitation she will have an opportunity to learn about the
psychological mechanisms of defense and the general problems of emotional adaptation. In short, in her daily work she will have ample opportunity to see the human mind functioning under stress. Under these
circumstances the opportunities for psychiatric training are great.

In addition to the patient's regressive tendencies the student nurse
will learn that she herself has regressive tendencies too. During periods
of emotional stress infantile attitudes of her own tend to be reawakened
which may complicate her relationship with fellow students, her superiors or her patients. When these tendencies affect her relationships with
patients they are referred to as countertransference (see Chapters I, II).
As she becomes alert to the manifestations of countertransference and
learns to master them, her usefulness as a nurse will increase. She will
become a better surgical nurse, a better medical nurse, a better obstetrical
nurse, but in the process will also be better prepared for the responsibilities of psychiatric nursing.

Training in the administrative aspects of nursing must be featured
more prominently in the curriculum of the student nurse. She should

learn how to manage a ward or a group of wards. As previously mentioned with respect to graduate training for psychiatric nursing, the student nurse should learn the principles of group psychology and techniques of education.

The team concept which is so important in the mental hospital operates in the general hospital, too. Most general hospitals have rehabilitation programs, occupational therapy, and recreational therapy. The student nurse can learn from the beginning of her training that she functions as part of a team, and that in certain important respects she is the leader of that team.

Thus, in the ordinary routines of the student nurse in the general hospital she will have experiences which will prepare her for duty as a psychiatric nurse, provided only that the teaching program exploits these experiences properly.

Relationship to the Attendant

Because of the major shortage of nurses in mental hospitals attendants have been compelled to assume some of the responsibilities of bedside nursing (see Chapter X). With recent improvements in attendant training programs an educationally superior group of young people have gone into the attendant field and have created a corps of workers specially trained for work on the wards of mental hospitals. In Saskatchewan the graduate attendant has even been given the title of "Psychiatric Nurse" and has been licensed as such. This designation as psychiatric nurse is acceptable as long as the training leading to that title is equivalent in all respects to that leading to the title of registered nurse. In general, however, the scientific training of the graduate nurse remains superior to that of the attendant. For that reason it would be an error to think that the need for graduate psychiatric nurses is being eliminated by such attendant training programs. On the contrary, the graduate psychiatric nurse can make her most useful contribution as co-ordinator and director of the treatment program on the ward level only if she has the assistance of a corps of well-trained psychiatric attendants.

SELECTED REFERENCES

BLACK, K.: *Psychiatric Nursing Today*. Proceedings of the First Annual Psychiatric Institute, New Jersey Neuropsychiatric Institute, 1953.
   An excellent critique of the inadequacies of current educational practices in nurses training with recommendations for improvements. Discussion of the graduate training benefits under the National Mental Health Act.

Careers in Mental Health as a Psychiatric Nurse. Public Health Service Publication No. 26. Supt. of Documents, U.S. Gov. Printing Office, Washington, D.C.
> A brief, simply written pamphlet which outlines the field of psychiatric nursing with suggestions for securing postgraduate training.

GROUP FOR THE ADVANCEMENT OF PSYCHIATRY: *The Psychiatric Nurse in the Mental Hospital.* Report No. 22, 1952.
> A brief report which highlights some of the unsolved problems in the field of psychiatric nursing.

HOULISTON, M.: *The Practice of Mental Nursing.* Baltimore: Williams & Wilkins, 1955.
> Practical and detailed in its description of the nurse's duties in a modern mental hospital.

LINTON, D.: A Nurse in Psychiatrics. Young Student Handles Tough Task on Way to Getting her R.N. *Life,* June 21, 1954.
> A photographic essay of the experiences of a student nurse on an "acute" ward of the Boston Psychopathic Hospital. Useful as educational material for young people interested in entering the field.

MARIMOTO, F. R.; GREENBLATT, M.: Personnel Awareness of Patient's Socializing Capacity. *Am. J. Psychiat.,* 110:443, 1953.
> The role of the nurse as the ward leader in promoting socializing activities among patients.

Psychiatric Nursing Personnel. Mental Hospital Service, American Psychiatric Association, Washington, D.C.
> A statistical study of the psychiatric nursing situation in 1950 covering patient-personnel ratios, educational programs, responsibilities of nurses and attendants, and personnel policies. Compiled by the Nursing Consultant to the Committee on Psychiatric Nursing of the American Psychiatric Association.

UNSIGNED: Study of Ward Patient Care in Hospitals for the Mentally Ill. *Am. J. Nursing,* 52:721, 1952.
> A description of a study currently in progress under the auspices of the Russell Sage Foundation for the purpose of improving psychiatric nursing services in mental hospitals. No results are reported in this article. However, the study seems worth watching.

Chapter XII

THE CHAPLAIN

The Psychology of Religious Feelings

Religious feelings are deeply ingrained in most people. Even in those instances where a person has been apparently nonobservant or agnostic, evidences of religious belief can often be demonstrated during periods of emotional stress. The reason for this is not hard to uncover. Freud has compared the relationship of the grown man to God with the child's relationship to his father. The helpless feelings which overwhelm the child are paralleled by similar feelings in certain tragic circumstances in the life of the adult. The child's faith in the omnipotence of his father has its counterpart in the religious faith of the adult. Freud concluded from these parallelisms that religious faith represents essentially a childlike attitude which will disappear when mankind becomes emotionally mature. Many psychiatrists would disagree with this conclusion. There are life situations today, and there always will be such situations, which will arouse dependency needs and feelings of helplessness in the most mature of people.

Periods of transition particularly are emotionally stressful. The change of status from childhood to adulthood, marriage, parenthood, loss of a loved one, incapacitating illness, all bring with them unforeseeable circumstances and the need for new adjustments. A previous state of balance existing between conflicting elements within the psychic apparatus is disrupted, temporarily at least, and anxiety is invariably increased (see Chapter I). In these circumstances religion may provide the individual with additional resources for dealing with emotional stress. An optimistic belief in a supernatural Being who is good may help to ward off pathological impulses to regression. Furthermore, ancient religious rituals, and beautiful ceremonials exert a potentially fortifying influence during periods of crisis. Finally, religion provides positive motivations and goals which exert a powerful impetus toward mental health. These religious standards lend substance and meaning to life. In the language of the psychiatrist, they provide outlets for the sublimation of many powerful human emotional needs.

The nonjudgmental attitude which the psychoanalyst assumes in his therapeutic relationship with patients has given rise to the misconception that psychiatrists are amoral and devoid of belief in ethical values. Nothing could be further from the truth. The highest values from the point of view of mental hygiene and religion coincide. A capacity to love and accept one's fellows, a belief that life is worth while, peace of mind, self-fulfillment—these are commonly sought for goals. We must communicate our unity of purpose to the ministers in the community. If we share our knowledge with them their pulpits may play an important role in the mental health of the community.

It must be evident that if religion plays so important a role in the functioning of the normal mind, it must be a potentially powerful therapeutic instrument in healing the sick mind. It is logical, therefore, to have chaplains on the staffs of state hospitals to participate in the therapeutic community.

Pastoral Psychiatry in a Mental Hospital Setting

The field dealing with the role of religion in fostering mental health has been called "pastoral psychiatry." A considerable literature has grown up on this subject, and several centers have been established in the country where ministers may receive training in pastoral psychiatry. The Menninger Clinic in Topeka and the St. Elizabeth's Hospital in Washington, D.C., are notable examples. Worcester State Hospital established such a center as early as 1925. As a result of this trend, the chaplain who presents himself for duties in a mental hospital will often come specially trained for the job. It has been recommended by one group (The Council for Clinical Training, Inc.) that no man be accepted for a hospital chaplaincy unless he has undergone at least one full year of clinical pastoral training. Ideally, at least some of the chaplains who come to the hospital should have pulpits in the community. In that way they can function more effectively as a bridge to the outer community for the patient in the hospital. As shall be seen subsequently, the chaplain's most important role in the mental hospital is that of a religious leader, and not at all as a psychotherapist in the secular sense of the word. To fulfill this function best he will require not only special psychiatric training but also special competence in his chosen work as a minister. This will include personal warmth, sincerity and a capacity to empathize with the patient's emotional needs.

In the 1953 report of the Council of State Governments, the following recommendation by the National Council of Churches is made:

> Every institution averaging approximately 150 patients per day (or over) under its care should have one full-time chaplain, representing the major faith group, and arrangements should be made with other clergy for ministry to persons of other faith groups.
>
> An institution having any second faith group represented in its population by 250 or more persons on an average daily population basis should have an additional full-time chaplain for that group. Additional full-time chaplains should be assigned for each 500 persons, or fraction thereof, of any faith group on an average daily population basis.
>
> Where the number of persons of any particular faith group is not sufficient, according to such standards, for a full-time chaplaincy—but large enough to demand time in the religious ministry—the institution should contract for the part-time services of a chaplain for that group.

A Training Program for Chaplains

Even if the chaplain has had previous instruction in "pastoral psychiatry," he should be included in the training program for hospital personnel (see Chapter XXIX). This program should aim to acquaint the chaplain with all phases of the treatment program as well as with the people who administer them so that he may integrate his contribution with theirs. A patient may communicate something to him which the social worker should know about, or the patient may tell something to the recreational therapist that the chaplain should know about. The chaplain should understand what every worker is trying to accomplish just as they should be instructed concerning his goals. In conjunction with the recreational therapy department the chaplain may organize a choir and arrange for rehearsals for religious services and special holiday celebrations. With the help of the occupational therapist he may have an altar built, or an ark for housing the Holy Scriptures in Jewish services, or benches, chairs and other objects of use in the chapel. In problems involving family relationships or the outside community the chaplain will often want to work in conjunction with the social service department. By thus co-ordinating his work with that of other departments the effectiveness of the treatment program is increased.

The chaplain should be included in classroom instruction devoted to problems of normal emotional development, symptom formation as an adaptational process, the nature of the unconscious, the phenomena of transference and countertransference (see preceeding chapters where these topics are covered).

The most important phase of the training program for chaplains will be in the form of seminars in which their experiences with patients are discussed with competent psychiatrists. Since this field is relatively new, careful records of these seminars should be kept. An attempt should be made to organize and publish these experiences for the benefit of workers in other hospitals.

Manifestations of Anxiety in the Chaplain

Whenever seminars of any kind are organized for instruction in mental hospitals, they invariably come to serve a group therapy function for the participants. It can be anticipated that the chaplains' seminars will be no exception to this rule. The divinity student or the young minister may be struggling with anxiety related to his first responsibilities as a religious leader in the community. At a time when he is called upon to guide others, his own anxieties impel him to regress and seek guidance himself. In this setting he may lose sight of the power of his own instrument for relieving human suffering and may seek to borrow from the psychiatrist's psychotherapeutic armamentarium. He may indulge in ill-advised attempts at psychotherapy, or may turn to psychiatrists for instruction in their techniques. When a minister develops doubts about the efficacy of religion to help those who consult him, he should be encouraged to turn first for help to his church superiors, to religious leaders who are older and wiser. Only secondarily should he turn to the techniques of psychiatry, and then to seek help for himself, not to use these techniques on his parishioners.

The chaplain who reports for duty in a mental hospital has special problems. The mentally ill arouse uncanny feelings in all who are technically uninformed about psychiatry (see Chapter XXXVII). In fact, even the most highly trained will experience anxiety from time to time in working with psychotic patients. The psychiatrist helps the chaplain to recognize the manifestations of anxiety in himself, particularly as they express themselves in inhibitions in carrying out his religious program. In group discussions the psychiatrist helps the chaplain to understand the origins of his anxiety and the technique for mastering it. In the religious program, as in all other aspects of the treatment program, anxiety in the members of the treatment team interfere with the most effective work in the patient's behalf.

The Separation Between Psychiatry and Religion

The chaplain must be acquainted not only with the nature of mental illness but also with the way in which the psychiatrist's proper domain differs from that of the chaplain. The problem of defining with ever increasing clarity the differences between the goals and responsibilities of the psychiatrist and those of the chaplain is probably the single most important point in the training program for chaplains. The following brief examples highlight these differences:

A. A person may fear to walk down a city street in broad daylight because of a fear of crowds, or because of a fear that he will have a heart attack in spite of reassurances by physicians to the contrary. Psychological and psychiatric studies may elicit the fact that these fears are based on unconscious infantile wishes, relating for example to a wish to exhibit the genitalia publicly, or to become involved in some other forbidden sexual activity. Making the patient conscious of these persistent childhood wishes will place him in better position to control them and as a result his fears will decrease. Reassurances and exhortations based on conscious reason are almost invariably of no avail because they do not take these unconscious motivations into consideration. To compel the patient to face situations that he fears without helping him to understand why he has these fears only intensifies his anxiety. The resolution of this problem clearly calls for the services of a psychiatrist.

On the other hand, a man may have fear as he goes into battle or when he is about to embark on a major enterprise the outcome of which is uncertain. Religious observances may add to his courage and resolve in meeting these crises.

B. A person may lose a loved one. Under such circumstances feelings of grief are normal. The religious leader may bring consolation from the Holy Scriptures, from the examples of courage and love presented by great Biblical figures of the past. In dealing with such real traumata the specific techniques of the psychiatrist are of little avail. But what of the woman who becomes depressed after having a baby? Or the man who becomes depressed, paradoxically, after achieving some great personal success? In these instances the basis for the feeling of depression is to be found in the unconscious meanings with which the individual has invested these situations. Once again, appeal to conscious reason is largely ineffective and the techniques of the psychiatrist are more useful.

C. A person may be guilt-ridden because of an act of unkindness to a loved one, or because of having been dishonest or unfair to others. The religious leader may give the sufferer an opportunity to atone for his wrongdoing and thereby diminish the intensity of his guilt. In mental hospitals, however, one commonly encounters people who torment themselves with guilty self-reproaches and who have no basis in contemporary external reality for their guilty feelings. The unconscious reasons for these feelings are usually not accessible to religious approaches and once again the special techniques of the psychiatrist must be called into play.

It follows that the chaplain should address himself to the real needs of patients rather than enter into futile disputations concerning phobias or delusions. The psychotic patient can be compared to a dreamer who is, at one moment, in the grip of a fearful nightmare and yet is able to tell himself that he is really dreaming. That is to say, there is a core of sanity within the most psychotic mind and it is with this part of the patient that the chaplain concerns himself. To do this most effectively the chaplain will have to be informed in general about the symptoms of mental illness and the emotionally adaptive function that mental symptoms serve (see Chapter I). In particular he will want to be informed by the psychiatrist about the clinical details of each individual patient who seeks his help.

The Special Power of Religion

The chaplain must be helped to appreciate the special power of his own instrument—religion. However deceptive the façade which some of these patients may present to the environment (in the form of anger, contempt, indifference), they are all, in a fundamental sense, the most helpless of human beings. If this were not so, it would not have been necessary to take them into the protective custody of the hospital. In their helpless state they have need of a strong leader. The chaplain derives from his specific religious symbolism a unique strength for many of these patients. They will attribute qualities of strength and wisdom to him which he may not feel personally as an individual but which he can feel if and when he understands the special power which is his to command by virtue of his position as a religious leader, by virtue of the religious wisdom which is at his disposal, and by virtue of the reassuring effects of ancient rituals, awe-inspiring and beautiful ceremonials which he alone is capable of administering. In short, his special contribution to the patient's welfare derives from the fact that he is a religious leader. If he keeps this fact before him, he will apply himself accordingly and will be less likely to waste himself in nonreligious psychotherapeutic techniques.

A striking example of the power of religion was related by a psychiatrist of Polish origin who was able to speak this language fluently in addition to English. On one of his back wards he had a chronic, so-called deteriorating schizophrenic woman who for years had been totally mute. Knowing that she too was Polish, he often stopped and addressed her in Polish, thinking that perhaps an appeal to her in her mother tongue would break the barrier of her psychotic inhibition. However, this was useless. One day, on an inspiration, he said to her sternly: "Woman, do you know your prayers? If you do, repeat them after me!" He then started to recite the Lord's prayer in Polish. What happened might have been described in days gone by as a miracle. The patient "came to life" and started to repeat the prayer with him. She fell to her knees with tears streaming down her face, and at the end she kissed his hands. The "miracle," alas, was not long lasting. She returned to her mute state and did not respond to his subsequent attempts in that vein. I think we would all agree today that this was no miracle, but rather a striking demonstration of several of the principles that have been mentioned—the accessibility of this "deteriorated" patient, the state of helpless dependency which led to such grateful acceptance of her doctor's prayer, the approach through reality and the extraordinarily powerful effect of religious feeling. That she relapsed so quickly is not as important as was the fleeting remission itself which proved so strikingly that religion provides an effective lever for prying open a mind that is locked by mental illness. Perhaps if this incident had occurred as part of the regular ministrations of a chaplain and was supplemented by a total religious program, the effects might have been longer lasting. We can only speculate at times concerning the thoughts within the mind of a psychotic patient. It is possible for example that this patient reacted with resentment when she realized that this prayer was offered up by a doctor, not by a minister. She may even have been aware of the fact that this doctor was not of her faith, and she may even have sensed some slight irreverence in his manner. In any case, we must not write off the importance of this approach because of the brevity of the result.

The Importance of Religious Services

If isolation and estrangement from fellow men are the common lot of psychotic patients, what could possibly be more logical than to bring these lonely people together in an emotionally meaningful situation? And what more natural group can we provide for them than that of the religious congregation. The repetition of carefully selected prayers in unison, responsive readings, and the singing of beloved hymns, particularly when instrumentally accompanied, will draw these lonely people together. In such group experiences the patient comes to recognize and accept the fact that he has more in common with his fellow man than he realized, that he is more human than otherwise.

The help of the doctors, nurses and attendants must be recruited in the attempt to give the greatest possible dignity and solemnity to the services. By the example of their presence and the reverence of their own bearing they can make an important contribution. Patients should be encouraged to wear their "Sunday-best" when going to services. In other words, if the therapeutic effectiveness of the religious services depends upon the specific impact of religious feelings, then every effort should be made to foster and intensify these feelings.

In an overcrowded state hospital all kinds of mix-ups can occur. Thus, patients of one faith have been taken to services of another faith—inadvertently or otherwise. Since a common chapel is employed by all religious groups, the symbolic devices of one faith may be in evidence during religious services of another. Such occurrences can be extremely confusing to patients, adding fuel to delusional fires, and even occasioning disturbed behavior. Needless to say, they should be avoided.

Regular worship services, frequently conducted (that is, more than once a week, if possible) should be the mainstay of the chaplain's contribution to the therapeutic community. All holidays should be celebrated with maximal regard for color and beauty of observance. The chaplain should build up to a holiday celebration with weeks of anticipatory activity in the form of sermons and in the mobilization of patient activities in the preparations (choir rehearsals, preparation of decorations).

Patient participation in services should be maximal, in the form of responsive readings, group singing, particularly of old familiar hymns, in distributing and collecting prayer books, posting announcements of services and special holiday celebrations. The fact that the psychotic patient can be more effectively reached through symbols and concrete acts than through the spoken word alone must be a guiding principle in planning the religious program. Services should not last more than forty minutes. Attempts should be made to arrange for services in the mother tongue of foreign-born patients. Sermons should be brief, not over six minutes, and should be devoted to topics readily understandable to the patient, and close to his current needs—for example, love, friendship, health, loyalty, work, ambition, home, family. The chaplain should address himself to the feelings of the patient, utilizing simple parables, concrete objects, and drawings on a blackboard. Abstractions and intellectualizations should be avoided because of the specific impairment in this type of thinking which characterizes many mental disorders. Prayers should be offered up for the doctors, nurses and attendants to bring out the unity of purpose that prevails in the mental hospital. Arrangements may be made to broadcast services over the public address system for patients who are too sick to go to the chapel. In areas where religious services are broadcast over television this may provide a particularly effective way of bringing religious comfort to patients confined to their bed or their ward.

The importance of these group worship experiences is indicated by E. E. Bruder's observation that patients will at times return for Sunday services after they have been discharged from the hospital. In this way the hospital provides continued emotional support and feelings of security to the patient in the community.

Work With Individual Patients

The chaplain traditionally includes visiting, counseling and praying with individual patients as part of his work. In these duties he should concern himself primarily with the chronically sick and bedridden who are unable to attend regular services. He should also try to see all newly admitted patients and give them support over the particular hardships of the first few days in the hospital. It is well to recall, in this connection, that psychotic patients have difficulty in tolerating too intimate a contact with other people. Excessive personal warmth on the part of the chaplain may arouse anxiety and the patient may react to an expression of love as if it were an attack. And yet the need for love which these patients have must not be omitted either. It often requires considerable sensitivity to arrive at the correct mixture of warmth and objectivity for approaching a psychotic patient with maximal effectiveness.

Other Duties of the Chaplain

The chaplain ministers to the spiritual needs of the acutely sick and dying just as he would in a general hospital.

He holds informal gatherings, adult classes, choir rehearsals and other activities to lift the spirits of patients and to help them live together in harmony.

He provides religious counseling services to doctors, nurses, social workers and others, both individually and in groups, for their guidance in working with patients and often for their own spiritual welfare.

He participates in the hospital's training program, not only contributing to the technical education of other members of the treatment team but also by training other clergymen so that they may better understand the special spiritual needs of the mentally sick.

He speaks before civic and church groups to tell them of the present knowledge of the cause and treatment of the various forms of mental illness and of religious observance as a mental hygiene measure.

The chaplain can play a very important role in the volunteer program (see Chapter XIII) by recruiting volunteers to help patients lead fuller, happier lives, and to aid in their improvement and possible recovery through games, hobby classes, and other creative activities.

These emotionally impoverished people need concrete evidences of affection. Bibles, and other comforting religious tracts, are often accepted in this way, not only for their printed content but for what they symbolize as gifts. Other gifts may be provided by the chaplain in the form of ornamental religious devices or books. Ideally, these gifts should emphasize the religious role of the giver, thereby providing the patient with a broader base of comfort and security than that which would result if the gift came simply from an unattached individual.

SELECTED REFERENCES

ALLPORT, D. B.: Religion and State Hospital. *Ment. Hyg.*, 27:574, 1943.
> Based on rich personal experiences, this paper contains many practical details concerning the conduct of the religious program in a mental hospital.
BRUDER, E. E.: A Ministry to the Mentally Ill in the Mental Hospital (see Maves).
> An excellent presentation, also based on great personal experience.
KEMP, C.: The Minister and Mental Hygiene: His Opportunity and Responsibility. *Ment. Hyg.*, 32:72, 1948.
MAVES, P. B., ed.: *The Church and Mental Health*. New York: Scribner, 1953.
> A collection of thoughtful essays covering the field of pastoral psychiatry in great detail.
SCULLY, A. W.: The Work of a Chaplain in a State Hospital for Mental Disorders. *J. Nerv. & Ment. Dis.*, 101:264, 1945.
> Describes a program for Catholic patients at the Massillon State Hospital in Ohio, centering about the construction of the shrine dedicated to Saint Dymphna, the Patron Saint of the mentally ill (see Chapter XXXV).
Training and Research in State Mental Health Programs. A Report to the Governors' Conference, 1953. Council of State Governments, 1313 E. 60th St., Chicago 37, Ill.
> Contains material relating to the role of the chaplain in the mental hospital, his training and recommended standards for a religious program in mental hospitals.

Chapter XIII

THE VOLUNTEER WORKER

The Specific Contributions of the Volunteer Worker

In recent years a new worker has joined the mental hospital treatment team, the volunteer worker. Properly integrated into the treatment program, his services have become well-nigh indispensable. In the Veterans Administration Hospital at Lyons, New Jersey, for example, between six and seven thousand volunteer hours per month are contributed by workers who travel many miles to reach the hospital. In the course of a single year almost a quarter of a million dollars worth of equipment and materials were brought into the hospital by these volunteers. By means of a volunteer program it has become possible in many hospitals to plan a genuine treatment program in spite of shortages of materials and paid personnel. However, it must not be thought the volunteer worker is a passing phenomenon whose usefulness will subside when these shortages are overcome. On the contrary, the volunteer worker brings something unique and irreplaceable into the therapeutic community. The patient reacts to the volunteer as to a friend from the outside world. The patient identifies with the volunteer more readily than he does with the paid hospital employee and frequently esteems him more highly. The presence of these voluntary representatives from the outer community has a reassuring effect upon the patient. He feels less ostracized. He is relieved to find that he himself and the hospital which confines him are not frightening to these ordinary citizens.

Because of the lack of self-esteem which is so regularly part of mental illness, it is a matter of therapeutic importance for these patients to find that there are others who want to help them purely because they feel they are worth helping. That this is so is indicated by the co-operative attitude which most patients display toward volunteer workers. They will do things to please the volunteer that they are indifferent about doing for themselves. In response to a volunteer's prompting an untidy patient becomes more concerned about her personal habits; a patient mute for many months begins to talk in the midst of a game with a volunteer. Volunteers have opened their homes to these patients and in the process have opened many new horizons for them.

The following case report quoted from Mrs. Marjorie Frank's excellent article on "Volunteer Work With Psychiatric Patients," exemplifies the way in which the volunteer worker can transform the life of a mental hospital patient:

> Special permission was obtained several weeks ago from the doctor in charge of the Continued Treatment Service, for a patient to visit the home of one of the men volunteers who organized the Camera Club. Through the Camera Club, this patient has become quite well versed in photography, but has never had the opportunity to learn the developing process, as the "dark room" at the hospital has not yet been completed. As a result, the visit gave him the opportunity to work in the volunteer's dark room and learn the various steps involved. This patient has been at the hospital for a number of years, so that the home atmosphere, too, was a very special treat. In the evening, they joined another man volunteer and his family and prepared a picnic supper outdoors.
>
> As a result of his photographic instruction, this patient has become the hospital photographer, available and prepared to record any special activity at a moment's notice.

Here is a form of treatment based upon the highest of human values, man's concern for his brother. It cannot be purchased with increased tax appropriations. It is available only as a gift from the patients' fellow citizens. In its qualities as a gift are to be found its special therapeutic importance. The beneficial effects of the volunteer worker's contribution go beyond their direct influence on the patient. Their activities have inspired the attendants and other regular workers in the hospital to set higher standards for themselves. It has been reported, for example, that the presence of a single volunteer worker may heighten the enthusiasm of an entire department. The benefits of their activities reverberate into the community as well. The voluntary status which encourages patients to an attitude of affectionate appreciation toward the volunteer influences people in the community to be favorably disposed to them also. The volunteer has a unique opportunity to tell the community about the hospital, the good things that go on within it as well as the bad things which should be corrected by public-spirited action. The best tribute to the influence of the volunteer worker on the community is the fact that no one is more effective than the volunteer in recruiting more volunteers for the hospital program. By bringing the mentally ill out of the hospital into close contacts and individualized relationships with citizens in the community at ball games, club meetings and in visits to private homes, volunteers have helped overcome many ancient prejudices concerning the mentally ill. They have fostered understanding, interest and genuine warmth in community attitudes concerning the fate of these patients.

Varieties of Volunteer Activities

Volunteers serve in many departments of the hospital. They participate in the recreation program, focusing as much as possible on the withdrawn patient. They plan parties for patients. They involve them in games, as individuals or in small groups, avoiding the more impersonal large spectator events. Volunteers serve in the athletic program, give courses in first aid and in swimming. They work in the library and the social service department. They supervise the activities of patients with deteriorated personal habits, either as a result of chronic psychosis or lobotomy. They may be involved in psychodrama in hospitals that employ this form of group therapy. Volunteers participate in the occupational therapy program and in the work rehabilitation program. They may make arrangements for teachers from vocational schools and local business experts to give lectures and help advise patients on their future plans for study and work opportunities after their discharge from the hospital. Volunteers may be assigned to educational therapy and conduct classes in typewriting, mechanical drawing, aeronautics, radio, shorthand, bookkeeping, languages, and mathematics. They make arrangements for guest speakers from the community to talk to the patients on current events, music, radio, labor relations, or travelogues. Many clubs from the community concerned with stamp collection, books, chess and photography hold special meetings at the hospital, get patients to start similar clubs of their own and invite their clubs to meet with them jointly in the community. They schedule trips to take patients to picnics, baseball and football games, plays, zoos, museums, broadcasting studios, municipal buildings and sight-seeing tours. Patients are also invited to leave the hospital for skiing parties, tennis and golf games, and for bowling and dancing classes in town. They visit country clubs and are invited to private homes. They attend meetings of various community groups such as the Rotary and Lions clubs, and enter into civic contests. Through the volunteer's contact with industries in the community, arrangements are made for patients to visit industries and businesses. Many of the industries visited have been most enthusiastic, planning tours of the plant, providing luncheon and scheduling conferences with the personnel department. Not only have these visits brought about increased understanding of mental patients but jobs have also been offered and accepted. Volunteers run annual benefit dances to raise funds for supplies. They type and edit the patients' newspaper.

Many patients are doomed to an especial loneliness because of the barrier of language. Volunteers who communicate with foreign patients may rescue some of these lost souls from oblivion. A patient who has no visitors or funds may be assigned to a volunteer as part of an "Adopt a Patient" program. A ward may be assigned to a group of volunteers as part of an "Adopt a Ward" program to arrange monthly parties for the celebration of birthdays, or to organize a ward gift and decorating project. A volunteer shopping service can be used to encourage an active interest in the community. For example, patients can be urged to follow the notices of special sales in the newspapers in planning their shopping. Volunteers can work in the beauty parlor, in the record room, in the secretarial department, or as receptionists on visiting days. This list cannot hope to exhaust the possibilities. Wherever a need exists within the mental hospital, volunteers can be found to fill it.

The Hospital Must Want a Volunteer Program

In view of the extraordinary contribution which volunteer workers can make, it may come as a surprise to learn that many medical directors are unfriendly to their presence. Indiscriminately selected volunteers, without proper training and without careful thought concerning their assignments, can without a doubt become a disruptive influence within a hospital, antagonizing employees, irritating patients and adding to the burdens of the already overburdened staff. Nathan S. Kline of the Veterans Administration has compared the gift of volunteer services to the proverbial gift of a white elephant; a beast of great potential strength which can be properly harnessed and utilized for the patient's welfare, can without proper direction become a trampling monster that leaves the wreckage of the hospital's treatment program strewn in its wake. To refuse this gift, however, because of the difficulties in using it properly, is certainly not the wisest choice. The medical director and his staff should acquaint themselves with the many advantages which accrue to the hospital from a well-run volunteer program. Appropriate literature should be studied (see references at end of Chapter). Experienced people should be invited to speak. If the staff is not thoroughly convinced of the importance of this form of treatment, it is better not to start it, since an inadequately run program is worse than no program at all.

The Hospital's Responsibilities to the Volunteer Worker

The hospital must prepare itself to make the volunteers feel welcome. If after subjecting themselves to the many inconveniences and personal sacrifices involved in becoming a competent worker, the volunteers are then permitted to feel like intruders, they cannot be blamed if they become halfhearted in their efforts or quit altogether. A well-qualified and personally interested paid staff member must be charged with the responsibility for co-ordinating, integrating and giving over-all direction to the volunteer program within the hospital. Preferably this should be a psychiatrist, the clinical director or one of his assistants. In each department of the hospital one person is made responsible for the volunteer workers assigned to it. The hospital has to provide for the health and safety of the volunteer workers and be prepared to give emergency medical care in the event of accidents incurred by volunteers while on duty. The hospital must provide physical facilities for the comfort of the volunteers, a place for their clothing, a room where they can relax between assignments, a headquarters where they can receive messages. The hospital may be able to provide them with lunch, but in any event will have to provide a comfortable place where they can eat.

Most of all the hospital personnel must be alerted against its own xenophobic tendencies. The volunteer worker comes as a friendly public-spirited citizen. He will contribute more if he is received as such by the hospital. Although the volunteer worker is not paid in cash, he gets a reward for his work, nevertheless, in the form of satisfactions that come from doing an important job and doing it well, in opportunities for intellectually broadening experiences and personal emotional growth, and in opportunities for developing qualities of leadership. The volunteer program provides students of medicine, public health, child welfare, nursing, psychiatry, religion and teaching with valuable preprofessional experience and insight into their future work. These are the only rewards which the mature worker seeks. It is the psychiatrist's responsibility to see that those rewards are forthcoming to the greatest extent possible. In addition, however, awards should be presented to volunteers who have made outstanding contributions.

Initiating the Program

When the medical director and his staff have decided that they want a volunteer program for their hospital, they contact the appropriate organization in their community and request assistance. The American Red Cross has become particularly experienced in this problem. Local chapters of the National Association for Mental Health or other representatives of the mental hygiene movement in the community, the American Friends Service Committee, the National Council of Jewish Women or other public-spirited organizations may be prepared to assume the responsibility for the community's side of the task. If several organizations are going to participate, a committee should be formed of representatives from each organization with one person, preferably a paid full-time worker, designated as the chairman and over-all director of volunteer activities.

The first thing that this committee will want to do is to conduct a survey of the hospital's needs. The community director of the volunteer program will meet with the director of the volunteer program designated by the hospital and together they will outline all the activities in which volunteers can be of help. They will make estimates of the number of people they can use and the amount of time they will want them to contribute.

Recruiting

Armed with this basic information, the committee will then enlist all available channels of public communication, including radio, television, posters in theaters and other public places, news releases and editorials in a call for volunteers. In pamphlets (see references) and in public meetings the volunteer program will be presented, including the responsiblities entailed in the assignments. Applicants will then be interviewed.

Selection and Screening

The selection of proper people for training is perhaps the most important phase of the entire program. Patients must be protected from those people with whom personal contact might be psychologically harmful. People who volunteer their services must be protected from undertaking a task which may be too taxing for them, mentally and physically. Applications are accepted through the community organization that has established connections with the hospital. The following suggested application form is from Nathan S. Kline's article on volunteer workers (see references):

1. Miss, Mrs., Mr. ....
2. Address ....
   Telephone Number ....
3. Date of birth...
   Place of birth ....
4. What foreign languages can you speak? ....
   What foreign languages can you read? ....
5. Can you provide your own transportation to and from the hospital if necessary? ....
   How many others can you accommodate? ....
6. Check your educational background:
   (a) High School ....
   (b) Business School ....
   (c) College ....
   (d) Major subject ....
7. Have you ever done hospital volunteer work before? ....
   What type? .... Length of time? ....
8. Interests and Training:
   (a) Have you ever belonged to a dramatic society? ....
   (b) Do you like to read aloud? ....
   (c) Can you play a musical instrument? ....
   (d) Can you sing? .... Direct group singing?..................
   (e) Can you teach any type of dancing? ....
   (f) Have you experience in directing games? ....
   (g) List games in which you are proficient (either indoor or outdoor) ....
   (h) With what types of handwork or crafts are you experienced? ....
   (i) What types of discussion groups, if any, have you conducted? ....
   (j) Have you had any library experience?....................................
   (k) If you have had any teaching experience, in what subject is it? ....
9. Can you type? .... Take dictation? ....
10. Have you had any training or experience in social work? ....
    If so, describe briefly ....
11. Availability:
    (a) Can you come throughout the year? ....
    (b) Will you be out of town at certain seasons? ....
        When? ....
    (c) Can you serve any day during the week? ....
        Can you serve in the evenings? ....
        Can you serve Saturdays? ....
        Can you serve Sundays? .... Holidays? ....
    (d) How many hours can you serve weekly? ....

Screening begins in the initial interview with the community director of the volunteer services. The applicant may be grossly unsuitable for one reason or another and be eliminated at once. After a thorough explanation of what the volunteer program entails, some applicants may choose to eliminate themselves. The community director will take into consideration such factors as sincerity, maturity as to motivation, an estimate of the capacity to accept direction from others, personal warmth, humor, dependability, patience, tact, kindness, general presentability and physical well-being. If acceptable, or if the community director feels that he should withhold a final decision, the applicant is interviewed by the psychiatrist or the hospital psychologist. Usually such interviews are conducted two or three times a year when large groups of volunteers can be seen in succession. The psychiatrist will look for evidences of manifest psychosis, psychoneurosis or any other form of incapacitating or disqualifying psychopathology. The applicant's motivation will concern him particularly. An excessively self-sacrificing attitude must be scrutinized with diagnostic care. Emotionally starved people who will find in the job a sole outlet for their needs are apt to run into trouble. A person who has been unsuccessful at a series of other jobs is apt to be unsuccessful at this one too. Persons who are motivated by mental illness in the family should be screened with particular care, and in any event should not be considered for assignment to the hospital in which the relative is being treated.

Psychological tests of one kind or another have been utilized for rapid screening of large numbers of applicants. A special "True-False Test for Volunteers" was developed by Nathan S. Kline and his co-workers in the Veterans Administration (see references). Whatever tests are used, an attempt should be made to check the test over a period of years as to its reliability as a selective device.

If the applicant passes the second echelon of selection, he is ready to begin his training. Further screening may occur following the lecture course. A final screening takes place on the job. Volunteers are accepted for a ten- to thirty-hour probationary period after which they may be turned down or accepted as regular workers. When volunteers are turned down, it should be explained to them that they have not failed but that rather that their particular aptitudes and abilities are unsuited for work with the mentally ill. If at all possible, properly motivated people should be switched over to volunteer work in other less sensitive areas. Those who are finally selected on the other hand, should be rewarded for their trials and tribulations by permission to wear a special uniform and insignia.

Training

It has been suggested that a minimal course of instruction consist of an introductory series of three teaching sessions given in the community followed by three sessions at the hospital. The introductory sessions should include lectures and discussions covering the basic needs and drives of people, facts and misconceptions about the mentally ill and their care, and community aspects of mental illness. Appropriate psychiatric motion pictures should be utilized in the course, and a selection of basic books should be made available to the students (see references to Chapters XXIX and XXXVII for film catalogues and suggested book titles).

In the hospital sessions, the class will be told about the hospital—what it tries to do and how it is organized to accomplish its goals. Procedures involved in the admission and discharge of patients are described. The importance of protecting patients by respecting their confidences and the need for continuity of service and dependability on the part of the volunteer are stressed. Types of mental illness are discussed. The volunteer is told about the reactions which he can expect from patients. He is also encouraged to ventilate his own anxieties concerning his forthcoming experiences on the wards. The role of anxiety in hospital personnel is discussed as a factor which interferes with effective treatment. Frank discussions in groups led by informed leaders as a means of diminishing anxiety will be stressed throughout their careers as volunteer workers. They are told about the role of the nurse, the attendant and all other departments involved in treatment. A volunteer worker who has established good rapport with a patient may be favored with many communications which the patient withholds from other members of the treatment team. The importance of the patient's remarks and actions for clarifying diagnoses and for individualizing treatment should be explained. They are taken on a tour of the hospital and are broken up into small discussion groups for questions and answers. A True-False examination provides a means for further screening at this point.

Work on the Wards

The probationary period of work on the wards is then begun. Experienced volunteer workers should accompany the newcomers on their first assignments. Reliability of their attendance is a matter of utmost importance. Patients gathered at a point of departure for an activity are unnecessarily traumatized if the volunteer worker does not show up. Confidential efficiency records are kept with the knowledge of each worker. Workers should be evaluated for qualities of leadership. Each day's group of volunteers must have an assigned leader for that day who must be notified if a worker cannot come, so that he has time to get someone else or to rearrange his assignments. Every department must have its own chief volunteer worker who is responsible to the day leader. In most hospitals volunteers work one day a week for a total of about one hundred hours for the year.

After the probationary period facilities for continued supervision should be maintained. Volunteers should be kept up to date on developments within the hospital through written instructions, group discussions, and a variety of visual aids including charts, posters, movies, and photographs.

The following suggestions are from the *Manual for Volunteer Workers* used at the Northville State Hospital in Michigan (Dr. Philip N. Brown, Director).

1. *Be a good listener,* but do not feel that you are obligated to act upon all the requests made of you. Patient requests may be channelled through proper sources. The most appropriate manner to meet frequent requests is to suggest to the patient that it be discussed with his or her doctor.

2. *Be friendly,* but remember that personal involvement will not accomplish what you are here to do. A friendly, impersonal approach is the best protection. We on the staff do not discuss our personal lives with the patients and feel that as a volunteer, you will use the same approach. If patients insist upon questioning you, a general reply to the effect that you are here as a volunteer and have been asked by the staff *not* to discuss yourself usually will suffice.

3. *Remember that poise, tact and a sense of humor* are helpful in your own reactions to situations and keeping any conversations on general subjects assures the patient of your sincerity.

4. *We always observe hospital etiquette,* such as checking with the Ward Supervisor before going on a ward, advising the supervisor if a patient leaves the ward with us, or if we are leaving any articles with the patient.

5. *Conservative dress, makeup and jewelry* are requested for obvious reasons.

6. *Withhold criticism* of the hospital, with patients, personnel and the public. If you have criticisms, please discuss them with the Director of Social Service who can advise you of further appropriate action.

7. *Remember the cardinal rule in any hospital. NEVER DISCUSS PATIENTS* in public or private outside the hospital, even among your closest friends. The information you obtain in the course of your work here is privileged and confidential.

PLEASE TRY TO AVOID THE FOLLOWING:
1. Appearing to be overly curious.
2. Discussing the patient's illness.
3. Handling any personal effects of patients.
4. Arguing with a patient.
5. Discussing religious matters with patient. (A note to our Chaplain may be left in the Social Service office advising him a patient wishes to talk with him.)
6. Mailing letters for patients or making telephone calls for them. (Refer these requests to the Ward Supervisor.)
7. Giving patients matches, nail files, razors or *any* items not cleared with Ward Supervisor.
8. Making promises unless they can be kept.
9. Giving your address or telephone number to a patient.
10. Making any speeches before groups in the community without clearing with the staff. The Speaker's Bureau of the Public Relations Committee can help you with this. They furnish speakers and can help with visual aids, facts and figures and other interpretation which will help to further the hospital's community program.

College Students as Volunteer Workers

In 1948 an interesting volunteer program was inaugurated by the student body of the University of Missouri. A recruiting drive was carried out by the local Y.M. and Y.W.C.A. Students were asked to work at the nearby State hospital on Saturdays for a two-hour period. Most volunteers went out every other Saturday. The names of the students who were accepted were sent out to the State hospital along with a list of activities in which each student was prepared to participate and the times when he would present himself for work. The student would be received at the hospital by a man designated as the director of this program. The director had the foregoing information concerning the student and was ready with an assignment for him. After the two-hour work period was finished the clinical director met with the volunteers for a group discussion of their experiences. Students reacted to this program with great enthusiasm. Many were motivated to choose careers associated with mental health. The interest of the entire community was stimulated; informative newspaper articles appeared; sound mental hygiene values were inculcated in all concerned.

SELECTED REFERENCES

DEUTSCH, A.: New Way to Help The Lost Ones. *Colliers,* Nov. 8, 1954.
    A popular presentation with photographs describing the Veterans Administration Volunteer Service (VAVS). Useful for recruiting purposes.

FECHNER, A. H.; PARKE, J. H.: The Volunteer Worker and the Psychiatric Hospital. *Am. J. Psychiat.*, 107:602, 1951.

Presents in brief outline a plan for organizing a volunteer service in a mental hospital. Based on experiences in V.A. hospitals.

FRANK, M. H.: Volunteer Work With Psychiatric Patients. *Ment. Hyg.*, 33-353, 1949.

An excellent summary by an outstanding authority. Distributed as a reprint by the National Association for Mental Health, 1790 Broadway, New York 19, N. Y.

FREEMAN, R. V.; SCHWARTZ, A.: A Motivation Center: A New Concept in Total Neuropsychiatric Care. *Am. J. Psychiat.*, 110:139, 1953.

Contains an example in which observations of a volunteer worker communicated to other departments contributed to improved treatment.

GRAY, J.: *Wanted, Your Magic.* New York: National Association for Mental Health, 1954.

Useful for recruiting volunteers.

HADDOCK, J. N.; DUNDAN, H. D.: Volunteer Work in a State Hospital by College Students. *Ment. Hyg.*, 35-599, 1951.

Describes the University of Missouri experience alluded to in the text.

KLINE, N. S.: Volunteer Workers. *Occupational Therapy and Rehabilitation*, 26:153, 1947.

Outlines plan for organizing a volunteer service. Contains application form (quoted in test) and a True-False Test for screening volunteers. Distributed as a reprint by the National Association for Mental Health.

MCBEE, M.; FRANK, M.: *Volunteer Participation in Psychiatric Hospital Services: Organization Manual and Program Guide.* New York: National Association for Mental Health, 1950.

A comprehensive treatment of the subject of basic importance.

STETSON, E. R.: The Role Played by Volunteers in a Mental Hospital. *Am. J. Occupational Therapy*, 5:203, 1951.

Contains excellent suggestions for utilization of the volunteer worker.

Part Three

THE PATIENTS

Chapter XIV

THE "CHRONIC" PATIENT

According to Kraepelin, dementia praecox, or schizophrenia, was a chronic progressive disease which culminated inevitably in a complete disorganization of the mental apparatus. The picture of the chronic schizophrenic patient hunched over on the floor in a foetal position, wetting, soiling, giggling and mumbling, is all too well known on the back wards of our mental hospitals and seems to be living proof of the correctness of the Kraepelinian contention. However, it has become manifest in recent years that what this picture represents is not so much a final result emerging relentlessly under all circumstances, but rather the course which the disease takes in the specific environment of the average mental hospital.

The Psychology of Schizophrenia

To start with, the schizophrenic patient suffers from an intolerable lack of self-respect. The characteristic way in which he protects himself against insult is by withdrawal from emotional involvements with other people. The resultant isolation is a protection against painful human relationships; but the loneliness contributes further to his lack of self-respect, and hence to further withdrawal. In his isolation the schizophrenic turns increasingly to daydreams for emotional gratification. In these fantasies he tries to overcome his feelings of loneliness and lack of self-esteem. In this sense his daydreams represent attempts at healing, albeit attempts that are doomed to failure as far as any realistic hopes of fulfillment are concerned. As is well known, these daydreams tend to achieve a vividness of hallucinatory intensity which is characteristic of schizophrenia, and in the course of which the patient attributes to others his own thoughts and feelings. His waking life partakes increasingly of the qualities of a persisting dream state. In fact, many of the modes of self-expression characteristic of dreams are employed by the schizophrenic in his waking communications with those about him. Thus, he confuses past and present, and things that happened long ago are mingled with current events. He treats as identities concepts which are in reality separate, but which are linked to each other by certain common denominators of thought and feeling. As a result, he becomes disoriented and he misidentifies. Infantile devices for self-expression are reawakened and the schizophrenic relies on bodily actions rather than words in relating to others (see Chapters VI and XVI). Thus, eating, urinating, defecating become invested with predominantly symbolic meaning for him. If the patient uses words, he tends to give them highly private meanings rather than the conventional ones employed by normal adults, or he may construct entirely new words out of fragments of old ones. All of these phenomena, so clearly seen in dreams, are observed in the waking state in schizophrenics and are expressions of what Freud called "primary process" thinking as contrasted to the "secondary process" which is logical and conventional and which characterizes normal waking thought.

The Relationship Between the Schizophrenic's Needs and the Realities of the Hospital

One conclusion that follows from the foregoing discussion is that the treatment of the schizophrenic ought to begin with an attempt to increase his self-esteem so that his impulse to retreat is diminished. Needless to say, this is easier said than done. The schizophrenic projects his self-hating attitudes onto those about him and he believes that others regard him with the same contempt in which he holds himself. He may be angered by this fancied belittlement and display "retaliatory" behavior, which in turn arouses genuine antagonism in the environment. The resulting unfriendly behavior which he experiences at the hands of others gives substance to his belief that the world is basically hostile. It takes deep understanding and self-discipline not to be seduced by the schizophrenic into treating him contemptuously. Since the schizophrenic needs to feel that he is accepted on his own terms before he is willing to conform to the positive values and expectations of those about him, such negative seductions serve to increase his isolation. The patient needs a sustained living experience with people who are kindly, who do not reject him in spite of what he does, and who are themselves reasonably mature emotionally, in order to convince him that his previous expectations are prejudices which do not hold true for all human relationships. In addition to such specially endowed people, the schizophrenic patient needs a program of activities which provides him with considerable freedom of choice, which encourages his initiative, and which is patterned consistently and meaningfully toward his rehabilitation.

Even a cursory consideration of the ordinary mental hospital shows the extent to which the schizophrenic's emotional needs are not met. His days are occupied with idleness or futile routine. The drabness of his surroundings and the way in which he is fed are to him degrading in the extreme. Most traumatic of all is his isolation from those assigned to care for him. Typically, his communications are not understood. Because of this, his behavior often elicits unjustifiably judgmental or punitive reactions from his environment. It is small wonder that he feels chronically frustrated in his search for a way of relating comfortably to the hospital environment and that as a result he becomes more deeply withdrawn.

This is precisely what the picture of extreme schizophrenic deterioration represents. It is the only way in which the patient with his schizophrenic illness can adapt to this particular environment. To paraphrase a remark of Stainbrook, the schizophrenic must learn through arduous trial and error how to become deteriorated. Deterioration represents the process of becoming a "successful" citizen of the society to which the hospital has assigned him.

The Social Psychology of Deterioration

A. H. Stanton, a psychiatrist, in collaboration with M. S. Schwartz, a sociologist, have made important contributions to the concept of schizophrenic deterioration as a psychosocial adaptive pattern. They have recently assembled their findings in an excellent book (see references). One of their working principles is the fact that a mental hospital ward is an interacting system in which the type of activity engaged in by any one person is to some extent determined by the other people who are on the ward. Another of their basic principles is that mental illness is not an entity residing within an individual but is rather a type of participation in a social process. By taking the foregoing propositions into account, it becomes possible to discern meaningful patterns in the occurrences in a mental hospital.

For example, they studied the symptom of wetting and soiling which is so common in chronic deteriorated schizophrenics. They point out that the term "incontinence" is a misnomer if by that term we mean loss of sphincter control. The so-called incontinent schizophrenic patient, they discovered, discharges his excreta in a highly controlled fashion. They were able to demonstrate that there were situations in which wetting and soiling rarely, if ever, took place, as for instance in group therapy sessions, in formal dances or parties, or in certain other hospital activities. On the other hand, soiling did take place in a specific constellation of circumstances under the pressure of an emotional need which had to be fulfilled. To understand the symptom it is necessary to refer to two sets of factors, the first one being the schizophrenic state of regression. As has already been mentioned, it is characteristic of the psychotic process that the patient, in his fearful withdrawal from normal human relationships, retreats from verbal means of communication to preverbal, somatic devices. The patient, like a small child, will involve some of his basic biological functions as a means of relating emotionally to others. This is described in more detail elsewhere (see Chapters VI and XVI). The other set of factors relates to the unconscious meanings with which the patient has invested these functions. As a result of these symbolic meanings the discharge of a biological function in a given situation makes sense to the patient, even though the observer who is not acquainted with them may find the behavior senseless. For example, one patient was mistreated by another. The victim avenged herself by soiling herself while sitting on the bed of her attacker. Here is an example of excreta used as a weapon to express feelings of hatred. One patient defecated immediately following a particularly kindly gesture by her therapist, in a manner reminiscent of the child who bestows the stool as a "gift" to the anxiously waiting mother. A patient who was fearful of human contact found that people left her alone when she had soiled. We might say that she used excreta like a skunk or a squid as a purely defensive device to keep enemies at a distance. A different patient, on the other hand, who hungered for the ministrations of a cleansing mother figure, soiled herself to compel such attentions from the nurses. Whereas the former patient would be silent after soiling, the latter clamored loudly until someone came to clean her. Where this patient wanted her excreta removed, another patient regarded her excreta as treasured productions which she hid, and the removal of which she resented. A male patient reported that the feeling of warmth and wetness from soiling was comforting to him during the night when he felt very lonely.

In all of these instances, the problem is complicated by the feeling of disgust which this symptom arouses in others. In spite of their best attempts to the contrary, nurses and attendants commonly find themselves angered or overwhelmed with feelings of futility in caring for a soiling patient. A soiling schizophrenic patient once said, "I stink. I disgust everyone!" In this particular instance, the therapist embraced the patient in complete disregard for his own cleanliness and said gently, "You don't disgust me. I like you." The patient, hitherto unapproachable, responded to this with deep emotion. It was the beginning of a highly successful therapeutic relationship with this doctor. Much more often the soiling patient does arouse feelings of disgust, with resultant further loss in self-esteem, which may result in violent outbursts or in feelings of despair and further withdrawal on the part of the patient.

A kindly female attendant once said to a male schizophrenic who kept disrobing himself, "I know you are a man. You can put your clothes on." The patient immediately obeyed her. It happens that this patient was indeed fearfully uncertain about his sexual identification, and his exhibitionistic behavior was an attempt to secure reassurance in this regard. This intuitive remark, made without feelings of shame or reproach, fulfilled precisely the patient's emotional need. Although further details are not known about this, the likelihood is that some immediately preceding blow to the patient's self-esteem precipitated this exhibitionistic episode. A punitive reaction by the attendant which registered disgust would have had the precise opposite effect. The patient's self-esteem lowered further, he would have experienced his exhibitionistic need with even greater intensity. This incident also emphasizes that in working with chronic psychotic patients, as in all psychotherapy, one must begin with the contemporary reality needs of the patient. Only secondarily do we consider the ancient deprivations which traumatized the patient in early childhood.

Practical Aspects of Treating the Chronic Schizophrenic

The reader may argue, "All these formulations may be very nice for those who are psychoanalytically trained or who have the time to individualize their approach to patients, but what practical good is all this on a crowded back ward of a mental hospital?" The fact is that these principles do have general, practical applicability. For example, instead of putting deteriorated patients on the worst wards, many have come to understand that they belong on the best. These, of all patients, have the greatest need for attractive surroundings. Instead of relegating them to the care of the least adequately trained attendants, they require the services of the best, those with most understanding of the schizophrenic process and with the greatest interest in patients.

A recent research study carried out at the Stockton State Hospital in California was designed to show the effects of adequate personnel and intensive treatment on a group of chronic mental patients who had failed to respond to routine treatment and who seemed destined to remain in a mental institution indefinitely. Three general objectives were set for the study:

To show whether adequate staffing and more intensive application of the treatments now commonly used could help recovery in a group of chronic, disintegrated patients, enough to permit some of them to be returned to the community.

To help determine what would be adequate staffing for a mental hospital.

To determine if adequate staffing actually would empty hospital beds.

The legislature of California provided sufficient funds for this study to sustain the research over a period of eighteen months. Additional professional and technical personnel were made available, and a carefully devised plan of intensive therapy was laid out.

Four hundred male patients were selected from the chronic group of patients previously relegated to "back wards." They were divided into two groups of two hundred each—an experimental group and a control group. Each patient in the experimental group was matched as closely as possible with a member of the control group for age, race, diagnosis, length of hospitalization, education, and other characteristics. Patients in the control group remained scattered throughout the chronic wards of the hospital and received the routine attention afforded these patients by the regular staff. The two hundred patients of the experimental group were placed in two special cottages. Each of the four hundred patients was rated regularly on a large number of points indicative of psychiatric condition.

The staff for the two special cottages was increased far above that of the ordinary ward. No types of therapy were employed for the experimental group that were not available in the rest of the institution, but the larger staff made possible increased utilization of available treatments.

Group therapy was given largely by the psychiatric ward aides and nurses, the physician acting primarily as teacher and co-ordinator for the rest of the staff. Aides and nurses met with small groups of patients for periods of reading designed to encourage communication in mute and withdrawn patients.

Electroshock and intensive psychiatric therapy were provided when deemed advisable. The preparation and serving of food received special attention. Medical attention was provided for many minor physical ailments of patients which ordinarily go unattended in crowded mental hospitals. In general, the attempt was to provide a total "milieu of therapeutic optimism."

The results of this project are not yet completely analyzed. The number of patients of the experimental group separated from the hospital, however, was more than two and a half times that in the control group. The number of visits which the experimental patients were able to make to relatives, leaving the hospital temporarily, also was increased about two and a half times. Patients remaining in the hospital were rated by the observers as showing more improvement under the experimental regime than those under regular hospital conditions.

Per patient costs, of course, also increased markedly during the experiment. Per diem costs rose from $2.52 to $5.38, an increase of $1,048 per year per patient. The savings, however, which will accrue from increased discharge of patients from the hospital are yet to be computed —to say nothing of the savings in terms of human values.

There is a tendency in mental hospitals to have male attendants care for male patients and female attendants for the women. And yet experience has shown that women attendants are more effective in taking care of disturbed men. It is quite possible that men assigned to the care of disturbed women might have a similarly beneficial effect upon them. The use of attendants of the opposite sex might help to bring disturbing homosexual impulses more completely under control. It might also intensify more normal socializing impulses by appealing to the relatively intact adult heterosexual part of the self.

A schizophrenic male patient was given a Rorschach test by a male psychologist on one day and by a female psychologist on the other. Even though his clinical picture seemed to be the same before each test, the results with the male psychologist were more grossly psychotic than those obtained by the female psychologist. Although this was not studied systematically, it seemed at the time as if the schizophrenic patient was more threatened by homosexual feelings in the test situation with the male psychologist, and that this was responsible for his greatly disorganized performance at that time. Here, it seems, is an interesting research problem which has practical significance for the care of psychotic patients in mental hospitals.

Patients need space to move around in, preferably with free access to the out-of-doors. A wide selection of activities should be made available with a policy of letting patients make spontaneous choices. The relationship of a given activity to future rehabilitation plans must always be held before the patient. Simple tasks should be presented as stepping stones to more complicated ones, with a realistic work program as the ultimate goal. The therapeutic value of a vocational program in which chronic schizophrenic patients are given the opportunity to contribute to the hospital's welfare in group work details has already been referred to (see R. A. Solow in Chapter V). Too often patients see the separate hospital activities in an unrelated and isolated fashion, and in a sense mirror their own inner feelings of fragmentation, in contrast to an integrating program which the patient needs.

Psychotherapy With Schizophrenics

It would seem from the foregoing that it is not imperative to impart understanding of dynamics to the individual patient. However, this does not mean that attempts to increase the self-understanding of patients should be neglected. The general importance for the hospital of intensive psychotherapy with individual patients has been taken up in Chapter I. There is no substitute for this type of relationship. Principles learned in psychotherapeutic relationships enhance our knowledge of the psychology of schizophrenia, thus enriching every detail of the treatment program of the hospital to the benefit of the individual patient who is treated.

It has long been known that generally competent psychotherapists may fail completely at intensive psychotherapy with individual schizophrenics. In a recent study by J. C. Whitehorn and B. J. Betz this fact was investigated systematically. They studied the work of two groups of resident physicians; members of one group were eminently successful in their psychotherapeutic results with schizophrenics (75 per cent improved on discharge), whereas members of the other group were outstanding in their failure (only 27 per cent improved on discharge). They found that physicians most likely to get good therapeutic results were those who *formulated* their cases with understanding of the personal motivational factors involved in the patient's reactions (see Chapter I, also Appendix A). Another factor which made for a successful psychotherapeutic result was the inclusion of a definite goal in the treatment plan in which the positive assets of the patient were called into action and an attempt was made to modify his personal defects. If a physician aimed simply at removing symptoms or planned vaguely for "better socialization," he was less likely to help his patient. Finally, the successful physician manifested initiative in sympathetic inquiries, expressed honest disagreements at times, sometimes challenged the patient's self-deprecatory attitudes, set realistic limits to what he could accept in the patient's behavior, and avoided becoming involved in a role of passive acceptance of the patient's obsessive-compulsive patterns of control and manipulation. These characteristics seemed to be manifestations in the therapist of self-confidence and self-respect, on the one hand, and sympathetic respect for the potentialities of the patient, on the other. An attitude of passive permissiveness, intellectualized interpretations, and a tendency to be didactic were associated with poor therapeutic results.

Group psychotherapy with schizophrenic patients has been discussed in Chapter II.

The Problem of Countertransference

Reference has frequently been made in these pages to the fact that anxiety suffered by members of the treatment team can interfere with their effectiveness as therapists. The psychiatrist in charge should provide his team with frequent opportunities for group discussion of experiences with patients. Difficulties with individual patients will often be found to result from personal emotional involvements on the part of the therapist. This phenomenon has been discussed in previous Chapters (I, II, V, etc.) as countertransference. With increased self-understanding, secured primarily in guided discussions in group seminars, countertransference can be diminished as an interfering factor in the treatment program.

Schizophrenic patients are particularly sensitive to conflicts between members of the treatment team. The relationship of pathological excited states to hidden staff disagreements has already been referred to in Chapter X. The inner conflict and confusion of the schizophrenic are intensified by evidences of conflict and confusion in the environment. Therefore, an important part of the psychotherapy of schizophrenia centers about the resolution of staff conflicts and the creation of an atmosphere of harmony and unity in the hospital environment.

Somatotherapy

Lobotomy and other forms of somatotherapy have been employed in treating chronic schizophrenic patients. Although the results have not been spectacular, controlled studies seem to prove that lobotomized chronic schizophrenics show symptomatic improvement with a frequency which is reliably greater than that of controls. Lobotomy and all other somatotherapeutic approaches must be integrated into the total treatment program. The importance of the social service department in achieving this integration is taken up in Chapter VIII.

The Results of Treating Chronic Schizophrenic Patients

Those who have approached a "chronic" ward in the manner outlined in this chapter, have experienced gratifying results, by and large, in the form of fewer violent outbursts, reduced wetting and soiling, and a de-

creased need for sedative medication. These are treatment results which
are important in their own right. They reflect a diminution in the
amount of human suffering if nothing else. However, this is not the
only level at which improvement occurs. In some instances, patients who
have been continuously hospitalized for years or even decades have been
reclaimed by such measures and have become self-supporting members of
the community.

It is striking how often families object to the rehabilitation of chronic
schizophrenic patients. Having adjusted over a period of years to the
absence of the schizophrenic member of the family, they may become
panic-stricken at the thought of his return. They may express a lack of
interest in the hospital's efforts and be unco-operative as far as making
plans for the patient's discharge. They may actively fight plans to discharge the patient from the hospital, even recruiting lawyers and con-
gressmen to help them. This resistance must be overcome. The patient,
too, in spite of mechanically expressed desires to leave the hospital, may
actually fear to do so when the opportunity is granted. For this reason,
"chronic" patients who improve enough to leave the hospital should be
prepared for their departure months in advance, with trial visits of increasing length, and in group therapy with similar patients. In addition,
the inertia of the staff should be mentioned. They accept the idea of
incurability as the line of least resistance, particularly where families and
patients object to rehabilitation. If the patient happens to be a good
worker in some vital department of the hospital, then the plan to discharge him meets with even further resistance, in the reluctance to part
with his services. In all these instances, the psychiatrist in charge of rehabilitating chronic patients should be guided by what is best for the
patient, not by any other considerations. Stringham commented that
when you read a note on a chart that a patient is "well institutionalized,
well behaved, good worker," he is probably a good candidate for a
"chronic" rehabilitation program.

Patients who have not responded to the hospital's acute treatment
program after six months to a year, are usually transferred to a building
which is called euphemistically the "Continued Treatment Building."
Continued treatment, so-called, is characterized typically by the absence
of a treatment program. Patients are interviewed less and less frequently,
the psychiatrist's notes get more and more perfunctory and routine. This
may continue for decades until senility sets in and introduces a few
changes in the clinical picture. There is a need for a genuine re-examination of each case at periodic intervals, with a social service report
and presentation at staff conferences. An active social service depart-

ment is crucial to the success of the chronic rehabilitation program. An attempt should be made to reformulate the case repeatedly in terms of changing realities and suitability for a rehabilitation program. The death of a parent or a spouse who has exerted an emotionally destructive influence on the patient may on occasion result in unexpected improvements. Foster home placement, vocational rehabilitation, sheltered residences, and other devices discussed in Chapter VIII may be called into play by the social service department in order to improve the effectiveness of the chronic rehabilitation program. With a liberal policy for returning patients to the hospital for physical or emotional complications, it has been estimated that approximately 60 per cent of chronic patients who have been improved enough to go out on trial visit will successfully re-establish themselves in the community.

Chronic Patients and Research

N. S. Kline and his associates at the Research Facility of the Rockland State Hospital in New York have taken up in detail the difficulties involved in proper case selection for research in schizophrenia. They point out the particular usefulness of the chronic schizophrenic population as a reservoir for cases for experimental study. After the first three years of hospitalization, the probability of discharge reaches a stable level of 10 per cent. Therefore, it is from patients hospitalized for at least three years that subjects may be selected with the expectation that the research group of patients will remain reasonably unchanged over the fairly extended period of time that a careful experimental study usually takes. Such patients, if they have not been out of the hospital, except possibly for brief visits, present a homogeneity of recent environment which is also desirable from an experimental point of view. Kline and his associates add certain other criteria for the selection of their particular group of experimental patients. For example, they have chosen an upper age limit of thirty-five years and a lower age limit of sixteen for admission to the hospital. Also, they decided for certain theoretical and practical reasons to work only with male patients. Thus, chronic patients are deserving of new interest on the part of psychiatrists because of what may be learned from them concerning the unsolved problems of psychiatry.

SELECTED REFERENCES

BICKFORD, J. A. B.: Treatment of the Chronic Mental Patient. *Lancet,* 266:924, 1954.
  A very useful description of the organization of an activities program for chronic patients.

KLINE, N. S.; TENNEY, A. M.; NICOLSON, G. T.; MALZBERG, B.: The Selection of Psychiatric Patients for Research. *Am. J. Psychiat.,* 110:179, 1953.
  A discussion of the place of the "chronic" patient in the research program of the hospital.

MILLER, D. H.; CLANCY, J.: An Approach to the Social Rehabilitation of Chronic Psychotic Patients. *Psychiatry,* 15:435, 1952.
  An analysis of deterioration as an artefact of ward "culture," with suggestions for overcoming this regressive milieu.

MURPHY, B. W.: Some Interpersonal Processes and Situations Delaying Discharge from a Psychiatric Institute. *Dis. Nerv. Syst.,* 12:273, 1951.
  An analysis of factors making for unnecessary prolongation of hospitalization.

SOLOW, R. A.: Group Work with Chronic Mental Patients. *J. Clin. & Exp. Psychopathol.,* 13:31, 1952.
  The therapeutic value of work, particularly when on-the-job social group formation is encouraged.

STAINBROOK, E. J.: The Schizophrenic, Manic and Depressive Behavioral Reactions. *Ann. Am. Acad. Pol. & Soc. Sci.,* 286:45, 1953.
  "Deterioration" as a specific cultural effect of mental hospital life.

STANTON, A. H.; SCHWARTZ, M. S.: *The Mental Hospital. A Study of Institutional Participation in Psychiatric Illness and Treatment.* New York: Basic Books, 1954.
  A study of this work is indispensable to the proper planning of a "chronic" rehabilitation program.

STRINGHAM, J. A.: Rehabilitating Chronic Psychiatric Patients. *Am. J. Psychiat.,* 108:924, 1952.
  An important contribution, analyzing factors which interfere with proper execution of a "chronic" rehabilitation program.

Training and Research in State Mental Health Programs. A Report to the Governors' Conference. Council of State Governments, 1313 East 60 Street, Chicago 37, Ill.
  Contains a detailed description of the "Stockton" study of the rehabilitation of chronic schizophrenic patients.

Veterans Administration Information Bulletin. Dept. of Medicine and Surgery, Psychiatry and Neurology Service, Feb., 1954. Available through the Office of the Chief Medical Director, Veterans Administration, Washington 25, D.C.
  Contains a report of a seminar for psychiatrists held at the V.A. Hospital in Downey, Illinois, on June 24, 25, 26, 1953, devoted primarily to the problem of rehabilitating the "chronic" mental hospital patient.

WHITEHORN, J. C.; BETZ, B. J.: A Study of Psychotherapeutic Relationships between Physicians and Schizophrenic Patients. *Am. J. Psychiat.,* 111:321, 1954.
  An instructive guide for establishing effective psychotherapeutic relationships with schizophrenic patients.

Chapter XV

THE AGED AND THE AGING

Statistics

In 1947, the number of people in New York State over the age of sixty-five was double the figure in 1920. However, the New York State mental hospital population for that age group quadrupled during the same interval. Furthermore, the number of first admissions in 1947 of patients over sixty-five *more* than quadrupled the figure for 1920. Percentagewise, 31.5 per cent of all first admissions in 1947 consisted of patients over sixty-five as contrasted to only 14 per cent in 1920. First admissions over forty-five years of age in 1947 consisted of almost 60 per cent of the total as contrasted to about 40 per cent in 1920. This trend in New York State has continued at an even higher rate since 1947 and holds true for all of America. These figures state quantitatively what every mental hospital psychiatrist already knows, namely, that the older age group is pre-empting more and more hospital beds. This is a statistic of major importance in planning the national mental hospital treatment program in all its details, the type of personnel required, the forms of therapy, the goals of therapy, the very form and arrangement of the buildings which are erected. It also indicates a problem in which the needs so far outstrip the available facilities that a new point of view and new solutions are urgently required.

The Reasons for the Problem

An obvious reason for this staggering increase in the aged population of our mental hospitals is to be found in the increasing average age of our population at large. Many more people are surviving to the age of sixty-five. Percentagewise and in absolute numbers, this figure is mounting at an increasing rate. So, in part, the mental hospital figures reflect those of the general population, not only in terms of new admissions but in the survival rates of chronically psychotic patients. Thus, in 1948, New York State had 307 patients who had been continuously hospitalized for over fifty years! Elderly patients who once quickly succumbed to injury and minor infection are now easily rescued from death.

However, as the figures in the foregoing paragraph bring out, the rate at which the older population in the state hospital has grown outstrips by far that which exists in the community. One reason for this is an undoubted rise in the actual incidence of mental illness in the older age group. Formerly old age was a time of surcease from the trials of life. It was in the words of Walt Whitman, "The teeming, quietest happiest days of all, the brooding and blissful halcyon days." No such poetic imagery applies to old age in our time. While science has added extra years to the life of the average man, it has not provided the means for the enjoyment of those years. Compulsory retirement at the age of sixty-five or earlier condemns many men to social and psychological oblivion. Many emotional needs are fulfilled by work (see Chapter V). Indeed, many men link their entire existence to their work. If they are devoid of outside interests, such as hobbies, avocations, family life, a love of continued intellectual growth, then they are divested of everything that makes life worth living when they are no longer employed. Between the ages of sixty-five and sixty-nine, 40 per cent of our male population is no longer gainfully employed. Between the ages of seventy and seventy-four, this figure rises to 60 per cent. After the age of seventy-five, 80 per cent of the male population is unemployed. In this older segment of our population are many thousands of men who are physically and mentally well preserved but who are nevertheless doomed to demoralizing idleness.

Whereas 90 per cent of men under the age of sixty-five are employed outside of agriculture, over the age of sixty-five only 75 per cent are so employed. That is to say, those who work in agriculture are able to stay on the job later than those who do not. Thus, as our population has become increasingly urban, opportunities for work in later years have declined sharply. Therefore, if work is a source of emotional stability, as indeed it is, socio-economic changes have undermined an important bulwark in the mental health of our older population.

The problem of adjustment in later years is much more difficult in many ways for the man than it is for the woman. The woman is able to continue pretty much at her old chores, shopping, cooking, cleaning and baby sitting for her grandchildren. The indignity of "just hanging around the house" as a superfluous member of the family is less frequently the woman's lot. However, the woman's capacity to adapt is often seriously taxed by the presence of the demoralized husband. It is striking, too, how many couples are able to accept each other only as long as the man is away for a good part of the twenty-four hours. When the man is no longer employed, and they are compelled as a result to spend longer time in each other's company, they may have to face, for the first time late in life, serious incompatibilities in their relationship.

In addition, there have been fundamental sociologic changes which have been traumatic to older people. Our urban population is apt to live in small apartments. Old people who cannot afford their own quarters are often compelled to live with their children. The frictions that seem inevitable when two different generations live in the same house are intensified by the overcrowding and lack of privacy which characterize life in the multiple dwellings of our cities. If, in such an environment, an older person develops the feeling that he is disliked or unwanted, there is often a substantial kernel of truth to this feeling, about which a paranoid delusional system can more readily crystallize.

These psychological traumata are part of our times and contribute to the real increase in the mental illnesses of late life. Altered family life, however, has contributed to the increased state hospital admission rate in still another way. More hospitals are available. The stigma attached to mental illness has decreased. Children have come to feel less deeply responsible for the welfare of aging parents. Because of these factors, elderly patients are often hospitalized today for mental changes that would never have resulted in hospitalization thirty-five years ago. For example, transitory confusion, irritability and a relatively mild memory impairment are often all that is found on mental examination of elderly patients committed to mental hospitals. There are thus essentially sociologic reasons for the increased population of elderly patients in mental hospitals as well as the previously enumerated psychologic ones. The sociologic aspects of the problem must be solved by sociologic techniques. That is to say, the psychiatrist can define them and call attention to them, but other groups will have to assume the responsibility for solving them. This matter will be considered later, in the discussion of treatment.

The Psychopathology of the "Senile" Disorders

During the nineteenth century, it was commonly held that the secret of each disease was to be uncovered in characteristic cellular abnormalities in the body. This approach which, for a time at least, was so fruitful in the elucidation of many diseases was singularly unproductive when applied to the main problems which concerned the psychiatrist. For most mental diseases, no characteristic cell changes could be found. A rare exception was general paresis. One could apply all the mechanical criteria of that era to this disease. Characteristic cellular changes could be demonstrated. The organic etiologic agent responsible for these changes could be defined; and with appropriate chemical and physical interventions, one could achieve a certain degree of restitution of cellular structure to normal, and the degree to which this could be accomplished measured the degree to which the patient could be cured. Nowadays, we know that this is a gross oversimplification of the problem. It omits, for example, reference to the basic personality of the patient as a factor determining the total clinical picture. It distorts and misinterprets others. For example, symptoms were understood simply as the product of altered cell function rather than as an attempt by the whole organism to adapt to emotional stress. However, rather than discuss general paresis in further detail, we will pass on to a consideration of the mental disturbances of old age which like paresis seemed to fit in with the cell pathology theory of disease, and which is more directly our concern in this chapter. Degenerative changes in brain cells characteristic of old age can be demonstrated, and they seemed to account for these psychiatric abnormalities. When at times, as in Alzheimer's or Pick's Disease, these changes appeared prematurely, then mental changes characteristic of senility appeared prematurely. These changes seemed to be the final, irrevocable evidences of the approaching end of life. And the patients, it seemed, were at the end of their road and there was nothing further to do except to tend them mercifully until their death.

Many things were wrong with this picture. Perhaps of greatest importance was the fact that the extent of organic degenerative change rarely paralleled the extent of the psychiatric disturbance. One found, for example, marked clinical deterioration with relatively minor organic change; and, conversely, advanced organic changes were not at all incompatible with a clinically well-preserved intellect. Furthermore, confusional reactions in the aged were found to be transitory and reversible, and seemed, quite often, to occur as a response to anxiety, a fact which could not be explained purely on the basis of irreversible cellular alteration. And finally, it was found possible to treat these people, to reverse many of the so-called senile symptoms and to restore them to the community in a much improved condition. All of these facts argued against the static and mechanical notion that the degenerative changes in the brain represented a pathognomonic and sufficient cause for the psychological abnormalities of old age observed by the psychiatrist.

The senile brain is different in its structure from the younger brain, and it functions differently, but the clinical psychological differences between the old and the young are to be understood only by taking into account all of the forces involved. This in turn can perhaps be rendered most simply by the use of a figure of speech. The senile brain functions like the youthful brain, only it does so in slow motion. For example, an older person can learn new material as well as can a younger one, only it will usually take him more time. Or, we have all had the experience of forgetting a name, or where we placed an object, or forgetting to do some minor chore of the day. Freud pointed out long ago that these little psychological "accidents" are not haphazard but occur rather in response to specific wishes or needs. The same is true of these occurrences in old age, only they are apt to occur more frequently and are less speedily corrected. We have all had the experience of seeing a stranger who looks familiar. Less common, possibly, but well within the limits of normal are similar instances involving the seeming familiarity of unfamiliar places (déjà vu). Such experiences are more apt to occur during periods of emotional stress, and it can often be demonstrated psychoanalytically that the error is in a direction which diminishes anxiety. Whereas the younger person readily brings this mistaken first look into congruence with reality, older people do this more slowly, and the result is a more or less sustained misidentification or disorientation. When older patients are tested psychologically, they may function at a high level during the earlier stages of the examination. However, they are soon fatigued or frustrated by the first difficult question, or hypersensitive about the implied question concerning their mental capacity. These are factors which operate in psychological testing at every age level, but in the older age group they are more apt to result in a sustained generalized inhibition of mental functioning which shows up conspicuously in the final score.

As the distinguished geriatrist, Stieglitz, once put it, the spots of the leopard do not change, they are only intensified. By and large, the behavior of old people is simply an exaggeration of lifelong patterns. The so-called second childhood of senility is characteristic primarily of those who never got over their first. The initial self-centered reactions of a lifetime are less readily corrected in response to a consideration for social convention and the demands of reality. Mild self-righteousness is easily caricatured into intolerable bigotry, parsimony into miserliness, generosity into an ill-considered dispersal of one's means. Fleeting doubts concerning a mate's fidelity may harden into grim delusion. It is all there in youth, but age congeals the process to a point where we can see the mental mechanisms in slow motion. The electroencephalogram often

shows a slowing of the rhythmic electrocortical activity which parallels
the foregoing psychological deceleration, and which may reflect an underlying neurophysiological mechanism which aids and abets it. A passive,
emotionally immature individual, who was inclined all his life to act
impulsively on first impression rather than on a more considered judgment, will naturally display these changes more readily with advancing
age. The emotionally mature individual may arrive at his final conclusion more slowly, more self-consciously and perhaps more painfully, but
given the opportunity, he is likely to turn up with the right answer in
spite of advanced age. In fact, such men often have so vast a life experience to draw upon that the resultant answer is apt to contain wisdom
which the more speedily arrived at conclusion of the younger person does
not have. Here is to be found the specific contribution of our savants and
elder statesmen.

In addition to these basic psychological factors, however, the underlying neurophysiological alterations also play a role which varies in its
quantitative importance from person to person. However, it does not
always play the fatalistically determining role that was commonly
believed heretofore.

Prevention

It is perhaps more urgent in a chapter on the aged and the aging
to begin a discussion of treatment with prophylactic considerations.
Treatment should begin with community education, and the mental
hospital psychiatrist must take leadership in that program. The public
must learn that a rational program to meet the emotional needs of older
people is a necessity. Automatic retirement based on chronological age
should be discouraged. Sheltered work situations must be devised in which
older people can continue to make socially useful contributions as long
as they are able. Special housing must be provided for the aged, low-
cost apartments which are small, simple to manage, and which have
access to suitable areas for rest and recreation. An encouraging trend, for
example, is the fact that 5 per cent of all units in New York State-aided
housing projects are now earmarked for the sole use of older persons.
There is a need for new housing facilities at a greater rate than this,
however. There is also a great need for "foster home" accommodations,
preferably with kitchen facilities, where sympathetic householders will
take older people into their homes and give at least minimal attention
to these forgotten and lonely people. More "homes for the aged" are
required in the community. Social security and old age assistance benefits

must be sufficient to meet the needs of old people without making them dependent upon the support of the younger generation. Some attempt should be made to provide them with spending money in addition to funds for the necessities of life. Community centers should be constructed either independently or as part of such housing projects, where old folks may congregate for companionship on any level which they may desire or need. The William Hodson Community Center in Old Burrow Hall, Bronx, New York, is an excellent example of this. Social workers trained in the problems of the aged should be available in such centers to provide guidance with respect to their health and their socioeconomic needs. Several homes for the aged are now setting up day center programs (see discussion of the "day hospital" in Chapter XXXV), consisting of educational, recreational and occupational activities to which old people in the community are invited. Thus, such programs benefit not only their own inmates but have significance for the welfare of the entire community. Churches are becoming active in setting up day centers for older people. Public libraries are setting aside special reading rooms for them. Through such centers, old people are being involved in civil defense activities, and in volunteer programs to provide simple, friendly services for other elderly people who are patients in hospitals for chronic disease. Psychological studies of patients in such programs give objective evidence of improved emotional balance. In addition, many patients so involved stop going to hospital clinics for various minor aches and pains, places which had constituted, unwittingly, an unwholesome kind of day center for many of them in the past. Nursing homes should be provided for the physically infirm, preferably with provision for keeping elderly couples together, with a suitable recreational and occupational program. Such infirmaries should be located in the environs of a general hospital where emergency medical and surgical care is readily available.

Such a program of prevention may sound complicated and expensive. It is simpler and cheaper by far than the current disorganized situation which is deluging our mental hospitals with old people.

Treatment: General Considerations

The fundamental principles of treatment in this age group do not differ from those which apply to younger patients. The psychiatrist collects his data from the usual sources—social service, psychological and clinical examination of the patient, and based upon this information he formulates a working hypothesis concerning the patient's illness. We are more apt to direct our effort toward environmental manipulation and reassurance rather than attempting fundamental revisions in the basic patterns of thought and behavior with which the patient deals with reality. However, a diminution in the emotional stress under which the patient is laboring remains the fundamental task.

A Geriatric Unit

Architecture. Elderly patients have such highly specialized physical needs that a special unit for housing them is clearly a necessity. These patients cannot climb stairs. Therefore, the geriatric unit should consist of one-story buildings with gently sloping ramps to the out of doors or higher buildings equipped with adequate elevator service. It has been observed that the more independence senile patients are given, the better preserved do they remain in their personal habits. Therefore, constructions should provide free access to sheltered outdoor areas with adjoining rooms for rest, music, television, radio, and other simple diversions. Patients should be admitted directly to such units and not changed from one section to another unless this is unavoidable, since each new environment poses a whole new series of problems of adaptation, each of which generates anxiety and results in regressive confusional states and habit deterioration. Plenty of fresh air and sunlight by day as well as illumination throughout the night tend to diminish confusional reactions. A fall, a broken bone, physical invalidism and mental deterioration progressing until death represent a common sequence in the mental hospital. Therefore, thoughtful provision must be made to prevent this series by preventing the fall which starts it. Floors should never be slippery, inclines never steep, handrails should be available in corridors and lavatories. Most of all, construction should be compact so that all the patients' needs can be provided for in a relatively small area. This should include ready access to X-ray as well as medical and surgical treatment facilities.

Personnel. The staff for the geriatric unit must be recruited from people who enjoy working with elderly patients. Nurses, attendants, and the various departmental therapists must be instructed concerning the emotional problems of the aged and their efforts geared in a continuous and meaningful way to their patients' actual needs. Mature people with a capacity for providing genuine motherly support are particularly valuable, yet pampering which fosters regression must be avoided. It has been estimated that one psychiatrist should be available for every hundred patients, one graduate nurse for every twenty, and one attendant for every twelve. One occupational therapist with ingenuity and training to meet the needs of these enfeebled people should be available for every hundred patients. Although these figures are rarely met in actual practice, a spirit of optimism should prevail because these patients can be helped with improvisations carried out by a properly motivated smaller staff.

Physical Methods of Treatment

Electroconvulsive Therapy (ECT). Senile patients with depression respond to ECT as well as do younger patients with this symptom. Patients in their ninth decade have been successfully treated. Complications are probably no higher in this group. Contrary to common expectation, old people suffer fewer fractures as a complication of ECT, although fractures which do occur are apt to be more serious in their long-term consequences. Curare which is employed to prevent fractures is particularly hazardous in older patients in whom some myocardial damage is the rule. An ambulatory patient with heart disease who is in danger of exhausting himself as a consequence of an agitated depression is more safely treated without curare. Severe hypochondriacal reactions, although less responsive to ECT in general, will respond favorably at times, particularly if depression is a dominant clinical feature. Senile patients who can be spared the major emotional dislocation of hospitalization are better treated under carefully supervised outpatient conditions. If the patient is suicidal and adequate protection is not available at home, naturally he will have to be hospitalized. ECT is usually given to older patients at more widely spaced intervals and in shorter series than in younger patients because of their greater readiness to develop long-lasting confusional states.

Medical Procedures. Any generalized metabolic abnormality can give rise to acute psychiatric disturbance in these patients. Therefore, careful supervision by an internist is of paramount importance. Many a senile psychotic reaction has been brought to an end when a failing heart was digitalized, or a pneumonic process properly treated with antibiotics. At seventy, the calcium requirement of the body is three times as great as it is between twenty and fifty years of age. There is also a great need for supplementary iron and vitamin B-12. An inadequate fluid intake is one of the most common errors in the dietary management of senile patients. All organic factors loom more important in the clinical psychiatric picture of aged patients than in the younger group.

Sedation in general is poorly tolerated by elderly patients. With continued use of most sedative drugs, delirium is almost unavoidable. If patients are kept up and about and diverted by day, they are less likely to wander during the night. Milk, a warm bath and reassuring words are usually all that is necessary to get these patients to resume their rest. Restraints are no less harmful than drugs in generating anxiety with resultant psychopathological regression. Nevertheless, bed sideboards may be used at night. Continued disturbed behavior in senile patients should always suggest careful medical study for possible toxic factors.

On the theory that confusional reactions are the result of impaired cerebral metabolism, various pharmacologic agents affecting metabolism have been tried. For example, cytochrome C was tried for a time but without success. Recently, S. Levy of Spokane, Washington, reported favorably on the oral use of metrazol (pentylenetetrazol) in combination with nicotinic acid. (To prepare a single dose dissolve 200 mg. of metrazol and 100 mg. of nicotinic acid in 4 cc. of compound pepsin elixir. This dose is repeated three times a day). In apparently well-controlled experiments, he demonstrated the usefulness of the mixture in bringing about improvements in subjective feelings, appearance and personal habits, general activities, sociability, attention and memory span, speech, work, eating and sleeping habits. He found it most useful in patients whose disturbance was mild. He felt that the drug can produce just enough improvement in some cases to tip the scales in favor of continued adjustment in the community, thereby postponing the necessity for hospitalization. Continued research along these lines is certainly indicated.

Chlorpromazine hydrochloride (thorazine) has been employed with considerable success to control acute agitated reactions in elderly patients. By means of this drug it has been possible to manage many disturbed patients, who would otherwise have required admission to a mental hospital, in their own homes with members of the family in attendance, in convalescent homes or in general hospitals. If the patient will not cooperate initially for oral medication, the drug may be administered parenterally. In elderly patients, particularly when hypertension is present, the first dose should be given while the patient is in bed and the blood pressure should be measured at frequent intervals for at least an hour. The effects of a sudden drop in blood pressure, which occurs occasionally, can be controlled by placing the patient in a recumbent position with legs elevated. Dosages have not been standardized but several hundred milligrams a day have been tolerated by many patients without harmful effect. Allergic skin reactions and jaundice due to liver damage are the main complications from the use of this drug. Fortunately, they occur infrequently and are readily controlled on withdrawal of the drug.

Psychotherapy

Psychotherapy with senile patients is feasible and practically useful. Working with individuals and with groups, it is possible to undo many of the regressive manifestations of the senium. Much of the elderly patient's struggle centers about the question of personal independence. To a large extent, all old people cannot accept the altered status that comes with retirement. The surrendering of authority, the loss of prestige, the economic uncertainties, the outright need in most instances of accepting some help, all clash with the independent conception of self which obtained up to that time. Much of the irritability of old people is an expression of their wish to display more strength and self-sufficiency than they actually possess. For this reason, every opportunity to demonstrate to a patient that he is not dominated should be exploited. Restrictions upon the patient's freedom of action should be imposed only when necessary. For example, if a patient requests a certain drug or asks to discontinue a certain treatment, a genuine effort should be made to accede to his request, when doing so will not harm him. Irritable rages against the therapist should be permitted. Whenever possible, evidences of respect for the older patient should be expressed. These are esteem-building maneuvers which represent the first step in a therapeutically meaningful relationship.

Of the various functions, physical and psychological, which go into decline in old age, none is more serious than the decline in motivation. The patient who is depressed, hostile and irascible is still fighting to keep his self-respect. When he decides that the battle is not worth the effort, then deterioration sets in. This is a psychological fact of no less importance than the neuropathological changes of the senium. The forgetful patient is often one who no longer cares to remember. If contemporary reality is particularly painful, ignoring it becomes a psychological act of self-preservation. This is usually what is behind the glibly recited formula that in senile patients memory for recent events is particularly impaired. If he chooses to occupy himself with less painful recollections from long ago, this is because it serves an emotionally adaptive function. Thus, deterioration in senile patients and in chronic schizophrenic patients have more in common than is ordinarily realized. Both represent attempts at adaptation to the particularly painful realities of the hospital ward. Both can be reversed to some extent with proper environmental changes.

The most fruitful psychotherapeutic approach with the aged has been in work with groups. Initially, an attempt is made to involve the patients as a group in simple tasks which show clear-cut results and which are obviously useful to the community, for example, cleaning windows or polishing eating utensils. The patient's abilities are explored for possible application in sheltered workshops outside of the hospital. Special training may be given in occupational therapy. As in the treatment of other psychotic patients, the therapist should keep in mind the fact that there always persists a core or a remnant of a previously intact ego, capable of rational thought and reality testing. It is to this that the therapist addresses himself, and it is this that he endeavors to mobilize and strengthen in purposefully directed group activities. Senile patients are capable of all the complexity of human relationship that younger patients are. Sexual interests are common in spite of lessened potency. Opportunities for mingling of the sexes in recreational areas should be provided. As with other patients, the effect of this is almost invariably beneficial, each sex tending to mobilize more adult controls in the other. Warm relationships can develop which contribute significantly to the development of restitutive motivations.

A particularly impressive report was that published by Linden of Norristown, Pennsylvania. He selected fifty-one chronologically senile women patients whom he thought he could help. For six months he worked with these women alone. Then he conducted his sessions in conjunction with a female group leader, a ward nurse who had been instructed in the principles and practice of group therapy. Linden found that the use of an auxiliary group therapist in the form of a female group leader greatly augmented the therapeutic efficacy of the group sessions. It was found that patients tended to ascribe softer, more protective and motherly qualities to the nurse and more disciplined reality functions to the male doctor. They would communicate material to the nurse that they would not tell the doctor, and vice versa. In this more complex interplay therapeutic effects were achieved which were not obtainable by either group leader alone.

Extramural Care

The same community facilities which would spare many patients the need to enter a mental hospital in the first place would facilitate the discharge of many others, for example, nursing homes for the physically infirm, low-cost housing projects, sheltered homes for the aged in the community, old age guidance centers, and sheltered workshops. In addition, foster home placement (family care, see Chapter XXXVI) provides a growing treatment facility which in time will contribute significantly to the discharge rate of senile patients. The hospital should maintain an outpatient clinic to which borderline problems can be referred by social workers from old age guidance centers. Useful pychotherapy on a purely supportive level (see Chapter I) can be done with older patients in an outpatient setting. A brief but friendly chat in which the patient is reassured of the doctor's continued interest, and from which he comes away with a present in the form of vitamins, a tonic or some other mild medication, can suffice to carry an anxious patient in the community for an indefinite period of time. The usefulness of ambulatory electroshock therapy in certain selected cases with adequate supervision in the home has already been indicated. If cases are seen in the outpatient clinic before being admitted to the hospital, the psychiatrist can eliminate unnecessary admissions to the senile wards.

Research

No discussion of this vast social problem would be complete without some reference to the need for research. The conception of the mental disorders of the senium as being preventable and curable is new. The mechanically pessimistic and fatalistic approaches of the past are being questioned. The problem must be re-explored at every level. The middle-aged should be studied for the purpose of identifying future candidates for mental illness and a preventive educational and group therapy program for them should be devised.

The various community facilities for the aged should be explored by sociologic and psychologic investigative techniques to see how effective they are and how their results can be improved. Realistic retirement plans should be investigated throughout business and industry, as well as the development of sheltered workshops for the aged. The psychology of old age must be studied continually by all means at our disposal, as well as the general physiology and neurophysiology of this group. Pharmacologic agents must be sought which may reverse some of the effects of the organic aging process. Group therapy with the aged is an almost unexplored field. In short, anyone who works with the aged should approach his task with some sense of its urgency and a considerable awareness that many facts remain to be discovered.

SELECTED REFERENCES

ARTHUR, J. K.: *How to Help Older Folk. A Guide for You and Your Family.* Philadelphia: J. B. Lippincott, 1954.

The material is presented in easily readable style. The case discussions and illustrations are well selected and make their points with conviction. The problems of financing old age homes for the well, and community care for the sick, ways and means of organizing clubs for recreational pursuits, are all well presented. There are several highly practical sections concerning mental illness. The appendices are unusually rich and furnish valuable information bearing on special problems of older persons.

CAMERON, D. E.: Day Hospital: One Approach to Expanding Hospital Facilities. In: *Proceedings of the Second Mental Hospital Institute of the APA Mental Hospital Service,* Oct., 1950.

This description of the "Day Hospital" is referred to here because it provides an excellent model for day centers for older patients.

GINZBERG, R.: Geriatric Ward Psychiatry. *Am. J. Psychiat.,* 110:296, 1953.

Contains theoretical considerations concerning psychotherapy of hospitalized elderly patients and describes the organization of a geriatric psychiatric ward service.

GROUP FOR THE ADVANCEMENT OF PSYCHIATRY: *The Problem of the Aged Patient in the Public Psychiatric Hospital.* Report No. 14, 1950.

Presents a brief survey of the problem with recommendations for future developments.

HILLIARD, R. M.: *Report of the Mayor's Advisory Committee for the Aged.* New York City, 1953.

A report compiled by experts based on considerable personal experience. Covers a wide range of geriatric topics, is rich in factual data concerning current facilities for the aged in New York City. Recommendations for future work are presented.

KUBIE, S. H.; LANDAU, G.: *Group Work with the Aged.* New York: International Universities Press, 1953.

A highly instructive and moving account of the history and activities program of the William Hodson Community Center, New York City. Innumerable program suggestions; rich illustrative material.

LAWTON, G.; STEWART, M. S.: *When You Grow Older.* Public Affairs Pamphlet No. 131, New York City.

The material in this pamphlet is drawn in large part from *Aging Successfully,* by George Lawton (New York: Columbia University Press, 1946). Covers a wide range of topics briefly, clearly and authoritatively. Contains an excellent list of references for those caring for older patients.

LEVY, S.: Pharmacologic Treatment of Aged Patients in a State Mental Hospital. *J. A. M. A.,* 153:1260, 1953.

Describes technique and results of the metrazol-nicotinic acid treatment of psychiatric disturbances of the senium.

LINDEN, M. E.: The Significance of Dual Leadership in Gerontologic Group Psychotherapy: Studies in Gerontologic Human Relations, III. *Int. J. Group Psychother.,* 4-262, 1954.

Describes a group psychotherapy program on a senile ward, utilizing dual (nurse-doctor) group leader technique.

MACLEAN, R. R.: A Special Center for Patients Over Seventy. In: *On The Positive Side.* American Psychiatric Association Mental Hospital Service, 1624 Eye St., N.W., Washington 6, D.C.

A facility for the separate care of patients seventy years or over is described. This report won the 1950 award of the APA Mental Hospital Service.

METROPOLITAN LIFE INSURANCE COMPANY: *Statistical Bulletin.* New York: 35:(No.)2, 1954.
   A study of the occupational record of people past sixty-five years of age.
NACE, F. D.: The Care of the Aged in a State Mental Hospital. *Am. J. Nursing,* 51:366, 1951.
   An extremely practical outline of nursing procedures for aged patients in mental hospitals from admission on. Highly recommended.
POTTER, H. W.; FREIMAN, G. V.: The Effect of Life Problems and Cerebral Pathology on the Mental Health of Aging Persons. *N. Y. State J. Med.,* 54:2826, 1954.
   A clear presentation of the role of psychological factors in the mental disorders of the senium.
STIEGLITZ, E. J.: The Aging Process. In: *Proceedings of the Third Mental Hospital Institute of the APA Mental Hospital Service, 1951.*
   Presented as an address on October 17, 1951. A highly recommended summary of basic geriatric principles as they apply to psychiatry.
ZEMAN, F. D.: Constructive Programs for the Mental Health of the Elderly. *Ment. Hyg.,* 35:221, 1951. Distributed as a pamphlet by the National Association for Mental Health, 1790 Broadway, New York 19, N. Y., 1952.
   Well written and factual, by a distinguished geriatric physician. Of value to laity and professional personnel alike.

Chapter XVI

CHILDREN AND ADOLESCENTS

Introduction

During the past fifty years, psychiatrists have systematically studied the emotional development of human beings. Under the theoretical and practical leadership of Meyer and Freud, they came to understand that the characteristic adult reactions to emotional stress are the outgrowth of thoughts and behavior patterns inculcated in childhood. The psychological life of the individual was seen to be a continuously adaptive one from its earliest beginnings, compounded of inner drives or wishes that strive for fulfillment, on the one hand, and various factors which interfere with these wish fulfillments, on the other. At first these data were arrived at from recollections or from reconstructions based on recollections of adult patients in analysis. In the well-known case of "Little Hans," Freud was able to collect data directly from observations on a phobic child which confirmed many of these reconstructions. Furthermore, he was able to demonstrate the usefulness of this knowledge in the successful treatment of the child for its incapacitating phobia. The psychoanalytic approach has had widespread application, with modifications to be sure, in the treatment of young patients in clinics and hospitals everywhere. Clinical experience has confirmed many of the psychoanalytic deductions, and added new details to the picture. In addition, direct study of the emotional development of the normal child has been considerably intensified in recent years. The following description is based upon data from these various sources.

The Emotional Development of the Child

In the beginning, the wishes of the child are simple ones, based on fundamental biological needs, the need for food, sleep, warmth and general physical comfort, the need to empty the bowels and the bladder.

However, more than simply the physical aspects of these needs must be provided for; the child needs tender, loving care as well. Without it, it may sicken physically as well as emotionally, and it may even die for lack of it. So complete is the child's dependence on the mother during the first few years of life that in a fundamental psychobiological sense mother and child constitute a single unit as real as that which obtained when the child lived in utero. In addition to fulfilling his needs, however, the mother is also a controlling and an inhibiting influence. During the first year of life she plays the latter role primarily in connection with the child's food intake. This period, referred to as the "oral phase of development," is discussed in further detail elsewhere (see Chapter VI). Attitudes of complete helplessness and dependency characterize it.

As the child matures psychobiologically the mother's expectations concerning him undergo a change. Gradually the mother, as a controlling influence, shifts her attention to the problem of bowel control. So deeply ingrained is the adult's disgust with feces, it is often hard for him to believe that there is a time in the development of a human being when feces are not taboo. If a little child were permitted the freedom to do so, it would play with its feces as with any other object, eating, smelling and smearing it with obvious pleasure. The revulsion and disgust which characterize the adult attitude must be learned; the child must be taught to cherish cleanliness. The rigid schedules involved in toilet training give the child a more vivid conception of time, and punctuality becomes a virtue. As a result of the mother's emotional involvement in the toilet training, defecation becomes invested with extra meanings, and the attitude toward it becomes a symbol for the attitude toward the mother and later on toward authority in general. Defecation in the proper place at the proper time becomes an act of compliance. The stool becomes a gift bestowed on the mother as a token of love. And if the mother expresses enough approval of the bowel movement, then feces comes to represent something most precious, though later on in life it may symbolize the most worthless thing. The child can express defiance by soiling itself, or by withholding the bowel movement. If the mother attempts to train the child before its neuromuscular apparatus has matured sufficiently, or if she is excessively punitive in the process, unnecessarily large quantities of anxiety may be liberated, and this may exert a lasting influence on the character structure of the child. This period has been called the "anal phase of development."

Because the child has not yet developed the capacity to communicate verbally, it is compelled to express its feelings by actions of one kind or another. At this time, "actions speak louder than words" because the child lacks words. The tendency to act impulsively as contrasted to the more controlled behavior which takes place after thoughtful reflection may have its origin in the unsuccessful resolution of conflicts during this preverbal phase of development. Psychosomatic disturbances, too, can be traced back similarly.

This is followed by a more complicated phase. The child can now communicate in words as well as in bodily actions. The biological problem about which the interpersonal drama centers is the control of urination. The child develops a sense of shame. Its horizon of interests broadens considerably. It begins to play with other children. It learns about the difference between the sexes, often interpreting the absence of a penis in the girl as a mutilation inflicted as a punishment ("the castration complex"). Out of this comes a fear of physical injury and death as a punishment for misbehavior. With the awareness of the difference in the sexes, the boy normally takes the father's behavior and aspirations as a model; the girl, the mother's. We speak of this modeling process as "identification." As one of the by-products of this process, the child conforms to the wishes of the parents not simply out of fear of loss of love or physical injury, but out of love for the parents. It now complies because it feels it wants to, not only because it is compelled to do so by external influences. It develops built-in controls, as it were, which are referred to collectively as the "superego." Another by-product of this identification process is an infantile ambition to displace the parent of the same sex from its major role in the family. The ideas and behavior patterns associated with this ambition are referred to as the "oedipus complex." Psychoanalysts first emphasized that masturbation occurs quite regularly, probably universally, during this time, and that at this early period it is already associated with fantasies involving the parents. This period has been called the "phallic phase of development."

Throughout these early years, the child's wishes encounter at every point the parents' wishes. Very often these are in open conflict. Until the conflict is resolved, the child may suffer from night terrors, transitory phobias, behavior disturbances, or other symptoms. These symptoms, almost universally present, are referred to as "the infantile neurosis." As the child's inner controls develop, it forgets many of the wishes which are the source of its troubles. We speak of this forgetting process as "repression." The repressed or forgotten wishes are now "unconscious" and collectively make up most of what is referred to as the "id." In addition to its controls, the child develops new channels of self-expression, so that forbidden unconscious impulses may achieve expression in roundabout ways. For example, an impulse to play with feces may be gratified in finger painting or in making mud pies; or the urge to masturbate may become transformed into pleasurable manipulations of toys, or the playing of various games. Such transformations of inacceptable unconscious impulses into socially acceptable or even praiseworthy activities are called "sublimations." Between the gradual development of inner controls and the growing capacity for sublimation, the stormy indecisions of these early conflicts are gradually resolved, and in the normal course of events a relatively peaceful period sets in which is called the "latency period." The psychological mechanisms and functions involved in harmonizing the opposing drives are referred to collectively as the "ego."

The development of the ego depends upon the presence of wholesome parental influences with which the child can identify, influences which are exerted at once lovingly but also in a firmly controlling fashion. Both aspects of these influences, that is, controlling as well as loving, must be experienced for normal ego development. If the child comes from a broken home, and if its opportunities for achieving proper parental identification are otherwise disrupted, normal ego development often will not ensue. As a result, the infantile neurosis is not resolved. Clinically, this may manifest itself as delinquent, neurotic or psychotic behavior during the latency period.

If a normal latency period has been achieved, the advent of puberty usually disrupts this hard-won truce. A combination of biological and sociological factors intensify wishes that had been brought under control. The overtly asexual tranquillity of the latency period is replaced by an intense and essentially uncontrollable interest in sexual matters. Masturbation is usually resumed at this time. The childhood fantasies that initially accompanied masturbation earlier in childhood remain repressed or re-emerge into consciousness in highly disguised forms. The unconscious meanings associated with adolescent masturbation are responsible for the intense guilt feelings which invariably accompany the act. Attempts to assuage the guilt feelings of adolescent masturbation by explanation and reassurance are usually of no avail because these attempts do not address themselves to the source of the guilt, namely the unconscious fantasies from early childhood involving the parents. Although some encouragement is given by parents to adolescent sexual interest, this is given ambiguously and, in any event, within sharply defined limits of expression.

Not only in the sexual sphere but in all aspects of life the adolescent is in an ambiguous position. His parents have mixed feelings or ambivalence about his growing up. He himself is ambivalent in this regard.

This is the specific battle of adolescence. New wishes, conscious ones, rooted in cultural as well as socioeconomic conditions take the center of the stage. Onto these conscious wishes, unconscious infantile drives become attached. For example, infantile exhibitionistic impulses may be mingled with an interest in acting, infantile sexual curiosity in a scientific interest in biology, sadistic impulses in ambitions to be a surgeon. In this process of compounding current drives with those of infancy, old neurotic conflicts tend to be reawakened. For example, ambitions to be successful in the family business may reawaken guilts related to the oedipus complex, schooling or a job involving travelling may reawaken old fears of separation from the mother. In any event, the patterns of adaptation which may have been adequate in latency no longer suffice in adolescence.

Conflicting drives must be reconciled and harmonized all over again. The new solutions must be predicated on an entirely new conception of one's self and one's relation to the outside world. Once again sleep disturbances, transitory phobias, behavior disturbances, psychosomatic disorders or other symptom formations may become clinically manifest. This is part of normal adolescent turmoil. If the adaptive mechanisms of the ego have been developed with sufficient strength up to this time and if the steadying influences of mature parent figures are available, the indecisions of adolescence are also resolved and a new period of peaceful growth sets in. On the other hand, if ego strength is insufficient, or if previously available parent figures or more recent substitutes are no longer available, for one reason or another, then the foregoing symptoms of adolescent turmoil may intensify and crystallize into mental disease.

Preventive Psychiatry

When the foregoing facts became known, many people thought we were on the threshold of the golden age of mental hygiene. If we educate parents and their surrogates in the schools concerning the emotional needs of children, so this thought ran, we will foster normal ego growth and mental illness will be thereby prevented. Unfortunately it has not worked out that way, at least as far as one can detect from the admission rates to our outpatient clinics and mental hospitals. The incidence of mental illness in our youngsters has not diminished. It is, in fact, definitely on the increase. Not only is there this quantitative change, but in the opinion of some there has been an unfortunate qualitative change as well. Where aggressively delinquent behavior used to predominate among young patients a generation or two ago, this has gradually given way to more malignant inhibited reactions, with severe psychoneurotic and psychotic symptoms predominating. It should be said at once that we do not know the reason for these changes, and that the elucidation of these changes represents a research problem of urgent importance for the sociologist as well as the psychiatrist.

The task of educating adults for mental health turned out to be easier said than done. As a result of their own neurotic problems, parents and teachers often rejected or misunderstood the teachings of preventive psychiatry. At times, the teachings themselves were incorrect, as during the era when the child's need for love was understood but not its need for adequate controls. People reasoned that since unsuccessful repression had something to do with mental illness, the thing to do was to eliminate repression. As a result of this unfortunate syllogism, parents and teachers often permitted the child free rein in the expression of its impulses. No attempt was made to instil controls that would make behavior more adaptive, more congruent to the demands of reality. Such lack of direction from adults undoubtedly contributed to developmental weaknesses of the ego in many instances.

As a result of the growing complexity of civilization, adults have been exposed to virtually unparalleled emotional stresses in recent times. A great cloud of uncertainty hangs over the future of mankind. The anxieties of the adult world undoubtedly percolate down into the children's world and contribute to their emotional problems. In addition, children are exposed to new influences, communication media like comic books and television, which present sexually provocative material and situations of raw violence with a uniquely vivid intensity. A debate is currently in progress on this subject. Some psychiatrists say these influences are not harmful. One has even said that they are beneficial because they give expression to unconscious fantasies which should be expressed. It must be clear, if normal ego development calls for repression of infantile impulses or at least their modification in socially approved sublimations, that the active indulgence in relatively undisguised infantile fantasies can serve no useful purpose. Surely it must be true that if children spent the same time absorbing positive life values, they would be better equipped to adapt to reality. In any case, here is a problem that calls for controlled scientific study, and the possibility, at least, exists that these influences may be contributing to what appears to be a deterioration in the mental health of the younger generation.

The foregoing remarks must not be construed to mean that preventive psychiatry through public education is useless and should be discarded. On the contrary, public education for mental health seems more urgently indicated than ever. As we perfect our knowledge with research and improve our means of communicating with the public, we should be able to establish a social milieu more favorable to normal ego growth.

Outpatient Psychotherapy of the Young

Whatever the prospects for preventive psychiatry, the fact remains that a vast practical problem confronts psychiatry, namely the task of treating those young people who are immediately in need of help. Important as the team approach is in the psychotherapy of the adult, it is even more urgently important in the treatment of the young. Although ego weakness is characteristic of the mentally ill of all ages, the fragility of the young ego is more marked because so much of its helplessness is based on reality. Physically, the child is weak. He cannot earn a living or otherwise provide for his physical needs. The task of developing a conception of one's role in life from a sexual and socioeconomic point of view as well as a capacity for sublimation lie before the child almost in their entirety. The young patient is less able to rebel against adult arbitrariness in the home, or independently to seek his fortune elsewhere if the family environment is unwholesome. For these reasons, the parents must be made part of the treatment plan from its inception.

It is necessary to appreciate the suffering that has usually taken place in a family before the decision is made to seek help for an emotionally disturbed youngster. The parents themselves may have emotional problems which they cannot master, and part of the child's illness may be found in his attempts to adapt to their difficulties. Parents usually have a deep feeling of guilt or personal failure when they bring their child for treatment. This may express itself in a hostile rejecting attitude toward the child, in an excessively self-punitive attitude, or in an attitude that is suspiciously objective and scientific because it is excessively so. If the psychiatrist or social worker can help the family to understand and accept its guilt and anxiety, a major hindrance to proper treatment of the youngster will have been eliminated. Although this task is usually assigned to the social worker, the psychiatrist may undertake the task himself if the home problem seems very formidable or, in a case where the emotional needs of the child are better met by the sex and temperament of the social worker, he may wish to assign the child to her care.

The treatment of the child differs from that of the adult in many fundamental ways. The clinic team may represent the first group of adults that the child has ever encountered upon whom it can depend, who will be accepting of his shortcomings, who will provide wholesome models with whom he can identify. The child enters into a more realistic relationship with the therapist than the adult parent. The latter comes into the therapeutic situation with more rigidly prejudiced expectations based on previous experiences, which is called transference (see Chapters I, II). The therapist, on his part, must be warm, generous and genuinely friendly to the child. He cannot afford to be an objective screen upon whom the patient projects his misconceptions about reality, as in analytically oriented psychotherapy with adults. The therapist depends less upon the verbal productions of the child for knowledge of his inner mental workings and more on deductions from his various play activities. For example, the therapist may use a set of dolls to reproduce the family constellation, and encourage the child to make up stories into which he will project his hidden thoughts and feelings. Similar use is made of drawings, games, and psychological test materials. As in the treatment of the adult, an attempt is made to understand the specific emotional stresses to which the child is subjected, and the way in which his symptoms represent attempts to adapt to these stresses. The symptoms are attempts to mitigate his fears and loneliness, and to fulfill whatever positive strivings he has.

Because clinic contacts are so brief, the main burden of emotional reconstruction falls upon the family. If they are reasonably well-balanced, responsible individuals, it may be possible to accomplish much in a few consultations.

For example, a very attractive thirty-five-year-old mother came to the clinic with her fifteen-year-old son because he displayed destructive outbursts in the home, smashing furniture, tearing his clothing and threatening her with physical violence on little provocation. In addition, he was truant from school and was involved in sexual escapades that were precocious for his age. The father was fifty-two years old, and an invalid. Frustrated in her relationship with the husband, the mother sought affection from her son. His adolescent behavior disturbance represented an attempt to defend himself against her "seductive advances." In two sessions, it was possible to give this woman sufficient understanding of the situation so that she was able to increase the emotional distance between herself and her son. His abnormal behavior subsided very quickly thereafter. The problem was explained to the family doctor and he was able to guide the family more effectively thereafter.

A young couple sought help because their six-year-old son was unwilling to leave the house to play with other children, although he would play quite normally with them if they visited him. In addition, he had night terrors. The father suffered from multiple sclerosis, as a result of which he was a semi-invalid. He was often hospitalized because of exacerbations in his illness. The child would limp and imitate other symptoms which the father displayed. The father had no conception of the emotional trauma which his frequent separations from the family inflicted on the youngster. He felt that the child was stubborn and disobedient, and as a result he often punished him. It was possible to show the father that the child's symptoms were the result of his fear of losing his father, and that by raging against the child, he intensified these fears. Gentler behavior with the child, including more complete explanations concerning his illness, resulted in improvement in the child's symptoms.

The Day Nursery should be mentioned as an outpatient treatment device of great value. Providing a "Day Hospital" type of program for children (see Chapter XXXV), it may carry a child through a period of crisis, thereby eliminating the need for intramural care.

Inpatient Treatment of the Child

If the home environment is not modifiable, or if the child's needs for supervision cannot be met in the home for other reasons, it may become necessary to hospitalize him. The young patient referred for hospitalization has usually been labeled by others as incorrigible and untreatable, and often has been rejected by the neighborhood and the community. In short, he usually presents a formidable problem as to management and treatment. People who are familiar with the severe limitations of our public mental hospitals will be shocked to learn that in many states, the state mental hospital is the only resource for the care and treatment of the seriously emotionally disturbed child. In a nation that concerns itself so with the welfare of its children, it is ironic that children should be the recipients of simple custodial care at a time when a rational program of treatment is becoming available for more and more of our adult mental patients.

In many mental hospitals, psychiatrists are being assigned the imposing task of setting up a children's service. In planning such a service, it is well to begin with a basic theory or philosophy. The aim of such a service should be to provide disturbed children with a new and gratifying living experience in a therapeutic environment. Psychotherapy with individuals or groups represents only a part of the total program. No less important is the presence of numerous accepting adults, group activities planned according to the emotional needs of each member of the group, occupational and recreational therapy, and above all an environment that the child knows will tolerate his deviations and will continue to help him in spite of them as he attempts to deal with his problems. All personnel associated with the children's service must be indoctrinated with the philosophy of the therapeutic community, so that each can bring to bear upon the child a corrective influence.

The psychiatrist in charge of the service may be assigned a building in which to set up his program. Here in the very structure of the building he may encounter his first obstacle. A young people's service has certain building requirements which, if lacking, may seriously undermine its therapeutic efficacy. For example, there should be facilities to separate the various diagnostic categories. The severely mentally retarded cannot be fitted into a therapeutic program designed for emotionally disturbed children of normal intelligence. Children with severe organic brain damage or with a malignant schizophrenic process that is showing rapid deterioration have different needs than others with a more hopeful prognosis. The aggressive delinquent child needs a program which emphasizes controls. The inhibited child with a neurotic or psychotic reaction needs a program which encourages his expressive impulses. Because of its underdeveloped ego, the child needs an environment which duplicates as far as possible a wholesome family environment. The cottage plan fulfills these needs particularly well, with its small groups of patients, the cottage parents, a living room and provisions for a certain amount of family life at mealtimes and in early evening activities. The mixing of age groups and sexes helps complete the resemblance to the organization of the normal family. In the adolescent age group, one is naturally concerned about acting out of sexual impulses. For this and for many other good psychological reasons, there should be provision for privacy in sleeping arrangements as well as in bathing. These special needs call for highly specialized architectural arrangements. If new buildings for the children's service are contemplated, it is probably well to avoid big investments in permanent buildings precisely because the field is new and in a state of flux. Simple huts like those employed by the Army are probably more flexibly applicable to the needs of a children's service than elaborate permanent structures representing an investment a hundred times as great.

The Intake Problem

The admission of a child into a mental hospital is inevitably much more disturbing to all members of the family than is treatment on an outpatient basis. The anxiety and guilt feelings of the parents must be dealt with, although very often the hospitalized youngster comes from a disrupted home in which a truly responsible parent is no longer available. In any event, the initial family contacts will serve not only to help the family over their emotional crisis, but will make it possible to plan the aftercare of the child at the time of admission. If the family lives far from the hospital, a social service agency which is physically accessible to the family should be brought into the treatment situation at once, to collect information and to assist in formulating the total treatment plan, including aftercare.

Much more traumatic than the parents' experiences is the impact that hospitalization has on the child. In many public mental hospitals no formal attempt is made to prepare the child. Ideally, the need for hospitalization should be discussed with the child in detail. The hospital should be described to him. If possible, preliminary visits to the hospital should be arranged, so that when the child comes to stay he is already familiar with the setup. He should be reassured that hospitalization is a temporary measure, that more normal living arrangements will be made for him after he is sufficiently improved. Other children in the institution should be properly prepared to receive the newcomer.

The Treatment Program

As in the case of the adult patient, the youngster's problem is formulated by integrating data from all available sources, and a plan of treatment is based upon it. In addition to psychotherapy with individuals and in groups (including psychodrama, patient government and other forms of group therapy as described in Chapter II), and the various activity programs already described for the adult patient in Chapter IV, there are many special details which apply to the treatment of children. For example, birthdays should be celebrated to emphasize the advantages of growing up. Properly selected gifts should be given to all children on appropriate occasions. Holidays should be observed with special pomp and ceremony. There should be adequate playground facilities and a swimming pool. Provisions should be made for summer holidays away from the hospital. Children are often helped by animal pets, although one must protect the animals from impulsively cruel behavior on the part of some children. Contacts with other children through the exchange of play facilities and in athletic competitions should be encouraged. The development of deep attachments to the hospital is not rare. In some institutions, discharged children return for holiday celebrations, or to share the joy of a new job, a promotion, a successfully completed period of military service, or a marriage, with cottage parents and other personnel, or to return for advice in time of trouble. The readiness to develop such attachments is part of childhood; they represent healthy psychological trends and should be encouraged by every possible means. The contention in some children's services that deep permanent attachments should be discouraged is only partially correct. If properly utilized, such attachments can be of profound psychotherapeutic importance.

Constant self-examination by ward personnel for emotional attitudes which interfere with a proper psychotherapeutic approach (countertransference) should be encouraged. Time should be devoted to the discussion of this problem in staff conferences. A problem that pertains particularly to a children's service is the development of rivalry between a cottage parent and the real parent. Needless to say, the cottage parent can never function as a rival, only as a therapist to the real parent as well as to the child in his care.

The educational needs of children must also be provided for. Accredited teachers must attempt to keep these children up to their proper school grade. Whenever possible, children should be placed in regular public schools in the community. Reading disabilities are very frequently present among emotionally disturbed children; arithmetic disabilities to a lesser extent. Remedial reading and remedial arithmetic classes are part of the educational program, but to no lesser degree a part of the treatment program. Remedial teachers are often in a particularly strategic position to deal with the child's emotional problems. At times, for example, the child may prefer to discuss personal matters instead of reading. The remedial teacher, therefore, must be kept informed of the total treatment plan, so that she may make therapeutic capital of such occasions.

The health program is also of special importance on the children's service. Youngsters are more susceptible to disease and require immunizations and more frequent physical check-ups; they have specific nutritional growth requirements; they require careful dental supervision. Neglect in these areas may aggravate an already complicated problem. Good care, on the other hand, may be a powerful cementing bond between the child and those who are trying to help him. Plastic surgery should not be omitted, particularly where cosmetic deformities have given rise to nicknames and have otherwise served to isolate a child from the group; nor should skin care be omitted, including the removal of scars and pitting by recently available surgical techniques. It should be recalled that surgical procedures of all kinds are emotionally traumatic to children of the youngest age groups. Preoperative care should include careful psychological preparation. Diet to correct obesity or excessive underweight may also be of great psychotherapeutic importance.

A regular religious program is omitted, by and large, from the children's service in mental hospitals, unless it happens to be run by a sectarian organization. In many hospitals, it is stated that religious training is given to the child if this is requested by the parents. When it is recalled how often the child comes from a broken home or one in which the parents themselves are deeply disturbed people, then this seems to be an absurd basis on which to include or exclude religion from the treatment program. It has been mentioned elsewhere (Chapter XII) that religion can fulfill deep emotional needs for people under stress. These rootless children in particular have need for the kind of support which religion can provide. It is true that many of these children are antagonistic to religion as they are to all expressions of parental influence. But this does not leave them less in need of an unfailingly accepting and forgiving parent figure of infinite strength. If presented meaningfully and with beauty, religion can only add to the ego supports of the youngster. To neglect it is to omit a readily available psychotherapeutic instrument of great potential power.

An adequate program of community relations is a particularly urgent matter for a hospital with a children's service. Very often the surrounding community is fearful and hostile in its attitude toward these young patients. This attitude can be modified by public education and can be transformed into a civic-spirited feeling of personal responsibility for the welfare of these youngsters. The police must be educated as to a proper attitude toward runaways. Volunteers (see Chapter XIII) can provide kindly parent figures who may help these children re-establish their faith in the world of grownups. They can teach hobbies and open up a whole world of auxiliary interests which will help each child discover the areas of sublimation best suited for his needs. They can invite into their homes and help open for them the doors of the community's schools and recreational centers.

Various physical agents have been used in the treatment of children. Amphetamine appears to have a beneficial effect, at least temporarily, on both overactive and inhibited children. Some success has been claimed for dilantin, particularly where there is reason to suspect that the disturbed behavior may be part of an epileptic syndrome. Electroconvulsive therapy (ECT) is reported to have beneficial effects on some schizophrenic children. Psychosurgery has been used with little success as an act of desperation in some instances of childhood schizophrenia. As a result of the equivocal results with all of these organic techniques, they are less widely used now than they were a few years ago. However, continued research in the use of such agents as adjuvants in the total treatment plan is certainly indicated.

Control of the Disturbed Child

As in the case of the adult, disturbed behavior never occurs without a reason. By and large, it is an attempt to deal with an intolerable frustration of some kind. Thus the control of disturbed behavior in the child begins with prophylaxis. Children, like emotionally disturbed adults, react to change of any kind with anxiety. Transition from one activity to another should be gradual. Adequate opportunities for the expression of pent-up aggression should be provided in the activities program. Personnel should be alert to signs of mounting tension in a child and should attempt to understand the reasons for it and to head it off by interventions based on an understanding of the case. (More details concerning prevention of disturbed behavior are to be found in Chapter X.)

In addition to genuine psychiatric emergencies, children present a constant need for the controlling influences of responsible adults. They must be taught the outer limits of permissible uncontrolled behavior at the same time that they are given love and acceptance. Thus, the ordinary disciplinary measures that parents employ with children should not be neglected. Deprivation of treats and privileges is the device most frequently used. Sometimes an overactive child will quiet down if placed at bed rest. Occasionally a period of isolation during which an outburst of fury may be given an opportunity to spend itself is useful. Corporal punishment is no more indicated in the treatment of children than it is in the treatment of adults.

Preparation for Discharge

When the child is admitted to the hospital, plans for his discharge should be set up at once. The use of social service agencies to work with families who live at a distance from the hospital has already been mentioned. Treatment of the child in a mental hospital consists of two parts, the therapeutic hospital experience and modification of the environment to which the child is returned. Ideally, he is returned to his own family. If this is therapeutically inadvisable, a foster home placement may be arranged. Some institutions have set up residence clubs, a cottage arrangement within the community, from which the youngster may go to school or to work. Such a sheltered residence may act as a halfway house between the mental hospital and unsupervised life in the community. At times a discharged youngster may be readmitted to the residence club for a period of care rather than be returned to the hospital proper. When the discharge plan has been arranged, the child should be notified of it months in advance, and should ge given an opportunity to try it out in visits of increasing length over a period of weeks before the final step is taken. It is advisable never to discharge an adolescent of working age unless he has been placed at a job. Naturally, not all patients will be discharged from the hospital into the community. Those who do not respond to treatment may have to be sent on to another mental hospital for custodial care.

The Reformatory

The reformatory has been renamed the training school for delinquent children. It is becoming increasingly apparent that the training school is not a school but a mental hospital. This was most dramatically brought out in the experience of the Hawthorne-Cedar Knolls School in New York. Initially it was set up to reform the delinquent child through discipline and redirection of its activities. Gradually it became apparent that there was a fundamental relationship between the delinquent child and the child who was clearly emotionally ill. Psychiatric treatment methods were introduced and found to be quite effective in helping these delinquent youngsters. With the passage of time and with alterations in the population from which it drew its patients, its facilities were employed more and more for the treatment of the emotionally ill youngster and less and less for the youngster whose difficulties involved infractions of the law. The program which had been worked out for the successful treatment of the delinquent child was carried over pretty much intact to the care of this new population of mentally sick youngsters. It proved to be quite effective in helping them, too. In short, the boundary line between the emotionally disturbed child who broke the law and the one who did not was entirely eliminated. This fact finds application in the widespread use of psychiatrists in our juvenile courts. It is being applied much more slowly to the so-called correctional institutions where many of these children are remanded. That these institutions ought to be converted to treatment centers for emotionally disturbed children is becoming more and more apparent.

Juvenile Narcotic Addiction

In recent years there has been a wave of increased narcotic addiction among the youngsters of our land. Although the newspapers did exaggerate to some extent the degree to which this problem existed, its major importance cannot be doubted. A great many of the youngsters who become addicted are emotionally disturbed to start with. Nevertheless, addiction introduces a complication into the task of emotional rehabilitation which may well be insuperable in many instances. In a fundamental sense, this is a sociologic problem. Penalties for peddling narcotics to youngsters should be made prohibitively heavy, so that the market is stamped out. As a matter of fact, the incidence of juvenile narcotic addiction seems to have fallen off considerably since an outraged public pressed for police action. This fact notwithstanding, young addicts present a knotty problem when they are referred for treatment. It is generally agreed that they should not be placed in a hospital with nonaddict children because of the likelihood that they may somehow obtain narcotics and seduce other children into becoming addicts. Recently, New York City set up a hospital for the treatment of young addicts. Unfortunately, among the so-called "young" addicts who were referred for treatment were many young married men with family responsibilities and corresponding social experiences whose needs were altogether different from those of children and adolescents. This fact seriously impaired the effectiveness of the program. However, they did demonstrate the feasibility and usefulness of involving community social service agencies in modifying the family milieu to which these youngsters were returned. The coordinated use of social service agencies in this manner represents a principle of broad applicability in the treatment of hospitalized mental patients of all ages. Where local facilities for treating young addicts are not available, it becomes an unfortunate necessity to refer the youngster to the Federal facilities in Lexington, Kentucky (see Chapter XVIII).

Training for Child Psychiatry

As the differences between adult and child psychiatry have been clarified, the need for specialized training for work with children has become increasingly evident. The policy adopted by the American Board of Psychiatry and the American Association of Psychiatric Clinics for children calls for two years of training in adult psychiatry before fellows are to be accepted for training in child psychiatry. It is preferable, naturally, that this training be dynamically oriented and contain careful individual supervision in all its aspects. The specialized children's training should deal with the emotional and intellectual development of the child, both in its normal and deviate aspects, with the parent-child relationship and its utilization in treatment, with psychological test methods for children, with problems of administering a children's hospital service or a clinic, knowledge of the community resources, schools, courts and social agencies, which must be utilized in treatment planning and, of course, the special psychotherapeutic techniques which are applied to children. Training should take place in a setting which routinely employs an integrated team approach to the problem of the child. Active clinical experiences, the use of small case seminars as teaching devices, and the emphasis on competent individual supervision constitute the basic foundations of the program.

Although no reference to classification has been made in this chapter, training in diagnostic evaluation should be accorded a place of proper importance. The American Psychiatric Association's *Diagnostic and Statistical Manual* should be followed (see Appendix E). At least equal in importance is the problem of diagnosis in dynamic terms, that is, training in the formulation of the child's problems in operational terms that can be utilized in planning a program of treatment (see Appendix A). (For more details concerning training, see Chapter XXIX.)

Research

Some areas which call for research have been mentioned earlier in this chapter. Reasons for the quantitative increase and qualitative changes in mental illness in young people must be investigated. The role of the current crop of television programs and "comic" books must be seriously studied under controlled conditions. These are psychological instruments of unprecedented power and should not be dismissed too lightly, as some individuals are inclined to do. New techniques for treating children in hospitals and clinics must be studied. For example, the use of the day hospital (see Chapter XXXV) for children has been relatively unexplored. The biological substrate of behavior, or what may be referred to as the constitutional factor in emotional disease should be studied in detail. The search for organic agents as adjuvants in treatment should not be neglected.

SELECTED REFERENCES

BOWLBY, J.; ROBERTSON, J.; ROSENBLUTH, D.: A Two-Year-Old Goes to Hospital. In *The Psychoanalytic Study of the Child*, Vol. VII. New York: International Universities Press, 1952.

COLEMAN, L.: Children Need Preparation for Tonsillectomy. *Child Study*, 1952.
　　Written by a surgeon, this is a sensitive and instructive account of the problem of preparing a child psychobiologically for surgery.

DEUTSCH, H.: *The Psychology of Women*, 2 Vols. New York: Grune & Stratton, 1944.
　　Contains invaluable data on prepuberty, early puberty, puberty and adolescence in the female. Rich in illustrative clinical material. Highly recommended.

EDITORIAL: Juvenile Drug addiction in the City of New York. *N. Y. Med.*, 9:682, 1953.
A detailed description of a treatment center for young narcotic addicts, describing pitfalls and failures. Invaluable for anyone involved in organizing such a center.

ELLIOTT, S. A.; KEITH-LUCAS, A.: A Mother's Movement Toward Responsibility During Her Child's Placement. *Soc. Casework*, 35:166, 1954.
A case history is presented, illustrating the way a social worker contributed to the successful therapy of a child by helping the mother to achieve a more genuinely maternal attitude in her relationship with the child.

FRAIBERG, S. H.: *Psychoanalytic Principles in Casework with Children.* New York: Family Service Association of America, 1955. (192 Lexington Avenue, N. Y. C., 16.)
A lucid and highly practical presentation of dynamic case work principles. Invaluable guide in work with children.

FREUD, A.: *The Ego and the Mechanisms of Defense.* New York: International Universities Press, 1946.
The phenomena of puberty are described as well as the defense mechanisms which are evolved in the attempt to master anxiety throughout life.

FREUD, A.: The Role of Bodily Illness in the Mental Life of Children. In *The Psychoanalytic Study of the Child,* Vol. VII. New York: International Universities Press, 1952.

FREUD, S.: Analysis of a Phobia in a Five-Year-Old Boy. *Collected Papers,* Vol. III. London: Hogarth Press, 1943.
This paper presents the case of "Little Hans," a pioneer study in the emotional illnesses of childhood.

GAVRIN, J. B., ed.: *Residential Treatment of a Schizophrenic Child.* Proceedings of Conference at the Hawthorne-Cedar Knolls School of The Jewish Board of Guardians of New York on October 5, 1952. Monograph No. 3.
Describes the Hawthorne treatment program. A multidisciplinary case presentation is discussed by a group of experts.

GILBERTSON, R. J. L.; SUTTON, H.: A Children's Psychiatric Service. *Am. J. Nursing,* 43:570, 1943.
A detailed and highly useful description of the role of the psychiatric nurse on a children's ward.

GROUP FOR THE ADVANCEMENT OF PSYCHIATRY: *Basic Concepts in Child Psychiatry.* Report No. 12, 1950.
A brief outline presenting developmental aspects of child behavior and psychopathology as well as suggestions for a training program for child psychiatry.

JENKINS, R. L., chairman: *Training Schools for Delinquent Children. A Guide to Planning with Particular Reference to Clinical Facilities.* Prepared by a Special Committee of the American Psychiatric Assoc. Mental Hospital Service, 1785 Massachusetts Avenue, N.W., Washington 6, D.C.
A brief pamphlet containing much valuable material prepared with the help of many experts.

JESSNER, L.; BLOM, G. E.; WALDFOGEL, S.: Emotional Implications of Tonsillectomy and Adenoidectomy on Children. In *The Psychoanalytic Study of the Child,* Vol. VII. New York: International Universities Press, 1952.

KANNER, L.: *Child Psychiatry.* Springfield, Ill.: C. C. Thomas, 1953.
This book has gone through two editions and many printings. It is a standard reference book in the field.

LEWIS, N. D. C.; PACELLA, B. L.; eds.: *Modern Trends in Child Psychiatry.* New York: International Universities Press, 1945.
A collection of papers by great authorities covering major aspects of child psychiatry.

LOURIE, N. V.; SCHULMAN, R.: The Role of the Residential Staff in Residential Treatment. *Am. J. Orthopsychiat.,* 22:798, 1952.
A helpful description of the organization of a treatment program for children in a mental hospital.

234 THE PATIENTS

MORAVIA, A.: *Two Adolescents*. New York: Farrar, Straus & Young, 1950.
    A sensitive study of adolescent psychology by a great Italian novelist.
REID, J. H.; HAGAN, H. R.: *Residential Treatment of Emotionally Disturbed Children*.
    New York (24 W. 40 St.): Child Welfare League of America, Inc., 1952.
    A descriptive study based on an analysis of twelve treatment centers for dis-
    turbed children in various parts of the country. An important survey of cur-
    rent experiences in a rapidly developing field.
Residential Treatment Centers for Emotionally Disturbed Children. Published by the
    Federal Security Agency, Department of Health, Education and Welfare, Chil-
    dren's Bureau. Available through Supt. of Documents, U.S. Gov. Printing Office,
    Washington 25, D.C.
    Lists 36 centers for the treatment of emotionally disturbed children, describing
    admission policies, physical plant, staff, treatment program and fees.
SCHRAGER, J.: A Focus for Supervision of Residential Staff in a Treatment Institution.
    Bull. Menninger Clin., 18:64, 1954.
    Describes the treatment program in a center for emotionally disturbed chil-
    dren with valuable illustrative case histories and critical comments.
The Children's Bookshelf. Published by the Department of Health, Education and
    Welfare, Children's Bureau. Publication No. 304. Available through U.S. Gov.
    Printing Office, Washington 25, D.C. (25c)
    A well selected booklist; of value in forming a library for a children's service.

Chapter XVII

THE ALCOHOLIC

Introduction

A psychiatrist in a State hospital once asked me, "What shall I do with the drunks that the police department deposits at my doorstep?" A colleague answered, "Leave them there. Tell the police to take them back to jail where they belong!" This condemnatory attitude was echoed by several others in our group. Yet alcoholism is one of the major public health problems of our time, ranking with cancer, tuberculosis and heart disease in its importance. The Metropolitan Life Insurance Company has estimated that there are 50 per cent more sufferers from alcoholism than from tuberculosis and that four million people in the United States are either actual or potential alcoholics. The ravages of chronic alcoholism are well known. It is a progressive disease leading to intellectual and physical deterioration, impaired earning capacity, and crippling organic disease and death. It is a major cause of broken homes. Its malignant effect upon family life wreaks incalculable harm in the emotional development of the young. This disease has other far-reaching social effects as well. It is a major cause of absenteeism in industry. It is a significant contributory factor in accidents of all kinds, but particularly in auto accidents, which represents in itself a major cause of death. It plays an important role in homicide, suicide and episodic sexual aberration.

I recounted these facts and then declared as emphatically as I could that the thing to do with the "drunk" was to hospitalize him and treat him. Whereupon someone else said, "We can't do that. The law says that the alcoholic without mental disorder is not eligible for admission to the State hospital—and it's a good thing, too, otherwise we'd fill up our beds with them." "If the idea is not to fill up beds," I answered, "why not pass a law against the admission of schizophrenics? Then you would have beds to spare! As a matter of fact, many of the alcoholics whom you turn away will come back to you later anyway, with delirium tremens, Korsakoff's psychosis, Wernicke's encephalopathy or any of the other forms of major mental disease which are associated with alcoholism. Why not treat them now before they are irreparably harmed or destroyed? This is the medical attitude toward all other diseases, why not to this one? And as far as the law is concerned, you are free to reject any chronic alcoholic who is without mental disease, provided, that is, you can find one. As a matter of fact, chronic alcoholism has its roots in mental disease almost without exception."

Alcoholism as a Disease

Alcoholics have been studied from a psychological point of view over a period of years. Certain common denominators of psychopathology have been found regularly. These people show evidences of arrested emotional development. They are impulsive and intolerant of tension. They are self-centered and incapable of entering into mature emotional relationships with men or women. Psychosexual abnormalities are regularly encountered. Under the influence of alcohol previously latent homosexual and exhibitionistic drives may become manifest. The frustration of emotional needs in childhood by the mother or by both parents is regularly encountered in the history of these patients. Psychological tests often bring out a persistent concern with the mouth which is a hangover from feeding experiences in early childhood, which were occasions for emotional frustration. Test results also confirm other aspects of their emotional immaturity, including oversensitivity and paranoid trends, poorly controlled aggression and anxiety and evidences of an inability to resolve the conflict between opposing drives.

Against this background it becomes understandable that these patients are excessively prone to mental disease in all forms, phobias, depressions, schizophrenic episodes, or any of the other manifestations of unsuccessful adaptation in the face of overwhelming conflict. Alcoholics are anxiety-ridden people who suffer from agonizing inhibition in a variety of social situations. Perhaps even more, they are subject to episodes of impotent rage of painful intensity. Alcohol enters into the picture in an attempt to adapt more successfully. It is a pharmacologic agent, a sedative which diminishes the intensity of these disagreeable symptoms. That is to say, alcohol diminishes suffering, for a time at least. It produces an impairment of consciousness which facilitates the denial of painful external realities and the repression of internal ones. As a result of the intensification of these defenses, the patient becomes euphoric. In this way alcohol produces a feeling of happiness. As a result of the diminished intensity of self-critical faculties, the patient dares to do things under the influence of alcohol that he shrinks from doing when sober. This includes socially useful activities as well as antisocial ones. A salesman may be able to face up to a client, a phobic to an otherwise intolerable train trip, a sexually inhibited man to a heterosexual situation. On the other hand, he may dare to talk back to his boss and lose his job, or accept the advances of a homosexual partner, or pull the trigger of a gun and end his life.

Social factors complicate the psychological problem of alcoholism. Some cultures tolerate alcoholism more than others and as a result are more apt to utilize alcohol in dealing with emotionally stressful situations (the Irish, for example, or the Indians, a few generations ago). People from cultures which are more intolerant of alcoholism (Greeks, Chinese, Jews) attempt to deal with their conflicts without it. This does not mean that the nonalcoholic groups have less mental disease; simply that alcohol is less likely to be involved in their failures in adaptation. Even tolerant cultural groups disapprove of its abuse. In fact, the cultural difference is apt to center about the question of what constitutes the abuse of alcohol. In any event, drinking to excess arouses disapproval from authority, from parents and the multitude of parental figures in society. As a result, drinking to excess may become an act of defiance, an act of aggression against an ambivalently regarded love object. It also leads to physical helplessness, as a result of which loved ones are compelled to give the tender loving care which these emotionally immature people long for. It also leads to sickness and social degradation which often fulfill masochistic wishes for punishment which obsess many of these guilt-ridden unfortunates. Thus, the psychological factors involved in alcoholism are numerous and complex.

In addition to the foregoing factors, certain physical changes supervene to complicate the picture. For example, during a period of prolonged drinking, an electrolytic and hormonal imbalance occurs which some people feel creates a craving for alcohol above and beyond that which derives from purely psychological factors. Alcoholics on a "binge" curtail their food intake sharply, and as a result nutritional deficiencies ensue. In time, these deficiencies result in widespread degenerative changes in the nervous system, including peripheral neuropathy, with weakness and loss of sensation in the hands and feet, optic neuritis with impairment of vision, brain stem changes with impairment of function of the third and fourth cranial nerves, nystagmus and ataxia as well as diffuse cerebral changes associated with various psychotic manifestations (including simple dementia, the silly confabulations of Korsakoff's psychosis, and under circumstances of withdrawal of alcohol, acute delirium). Alcoholics often sustain head injuries as a result of their ataxia and impairment of consciousness. As a result of Vitamin C deficiency a relatively minor head injury may result in a subdural hematoma with concomitant mental disturbance. These central nervous system effects of alcohol are naturally of primary concern to the psychiatrist. However, the well-known liver changes, the anemia, the myocardial damage can all contribute secondarily through a generalized toxic state to abnormalities in mental functioning.

In short, when the policeman deposits the drunk on the doorstep of a mental hospital, he knows what he is doing.

Acute Alcoholic State

The term acute alcoholic state is used in a double sense. It refers to the general condition of an individual after the high consumption of alcohol over a relatively short period of time. This can occur for example in an individual who is not an alcoholic in the ordinary sense of the word, and never will be, but who is involved in a youthful experiment. It can occur as an episode in an individual whose degenerative somatic changes identify him as a chronic alcoholic. It can also occur in an individual who is an alcoholic but early enough in his career so that irreversible somatic changes have not yet occurred. Such a person, usually a youthful drinker, can also be referred to as an acute alcoholic as contrasted to the permanently crippled chronic one.

A state of acute alcoholic intoxication exists when the quantity of alcohol in the blood reaches a certain level, usually around 150 mg. of alcohol per 100 cc. of blood. The chronic alcoholic may walk around with higher blood alcohol levels without overt manifestations of intoxication. Also individuals who are in an extreme state of tension, associated primarily with suppressed rage which is controlled with the greatest of difficulty may respond to lower blood alcohol levels with violent abreactions characterized by uncontrolled destructive fury, followed by an amnesia for the acute episode. This is designated as pathological intoxication. While an individual may give a history of repeated episodes of pathological intoxication which suggest that he has some constitutional sensitivity to alcohol, many individuals during periods of stress and repressed rage may show this reaction to alcohol as an isolated episode. This was observed, for example, in World War II in overseas rest areas where combat infantrymen had returned from the front.

Although there are considerable individual variations, if a person consumes about three fourths of an ounce of whiskey in an hour, he has a blood alcohol level of 10 mg. per cent and shows no overt evidence of the effect of alcohol. An ounce of whiskey yields a somewhat higher blood level (20 mg. per cent) and may result in pleasant sociable behavior where inhibition was previously present.

Two to three ounces of whiskey in an hour yield a blood level of approximately 50 mg. per cent and is associated with definite euphoria.

Five to six ounces yield a blood level of 100 mg. per cent and is associated with some slurring of speech and moderate impairment of motor skills.

A half pint consumed in an hour yields a blood level of 150 mg. per cent and is associated with marked motor inco-ordination and slowing of reaction time. A person showing this blood alcohol level is drunk by official designation.

Ten ounces of whiskey in an hour (blood level 200 mg. per cent) result in loss of emotional control, motor helplessness, nausea and poor sphincter control.

A pint of whiskey (blood level 300 mg. per cent) results in stupor.

Twenty-four ounces (blood level 400-500 mg. per cent) result in deep coma. Higher levels result in respiratory paralysis and death.

Acute alcoholic intoxication is the leading cause of coma. However, this is always a perilous diagnosis because the unconscious patient with an alcoholic breath can also have suffered a head injury, a coronary occlusion or a cerebral vascular accident. The stomach should be emptied at once by lavage and oxygen may be administered where respiration and color are not good. Caffeine may be given in addition. If there is not a relatively rapid response, one must suspect the possibility of a more serious underlying condition.

Treatment of the Immediate State

Let us assume that there is nothing more than alcoholic intoxication, or that the patient was not in coma at all but walked in in a drunken state and asked for help. It would be a grave error to conceive of the physician's role at this time to consist simply in sobering him up. This is the time to take hold of the alcoholic and to begin the process of rehabilitation. The hospital is the ideal place to carry this out. Separation from his home environment may immediately diminish the stress he is under. A complete physical examination with laboratory studies should be carried out as soon as practical. Replacement of sodium chloride, which is lost in significant quantities during a period of heavy drinking, is the first step in treatment: two to four grams in the first twenty-four hours of which not more than two grams should be given intravenously. Intravenous glucose should be given with it.

Large doses of vitamin B complex and at least 0.5 to 1.0 gram of vitamin C should be given daily for the first two or three days.

Adrenal cortical hormones have been found to exert a specifically beneficial effect in acute alcoholic intoxication. These may be given as the aqueous cortical extract (ACE), in which case 20-60 cc. should be added to 1000 cc. of the dextrose and saline infusion; 25 mg. of ACTH may be used, instead, in a similar infusion. The infusion should be administered daily over a period of six to eight hours for several days. This management has been particularly effective in warding off impending delirium tremens.

Barbiturates should be avoided if possible, as well as chloral during the stage of acute alcoholic intoxication. Although sedation should be avoided if possible, paraldehyde is probably the sedative of choice.

Long-Term Treatment of Alcoholism: General Remarks

After the acute alcoholic state has subsided, it becomes necessary to plan the next stage in rehabilitation. The mainstay of any successful treatment is a combination of a plan for maintaining sobriety and a program of psychotherapy. Either by itself is unsuccessful.

Alcoholics Anonymous

The most readily available, by far the safest, and probably the most effective treatment plan of all is that of Alcoholics Anonymous (AA). Most psychiatrists are familiar with their program and most mental institutions have an affiliated chapter. AA starts with the assumption that only an alcoholic who has suffered deeply as a result of this disease can empathize with the problems of another alcoholic and can lead him to sobriety. Though informal in its observances, the movement is deeply religious. Each individual begins by acknowledging his own personal helplessness and his need for assistance from a Superior Power. They join with each other in a mutual assistance pact. Their thesis is that the alcoholic has a physical abnormality of metabolism as a result of which alcohol paralyzes his will in a way which is not experienced by the normal drinker. As a result, they insist on complete sobriety. When a member feels a growing urge to drink he calls upon a fellow member for assistance. One or more members will respond to his call and stay with him until the emergency is over. When a member lapses from sobriety, the reaction of the others is one of acceptance and understanding. Each year of sobriety is celebrated as a birthday as if the nondrinking life represents a rebirth, which in a fundamental psychological sense it is for so many of these people. In their public meetings, they tell each other of the suffering and degradation which was their lot as alcoholics. Oftentimes these autobiographical accounts are told with much humor, so that they develop a capacity to laugh at their own foibles as alcoholics. For many, the conversion to sobriety comes as a deeply moving religious experience in which continued religious observances play an important role. For all of them, it is an intensely social experience in which they stand prepared to give of themselves and their time unstintingly to their organization and the needs of a fellow sufferer. The psychological mechanisms whereby they achieve their results have not been studied systematically, but it can be surmised that many complex factors are involved. They have brought more people into a state of continued sobriety than any other purely spiritual or psychological approach. For this reason, it would seem logical to refer the alcoholic patient first to them. The psychiatrist should know the members of the local chapter. He should read their literature so that he understands their program clearly. He should work with them sympathetically and gratefully as effective members of the therapeutic community.

However, AA is not successful with everyone who tries it. The criteria for the selection of those patients for whom the program works is a project for psychological research. In the meantime, a trial of treatment is the best method of selection. For patients who have not responded to AA, other methods have proved of value. These will be discussed in the following pages.

The Conditioned Aversion Technique

In this procedure, the psychiatrist aims to establish a conditioned reflex in which the sight and smell of alcohol will arouse in the patient a feeling of revulsion. Although the details vary, the following example makes the method clear: Two or more patients are placed in an empty room where they are not permitted any food or water. They are given only alcoholic beverages and injections of apomorphine at appropriate intervals to promote emesis. The room is not cleaned and the ordeal continues until a conditioned reflex is established, usually in about forty-eight hours. Such an experience can indeed establish an aversion to alcohol which may last for many months. Unless it is supplemented by psychotherapy, however, relapses occur almost invariably.

Disulfiram. Probably the most important advance in the medical management of the alcoholic has been the use of disulfiram (tetraethylthiuram disulfide, formerly called antabuse). This drug reacts with alcohol in the blood stream to release acetaldehyde. This has a profoundly sickening effect on the patient and may be associated with alarming physical symptoms. If a patient has been medicated with disulfiram and then takes a drink, symptoms appear in about fifteen minutes—headache, flushing, nausea, salivation, burning of the eyes, and dyspnea. If the reaction is severe, as for example after the ingestion of a large dose of alcohol, the patient may become weak, suffer anginal pains and go into shock. The reaction is treated with intravenous antihistamines and the usual treatment for shock.

Most people feel that the patient should have a controlled alcohol-disulfiram reaction in the hospital, although some feel that this is not necessary. When a patient stops disulfiram, the alcohol effect can be elicited for three to five days afterwards. Patients develop a profound respect for the severity of the reaction and having once decided to start the medication, they are not likely to take a drink in a moment of rage or anxiety. Many patients in an embittered moment will stop the medication in a determination to resume their drinking but when three or four days have passed and they dare to try a drink the mood will often have passed and they will resume the medication.

The usual dose is a half gram tablet daily. Some patients react with persistent drowsiness. If so, the medication is given at bedtime and usually by the next morning this effect of the drug will have subsided. Other reactions include headache, weakness, nausea and loss of appetite. Some have complained of abdominal cramps, diminished potency, a metallic taste and a rash. Usually these side effects wear off after a week or two. If not, or if they are severe, then the dose may be decreased to half a tablet (0.25 gram) or even a quarter (0.125 gram). These reactions are rarely serious. A more serious reaction is the eruption of a psychosis. It was speculated by some that the psychosis had been held in check by alcohol and that with the removal of this support, the latent psychosis could no longer be kept in repression and therefore became clinically manifest. If this were true, one would expect psychotic episodes to follow the sudden sobriety which Alcoholics Anonymous imposes. If these do occur, they are rare. In any event, a much simpler explanation is to be found in the fact that in the early days of high disulfiram dosage, psychoses were seen in as many as 10 per cent of treated cases. Since the dose has been reduced, these reactions have become very rare. Disulfiram can produce abnormalities in the electroencephalogram. These factors, along with its capacity to produce drowsiness, suggest the more obvious idea that the psychoses were the result of toxic effects upon the cerebral cortex.

In fact, I believe that herein lies the secret of disulfiram's success. It produces an intolerance for alcohol but provides, simultaneously, a sedative effect which gives pharmacologic support to the patient who has been deprived of his alcohol. This idea is supported by the fact that disulfiram and chlorpromazine (thorazine), the recently discovered central nervous system depressant (see Chapters III, XV) potentiate each other. When given in combination, they produce a more profound and restful sleep than either one given separately.

Contraindications to Disulfiram. Disulfiram should be given with particular caution, if it is given at all, to patients with myocardial damage. Where the alcoholic debauchery seems to be adversely affecting the heart, the administration of disulfiram may conceivably be a life-saving measure. However, the fatalities which have been reported after the ingestion of alcohol by patients on disulfiram may be related to existing myocardial damage, although this is not a certainty. A report from Denmark lists five deaths due to the pharmacologic action of disulfiram in 11,000 treated cases. When this is compared with the incidence of complications of all kinds in untreated alcoholism it is felt to be a favorable ratio.

It has usually been stated that patients who have been drinking should have at least one week of sobriety before disulfiram is given. Recently, however, it was found that one can start the alcoholic patient on disulfiram at once, provided he is given 100 mg. of chlorpromazine with the initial 0.5 gram tablet of disulfiram. Chlorpromazine is repeated six hours later in a 50 mg. dose. The following day the 0.5 gram tablet of disulfiram is given with 50 mg. of chlorpromazine. The next day, the disulfiram tablet is given with 25 mg. of chlorpromazine. Thereafter, disulfiram is given alone. By this method, the nausea and vomiting of the disulfiram alcohol reaction is eliminated entirely. What is more important, patients who would be expected to show some psychomotor agitation on removal of the alcohol remained drowsy and calm. Some even sleep ten to twelve hours after the initial dose and wake up refreshed. On this regimen, many severely alcoholic patients are able to return to work within seventy-two hours without having experienced the common withdrawal symptoms. Either drug by itself is ineffectual. Only the combination as described is successful.

Patients on disulfiram have gotten severely ill as a result of inhaling the fumes of an aftershave lotion, after taking a medicine containing an alcoholic elixir or eating food prepared with a wine sauce. These are minor inconveniences against which the patient must nevertheless be warned.

Psychotherapy

To omit psychotherapy with these patients is to fail to understand the role which alcohol has played in their lives. Unable to resolve their emotional conflicts on their own, they turn to alcohol to supplement their defenses. The fact that alcohol proved to be a poor helper does not negate the fact that it contributed in some measure to their adaptation. In any event, these are people who have a tendency to employ infantile techniques for the solution of adult problems. To take away their alcohol and give them no protective devices in return is to increase the likelihood of relapse many times over.

Prior to disulfiram, psychotherapists were always defeated by the ease with which the alcoholic could relieve an exacerbation of anxiety by means of alcohol. The release of anxiety in the course of treatment resulted not in opportunities for new insights as with other patients, but more often in new alcoholic debauches. In the treatment of a phobia, for example, it becomes necessary sooner or later for the patient to face up to the situation in which his anxiety is intensified. Only in this way will the patient be able to learn the unconscious meanings of the situations which are responsible for these exacerbations. If, on the other hand, he is never able to mobilize the courage and the control to face the phobic situation realistically for even a few moments, then the understanding requisite to master the phobia will never be forthcoming. The alcoholic is like the phobic patient (indeed very commonly his underlying condition is a phobia), only instead of absenting himself physically from the phobic situation, he absents himself psychologically by obtunding his conscious awareness of reality. As a consequence therapeutic results were poor and psychiatrists approached the psychotherapy of alcoholics with much pessimism. The success of disulfiram in producing extended periods of sobriety has replaced this feeling with a wave of optimism. Reports are appearing in the literature of psychotherapeutic successes with alcoholics both in individual and in group psychotherapy. Ruth Fox of New York, for example, in a discussion of 150 alcoholics in psychotherapy, stated that close to 70 per cent of her patients were well along the road to complete rehabilitation. She estimated that without the aid of disulfiram, she could not have hoped for success in more than 10 per cent.

With the achievement of sobriety, the psychotherapy of the alcoholic becomes the same as that with other patients, that is to say, no less difficult, but on the other hand, not as hopeless as it seemed in the past. The underlying psychopathologic process emerges without the confusing overlay secondary to the alcoholism. The patient may then be seen to have a phobia, a depression, or a schizophrenia. As in other cases, data are collected from personal examination of the patient, from psychological testing and from social service. On the basis of this information, a working hypothesis concerning the patient's emotional maladaption is formulated, goals of therapy are set, and therapy is carried out in the prescribed fashion (see Chapters I, II).

A word might be added about countertransference. Very often, the patient will maintain sobriety as an act of love for his psychotherapist. Sometimes, the psychotherapist is seduced into counterfeelings of affectionate appreciation for this gift. When this happens, a trap has been set. The patient becomes aware of the personal emotional importance of his sobriety to the therapist. Sooner or later, the patient will avenge himself on the psychotherapist for the disappointments which he suffered early in life. If the therapist then reacts with disappointment, the patient's guilt feelings are intensified and his masochistic impulses to degrade himself become correspondingly greater. The therapist must make it clear that alcohol has severe limitations in its usefulness as a means of adaptation, but that its use represents to him an understandable attempt to diminish his own suffering and nothing more. Also, he explains to the patient how the continued use of alcohol makes it difficult or impossible to improve the patient's understanding of reality. However, he must add that the patient's sobriety is in no sense a personal favor or a gift as far as the therapist is concerned. In short, the therapist must discipline himself not to be too ambitious for a good therapeutic result, since the psychotherapist is apt to be most successful when he strives least for success.

Miscellaneous Considerations

Because of the popularity of psychosurgery in mental hospitals today, the question of lobotomy is brought up from time to time as a treatment of alcoholism. The suggestion is not without a certain logic. If alcoholism is a reaction to psychic anguish, and if lobotomy diminishes the intensity of this anguish, then lobotomy might seem indicated in some cases of alcoholism. As a matter of fact, it has not worked out that way. B. Talbot and his co-workers in Boston compared the drinking habits of 179 patients before and after lobotomy. There was no change in the drinking habits of 93 per cent of those who were returned to the community. Out of 167 nonalcoholics 5 patients became alcoholic for the first time after the operation. Of the 12 known alcoholics in this group, 4 drank more after the operation than previously. Only 3 stopped drinking entirely, leaving 5 in whom the drinking habits were unchanged. Deteriorated alcoholics have been lobotomized, too, without improvement. The reason for this lack of success is probably related to the curious intensification of oral drives which is commonly seen after lobotomy and which result so often in considerable weight gain postoperatively.

Alcoholism as a major cause of absenteeism is a matter of concern to business and industry. This provides an opportunity for the mental hospital psychiatrist to establish a liaison with the community which will be invaluable not only in the treatment of his alcoholic patients but in the entire treatment program of the hospital. There is a need to explain alcoholism as a disease and to educate management to stand by families with insurance plans and sickness benefits to cover alcoholic episodes in their workers. Furthermore, industry is in an excellent position to motivate their alcoholic workers to accept rehabilitation. The Consolidated Edison Company of New York, for example, instituted a program within its own organization, and over a period of two and a half years, succeeded in rehabilitating 52 per cent of its alcoholic workers.

When a psychosis occurs in an alcoholic patient, there is inevitably a discussion concerning the relationship between the psychosis and the alcohol. In some instances, as in clinically typical delirium tremens, there seems to be no question about the psychosis as an event which is specifically part of the alcoholic syndrome. Sometimes, however, a manic person will drink to excess as part of his general excesses, and a depressed man will drink to excess in a quest for sedation. A patient may be admitted with a schizophrenic episode which seems to have been precipitated by alcohol. This same patient may go into remission and have a second episode while in the hospital when access to alcohol is impossible. Thompson and Bielinski of California described six alcoholic patients, three with paranoid schizophrenia, and three with agitated involutional melancholia. In each case, the craving for alcohol was removed by the conditioned aversion treatment, using a mixture of emetine, ephedrine, pilocarpine and strychnine. It was planned to treat the psychosis after the alcoholism was interrupted. In each case, the state of continued sobriety was followed by a rapid improvement in the psychosis, indicating further the difficulties in elucidating the role of alcohol in the total adaptive mechanism of the patient.

The need for research in alcoholism provides another reason why the alcoholic belongs in the mental hospital. Much can be learned about mental mechanisms and psychosis in general from a study of the alcoholic psychoses. Many problems of group therapy with alcoholics under disulfiram remain to be worked out, as well as a more detailed psychological understanding of the AA program. This might lead, for example, to a more accurate way of selecting patients for AA, as well as a broadening of the AA program to the treatment of nonalcoholic patients.

SELECTED REFERENCES

Alcohol, Science and Society. Twenty-nine Lectures with Discussions as given at the Yale Summer School of Alcohol Studies. *Quart. J. Stud. Alcohol,* New Haven, 1945.
  May be employed in hospital training programs.
Alcoholics Anonymous. The Story of How Many Thousands of Men and Women Have Recovered from Alcoholism. New York: Works Publ., 1948.
  An official presentation of the AA program with considerable illustrative material.
ALLEN, E. B.; PROUT, C. T.: Alcoholism. Chap. XXIX in *Progress in Neurology and Psychiatry,* VIII. New York: Grune & Stratton, 1953.
  A valuable summary of experiences with disulfiram.
BROY, W. R.; TUPPER, W. E.: Sobering the Alcoholic Patient. *Northwest Med.,* 52:731, 1953.
  A recommended procedure for treating acute alcoholic intoxication.
CONSTANT, G. A.: Alcoholism—A Public Health Problem. *Texas State J. Med.,* 50:136, 1954.
  Contains useful statistics concerning ravages of alcoholism.
CUMMINS, J. F.; FRIED, D. G.: Use of Chlorpromazine in Chronic Alcoholics. *Am. J. Med. Sci.* 227:561, 1954.
  Describes a regimen for treating impending delirium tremens with a combination of disulfiram and chlorpromazine.
FELDMAN, D. J.; ZUCKER, H. D.: Present-Day Medical Management of Alcoholism. *J. A. M. A.,* 153:895, 1953.
  A comprehensive summary of medical aspects of the treatment of alcoholism.
GREENBAUM, H.: Group Psychotherapy with Alcoholics in Conjunction with Antabuse Treatment. *Int. J. Group Psychother.,* 4:30, 1954.
  A preliminary report of a useful approach that deserves further study.
LOLLI, G.: On Therapeutic Successes in Alcoholism. *Quart. J. Stud. Alcohol.,* 14:238, 1953.
  Takes up countertransference problems in the treatment of alcoholics.
MARTENSEN-LARSEN, O.: Five Years Experience with Disulfiram in the Treatment of Alcoholics. *Quart. J. Stud. Alcohol.,* 14:406, 1953.
  Unusually extensive experiences with disulfiram are summarized. Based on studies in the Alcoholics Treatment Center, Copenhagen.
MC CARTHY, R. G.: What Shall Our Schools Teach About Alcohol? *Nat. Parent-Teacher,* 48:19, 1954.
  Stresses the need for early widespread education concerning the dangers of alcoholism. Useful for public education programs.
SELINGER, R. V.: Present-Day Status of Medical-Psychological Aspects of Alcoholism. *Ment. Hyg.,* 33:570, 1949.
  A Summary of psychological findings in alcohol addicts.

—— Alcohol and Crime. *J. Crim. Law, Criminol. & Pol. Sci.*, 44:438, 1953.
     A statistical study of the role of alcohol in crime.
SHUPE, L. M.: Alcohol and Crime. *J. Crim. Law, Criminol. & Pol. Sci.*, 44:661, 1954.
     More statistics about the role of alcohol in crime.
THOMPSON, G. N.: BIELINSKI, B.: Improvement in Psychosis Following Conditioned-Reflex
     Treatment of Alcoholism. *J. Nerv. & Ment. Dis.*, 117:537, 1953.
TUREEN, L. L.: Some Observations on the Behavior Pattern of Alcoholics on Antabuse
     Therapy, *J. Nerv. & Ment. Dis.*, 119:43, 1954.
     Experiences are presented concerning psychotherapy with alcoholics receiving
     disulfiram.

Chapter XVIII

THE ADDICT

Introduction

Although the psychiatrist in the mental hospital does not ordinarily think of the drug addict as coming within his professional purview, the fact is that drug addicts are not infrequently admitted because of psychosis related to addiction. Bromides are an ancient offender in this regard. In recent years, barbiturate addiction has become a problem of major importance. Psychotic reactions may also occur with the use of marihuana, cocaine and amphetamine (benzidrine). In addition, an addict may request treatment in a mental hospital, at least as far as withdrawal of the drug is concerned. Here, as in the case of alcohol addiction, the psychiatrist is obligated to think of the withdrawal process as a springboard to a program of total psychiatric rehabilitation, never as an end in itself.

Definition of Addiction

Drug addiction is a condition in which an individual has become so accustomed to the repeated daily use of a drug that he is dependent upon it for his sense of well-being. If forced to abandon it, he suffers a psychic craving and may (although not with all drugs) develop a characteristic abstinence syndrome which is due, in part, to physiological alterations brought about by the drug. It has also been defined as a compulsive use of chemical agents which are harmful to the individual, to society, or to both.

Popular Misconceptions Concerning Drug Addiction

The following frequent misconceptions are from the brochure by Howe and Morris (see references):

Cure and Withdrawal: Measures directed to the relief of abstinence symptoms must not be regarded as a "cure." Unfortunately, at the present time, we have no successful method of curing drug addiction. The use of the drug may be stopped, whereupon addiction may be said to be arrested; social rehabilitation then may be effected. However, *a single dose of the addicting drug usually will induce relapse.*

Addiction and Habituation: Associated with addiction is a cellular dependence with definite withdrawal symptoms. In contrast, habituation is a psychic fixation. To illustrate, cocaine is not an addicting drug, for administration can be interrupted without significant somatic disturbances. Habituation must not be regarded as necessarily less serious than addiction for it may be practically as binding. The likelihood of a permanent cure in an individual who has used cocaine over a long period is poor. The difficulty many individuals encounter in trying to give up smoking is a matter of common experience which needs no further comment.

There has been much written concerning the psychologic make-up of individuals who become addicted, and many authorities hold that only the emotionally unstable can become involved. These authors seem to have overlooked the fact that addiction is, unlike habituation, principally a physiologic condition and not a mental state. No one would deny that certain people have a lower threshold for pain and discomfort than others and may become more readily affected by narcotics than those individuals with a more stable make-up. However, *addiction can occur in any one.* The belief that addiction is limited to the mentally or emotionally unstable has been widely held, is taught in medical schools, and frequently stated in the literature. Many intelligent persons have thus considered themselves immune from the danger of addiction. They have used these drugs, particularly Demerol, only to find themselves helplessly bound to a narcotic.

Addiction as an Illness, Not a Vice: Although from one point of view narcotic addiction may be looked upon as a "vice," dealing with it as such is singularly ineffective. The only proper and reasonable course is to recognize the condition as a disease which cannot be overcome merely by depriving the patient of his drug. Physicians must recognize at the outset that, to the one addicted, the drug seems to be the one supreme necessity of life.

The Addict "Against the World": Drug users are often judged with undue harshness. They try to preserve their place in society and protect themselves from the criticism and censure of their friends, from difficulties with the police, and from the sting of well-meaning but misguided public opinion. Because of their usual denial of drug use, addicts are commonly charged with being notorious liars and totally unreliable. Most drug users honestly believe they would die or go insane if deprived of their drugs. Thus they feel justified in doing anything necessary to protect themselves against either contingency.

The Addict and Crime: Individuals who have no difficulty in obtaining their drug, and to whom the cost is not a burden, do not as a rule constitute a danger to society. When the cost of the drug is beyond their means, as it usually is, addicts may turn to crime for the drug money. As a logical corollary some have proposed that we legalize the administration of narcotics to addicts by physicians, to protect them against the "dope peddler" and to destroy the illegal narcotic traffic by taking the profit out of it. This plan has worked out successfully in England.

Social pressures may intensify paranoid trends and result in overtly psychotic behavior.

Psychological Factors in Addiction

The capacity to develop in the user a state of psychological dependence is perhaps the outstanding characteristic of all habit-forming drugs. This in turn is based on the capacity of these drugs to reduce suffering which is the result of unresolvable emotional conflict. As in the case of the alcoholic, the drug addict, by and large, is apt to suffer from arrested emotional development. He is self-centered, has a low frustration tolerance, and a great need to be loved and protected. Psychological studies show that the drug addict, like the alcoholic, has a special preoccupation with the mouth which is rooted in frustrating relationships with parents in early childhood. For example, the father of the addict typically has played little or no role in the upbringing of the patient, whereas the mother has been an excessively protective and controlling person, toward whom the patient has deeply ambivalent feelings. Depressive, phobic and schizophrenic mechanisms are commonly encountered (see Chapter XVII).

In these patients, the drug is used as part of a pattern of emotional adaptation. During certain limited intervals, the individual may indeed adapt more successfully to the demands of the environment as a result of its use. However, relatively soon physiological and psychological alterations secondary to the use of the drug result in harmful effects which outweigh by far any limited benefits derived from it. The opiates (methedone especially) are particularly seductive to these psychological sufferers because of their ability to reduce anguish without seriously impairing the sensorium or the effectiveness of internalized behavior controls. Psychological test results in morphine addicts, for example, show a more "mature" record following an injection of morphine than that which existed before.

Drugs like the barbiturates, bromides and alcohol, on the other hand, reduce anguish but reduce all other higher functions as well, so that there is a clouded sensorium, an impairment of fine motor skills, and of inhibition. The difference between the opiates and other central nervous system depressants resides most likely in a demonstrable physiological difference in their action on the central nervous system. The opiates seem to act selectively on the nervous system (on long circuited internuncial chains, and most probably on the many synapses in such chains), whereas the other agents are more diffusely depressant in their action.

Even though the addict may have used the drug initially to improve his adaptation to reality, sooner or later it becomes a substitute for reality. Needs which required active social relations heretofore are obliterated completely by the drug or find substitute fulfillments in drug-induced reveries. The result of drug addiction, therefore, is a progressive surrender of all real emotional involvements in other human beings except as they are a source of drug supply.

In addition to the psychological factors, secondary needs develop in the addict, depending upon which drug is used, because of physiological alterations in the body. This can be shown with particular clarity in the case of morphine. Morphine produces simultaneously depression of some functions in the nervous system and excitation of others. The excitation appears to outlast the depression, and hence for a time after recovery from the depressant effect the level of excitation of the nervous system is higher than before the drug is administered. A second injection of morphine at this time will therefore have less of a depressant effect, and after recovery from depression, excitation will be enhanced still further. The same cycle of events follows each succeeding injection of morphine. This growing state of central nervous system hyperirritability is experienced as anxiety. It generates a new organisimal need which when gratified brings pleasurable relief. Eventually the gratification of this artificially induced need for the drug becomes an end in itself which displaces any other life goals which the addict may have cherished up to that time.

Cultural factors, too, play a role in the psychological mechanism involved in drug addiction. For example, the use of opiates involves the defiance of federal law. A particularly hostile attitude toward authority is not uncommon among prisoners who have been incarcerated for violation of the Harrison Narcotic Act. Many barbiturate addicts avoid alcohol because of intolerable guilt attendant upon its use. When they take a "medication," they do not feel that they are doing something wrong, as when they take a drink. The need to control overt expressions of aggression has led to the condoning of opiates by the Chinese, whereas they abhor the more generalized loss of control associated with alcohol. Our more aggressive culture, on the other hand, has been more accepting of the boisterous release associated with alcoholism than it has of the controlled reveries of opiate addiction. The initial use of narcotic drugs is due ordinarily to one of two general circumstances. In the older age group many instances of addiction are caused by injudicious medical use of addicting drugs. These should be employed with great caution or not at all in chronic painful conditions which are not expected to be terminal. Curiosity and imitativeness are the principle motivations in the adolescent group among whom alcohol and marihuana frequently precede the use of the opiate. Passive insecure youngsters are more likely to be seduced into the use of these drugs than those who are emotionally sound.

Tolerance and Physical Dependence

Tolerance and physical dependence are two characteristics of drug addiction. Tolerance refers to the diminishing effect on repetition of the same dose of the drug during continuous regular use. This seems to be the outcome of a metabolic change as a result of which the organism alters or destroys the drug at a more rapid rate. Physical dependence refers to the fact that the abrupt withdrawal of the drug after a period of continuous use results in the eruption of a group of disagreeable symptoms referred to as the abstinence syndrome. One mechanism whereby physical dependence can develop has already been described. Whatever the mechanism, physical dependence refers to the fact that the organism has adapted in its physiological function to the presence of the drug and in this sense the drug has become essential for health. In its absence, the physiological mechanisms become temporarily deranged; the individual becomes sick, and the disturbance may even be severe enough to cause death.

The Addicting Drugs

From a chemical point of view, addicting drugs fall into two categories: (1) opium, morphine and its transformation products, and (2) the synthetic analgesics.

Compounds Related to Morphine
1. Opium
2. Morphine
3. Codeine
4. Heroin
5. Dihydromorphinone Dilaudid
   Hydrochloride

6. Metopon Hydrochloride
7. 6-methyldihydromorphine
8. Racemorphan Hydrobromide
9. Dihydrocodeinone Bitartrate
        Hycodan Bitartrate, Dicodid

Though the various transformation products of morphine are members of the same family, they differ in their narcotic effect and their ability to produce addiction. Their effects are usually described in comparison with those of morphine. Codeine has such a slight narcotic action that it is not tempting to addicts. Recorded instances of addiction are infrequent. Heroin is rapidly acting and rapidly addicting. It is highly potent; its effects are produced by one quarter of the dose of morphine. As heroin is unnecessary for medical purposes its manufacture and importation are prohibited in this country and Canada and its use is discouraged by many other nations. The action of Dilaudid is nearly identical with that of morphine. Metopon is another highly potent member of the family with addicting properties. A related drug, 6-methyldihydromorphine, is reputed to have the analgesic properties of morphine, but with slightly less tendency to addiction, or at least milder withdrawal symptoms. Dromoran (Racemorphan) is at least four times as toxic and four times as analgesic as morphine, but has the same rate of tolerance production. Another derivative of morphine, dihydrocodeinone, is currently used in cough remedies.

The Synthetic Analgesics
1. Meperidine Hydrochloride (U.S.P.) — Demerol Hydrochloride, Isonipecaine, Dolantin, Pethedine hydrochloride (B.P.)
2. Methadone Hydrochloride — Methadone, Dolophine, Amidone, Miadone, Adanon Hydrochloride, Physeptone

The introduction of a totally new synthetic compound in 1939 was a chemical landmark, because some of the actions of morphine were achieved but with an entirely different chemical formula. This compound was marketed as Demerol, Dolantin and Pethedine, but is now officially termed meperidine hydrochloride. Similar in action to morphine, meperidine has proved to be just as addicting. Alteration of this new formula has yielded such drugs as ketobemidone (Cliradon) and Nisentil.

Methadone, another synthetic compound, has high analgesic action.

dl-Isomethadone, a related substance, was found to have only about one third the analgesic activity of morphine.

The most recent and unheralded analgesic synthetic compounds are the Diethienylbutenes, some of which are as potent as morphine, and also as addicting.

The Opiate Abstinence Syndrome

In the early stages of opiate addiction, withdrawal of the drug results in restlessness, depression and mild disturbances in the autonomic nervous system. These symptoms are not unendurable and they disappear within a few days. If the patient is chronically addicted and the drug is abruptly withdrawn, the patient shows some drowsiness for the first day. Restlessness, yawning, perspiration, rhinorrhea and lacrimation then appear. This is followed by dilation of the pupils, muscle twitching and goose flesh. Anorexia sets in, with vomiting and diarrhea, as well as generalized muscular aches and insomnia. Considerable weight may be lost in a single day. There is often low-grade fever. The blood pressure, heart rate and respiratory rate are increased. There is some hyperglycemia and leukocytosis. Increased red cell count, and hemoglobin and hematocrit readings reflect the considerable dehydration due to generalized fluid loss. The symptoms reach maximum intensity forty-eight hours after the last dose and remain severe during the next two days, following which there is a gradual decline of the symptoms. In seven to ten days after withdrawal, all acute manifestations subside, but patients complain of weakness, insomnia and nervousness for many months.

The symptoms so far described are all expressions of the physical dependence which the opiate has produced. They are stereotyped, follow the same pattern in all patients, and are expressions of the physiological reorganization which must take place in the absence of the drug. In addition, there are emotional reactions during withdrawal which are more individualized expressions of the patient's wish for relief. Various psychoneurotic manifestations may occur, but psychotic reactions are rare. When the patient's agonized pleas are met with a firm uncompromising attitude on the part of the physician, both components of the syndrome tend to be shortened. That there is a psychological factor in the physical component is further verified by the fact that delayed physical manifestations of the abstinence syndrome can appear weeks or even months later, after an extended period of physical comfort, when the patient is discharged from the hospital and drugs are once again available. The temptation, a purely psychological experience, can trigger off these symptoms again, as if through a conditioned reflex.

Diagnosis of Opiate Addiction

Usually the diagnosis of addiction is made on the patient's direct history. However, addicts may attempt to conceal the fact of their addiction at times, and the diagnosis must be made by other means. Physical examination may show healed or recent hypodermic puncture lesions which may be found over veins or in any portion of the body which is accessible to self-injection. Multiple abcesses or scars of healed abcesses are suggestive as are a dry tongue and constricted or nonreactive pupils.

A definitive diagnosis of addiction to morphine or similar drugs depends upon the demonstration of the characteristic signs of abstinence following complete and abrupt withdrawal. Recently, N-allylnormorphine (Nalorphine, Nalline) has been introduced as a rapid diagnostic device for establishing the existence of a state of opiate addiction, since its injection into the addict produces withdrawal symptoms at once. It will not precipitate abstinence symptoms in demerol addiction unless the patient is taking 2,000 mg. or more a day. The test must be carried out with great caution since an excessive dose of Nalorphine may be dangerous to the life of an addict. The recommended procedure is to examine first for the presence of withdrawal symptoms. If absent, the patient is given 3 mg. of Nalorphine subcutaneously. If the patient has been taking as much as 120 mg. of either morphine or methadone daily for fifteen days or more, definite abstinence symptoms will appear within twenty minutes. If these symptoms are not seen at the end of this period, an additional 5 mg. of Nalorphine is injected and the patient is observed for an additional twenty minutes. If abstinence symptoms have not appeared and if typical nalorphine effects are evident (pupillary constriction, pseudoptosis, slurring of speech and reduced respiratory rate), it is safe to conclude that the patient has not been taking morphine or methadone in sufficient dose or at sufficiently frequent intervals to create a significant degree of physical dependence. If a positive test is obtained, the patient should be given 15-30 mg. of morphine or methadone. Symptoms of abstinence precipitated by nalorphine will decline gradually during the course of two or three hours. If a negative test is obtained, the patient should be kept under observation until the direct effects of nalorphine have subsided; this will require about four hours. The procedure is contraindicated in addicts suffering from any serious organic disease. The American Medical Association recommends that it should never be carried out without full explanation to the patient and without written consent. Another physician should always participate in the proceedings as a witness in documenting the diagnosis of addiction.

Treatment of the Opiate Abstinence Syndrome

Morphine, heroin and diaudid are associated with the most severe abstinence syndromes. Codeine and Demerol yield qualitatively similar reactions but milder in intensity. Abstinence from methadone differs, in that few signs of disturbed autonomic function are seen, the onset is slow, the intensity mild and the course prolonged. The relative mildness of the methadone abstinence syndrome suggested its suitability in the management of the abstinence syndrome. Abrupt unaided withdrawal of opiate medication from an addict may be agonizing and sometimes dangerous to life. By the expedient of replacing the withdrawn morphine (for example) with methadone and then gradually reducing the methadone to zero abstinence can be achieved with less suffering and danger. A typical methadone withdrawal schedule is as follows:

Day	Stage	Drug	Amt. per Dose (Milligrams)	No. of Doses per day
1	addiction	morphine	90	4
2	substitution	morphine	45	4
3	substitution	methadone	15	4
4	substitution	methadone	22.5	4
5	reduction	methadone	10	4
6	reduction	methadone	10	4
7	reduction	methadone	5	4
8	reduction	methadone	5	4
9	reduction	methadone	4	4
10	reduction	methadone	2.5	4
11	reduction	methadone	2.5	3
12	reduction	methadone	2.5	2
13	reduction	methadone	2.5	2
14	reduction	methadone	2.5	1
15	abstinence	none	0	0

The methadone dose should be regulated so that it does not eliminate abstinence symptoms entirely. In patients with physically debilitating illness, the reduction process should be extended for thirty days or more. Supplementary sedation may be given at night during the second and third weeks of withdrawal, but excessive sedation should be avoided. Although methadone mitigates the intensity of the suffering and eliminates much of the physical danger, it also extends the period of suffering, a fact which makes it objectionable to many addicts. Experience has proven that the treatment of choice from the addict's point of view consists of abrupt withdrawal of all opiates with supportive treatment for the withdrawal symptoms. Initially, addicts will choose the metha-done procedure but with repeated experiences they object to it increas-ingly, not only because of the prolongation of the abstinence reaction but because of the extended period of generalized physical debility which follows it.

Various agents have been used for supportive purposes. Hyoscine, insulin in small doses, calcium gluconate in combination with nicotinic acid and barbiturates, and prolonged narcosis are examples. Prolonged narcosis is a hazardous procedure unless carried out with expert around-the-clock nursing. In recent years electroconvulsive therapy (ECT) has been used increasingly with satisfactory results. The availability of this procedure and personnel who are expert in its application make it particularly suitable for a mental hospital setting. Patients with severe addiction are taken off the drug at once and are given ECT. This is repeated symptomatically. They usually require three to four treatments during the first twenty-four hours, two or three treatments during the second twenty-four hours, and one treatment a day for about a week. After this period a treatment is given on alternate days and at increas-ingly less frequent intervals, depending on the patient's needs. Most patients require a total of about twelve treatments although some manage with much less and others require considerably more. This seems to be the simplest and probably the safest of all the withdrawal procedures.

Drug addicts are usually in poor physical condition on admission to the hospital. The initial task is to improve the general condition of the patient as quickly as possible. Parenteral fluids and vitamins in high dosage are essential. Careful diagnostic studies should be carried out, including serologic tests for lues, chest X-ray, and complete blood studies.

Howe and Morris state that there are four cardinal principles in the treatment of addiction:

Institutional treatment is essential to successful therapy; outpatient treatment never should be attempted.

Narcotic drugs should never be prescribed to an addict for self-administration.

Addicts are ill persons and should be treated as such.

Upon the discovery of the presence of addiction, immediate treatment should be instituted before withdrawal symptoms become manifest.

It is clear from the foregoing material that the treatment of the addict must take place in a hospital and that the mental hospital, or even the general hospital, is well equipped to deal with this problem.

The Habituating Drugs

Cocaine, marihuana, the drugs of the amphetamine group, the barbiturates, bromides and other drugs may be habit-forming but do not give rise to the state of physiological dependency characteristic of the addicting drugs. That is to say, abrupt withdrawal of these drugs does not result in a characteristic and unvarying series of somatic disturbances.

Cocaine. At the present time the use of cocaine, in this country, is principally confined to occasional indulgences by individuals addicted to heroin or morphine. Their purpose is to obtain a euphoric experience which no longer accompanies the use of opiates.

While opiate addiction may result from the legitimate medical use of these drugs, the use of cocaine for its intoxicating effects usually results from an effort to experience various kinds of emotional or sensual gratification.

Cocaine, by whatever route it is administered, produces a euphoric reaction with elevation of mood, a feeling of physical and mental prowess, and hallucinations which are usually pleasurable and may be sexually oriented. As cocaine is rapidly destroyed in the tissues and the subjective stimulation lasts but a few minutes, the habitual user repeats the administration every ten or fifteen minutes, sometimes for several days. Tolerance does not develop to the extent noted with opiates; however, amounts up to ten or fifteen grams daily have been used. The size of a fatal dose is unknown; death results from paralysis of respiration.

Continued use of cocaine frequently results in a toxic psychosis with paranoid delusions. The persecutory delusions are associated with terrifying auditory and visual hallucinations which may cause the addict to be destructive to himself and to anyone with whom he may come in contact.

In spite of legislation to control the indiscriminate sale of barbiturates, habituation to these drugs remains common. As previously mentioned, the barbiturates, like alcohol, have a more diffusely depressant effect upon the central nervous system. Although the opiate addict may appear alert and in full possession of his faculties, the chronic barbiturate addict is confused and irritable, reacts and speaks slowly, exhibits somnolence, dysarthria, nystagmus and ataxia. The presence of round, punched out ulcers in the skin of the extremities may be due to subcutaneous injections of barbiturates or attempts to inject them intravenously. Confirmatory evidence of chronic barbiturism may be found in an electroencephalographic record characterized by diffuse fast activity.

The clinical features of the abstinence syndrome when barbiturates are withdrawn vary, and are probably related to the duration of the habituation and the amounts of the drug to which the individual has become accustomed. In some, grand mal convulsions may appear suddenly between the twenty-fourth and forty-eighth hours. In others, the seizures may be preceded by tremors, choreiform and athetoid movements or bizarre involuntary movements of whole extremities; these may occur without subsequent convulsions. Usually such symptoms are preceded or accompanied by intense diffuse anxiety, generalized weakness, low blood pressure and high nonprotein nitrogen in the blood.

Between the fourth and the seventh days further personality changes may occur in some individuals, including anxiety attacks, homosexual panic and paranoid reactions, hallucinatory delusional states, delirium, and amnesic confabulatory reactions. These may be seen in different patients and in the same patient at different times. These reactions may go on for several weeks. Recovery, however, appears to be complete.

If barbiturate intoxication is not suspected, a host of erroneous diagnoses may be made, such as hysteria or other types of psychoneurosis, epilepsy, schizophrenia, alcoholic delirium tremens or Korsakoff's psychosis. If these mistakenly diagnosed conditions are then treated with barbiturates, a vicious cycle may be set up which will continue until the proper diagnosis is made. A careful history and physical examination, with an electroencephalogram and a blood nonprotein nitrogen determination should make the proper diagnosis possible in most cases.

Management of the barbiturate abstinence syndrome consists primarily of slow withdrawal of the drug over a period of a month. This will usually prevent the convulsions characteristic of the first stage. Psychotic reactions, however, may emerge notwithstanding. If exhausting hyperactive reactions ensue, the patient may be sedated by means of electroshock therapy.

Bromide addiction can produce a similar clinical picture, although the incidence of this drug as an offending agent has decreased sharply in our time. The presence of the acneform eruption characteristic of bromide intoxication and a blood bromide determination if this is available in the hospital laboratory will establish the diagnosis.

Long-Term Treatment of Addiction

The management of the acute withdrawal reaction represents only the first phase in the treatment of drug addictions. The long-term treatment of the drug addict is as difficult as the treatment of alcoholism was prior to the introduction of disulfiram. That is to say, the incidence of relapse is very high and understandably so when suffering is intense and pharmacologic relief immediately at hand. Nevertheless, successful treatment depends ultimately on psychotherapy carried out during an extended period of abstinence. The most optimistic estimate of "beneficial" results from adequate treatment is in about 35 per cent of treated addicts. The possibilities of group therapy in the treatment of addicts are in their early phases of exploration. A program for addicts paralleling Alcoholics Anonymous is also in its beginnings (Narcotics Anonymous, c/o YMCA, 215 West 23 Street, New York City). One day, a pharmacologic agent corresponding to disulfiram may become available in the management of drug addiction too.

Finally, the psychiatrist can make a prophylactic contribution in the form of public education concerning the dangers of addiction, the need to regard addiction as a sickness, and the provision of treatment facilities in the community, particularly for the young addict (see Chapter XVI). Continued research in group techniques of treatment is a matter of top priority.

SELECTED REFERENCES

COUNCIL ON PHARMACY AND CHEMISTRY REPORT: What to Do with a Drug Addict. *J. A. M. A.*, 149:1220, 1952.
    A statement prepared for the general practitioner by the Committee on Drug Addiction and Narcotics of the National Research Council giving pertinent Federal regulations, diagnosis, disposition and recommendations concerning treatment.

EDITORIAL: Rapid Diagnosis of Addiction to Morphine, *J. A. M. A.*, 154:414, 1954.
    Describes the "Nalline" technique of diagnosing opiate addiction.

FORT, J. P., JR.: Heroin Addiction Among Young Men. *Psychiatry*, 17:251, 1954.
    Presents psychological findings and suggestions for group and individual psychotherapy.

FRASER, H. F.; ISBELL, H.; EISENMAN, A. J.; et al.: Chronic Barbiturate Intoxication: Further Studies, *A. M. A. Arch. Int. Med.*, 94:34, 1954.
    Describes the characteristics of barbiturate intoxication including psychological, electroencephalographic and biochemical data.

HOWE, H. S.; MORRIS, L. S.: *Treatment of Withdrawal Symptoms of Persons Addicted to Narcotic Drugs*. Welfare and Health Council of New York City, 44 East 23 Street, New York 10, N. Y.
    A pamphlet which is extraordinarily rich in data of practical importance concerning the diagnosis of drug addiction and the treatment of the abstinence syndrome.

WIKLER, A.: *Opiate Addiction. Psychological and Neurophysiological Aspects in Relation to Clinical Problems*. Springfield, Ill.: C. C. Thomas, 1953.
    A short monograph detailing the important contributions of Wikler and his associates. Contains an excellent bibliography, particularly as it concerns experimental aspects of addiction.

—— Drug Addiction. In: Tice's *Practice of Medicine*, 8:17, 1953. Hagerstown, Md.: W. F. Prior Co.
    A summary of clinical aspects of drug addiction. Contains a description of methadone withdrawal procedure.

Chapter XIX

THE MENTAL DEFECTIVE

Introduction

It has often been said that mental deficiency is the stepchild of psychiatry. To a considerable extent this is understandable. The problems of diagnosis and treatment are no less formidable than they are in the field of psychiatry in general, yet the achievements often seem less gratifying because of the lesser apparent social usefulness of the patients treated. Let us leave aside the fact that many kindly mental defectives contribute richly to the happiness of those about them; or that many of the evils in the world today are the contributions of their more intelligent brothers; the basic fact is the physician's obligation to do his utmost to help all who need it, even when his patients are mentally defective. In the words of Helen MacMurchy,

> The Golden Rule applies to them. We are to do for them what we would others should do for us. Give them justice and a fair chance. Do not throw them into a world where the scales are weighted against them. . . . But give them one chance to bring out the best that is in them. This is but a fair request on behalf of human beings who nevertheless are permanent children and who will never grow up—whose joys and sorrows, and sins and virtues are all on a childish scale. Responsibility, except so far as a child understands it, is not their portion. The achievements of life, for them, are bounded by their mental make-up and character—just as our own achievements are, though on a little larger scale.

Fatalism and defeatism have no more place in regard to mental deficiency than in any other category of disease. Mental defectives present problems for solution. In the search for answers, methods of prevention and treatment inevitably appear, and no one can presume to guess what the ultimate contributions may be. Furthermore, however little we can do

262

for them, these patients can do a lot for us. To the physician, they present a wealth of neurological material and some of the most tantalizing problems in physiological chemistry and embryology. To the psychologist, the relative simplicity of the mind of a mental defective with its freedom from complicated cultural overlay, presents an ideal experimental preparation. They offer a unique opportunity for the study of emotional development and expression, psychological mechanisms of defense, the learning process, new psychological test procedures, and techniques of play therapy. To the teacher, the social worker, the lawyer, the law enforcement official, these patients have much to teach about those who are less crippled intellectually.

Most important of all, the psychiatrist cannot avoid the problem of mental deficiency. In his clinic work, mentally defective patients will doubtlessly be referred for diagnosis and disposition. He will have to guide parents, teachers, social agencies, courts and law enforcement officials in their problems with mental defectives. He may be called upon to deal with the emotional havoc wrought in a family by the presence of a mental defective—the alcoholism of a father, the depression of a mother, the behavior disturbance in a younger sibling. And even though the vast majority of institutionalized mental defectives do not reside in mental hospitals, psychotic outbreaks do occur among them, and an understanding of their capabilities and their limitations is essential for proper treatment planning.

Definition of Mental Deficiency

Mental deficiency has been defined as a condition of arrested or incomplete mental development existing before adolescence, caused by disease or genetic constitution, and resulting in social incompetence. Thus, there are sociological factors embodied in the concept of the social inadequacy of the defective, psychologic factors which are embodied in the concept of arrested or incompleted mental development, and biological factors which are contained in the reference to disease and genetic factors. By this definition, mental deficiency is not a single condition but a symptom which can occur as a result of many causes and in association with many other manifestations.

Diagnosis and Classification

Psychological testing is of foremost importance in establishing a diagnosis of mental deficiency. By comparing the performance of an average population of a given age on a variety of standardized test situations, it becomes possible to establish test norms for each age level. If an individual of age ten, for example, should then achieve a score which is equal to that achieved by the average child of five, it was common to say that this child of chronological age (C.A.) ten had a mental age (M.A.) of five. If his mental age was then divided by his chronological age and multiplied by one hundred, a figure was obtained which was called his intelligence quotient (I.Q.).

$$\text{I.Q.} = \frac{\text{M.A.}}{\text{C.A.}} \times 100$$

In the foregoing example, $\text{I.Q.} = \frac{5}{10} \times 100$ or 50.

D. Wechsler found that it was fallacious to compare the performance of an adult with the performance of a child because intelligence is compounded of many factors which change unequally as the individual grows older. He devised a battery of tests (see Chapter IX) which were standardized for large populations of adults at all age levels so that it became possible to compare the performance of an adult of a given age with the average performances of other adults of that same age. The intelligence quotient was then calculated, not on the basis of the performance of a child of a vastly different age, biological development and life experience, but on the basis of the average level of performance for that age which was scored as an I.Q. of 100. Recently, Wechsler devised a similar test scale for the improved measurement of the intelligence of children.

On the basis of their performance on mental tests, defectives are usually divided into low, middle and high grade levels of mental deficiency.

The low grade defective, or idiot is said to have less intelligence than the average three-year-old child. In more modern terminology, we say he has an I.Q. of 20 or less. He does not have enough understanding to stay out of danger. Often he does not seem to distinguish between food and inedible objects. Toilet habits are usually lacking in spite of attempts at training. He may be able to utter a few words. He may be capable of showing affection as well as outbursts of anger and excitement.

The middle grade defective, or imbecile has been compared to the average child of between three to seven. He has an I.Q. of 20 to 49. He has enough understanding to avoid obvious danger. He can speak simple phrases, write his name, and perhaps read short sentences. He is capable of learning personal cleanliness and can carry out simple useful tasks like sweeping a floor, if he is supervised.

The high grade defective, or moron, has been compared to the average eight- to eleven-year-old child. He has an I.Q. betwen 50 and 75. He may be able to complete the sixth grade in school. Often he can be a wage earner trained to do unskilled or even semiskilled work. Unlike the foregoing categories, the high grade mental defective usually appears normal and goes unnoticed except for his inability from time to time to manage his affairs or to solve ordinary problems. Because of his incapacity to understand the need to conceal his sexual excitement, he may be arrested for exhibitionism or other perverse sexual activities. Because of the failure to understand the need for contraception, illegitimate pregnancies are common. Mental deficiency rather than abnormally intense sexual drive is responsible for this behavior. In school, his intellectual limitations may not be appreciated and he may be plied with tasks which are beyond his ability. As a result, he may become truant. His increased suggestibility makes him prey to more domineering delinquent companions. All these factors contribute to patterns of antisocial conduct which are not uncommonly seen in this group.

The foregoing classification has the disadvantage of being excessively mechanical, and presents a falsely rigid conception of the problem. It omits the fact that the pattern of adaptation displayed by the mental defective is the product of genetic, physical, cultural, socioeconomic, educational and emotional determinants, some of which are subject to considerable alteration through appropriate intervention. For this reason, Kanner has suggested that mental deficiency be divided into: (1) absolute retardation, in which a primary irreversible intellectual deficit is of greatest importance; (2) relative retardation, in which modifiable emotional and situational factors play a critical role in determining the capacity for adaptation in the community of a person with borderline intelligence; (3) pseudo retardation, which resembles mental deficiency in some of its clinical manifestations but is associated with normal or above average intelligence. Sometimes this may represent a passive dependent way of relating to others which is part of a severe psychoneurosis. Children with so-called infantile autism, or with childhood schizophrenia refrain from talking, fail to respond to stimuli, or to engage in intelligent activity. In these instances, the picture is the result of an emotionally determined withdrawal of attention or an inhibition of emotional expression in individuals of normal intelligence. Certain specific disabilities which interfere with learning may contribute to a syndrome of pseudo retardation, such as impaired hearing or vision, reading disability, word deafness, and minor motor handicaps. In addition to the intellectual deprivations which inevitably result from these disabilities, emotional disturbances may arise which intensify the picture of pseudo retardation.

This approach emphasizes the fact that the problem of the mental defective, like that of all the mentally ill, should be formulated dynamically on the basis of data concerning the patient and his home environment collected from all the usual sources, utilizing the services of the social worker, the psychologist, the teacher and all the activities directors who are involved with the child, as well as from clinical observation by the psychiatrist himself. In short the psychiatrist should attempt to visualize what a patient is trying to achieve in life, what factors are frustrating him, and how his clinical picture represents a compromise or an attempt to adapt to these conflicting forces. From this point of view, the I.Q. is only one item in a much larger picture in which emotional factors assume a role of predominant importance in the majority of cases (see Chapter IX for further discussion of this point).

Somatic Factors in Mental Deficiency

Multiple Genes. Approximately 30 per cent of all mental defectives show no clinical manifestations aside from intellectual impairment. This group has been referred to as the undifferentiated form of mental deficiency. Because of the frequency with which parents, siblings and cousins are similarly affected, it has also been called the familial form of mental deficiency.

The distribution of intelligence quotients in our general population tends to follow the bell-shaped curve of Gauss. Just as the majority of people of average intelligence tend to cluster about the peak of the curve, so do the majority of these undifferentiated cases of mental deficiency represent the lower part of that curve, and are as integral a part of the population as individuals of superior intelligence with I.Q.'s over 130, who make up the other end of the curve. From the form of the curve it could be predicted that the majority of this group of cases would be high grade mental defectives, with only a very small number of cases in the low grade category. This prediction conforms with the actual facts.

The available evidence indicates that intelligence depends upon the combined action of many genes, each alone producing a small effect. It is safe to assume on the same basis that the undifferentiated type of mental deficiency is also determined by multiple genes. The frequent familial incidence of this type of deficiency is in accord with this hereditary hypothesis. It should be reiterated that emotional, physical and sociological deprivation plays a role of critical importance in many of these cases.

Dominant Genes. When a disease which is present in one parent is invariably transmitted to the offspring, it is said to be carried by a dominant gene. Tuberosclerosis, neurofibromatosis, and nevoid idiocy, a group of diseases in which mental deficiency is associated with characteristic skin lesions, are instances of such defects. Often the defect appears in incomplete form in one generation and becomes more severe in a subsequent one. The occurrence of sporadic cases is explained by assuming a new mutation in a parental germ cell.

Recessive Genes. A disease which becomes clinically manifest only through the combination of genes from both parents is said to be carried by recessive genes. Amaurotic family idiocy, gargoylism, phenylpyruvic idiocy, hepatolenticular degeneration, and some cases of diffuse sclerosis, are examples of this. The incidence of consanguineous marriages is significantly higher in this group than in the general population.

Infections in the Mother. Syphilis in the mother accounts for a small per cent of mentally defective children. With modern methods of detection and cure, this cause is decreasing even further in importance.

Rubella, or German measles during the first three months of pregnancy often results in severe mental deficiency in the child. Besides intellectual impairment, these patients often show deafness, congenital anomalies of the heart and eyes and microcephaly.

It is a fact that many mothers of mentally defective malformed children suffered from acute virus disease during pregnancy with a greater frequency than mothers of normal children.

Infection in the Children. In 10 to 20 per cent of all institutionalized defectives, the intellectual abnormality was the result of an encephalitis of viral or bacterial origin. In the past few years, the increased use of antibiotics has resulted in a decreased death rate from this cause, but also in a noticeable rise in the number of partially recovered defective patients. The degree of mental deficiency in postencephalitic children varies considerably from case to case, and in a given case from month to month, prior to stabilization. It is said that episodes of overactivity, restlessness, impulsiveness, assaultiveness, and destructiveness, characterize this group. While this is often true, the general reaction is determined by the previous personality traits of the child and by environmental stress rather than by the specific effect of the encephalitis per se.

Trauma. About 20 per cent of all institutionalized defectives are victims of birth trauma. Difficult labor and prematurity are the most frequent immediate causes of asphyxia, anoxia and cerebral hemorrhage. However, it should be emphasized that over 50 per cent of all children with clinical evidence of birth injury are not mentally defective.

Toxic Factors. Eclampsia is a factor in some cases of mental deficiency. Deep X-ray treatment to the abdomen during pregnancy can result in mentally defective children with microcephaly and other congenital abnormalities. This rarely occurs now since pregnancy tests are made routinely before irradiating women of childbearing age.

Blood incompatibility due to the Rh. factor is the cause of a very small per cent of mental deficiency.

Mongolism makes up 5 to 10 per cent of all defectives. It shows characteristic physical manifestations in the fetus prior to the third month of development. Although etiologic factors are not understood, it is regarded as a consequence, somehow, of advanced age in the mother, with associated endocrine disorders and pathological lesions of the uterus.

Endocrine Factors. Although endocrine abnormalities are quite common in mental deficiency, these play a primary etiologic role infrequently. Cretinism is the best known example of mental deficiency caused by endocrine defect occurring endemically in some geographic areas and sporadically elsewhere. Froehlich's syndrome, based on a hypopituitary state, is associated with obesity, hypogenitalism and at times with mild mental deficiency.

Outpatient Treatment of Mental Deficiency

It has been estimated that 1 per cent of our population, or approximately one and a half million peole, suffer from mental deficiency. Only 10 per cent of these, however, are institutionalized. Thus, the vast majority of mental defectives are cared for in the community. In part, this is due to overcrowding of available facilities. In addition, however, this is made possible by the availability of special classes in the public schools, social service help for families, guidance in mental hygiene clinics by psychiatrists, organization of parents into mutual help groups, and by foster home placements.

The following are a few basic principles (see *Forgotten Children,* references) with which families of mental defectives should be acquainted:

The condition is not curable nor will the child "outgrow" it. At first, this is not easy to accept, but it is wise to face it.

Though the child cannot become normal, parents can do much for his welfare.

Social service agencies stand ready to help, and many states and towns have mental health clinics, where psychological examinations can be carried out. Social workers help the family to understand the nature of the child's handicap and provide whatever other help they can.

Habit and character training is possible for the mentally retarded child, even the low grade. Agreeable manners can help offset the child's other limitations.

Parents should not prevent their mentally retarded child from doing the simple work he can do. Participation in household chores should be required. Disciplined and systematic training should be a daily affair.

Avoid overprotection. Facilities should be arranged for enjoyable times outside the home. At times, he may be able to play happily with younger children.

Parents should be particularly mindful of the susceptibility of these handicapped children to antisocial and delinquent influences, and supervise their social activities accordingly.

The mental health of an entire family should not be jeopardized by the mentally retarded child. This may be a factor necessitating institutional care.

A few states have a home training program for defective children. The availability of such facilities should be explored. Home training for mental defectives can be carried out only under favorable circumstances. The capacities of the child must be evaluated. This calls for detailed physical, laboratory, psychological and psychiatric studies of the child. The capacity of the home to meet the need of the child must also be evaluated. This calls for careful social service study. If on the basis of these findings it is felt that the child is suitable for home training, this can be carried out by the mother under the direction of a properly trained worker. An unusually fine program for home training is to be found in an article by M. J. Gianini and co-workers which is reprinted in Appendix D.

There are several voluntary organizations of parents and relatives of mentally defective children to promote public education, improvement of state institutions, material and voluntary service contributions to these institutions, legislative reforms and better facilities for the education of retarded children in the schools (for example, the Association for the Help of Retarded Children, Inc., 323 Fourth Avenue, New York City; also see references).

It has been estimated that 2 per cent of all school children are in need of special training because they are mentally defective. Schools should be on the alert for this problem. Specially trained teachers and separate classes should be provided. Reading and writing instruction are minimal, and geared to the practical needs of life rather than the child's leisure time pleasure. Most instruction is given through field trips and demonstrations. Handwork and manual training as well as practical experience in shops and kitchens are important. Daily experiences should put emphasis on personal hygiene, speech correction, good manners, orderliness and punctuality.

Vocational guidance for defectives is important in the extreme. They should have work which is compatible with their limited ability. They need an employer who will maintain a personalized parental relationship. They must be taught to save their earnings. Employment should be year round and frequent changes should be avoided. Large numbers of boys are in agriculture, mills or in shops, and a few are in transportation work. Girls find occupation in factories, laundries, homes and restaurants. Thus, with proper training and sympathetic after-school supervision, they can become ordinary, decent, working citizens who attend to their own business and make their own way in such a manner as to be in no sense a social burden or a menace.

An important development in the outpatient treatment of mental defectives is the sheltered workshop. These shops serve two functions; as a training school to prepare the trainee to be useful and independent, and as a permanent job to help the more severely limited person to be as useful and as happy as possible. The organization of a sheltered workshop is a complicated process. A full-time director is necessary, also work space, a staff for psychological testing and training, public support, contracts and subcontracts, and liaison with industry for placing trainees. Such shops are rarely self-supporting although an important part of its funds can come from the sale of its products. The remainder of its funds must be derived from tuition, membership dues, donations, and grants from agencies. Applicants must be screened socially, in terms of the capacity for self-care, co-operation, group relationships and motivation. They must also be screened psychologically in terms of academic achievement, performance on tests, social maturity, manual dexterity and prognosis. The psychiatrist's evaluation takes in the problem of emotional stability, the presence of overt emotional disease, the need for psychotherapy or special work assignments. The general medical and neurological examination takes into account physical appearance, the presence of seizures and the need for anticonvulsive therapy, and the presence of other forms of physical disability.

The staff works with the family as well as with the trainee for the improvement of the home environment. Social service maintains a liaison with other agencies, including the state vocational rehabilitation agency and the State Employment Service (see Chapter V). Although many trainees can ultimately be placed on farms, as domestics, or as janitors, most trainees utilizing the services of such centers require permanent vocational shelter. The program should be organized accordingly. Examples of jobs that have been successfully handled by such shops include sorting newspapers, burlap bags, repairing furniture, packing and assembling toys.

To complete the possible functions of a sheltered workshop it should also serve as a recreation center, arranging for parties, dances, movies and trips.

(More information concerning the successful operation of a sheltered workshop can be obtained by writing to Mrs. P. Hoffman, workshop chairman, Sheltered Workshop of the Aid to Retarded Children, Inc., 1820 Balboa St., San Francisco, Calif.)

The Role of Social Service

In those instances where social service finds that the home of the mentally defective child cannot meet his emotional needs, foster home placement may be arranged (see Chapter XXXVI). Such placement may be arranged directly or more frequently after a period of treatment and training in an institution. Ideally such placements should be undertaken as temporary measures with an independent job in the community and return to an improved home environment as the goal.

Groups of mental defectives may be placed in a home in the community which is sometimes referred to as a "colony." The colony is usually provided with a full-time house mother and a treatment team to assist the residents of the home in achieving maximal self-fulfillment in the community. The social worker, under the direction of a psychiatrist, can conduct group discussions as well as individual casework. The colony maintains a recreation program and facilities for education and training. The colony social worker may provide for summer camp or other vacation opportunities. Residents are usually placed at jobs in the community from which they return in the evening to the colony. Here as in foster home placement the goal is an independent job in the community and return to an improved home environment.

The social worker involved in the foster home or colony placement establishes liaison with social service agencies in the neighborhood of the patient's family, so that social casework with the family can go on with maximal effectiveness during the period of placement, and aftercare can be provided for the patient more conveniently when he returns to his own home.

The social worker plays a crucial role in maintaining a maximal number of mental defectives in the community as independent and effective individuals. For this reason states should seek to expand their social services for mental defectives. Actual field studies have repeatedly demonstrated that increased expenditures for social services are more than compensated for by savings in extramural placements.

Institutional Care of Mental Defectives

The available public institutions for mental defectives have many serious limitations. In a survey carried out by the American Association on Mental Deficiency a few years ago, it was reported that the average overcrowding in institutions was 20 per cent; the majority of the institutions did not have a formal course of training for attendants; 51 per cent of the institutions believed that their fire protection facilities were inadequate; 72 per cent felt that their psychological facilities were inadequate; the majority did not have a college graduate dietitian and felt that their dietary facilities were otherwise inadequate; 75 per cent felt that their X-ray facilities were inadequate; 45 per cent similarly criticized their laboratory facilities; 35 per cent their hospitalization facilities; 45 per cent their dental care; 66 per cent their facilities for patient activities; and 72 per cent the facilities of the school department. The biggest handicaps in order of importance were listed in the following categories: personnel, budget, buildings, and equipment.

The situation since that report has, if anything, deteriorated. The number of patients referred for admission is increasing. Among them the percentage of trainable people is falling off steadily. Low grade mental deficiency is being diagnosed much earlier, and pediatricians are urging families to institutionalize these infants at once. This may be good advice, but waiting lists are long and nursery facilities for these youngest defectives are in greatest shortage of all. As a result of medical advances the longevity of low grade defectives has increased considerably. These severely retarded patients are being admitted earlier and are living longer than ever before. The resultant overcrowding inevitably impairs the effectiveness of the training program for those who can be rehabilitated.

With all these disadvantages, there are many situations in which institutionalization is unavoidable, when, for example, the defective is without a home or is not well taken care of in his home; or when he is a major disrupting force to the mental health of the rest of the family; if the community or school lacks training facilities for the mentally retarded; and in cases in which the child tends to be a danger to himself or those about him. Many times youngsters suitable for training cannot be admitted and the optimal period for training may be lost, only to have them admitted later as an emergency problem in the community. In the meantime, siblings may develop behavior disturbances, parental discord with alcoholism, depression and broken homes may all follow in the wake of retardation. It is apparent that expanded training facilities for mental defectives are urgently needed.

Institutional care for the lowest grade mental defectives is unavoidably custodial. However, for the others there must be a treatment program which rests on the four pillars of education, vocational training, proper placement in the community as far as job and family life are concerned, and mental hygiene. The latter calls for all the techniques of mental hospital treatment that can be marshaled in the institution. Special group therapy techniques with mental defectives must be evolved. The possibilities of play therapy should be explored further. A volunteer program for expansion of activities should be organized, if possible. In search for sheltered work situations, we should not lose sight of the state institutions themselves which in many ways may provide the finest sheltered work situations of all. When patients are sufficiently improved, they can be discharged from their status as patients and placed on the payroll, not only in their own hospital but in other public institutions. This holds true, of course, not only for the placement of mental defectives but for general psychiatric patients as well.

Delinquent defectives present a special problem. It is universally accepted that they require separate facilities. The expediency of mingling them with other intellectually normal delinquents or with nondelinquent defectives carries with it obvious hazards.

Somatotherapy in Mental Deficiency

Cretins are capable of considerable improvement if given thyroid early in life and for long periods of time. Surgical removal of diseased brain tissue results in improved mental function in some defectives. Glutamic acid has been used with equivocal results. Electroconvulsive therapy is useful in the treatment of mental defectives for the same conditions as in patients with normal intelligence, namely for the symptomatic relief of depression and for acute psychotic disturbances. Although some defective patients have been reported benefited by lobotomy, often this may result in further disorganization of behavior. In any event, cases should be selected with great care.

Sterilization of Mental Defectives

Sterilization is often advocated in the treatment of mental deficiency. In some states it is sanctioned, and in others it is, under certain circumstances, even required. In the case of dominant gene disorders sterilization of affected adults seems biologically justifiable. However, it is not always possible to recognize the incomplete forms of these syndromes. Moreover, fresh mutation will continue to produce other new affected individuals.

In the case of recessive gene disorders, parents with affected children should be discouraged from having further offspring as well as from permitting consanguineous marriages among other members of the family. However, sterilization of parents in these circumstances is rarely countenanced, since they are in all outward respects entirely normal and since the likelihood of having normal children exists.

Prevention of the undifferentiated form of mental deficiency in which multiple genes play a role should be based on the justifiable assumption that these defectives should not marry among themselves and should not have children. As a matter of fact, the exact opposite is usually the case. Intermarriage is quite frequent among them, in addition to which their fertility is quite high. As a result it is not rare in the family history of institutionalized defectives of this category to find that one or both parents were themselves institutionalized because of mental deficiency. Segregation of defectives in institutions during the reproductive period is both common and effective, but it is also expensive and inhumane. Sterilization seems to be a more rational and humane way of dealing with this problem.

Prevention by Other Means

Improved obstetrical technique and care of prematures, treatment of syphilis, interruption of pregnancy following rubella or other severe virus infections during the first trimester, proper management of Rh. negative pregnancies, encouraging childbearing during the younger child-bearing years, can all diminish the likelihood of some forms of mental deficiency.

Training and Research

It was previously stated that the major handicap facing institutions for mental defectives is the shortage of personnel, particularly in the professional categories. A strong emphasis on training and research is far and away the most effective device for attracting superior personnel. Some aspects of training are taken up in Chapter XXIX. Throughout the foregoing discussion, important areas for research have been touched upon, in physiological chemistry, embryology, neurology, neuropathology, the development and evaluation of new psychological tests, research in perception, emotional development and expression, in mental mechanisms, psychological methods of treatment, in groups and with play techniques, somatic methods of treatment including drugs to increase the I.Q., drugs and other devices to modify mood in a more constructive direction. Sociological studies of institution cultures as well as the relationships of the defective to the community on the outside, legal reforms and many other areas wait to be explored.

Medicolegal Aspects of Mental Deficiency

In New York State, a mental defective who is not confined on a criminal charge may be admitted to and confined in a state institution for mental defectives, or in a licensed private institution, by compliance with any one of the following admission procedures:

a) On voluntary application
b) On certificate of one physician or one psychologist
c) On court certification.

a) Voluntary application may be made on a form prescribed by the Department of Mental Hygiene. If the patient is less than twenty-one, this application is made for him by his parents or some responsible surrogate. After accepting the patient, the director of the institution is authorized to detain him up to sixty days for care and treatment. Within ten days after the patient is admitted, the director of the institution must notify the Department of Mental Hygiene which decides if patient is suitable for continued care as a voluntary admission, or if commitment proceedings should be instituted. After sixty days, the applicant may apply for discharge. If the director deems that this is inadvisable, he has fifteen days in which to have the patient committed. Unless regular commitment through a court order is obtained by then, the patient must be released by the fifteenth day after his application for discharge.

b) The mental defective may also be admitted if he presents himself willingly to an authorized institution for admission with a certificate from an accredited examining psychiatrist or psychologist. As in the instance of voluntary application, the patient is free to apply for discharge after sixty days, and the director of the institution has fifteen days in which to comply or to secure a court order for further care.

c) Any responsible individual may file an application for the commitment of a patient because of mental deficiency. This application, called a petition, is made out on a form prescribed by law. Along with this there must be certificates from two accredited examining psychiatrists or one certified examining psychiatrist and one certified psychologist agreeing to the patient's commitment. The judge sees the patient, although he may omit this step if he agrees that it would be detrimental to the patient's welfare. If the judge feels that commitment is indicated, he issues an order committing the patient for observation. Within sixty days, the institution must file a certificate setting forth the findings and indicating the need for continued care. When such a certificate is filed, the order issued by the judge becomes a final order and the patient can then be confined until he has improved to a point where the doctors feel it is proper to release him.

In Chapter XXXI, there is a discussion of provisions to protect the property of a committed patient, his testamentary capacity and his capacity to enter into business contracts, the validity of an adoption surrender document made out by a committed mother, legal competence and the need for formal judicial proceedings in order to declare a person incompetent. In the case of incompetence, the procedure of appointing a committee is taken up. In the discussion of the sex offender in Chapter XXIII it is mentioned that the mental defective is a major contributor to this problem. Criminal responsibility is discussed too in Chapter XXIV, along with the problem of deciding whether a person confined on a criminal charge is suffering from a defect of reason from disease of the mind. If such a defect is found to be present, the psychiatrist is asked to decide whether or not this illness makes it impossible for the accused to participate in or co-operate in his own defense. If the patient is remanded for trial, the psychiatrist must also express an opinion if the defendant can be held legally accountable for his actions at the time of the alleged crime. In all of these instances, mental deficiency may be the disease of the mind which is producing the defect of reason in question. For these reasons, it is well for those who work with mental defectives to understand such problems in forensic psychiatry. It is no less imperative for the psychiatrist to acquaint himself with the field of mental deficiency.

SELECTED REFERENCES

CAPA, C.: Retarded Children. *Life*, Oct. 19, 1954.
　　A sympathetic presentation with photographs of the problem of mental deficiency in the U. S. Useful for public education.
COBB, D.: Preparing the Mentally Defective Child for Community Adjustment. *Am. J. Ment. Deficiency*, 58:664, 1954.
　　The great importance of the social worker in the rehabilitation of mental defectives is well brought out, with illustrative material.
Forgotten Children. A pamphlet available through the National Association for Mental Health (1790 Broadway, New York 19, N. Y.).
　　Presents basic facts in language readily understandable to the laity; with suggested reading lists for parents, teachers and social workers; sources of additional information about mental deficiency; and the addresses of several parents' groups for the aid of retarded children.

GIANINI, M. J.; et al.: A Home Training Program for Retarded Children. *Pediatrics*, 13:278, 1954.
  Part of this important article is reprinted in this book as Appendix D.
JERVIS, G. A.: The Mental Deficiencies. *Ann. Am. Acad. Pol. & Soc. Sci.*, 286:25, 1953.
  A concise and authoritative summary of the field.
KANNER, L.: *Child Psychiatry*. Springfield, Ill.: C. C. Thomas, 1953.
  This basic text contains much useful material concerning mental deficiency.
KUGELMASS, I. N.: *The Management of Mental Deficiency in Children*. New York: Grune & Stratton, 1954.
  Contains a useful summary of the technique of examining the retarded child and suggestions for general care, training and education.
MACMURCHY, H.: *The Almosts. A Study of the Feebleminded*. Boston: Houghton Mifflin, 1920.
  This book consists of excerpts from the works of great writers as these have dealt with mental defectives. Contains many valuable insights.
WECHSLER, D.: *Wechsler Intelligence Scale for Children (WISC)*. New York: Psychological Corporation, 1949.
  A manual and test materials for a procedure of great value in the psychological examination of children.
ZEHNDER, J.: Sheltered Workshops for Mentally Retarded Adults. *Exceptional Children*, 20:216, 1954.
  A detailed and highly useful account of this aspect of rehabilitating mental defectives.

Chapter XX

THE EPILEPTIC

Introduction

In recent years the number of patients institutionalized for epilepsy has fallen off considerably. The reason for this is not hard to find. Developments in treatment of the convulsive state are among the more dramatic chapters in modern medicine. The formerly familiar picture of the epileptic with physical scarring, mental confusion and general dilapidation no longer obtains. With modern methods of treatment most seizures can be controlled completely. Lennox has estimated that the total number of seizures in 1954 was certaintly less than one half the number for 1934 despite the considerable growth in population which occurred in the meantime. Opportunities for normal existence for the epileptic are greater now than ever before. Many institutions for epileptics have been so affected by this development that they have been transformed into regular mental hospitals. Only about six public institutions specifically designated for the care of epileptics remain in the country. In the others, patients have been re-examined, reclassified and placed on modern methods of treatment. Hundreds of epileptics have been rehabilitated in this manner. Many of them are working productively in the community after decades of institutional care. The remainder are mental defectives with epilepsy, psychotics with epilepsy or physically handicapped patients with epilepsy. In almost all of these cases, further institutional care was necessary not because of the epilepsy but because of the other conditions. Thus, there is probably no indication for chronic hospitalization of the epileptic unless he is suffering from a primary neuropsychiatric disorder, in which case he should be sent to an institution with a program for the treatment of that disorder.

In spite of the fact that so many more epileptics can now be controlled in the community, there are still many points of contact with the mental hospital psychiatrist. Certainly it will arise in his outpatient work. Even though epilepsy is regarded primarily as a neurological problem, it has many psychiatric aspects. For example, it is generally agreed that emotional tensions can increase the number of seizures, and that resolution of conflict can decrease them. A vicious circle occurs when nervous tension increases seizures, and they in turn, by complicating the personal circumstances of the patient, increase tensions. This calls for a total treatment plan in which pharmacologic therapy is only a part. In addition, mental disturbance is not infrequently part of the epileptic attack, as a consequence of which the patient may be admitted to a mental hospital. Epileptic seizures may occur in the process of recovering from a toxic psychosis (barbiturates and alcohol, for example), or may occur, apparently unrelatedly, in a schizophrenic process. In any event, the evaluation of the relationship between epilepsy and a given psychotic reaction is often difficult. There are practical problems as well as theoretical reasons, to be discussed later, why this disease process is of such great importance to the psychiatrist.

What Is Epilepsy?

Epilepsy can be described as a chronic paroxysmal disorder of cerebral function characterized by recurrent attacks of altered consciousness, sudden in onset and brief in duration. The epileptic attack tends to follow certain stereotyped patterns which express the fact that essentially normal, universally present physiological mechanisms are involved. Typical epileptic patterns can be evoked from the normal brain of all mammals, including human beings, by appropriate electrical and chemical stimuli. In this sense, epilepsy is not a disease but a symptom complex which is touched off by a variety of pathogenic agents. Almost three hundred years ago Thomas Willis likened the force that caused the convulsion to a flash of lightning. In 1929, Berger demonstrated that the epileptic attack is indeed associated with an electrical storm in the brain which parallels the clinical picture in its sudden onset and termination, and which can be detected by appropriate electrical measuring devices when brought into physical relationship with the cerebral cortex.

In some instances we know the central nervous system irritant responsible for recurrent attacks, in which case we say that the epilepsy is symptomatic. Organic lesions of the brain which can play such a role include tumors, abscesses and other inflammatory processes, so-called degenerative disorders, and scar tissue formed after trauma or vascular accident. Birth trauma to the head is of particular importance. Adult head wounds which penetrate the dura are very likely to be followed by epilepsy whether occasioned by war, civilian accident or as a result of a neurosurgical procedure. Physiological disturbances which can result in seizures include abrupt circulatory changes in the brain due to cardiac or local causes, carotid sinus syndrome, hypoglycemia due to insulin overdosage, adenoma of the pancreas or other endocrine disease, toxic agents like barbiturates and alcohol, particularly when these substances are abruptly withdrawn, uremic states, a variety of convulsant drugs and acute febrile states in early childhood.

In the vast majority of epileptics (about 75 per cent), we are not able to identify the factor which precipitates the epileptic attack. These constitute the cases of so-called idiopathic epilepsy.

It has been estimated that less than one half of one per cent of the general population is affected by epilepsy. Males are more frequently affected than females. The highest incidence of epileptic seizures occurs during the first two years of life and during adolescence. In general, it may be said that "idiopathic" seizures tend to diminish with age, so that it is fair to say that time is on the side of the epileptic. However, over 30 per cent of all cases of "idiopathic" epilepsy begin after the age of twenty, a factor of clinical diagnostic importance, since it is sometimes said, erroneously, that epilepsy which begins in the adult is usually symptomatic.

Classification of Epileptic Seizures

Although seizures are almost infinitely varied in form, four main types are generally recognized.

The majority of adult cases fall into the category of "grand mal" epilepsy, or epilepsy with generalized convulsions. In over 50 per cent of the cases, the seizure begins with a preliminary warning called the aura. This may consist of strange visceral sensations or other feelings, headaches, visual disturbances, vague premonitions, bizarre repetitive thoughts or phrases. At times, the patient utters a characteristic cry and then falls to the ground in a coma. As a result of the fall he may injure himself severely. The muscular system then goes into a sustained spasm called the tonic phase of the seizure. This is followed by alternating muscular contractions and relaxations resulting in characteristic generalized movements, called the clonic phase. Urinary and fecal incontinence may occur at this time or at the onset of the fit. Generalized sweating, cyanosis and excessive salivation, which is often blood-tinged, complete the clinical picture. The average attack lasts two to five minutes. On regaining consciousness the patient is frequently drowsy and confused. A positive Babinski and other neurologic abnormalities are often demonstrable at this time as transitory phenomena. Typically, there is an amnesia for the attack. Seizures can occur from one or two times in a year to several times in a day. Status epilepticus is a condition in which one grand mal attack follows immediately upon another, without intervening periods of consciousness. This symptom is usually associated with organic brain disease. This is a serious condition which may result in the death of the patient from exhaustion if not successfully interrupted. In about 85 per cent of patients subject to grand mal seizures, the resting electroencephalogram (EEG) is abnormal. However, in all cases, the EEG record becomes abnormal during an attack, showing high voltage spikes of twenty-five to thirty per second frequency.

"Petit mal" represents the most common form of childhood epilepsy. This type of seizure is manifested by a transient clouding of consciousness lasting one to thirty seconds with or without associated movements of the head, eyes, and extremities, or loss of muscular tone. The patient suddenly stops an activity in which he is engaged and resumes it when the attack is over. As part of an attack, he may suddenly fall to the ground, or drop an object (including a baby if the patient happens to be a young mother). Seizures often occur several times in one day. Although many children can outgrow this form of epilepsy, about one in three later develop grand mal seizures unless adequately treated. The EEG during a petit mal attack is highly characteristic, consisting of a series of spike and dome complexes at a rate of three per second.

Psychomotor epilepsy consists of paroxysms of altered consciousness in the course of which the patient carries out in an automatic fashion some complicated act. This may consist of a series of apparently purposeless movements as in the case of a man who would seize curtains, drapes or tassels of blinds and act as if he were trying to climb them. The episode may be characterized by a temper tantrum, destruction of furniture, and occasionally by assaultive behavior. It may last from a few minutes to hours. The patient may react to a vivid dreamlike aura with psychotic behavior that may last for hours. When such behavior begins abruptly, is contrary to the patient's ordinary character, and is not remembered by the patient, it is suggestive of epilepsy. In many instances, parents or other people may find it hard to believe that the patient's behavior is not willful, and as a result they may be unjustifiably rejecting and punitive. The EEG characteristically shows a frequency of three to six waves per second, an abnormality which is invariably present during the psychiatric disturbance if the latter is really part of a psychomotor seizure.

Focal or Jacksonian epilepsy begins with paroxysmal clonic movements or paresthesias in some small part of the body—in the hand, the face or the foot, for example. They tend to spread unilaterally, or bilaterally to become a generalized grand mal attack. However, they may remain focal, in which case the patient remains fully conscious and represents an exception to the general rule that the epileptic attack is associated with a disturbance in consciousness. This form of epilepsy is usually the result of a focal organic disease process in the cerebral cortex, the location of which can be deduced from the point of origin of the seizure.

Diagnosis of Epilepsy

A careful history is of great importance in the diagnosis of epilepsy, including the family history concerning seizures, the onset of the attacks, the frequency and time of day of occurrence, a careful eyewitness account of the attack, the previous occurrence of head injury, including an obstetrical history, previous intracranial inflammatory disease, the use of alcohol, and the exposure to industrial poisons. Although the EEG is helpful, abnormal records can be obtained from people without epilepsy, and a normal EEG record can be obtained from 15 per cent of known epileptics if the record is taken between seizures.

A thorough diagnostic work-up for epilepsy requires the facilities of a neurologic service in a general hospital where an expert neurologic examination can be carried out, including pneumoencephalography if necessary, complete cerebrospinal fluid studies, and EEG.

Treatment of Epilepsy

The mainstay of treatment of epilepsy are the pharmacologic analeptic agents. In 1857, bromides were introduced. Phenobarbital introduced in 1912 represented an important advance. In 1937, Putnam and Merritt carried out an exhaustive study of hundreds of drugs. As a result, they discovered the specific usefulness of dilantin. It proved to be the first drug capable of controlling grand mal seizures without exerting a generalized hypnotic influence. This drug opened up new possibilities, not simply for the control of epileptic seizure, but control in a setting of alert consciousness not previously attainable. This opened up an entirely new conception of the clinical course of epilepsy from a general psychiatric point of view and of the possibilities for rehabilitation. After the discovery of dilantin many other useful drugs were found—mesantoin for grand mal epilepsy, tridione for petit mal, phenurone for psychomotor seizures, and several others which are still in the process of evaluation. Each of these drugs has advantages and important disadvantages which must also be taken into account when they are used.

Although the details of pharmacologic treatment of epilepsy are only secondarily germaine to the main purpose of this book, a brief review of this problem may be useful.

The question has been raised whether individuals having infrequent seizures (one a year or less) should be treated at all. The answer is yes. Moderate doses of phenobarbital, alone or in combination with dilantin may be sufficient. If the seizures occur more frequently, dilantin is the drug of choice. The patient is started on one decigram (0.1) of dilantin three times daily, the timing depending on when the seizures occur most frequently. If the aggregate daily dose does not control the seizures, it may be increased by an additional decigram a day until the attacks are controlled, or until toxic symptoms appear (rash, confusion, nausea, vomiting, unsteady gait and hypertrophy of the gums). If toxic symptoms have appeared and the seizures are still not controlled, other anticonvulsants such as mesantoin, mysoline, phenobarbital, in similar doses, alone or in combination, may be substituted.

Amphetamine sulfate is a valuable adjunct to the treatment of seizures for two reasons. The first relates to the fact that many seizures are precipitated by drowsiness. Indeed, electroencephalographers study brain waves with particular care during spontaneous or drug-induced drowsy states for this very reason. Amphetamine diminishes seizures by decreasing diurnal drowsiness. As a second reason, amphetamine counteracts the sedative effect of anticonvulsant drugs and so permits a larger dose to be given without toxic clouding of consciousness.

For patients who have repeated daily convulsions which resist the usual treatment Putnam and Rothenberg have recommended a drastic four-day "sleep" treatment requiring hospitalization, in which dilantin is given in doses up to sixty grains daily, combined with paraldehyde or other hypnotic agents to produce a narcotized state. Ketosis from starvation is allowed to develop. Intravenous fluids containing glutamic acid are administered. Inhalations of 10 per cent carbon dioxide and 90 per cent oxygen are given for ten minutes every hour. Penicillin is given intramuscularly in a dose of 300,000 units daily in order to prevent respiratory infections. After four days on this program some previously uncontrollable cases can be rendered seizure-free. By this means Putnam and Rothenberg were able to bring about a relatively seizure-free state in 77 per cent of the cases they treated.

Petit mal seizures are more resistant to treatment, and tridione in three decigram (0.3) doses, three or four times daily has been found most effective. It has the disadvantage of causing aplastic anemia, and indeed, fatalities have been reported. Frequent blood counts should be done and the drug discarded immediately when blood changes are found. Paradione seems to be less dangerous in this condition.

Where neurologic studies reveal an underlying organic process, this should be treated medically or surgically as indicated. Penfield and his co-workers have led the field in the successful excision of diseased cortical areas in the treatment of epilepsy with focal characteristics. In certain cases showing predominantly psychomotor changes, EEG abnormalities localized to the tip of the temporal lobe have been found. When neurosurgical exploration shows abnormal tissue in this region, excision may result in favorable clinical changes.

Some Psychiatric Aspects of Treating Epileptics

It was previously mentioned that emotional tension can increase the frequency of seizures. In some respects the seizure seems to supervene as a kind of desperate act of defense, representing a total withdrawal of consciousness from a psychologically intolerable situation. A rational plan of treatment should therefore include a consideration of the emotional problems of the patient. Naturally, this calls for a careful psychiatric history and detailed clinical observations. The data should be supplemented by social service and psychological studies in formulating the case and planning treatment. The usual psychiatric techniques are brought to bear on this problem, including a full program of activities— educational, recreational, and vocational. The services of the social worker should be employed for job placement, or the services of the special vocational rehabilitation officer if one is available (see Chapter V). It goes without saying that in an epileptic the seizure itself plays a major traumatic role in the total picture. Psychological studies of epileptics often highlight the deep-seated fear of falling and loss of conscious control by which they are haunted, intensifying their insecurity feelings and anxiety.

Occasionally the psychological significance of a seizure is more complicated. For example, the psychoanalysis of a young epileptic woman brought out the fact that the loss of consciousness preceding the convulsions had for her the symbolic significance of an orgasm. This she both desired and dreaded because she also equated it with death. The curious fact that seizures can be invested with pleasurable meaning is also indicated in a few reported instances of children who could induce seizures in themselves by a flickered light stimulus which they would produce at will by rapidly oscillating the hand between themselves and the light. They would induce seizures in themselves in this manner as a form of play.

A need to inculcate an understanding of this disease is a matter of major psychotherapeutic importance. The patient should be taught, for example, that with relatively few restrictions of one's activities there is little real danger to life and limb, and that with conscientious observance of the medical regimen most seizures can be controlled. Because of the horror which the very term "epilepsy" engenders, it has been proposed that this term not be used with patients. On the other hand, some have felt that a realistic acceptance of the term and all that goes with it makes for better mental hygiene. Genuine understanding of the condition does call for an acceptance of certain inevitable physical limitations. Driving a car, running an elevator, working near moving machinery or similar activities are unwise. The epileptic should not swim alone. On the other hand, he is capable of functioning satisfactorily at a wide range of occupations including medicine, law, the ministry, engineering, teaching, selling, farming, clerking, laborer, mechanic, stenographer, dressmaker, newspaper reporter, interior decorator, factory worker, beautician, actress, dancer, writer, plumber, and musician. Such companies as International Business Machines and the Ford Motor Company are among the employers successfully hiring epileptics. Supervisors at the Ford plant in Dearborn state that epileptics are unusually conscientious and that their records of performance and safety are excellent. A good confirmation of this conclusion is to be found in the fact that the Association of Casualty and Surety Companies in no way opposes the employment of epileptics, for they recognize that when properly placed they are satisfactory workers. Government Civil Service has many posts open to epileptics if seizures can be adequately controlled. Even military service is open to the epileptic if his seizures are controllable with medication. It is a good idea to refer the epileptic patient for membership in the National Epilepsy League, Inc., at 130 North Wells Street in Chicago, or the Epilepsy Association of New York, at 186 Fifth Avenue in New York City. In these organizations he will learn more about his disease and how other epileptics have succeeded in overcoming their handicap.

Part of the problem of enabling the patient to cope with his seizures consists in persuading his environment to accept them. Oftentimes family life is disrupted and one or more members may need psychiatric help as a result. Social service liaison is invaluable in such instances. At times it is useful to meet with the parents of epileptics in group therapy sessions with or without the patient.

Perhaps the greatest need of all is for a program of public education. Lennox has commented that were Hippocrates to visit the earth today, he might well regard with incredulous admiration the advances that have been made since his clinical description of the disease. However, he would probably be no less incredulous of the unjustified horror with which the general public reacts to this condition. The Greeks regarded the epileptic as somehow divinely endowed, and provided him with a position of respect, with rights to education and employment, the last of which are too often denied the epileptic today. Teachers and the entire public education system require instruction concerning epilepsy. Children in the classroom are remarkably tolerant of epileptic seizures if the teacher herself maintains a rational attitude. Some of the enlightened employers mentioned earlier can lead the way. The Veterans Administration has prepared a film called "Seizure," which is very useful in a campaign to educate the public. In some states traveling clinics (see Chapter XXXV) play an important role in the treatment of epileptic patients in the community. In addition to assuming responsibility for the pharmacologic aspects of therapy, travelling clinic personnel deal with the emotional problems of epileptics and their families, assist in job placement, survey community reactions, and further public education.

Institutional Care of Epileptics

The vast majority of epileptics are neither psychotic nor feeble-minded. Many of the supposed deteriorative aspects of the disease are now known to be the result of toxic drug effects, and the inevitable emotional and intellectual dilapidation which are part of adaptation to the average institutional milieu (see Chapter XIV). As was mentioned earlier, colonies for epileptics have been re-examined from a diagnostic point of view, and in terms of a genuine treatment and rehabilitation program. As a result of the application of modern methods of treatment, family care (see Chapter XXXVI) and vocational guidance, many hundreds of epileptics have been rehabilitated and discharged into the community as self-supporting individuals and have earned the reputation of being conscientious and dependable workers. Many others were transferred to institutions for mental defectives or to mental hospitals where the psychiatric disorder of primary importance could be more adequately treated. It has become abundantly clear that separate facilities for the institutional treatment of patients with epilepsy are not necessary, that indeed institutional care for epileptics is rarely if ever indicated unless there is present in addition to the epilepsy another neuropsychiatric problem which necessitates it.

The Relationship of Epilepsy to Other Psychiatric Disorders

Occasionally the psychotic episode for which a patient is admitted to a mental hospital is part of an epileptic attack (see Chapter XXXII). In such a case, treatment of the psychosis consists of treatment of the epilepsy. Such psychotic episodes are characterized by their paroxysmal character. They start and end suddenly, are usually associated with amnesia for the psychotic experience, show characteristic EEG changes during the attack and a favorable response to medication. More often the psychosis is only secondarily related to the epilepsy, if at all. Years ago various people held to the theory that epilepsy and schizophrenia are mutually exclusive. Treatments were based on this hypothesis. One of these treatments was the pharmacologic induction of convulsions in the treatment of schizophrenia introduced by Meduna. Time has proved that the theory is wrong but that the treatment upon which it was based is nevertheless of value. That the efficacy of the treatment is utterly unrelated to this theory is perhaps best proven by the fact that convulsive therapy is of greatest value in the affective disorders, not in the schizophrenic reactions for which it was originally proposed. If a schizophrenic patient has epileptic seizures and his psychosis continues without remission it might be supposed that the induction of further seizures electrically would be of no therapeutic value. In actual practice seizures induced for therapeutic purposes often do result in clinical improvements which do not occur after the spontaneous seizures. This may be because the passage of the electrical current itself, above and beyond the seizure which follows it, produces brain changes which favorably affect the clinical picture. Similarly, lobotomy has been utilized reluctantly in epileptics with psychosis because of the fear that the frequently seen postlobotomy seizures would aggravate the existing epileptic state. Nevertheless, epileptics with seriously aggressive outbursts or with other psychotic reactions have been lobotomized with favorable clinical results without increasing the incidence of seizures. In fact, a decreased incidence of seizures sometimes occurs as a result, possibly, of the relief from emotional tensions which had previously precipitated them.

Epilepsy rarely begins as a sequel of electroconvulsive therapy. As a sequel of lobotomy, on the other hand, it is quite common. It is good practice to put all postlobotomy cases on anticonvulsant medication for at least a year after operation.

When phenurone was first introduced in the treatment of psychomotor epilepsy, it was soon observed that the relief of the psychomotor attack from this drug was often followed by a sustained psychotic reaction of even graver clinical import than the psychomotor attacks themselves. It has already been pointed out that the pattern of epileptic discharge seems to be part of the organization of the normal central nervous system. What relationship, if any, does this mechanism have to the psychological workings of the normal human mind? It has already been mentioned that the epileptic attack seems to occur, in some instances, at least, as a total withdrawal of consciousness from a psychologically intolerable situation. The studies of Penfield and others suggest that a part of the temporal lobe in association with other cerebral and brainstem structures plays a role in the control of consciousness, increasing or decreasing the general level of alertness in various psychological circumstances. In addition, this mechanism seems to play a role in a more circumscribed fashion, too, helping to bring specific psychological areas in the field of attention more or less clearly into focus. Thus, it may play a role in the recall of repressed memories or in the initiation of repression. Penfield and his co-workers have been able to bring forgotten experiences into consciousness by cortical stimulation to specific temporal areas. On the other hand, observations by Ostow on patients with focal EEG abnormalities in the temporal lobe are strongly suggestive of the importance of the temporal lobes in repression. We seem to be on the verge of a renaissance of research in the brain-mind borderland. Epileptic patients give promise of particularly fruitful data for illuminating this field.

Heredity in Epilepsy

The brain-wave pattern is an inherited trait. Thus, among identical twins without brain damage, the presence of a spike and dome complex characteristic of petit mal in one is associated with a similar pattern in 94 per cent of the other. Concordance of this pattern in nonidentical twins is only 6 per cent. An inherited dysrhythmia probably constitutes a predisposition to epilepsy. However, the incidence of actual epilepsy is much lower than the incidence of such dysrhythmias. Thus, one cannot say that epilepsy per se is inherited, only that certain factors which excite the epileptic state are more apt to make the disease manifest in predisposed people than in others.

This question touches upon the problem of marriage and childbearing. In several states, obsolete laws prohibit the marriage of epileptics. In those areas, this question is unfortunately academic. As a rule, an epileptic can marry happily and successfully provided that the marriage is "right" from all other points of view, and that the seizures themselves are not inordinately difficult to control. Sexual intercourse and pregnancy do not alter the course of epilepsy significantly, except possibly as contentment and a sense of fulfillment may decrease emotional tension and decrease the number of seizures that come from that cause.

A generation ago most doctors would have advised an epileptic against having children. Nowadays, the majority would sanction it if the epilepsy is reasonably well controlled or, when the epileptic parent is the mother, if the care of the child can be supervised against injury during seizures. It has been estimated that the likelihood of an epileptic parent having an epileptic child is one in forty in his or her favor. This is considerably higher than the one in two hundred chance for the average parent. Nevertheless, the figure is still not high in absolute terms. When one adds to this the fact that epilepsy is so much more easily controlled today, and that epileptics often have other admirable qualities worth preserving genetically, then there is cause for optimism here.

Medicolegal Aspects of Epilepsy

In New York State epileptics can be admitted to a public institution set aside for the care and treatment of epileptics or to an accredited private hospital on voluntary application by the epileptic or his guardian, or on temporary certification by one physician or on certification by a court of law. In the first two instances, the epileptic can be detained up to sixty days, after which he can apply to the director of the institution for discharge. If the director feels that this is inadvisable, he has fifteen more days during which he is permitted to detain the epileptic pending action by the court. Unless the court takes appropriate action, he must discharge the patient by the end of that time. Court certification is obtained if a petition for certification is drawn up by a properly qualified petitioner and presented to a judge of an appropriate court with official statements from two accredited examining psychiatrists certifying that the patient needs institutional care. If the judge agrees that a court appearance of the patient would be harmful to his health, he may dispense with it. If on the basis of the data the judge rules that institutional care is necessary, then the patient is committed, and may be detained until the director feels that his condition has improved sufficiently to permit his discharge.

Episodes of destructive and assaultive behavior can occur during an attack of psychomotor epilepsy, or in clouded states of consciousness associated with grand mal. As a result, the question of an epileptic's legal responsibility may come up in a case of homicide or in other infractions of the law (see Chapter XXIV). The demonstration of an electroencephalographic abnormality during the period of mental disorder which also coincides with the episode in its onset and termination is proof of the epileptic nature of the psychic abnormality. EEG abnormalities which are not so restricted in their occurrence are more difficult to evaluate. In these instances the electroencephalographer will have to evaluate the EEG record in the light of the total clinical picture.

SELECTED REFERENCES

BARKER, W.: Studies on Epilepsy: The Petit Mal Attack as a Response Within the Central Nervous System to Distress in Organism-Environment Integration. *Psychosom. Med.*, 10:73, 1948.

BICKFORD, R. G.; DALY, D.; KEITH, H. M.: Convulsive Effects of Light Stimulation in Children. *A. M. A. Am. J. Dis. Chil.*, 86:170, 1953.
　　The use of flickered light in playfully self-induced seizures in children is described.

HILL, D.; SARGENT, W.; HEPPENSTALL, M. E.: A Case of Matricide. *Lancet*, 1:526, 1943.
　　This article discusses the use of the EEG in evaluating the role of epilepsy in an act of violence.

KALINOWSKY, L. B.; HOCH, P. H.: *Shock Treatments, Psychotherapy, and Other Somatic Treatments in Psychiatry*. New York: Grune & Stratton, 1952.
　　Experiences with electroconvulsive therapy and lobotomy of epileptics are summarized.

LENNOX, W. G.: *Science and Seizures: New Light on Epilepsy and Migraine*. New York: Harper, 1946.
　　Written for the laity, this is useful for the education of the epileptic, his family and the general public.

—— The Social and Emotional Problems of the Epileptic Child and His Family. *J. Pediat.*, 44:591, 1954.
　　Summarizes many facts of general clinical importance. Contains a case history showing the interaction of emotional disturbances and seizures in an epileptic child with an emotionally disturbed mother. The role of the social worker in such situations is emphasized.

OSTOW, M.: Fluctuation of Temporal Lobe Electroencephalographic Abnormality During Psychic Function. *Am. J. Psychiat.*, 110:55, 1953.

—— Psychodynamic Disturbances in Patients with Temporal Lobe Disorder. *J. Mt. Sinai Hosp.*, 20:293, 1954.
　　These papers deal with the relationship of the temporal lobe to repression of painful memories.

PENFIELD, W.: Epileptic Automatism and the Centroencephalic Integrating System. In: *Patterns of Organization of the Central Nervous System*. (Proceedings of the Association for Research in Nervous and Mental Disease, 30:513), 1952.

Clinical psychiatric implications of this great investigator's researches on the cerebral cortex are presented.

PUTMAN, T. J.: *Convulsive Seizures: A Manual for Patients, Their Families, and Friends*. Philadelphia: Lippincott, 1945.

A highly useful book.

——, ROTHENBERG, S. F.: Results of Intensive (Narcosis) and Standard Medical Treatment of Epilepsy. *J.A.M.A.*, 152:1400, 1953.

Describes technique for controlling refractory cases, a group more likely to be of interest to the mental hospital psychiatrist.

RANDALL, G. C.; ROGERS, W. C.: Group Psychotherapy for Epileptics. *Am. J. Psychiat.*, 107:422, 1950.

Describes a therapeutic approach that deserves wider application and study.

WECHSLER, I. S.: *Textbook of Clinical Neurology*, 7th ed. Philadelphia: W. B. Saunders, 1952.

A standard source of neurological information. Highly recommended for the hospital psychiatrist.

WEINSTEIN, E. A.; ALVORD, E. C., JR.; RIOCH, D. M.: Disorders Associated with Disturbance of Brain Function. *Ann. Am. Acad. Pol. & Soc. Sci.*, 286:34, 1953.

Includes a concise description of the nature of the epileptic seizure.

YAHRAES, H.: *Epilepsy—The Ghost Is Out of the Closet*. Public Affairs Pamphlet No. 98. Public Affairs Pamphlets, 22 East 38 Street, New York 16, N.Y.

Written for the laity, this brief pamphlet presents in simple language basic facts for epileptics, their families and the general public.

Chapter XXI

THE PREGNANT PATIENT

Introduction

A colleague once related that on his first day in a state hospital, a schizophrenic patient gave birth to a baby. He was impressed by the professional skill with which one of the regular staff psychiatrists delivered the baby, directed the establishment of a small nursery, gave the mother postpartum care, and arranged a schedule of artificial feedings for the baby. He was too overwhelmed with the complexity of his own responsibilities during those first days as a state hospital psychiatrist to think more deeply about the situation, but subsequently, he said, he came to appreciate the psychiatric problems condensed in that obstetrical drama: When was the pregnancy first discovered? Was interruption of the pregnancy ever considered? What effect did the pregnancy have on the course of the mental illness? If the pregnancy had been interrupted, what effect would that have had? Did the pregnancy modify in any way the treatment that this patient received? What maternal reactions did the patient show? What arrangements were made for the subsequent care of the baby? If the baby was given out for adoption, what were the legal technicalities of an adoption proceeding involving a psychotic mother? What is the mental health of that baby today? What was the psychiatrist's opinion about future pregnancies for that patient? If he felt that further pregnancies were ill advised, did he do anything to prevent them? If so, did such advice include sterilization, contraception, or abstinence?

Psychological Aspects of Pregnancy

Let us consider first some basic psychiatric principles which are relevant. Pregnancy, childbirth and motherhood together represent ultimate fulfillments for the biologically mature woman. Her physical and emotional development up to that point is calculated to prepare her for these momentous events. Her play in early childhood, her adolescent daydreams, her hopes and ambitions as a young woman center to a considerable degree about this theme. And at the menopause, related problems which had become quiescent over a period of years erupt anew. It should come as no surprise that these problems taken together represent the greatest source of emotional stress and therefore of mental illness for the woman. It has been said that if a woman can go through a pregnancy and a delivery and then through the trials and tribulations of the first year of motherhood without overt mental illness, she is usually able to handle any of the situations which life has to offer. On the other hand, a painstaking obstetrical history from a psychosomatic viewpoint should constitute an important part of every psychiatric anamnesis on a female patient. Many an emotionally immature young woman is able to make an acceptable adaptation until she becomes a mother, at which time the weaknesses of a pathologically narcissistic orientation to life may, for the first time, come to the surface. As long as she can play a protected, passive, dependent role, she can adapt. As soon as she is called upon to play an active, giving, protective role, she is found to be lacking in emotional equipment. As a result, many acute or chronic emotional disorders become clinically manifest at this time.

A young woman, age twenty-five, was happily married for six years. She and her husband worked in different departments of a large factory. She had many friends, lived an active social life, and displayed no evidence of emotional disorder. She and her husband practiced birth control. In her twenty-fourth year she became pregnant. Although the pregnancy was unplanned, she was quite happy about it and went to term uneventfully delivering a normal male infant. During the postpartum period she was tearful and frightened. Upon her return home her widowed mother left her job and moved in to help with the care of the baby. The patient became more deeply depressed. Her mother found herself equally occupied with the newborn baby and the patient. After several weeks her mother had to return to her job and the husband had to take time off from work to look after the patient and the baby. She was anorexic, with a weight loss of 15 pounds, sleepless, agitated and suicidal. She felt unable to care for the baby and reproached herself constantly as an unfit mother. A course of electroconvulsive therapy did not relieve her. She was then treated with analytically oriented psychotherapy. During this time her basically infantile conception of herself emerged. She became aware of her characteristic patterns of helplessness and childish irresponsibility in her relationship with her husband and mother. The birth of the baby awakened childhood recollections concerning her play with dolls, during which she had had fantasies of getting rid of her mother and marrying her father. These recollections seemed to account for the intense guilt feeling she was suffering and her need to abdicate any pretense of motherhood. In her behavior she seemed to be showing her mother that she was a helpless baby and not a rival for her place in the family. With the elucidation of these mechanisms her symptoms gradually lifted and she was able to assume the care of her baby.

Many women develop a postpartum emotional disorder from which they emerge with the determination to have no more babies. They develop a distaste for sexual intercourse based upon their deep-rooted fear of future pregnancies. After years of frigidity and an inhibited neurotic adaptation to life, they may become overtly ill again at the menopause. An inadvertent pregnancy in such patients is often catastrophic from a psychiatric point of view.

Therapeutic Abortion on Psychiatric Grounds

Unequipped as a woman may be for motherhood, one must not lose sight of the psychological trauma which may result from the interruption of a pregnancy. Women may react with overwhelming guilt feelings following an abortion which can then touch off a psychiatric illness of major proportions. I have seen several severe phobic reactions begin under such circumstances.

A thirty-year-old woman developed a depression and a fear of crowds following the birth of her daughter six years previously. This subsided gradually over one year without treatment. Thereafter she displayed a fear of pregnancy which resulted in frigidity and infrequent sexual relations. In spite of this she became pregnant. She obtained an illegal abortion without telling her husband. The physician who carried out the procedure showed her the curetted material in a jar. The patient reacted to this sight with a feeling of horror. On her way home she experienced a fear that a foreign body would fly into her eye. Thereafter this fear intensified, so that she refused to go out of doors. She would compel her husband to examine her eyes in an obsessive-compulsive ritual many times each day to see if a foreign body had actually entered. She gradually withdrew from all social contacts. In analytically oriented psychotherapy she often returned to the horror she experienced at the sight of the fetal fragments. She recalled, with intense guilt, hostile feelings toward her daughter which she experienced during her previous phobic episode. The eye symptom became understandable as an attempt to repress her murderous impulses toward her daughter. This in turn recalled similar attitudes in childhood toward siblings, with whom she had to share her mother's attention. Like the patient in the previous case history, she showed striking evidences of emotional immaturity, with a wish to be "babied." There was a gradual improvement in her symptoms.

Often, symptoms may recur years later in the obsessive self-reproaches of an involutional melancholia. Such harmful effects of induced abortion, immediate and delayed, must be taken into account in one's deliberations concerning therapeutic abortion.

In thirty-one states there is legal sanction for the interruption of a pregnancy if it is done to save the life of a mother. In some states, however, it is ruled that the peril to life need not be immediate or imminent, that it is sufficient only that the peril to life be potentially present. It is not essential that the doctor believe that the death of the patient would otherwise be a certainty. In a state whose statute read that abortion may be done only to save the mother's life, it was said in a court ruling that "a physician may lawfully procure the abortion of a patient if in good faith he believes it necessary to save her life or to prevent serious impairment of her health, mental or physical." In other words, the court recognized the fact that danger to life and danger of serious impairment of health are really different aspects of the same problem. Some states (Colorado, Maryland, New Mexico, and District of Columbia) legalize this fact in the specific statement that abortion may be performed to safeguard the health of the mother.

With the development of modern medical techniques, it has become possible to carry through to successful delivery many women who might not have survived a generation ago, so that the number of medical conditions that represent unequivocal indications for abortion has steadily decreased. Ectopic pregnancy, hydatidiform mole, serious recurrent uterine hemorrhage, certain Rh. negative states, pre-eclampsia, class III and IV cardiac conditions, active cases of tuberculosis and breast carcinoma remain as important indications. Abortion is carried out in certain heredo-degenerative conditions such as amaurotic family idiocy, Leber's disease and Huntington's Chorea, even though the laws do not specifically legalize abortion for hereditary disease. In such instances most physicians justify the procedure on the basis that they are thereby preventing serious mental illness in the mother.

It is a curious fact that concern for the unborn infant seems by and large to be absent in legal considerations of this problem. It is not enough to be concerned with saving the life of an embryo if no constructive opportunity is provided for that life to be developed. Associated with emotional disorder in the mother is often a significant impairment in the woman's capacity for maternal response. Overt or unconscious rejection of the child is almost universally present in the emotional illnesses that become clinically manifest after childbirth. In some psychotic women, this may result in actual infanticide. In others, there may develop a fear of harming the child. Still others may be able to go through the overt expressions of maternal behavior, yet be devoid of genuine warmth in the process. In these latter instances, the child often suffers genuine emotional deprivation which may stunt his emotional growth and lay the groundwork for a variety of psychiatric disturbances later on in life. Surely these are matters to be taken into consideration in evaluating the total picture.

Concern for the welfare of the infant as well as an improved understanding of the psychodynamics of motherhood have contributed to the increased interest in recent times in mental illness as an indication for therapeutic abortion. Naturally, each case that is referred must be considered individually. However, the following psychiatric indications have been suggested as a guide: Overt manic-depressive psychosis and schizophrenia which have not responded to previous attempts at treatment; a history of episodes of acute mental illness precipitated regularly by pregnancies in the past; adolescent youngsters who are obviously not ready for the emotional experience of either pregnancy or childbirth. It has been suggested that a previous lobotomy weigh heavily as a factor in favor of abortion because of the fragility of the adaptive mechanisms in such patients.

It may be decided that some patients in the foregoing categories are not endangered by pregnancy. On the other hand, the list presented here is not exhaustive, and other clinical situations may arise in which the psychiatrist may want to recommend abortion. In any event the decision is usually a difficult one, and is practically never decided on the basis of a single psychiatrist's opinion. Two or more psychiatrists should consider the problem independently and in concert. Personal feelings and general philosophical considerations should play no role in the conclusion. One has to be guided by the facts and the laws of the state.

Treatment of the Pregnant Patient in a Mental Hospital

All female patients newly admitted to a state hospital should have a gynecologic examination. A surprising number of early pregnancies will be picked up in this way, a fact of importance in planning the patient's treatment. If the pregnancy should be interrupted for psychiatric reasons, it should be done as early as possible. Many pregnant patients have been treated successfully with electroshock therapy (ECT) in every stage of pregnancy without adverse effect. The convulsions did not induce labor pains or rupture the membrances, even in patients treated at term. Vaginal bleeding and temporarily impaired fetal circulation has been reported in the literature but no serious damage to mother or child. Insulin shock therapy, on the other hand, seems to be more hazardous in that stillbirths have been reported in some cases. However, fetal death does not occur in every instance. It is necessary as always to weigh all the factors involved and to proceed in accordance with the needs of each individual patient.

Prevention of Conception

The problem of therapeutic abortion is inevitably connected with the problem of contraception. Where this is not prohibited by religious belief, the psychiatrist may want to suggest the use of contraceptives in the treatment of a patient. Satisfying sexual relations play an important role in mental health, and the psychiatrist may want to foster this in instances where pregnancy itself is nevertheless inadvisable. He will inevitably address this contraceptive advice to the spouse who is not mentally ill, or at least is not in the hospital. He may want to do this personally or with the help of the social worker. In any event, it is a matter to be given careful consideration before a married patient leaves the hospital, particularly if the wife is the one who is ill. If she returns pregnant (and this is not at all infrequent), it inevitably complicates the management of the case, not only in terms of treatment in the hospital, but in terms of the effect of such an event on an already broken family and in terms of the psychosocial reverberations in the community.

Sterilization as a way of preventing conception is a more serious matter. The permanent loss of the ability to procreate may have a shattering effect upon the self-esteem of a patient. If the psychiatric indications for therapeutic abortion are few, then the indications for sterilization on these grounds must be rare indeed. These two procedures are sometimes linked in an unwarranted fashion and the statement will be made: "I will agree to therapeutic abortion only if it is also agreed that we sterilize the patient." Although this is usually rationalized scientifically, it often contains punitive overtones. The two procedures are different in their indications and in their long-term effects upon the rehabilitation of the patient. A patient may require a therapeutic abortion now, yet later in life be mature enough to undertake the role of motherhood successfully. There are instances, however, particularly among mentally defective girls (see Chapter XIX), where the capacity to exercise proper judgment and control in sexual situations is permanently and hopelessly impaired. Many such patients become pregnant as soon as they are released from the institution. Their offspring inevitably become public charges, and through the hardship which they must undergo give rise to a new generation of mental sickness. Except for their propensity to become pregnant, these young women are often able to adjust in the community and to support themselves. In some instances, sterilization would seem to be an act of kindness, if as a result the patient is liberated from the need to live for years in an institution. This procedure should be considered, therefore, in states that have laws permitting it.

Disposition of the Baby

When a schizophrenic woman becomes pregnant, she may invest her pregnancy with mystical and religious delusions. In more deteriorated schizophrenic states, she may take no notice of it at all. In either event, the attitude to the pregnancy is divorced from reality, and following the birth of the child, normal maternal reactions rarely if ever occur. It is quite clear that the infant can rarely be left with the psychotic mother, even if she has improved enough to adjust at home. Some disposition of the baby must be made. Ideally, the baby is placed with some responsible member of the family. If such a person is not available, the problem of adoption may be raised. The question is then asked, can a psychotic mother sign over her child for adoption? According to some authorities, the mere fact of psychosis does not in itself invalidate an adoption order. What must be demonstrated is that the patient understands that the child is her own and that what she is doing is to relinquish permanently her legal relationship to that child as its mother. In short, she must be able to understand that she is giving her child away for adoption. This reasoning which, incidentally, is accepted in most courts, is based on the fallacious and now largely outmoded idea that a person can be partially insane (see Chapter XXIV). In the words of Davidson, "The psychiatrist knows that a delusional system is never watertight and that it reflects a disorganization of thinking that may contaminate all of the patient's thought processes." The fallacy of "partial insanity" is confirmed by actual clinical and medicolegal experience. A psychotic mother may recover and her previous attitude of rejection or indifference may be replaced by one of intense maternal devotion. At such a time she may be deeply traumatized by the loss of her baby. For this reason, Davidson urges placement within the family if it is at all possible, with the use of adoption as a last resort. Many such children are doomed to lives of misery and stunted emotional growth. One must conclude from this that the possibilities for a reasonably normal family life for the offspring should be included in one's deliberations concerning the indications for therapeutic abortion.

SELECTED REFERENCES

DAVIDSON, H. A.: *Forensic Psychiatry.* New York: Ronald Press, 1952.
A comprehensive and authoritative summary of existing practices. Contains a discussion of adoption proceedings.
—— Appraisal of the Witness. *Am. J. Psychiat.,* 111:481, 1954.
Comments on the fallacy of "partial insanity."
GUTTMACHER, A. F.: Therapeutic Abortion: The Doctor's Dilemma. *J. Mt. Sinai Hosp.,* 82:111, 1954.
A conservative point of view concerning therapeutic abortion for psychiatric reasons.
KALINOWSKY, L. B.; HOCH, P. H.: *Shock Treatments, Psychosurgery, and Other Somatic Treatments in Psychiatry.* New York: Grune & Stratton, 1952.
Contains data concerning the effects of pregnancy in modifying the applicability of somatotherapeutic procedures.
ROSEN, H., ed.: *Therapeutic Abortion. Medical, Psychiatric, Legal, Anthropologic and Religious Considerations.* New York: Julian Press, 1954.
A collection of essays by distinguished authorities surveying the subject with great thoroughness.

Chapter XXII

THE VETERAN

When a patient is admitted to a mental hospital, it is ascertained routinely if he is a veteran. If he is, a description of his military history should be incorporated into the psychiatric record and steps taken to determine his eligibility for veteran's benefits.

The Veteran's Rights

Within twenty-four hours after the veteran is admitted to the mental hospital, V.A. form "10-P-10" should be completed by the physician and forwarded to the chief contact representative of the Regional Office of the Veterans Administration. From the data on this form his eligibility for V.A. hospitalization will be determined. On this form and on any other V.A. forms that the physician may be called upon to complete the nature of the illness should be fully and clearly explained as well as the extent of the disability resulting from the illness. Otherwise a lay member of a claims board may not appreciate the severity of the veteran's condition, and injustices might occur inadvertently. Any person who has had wartime service in the Armed Forces of the United States is eligible to apply for admission to a V.A. hospital. His eligibility for such care is highest if his mental illness is service-connected. If the illness started within a two-year period following his discharge from the Army it is regarded as presumptive evidence of service connection. Even if his illness is not service-connected, he will be admitted to a V.A. hospital if a bed is available and he certifies that he is financially unable to pay hospital charges elsewhere.

If a bed is available in a nearby V.A. hospital, the eligible veteran is transferred. At times this means a better level of psychiatric care than that which was available in the previous mental hospital. In the process it will also release a bed for a patient not eligible for care elsewhere.

Because of the great demand for psychiatric treatment, however, beds for nonservice-connected cases are seldom available. The V.A. will pay the cost of hospitalization in some other facility if no bed is available for a service-connected case.

In addition to hospitalization there is the matter of financial benefits. If the mental illness is directly or presumptively service-connected, the patient and his dependents are eligible for compensation. In the event that he is permanently and totally disabled by his illness, he is eligible for a pension even when this illness is not service-connected. These facts should be explained to the veteran and his family so that they may file a formal application for compensation or pension with the Regional V.A. Office. This is done on V.A. "form 8-526." It is important to file this application promptly. If it is acted upon favorably, benefits will become available to the veteran retroactively. If there is a delay in filing it, his dependents will be unnecessarily deprived of funds.

Patients who are eligible for V.A. compensation are also eligible for outpatient treatment. In view of the excellent psychiatric clinics maintained by the V.A. throughout the country, this may mean earlier discharge from the mental hospital and better aftercare.

Veterans disabled by service-connected mental illness are eligible for education and training at government expense with tuition, supplies, and in many cases a subsistence allowance under the provisions of the Vocational Rehabilitation Act. This is a fact of considerable importance in planning the veteran's treatment program. Some veterans qualify for "GI" loans which they may use in starting a business, a farm or in purchasing a house.

If the veteran remains in a disabled condition following his discharge from the hospital, he may be entitled to disability compensation. The extent of his disability will be decided by a rating board on the basis of information provided by his physicians. If the veteran is rated 50 per cent or more disabled, he may receive additional sums for dependents. Veterans with disabilities which are not service-connected may be entitled to a pension provided their earned income is below a certain fixed limit.

If the veteran dies in a mental hospital from a service-connected illness his widow, his children or other dependents may qualify for death compensation and burial benefits. The widow and children of certain deceased veterans may be entitled to death pension benefits in cases where the cause of death was not a service-connected illness.

In all of the foregoing instances, the contact representative of the V.A. Regional Office will assist in securing benefits to which the veteran and his dependents are entitled. He may be consulted in the Regional Office by members of the veteran's family. If this is impractical, then an itinerant contact representative may be dispatched by the Regional Office to the veteran's home or to the mental hospital. If a V.A. hospital is in the immediate vicinity of the mental hospital, its contact representative may be able to assist the veteran and his family.

It is important to add to the foregoing that no one in the mental hospital should make statements to the veteran patient or his family concerning eligibility for compensation or degree of disability. This may create erroneous impressions, intensify paranoid litigious tendencies or otherwise complicate the management of the case.

The Value of the History of Military Service

The patient's service history is important to the psychiatrist for many reasons. The Armed Forces in wartime represent an emotionally stressful situation for the average person. His capacity to adapt successfully to that environment bespeaks a certain ego strength which has prognostic implications. We will want to know his rank on entering the service and that on leaving it. Promotions will be indicative of a well-integrated personality; the absence of promotions may express a marginal capacity for adaptation. The record of disciplinary actions is also important as a source of further data concerning the patient's capacity for adjustment and the characteristic patterns of adaptation which he employs under stress. There may be a history of deviant sexual behavior, episodes of violence, alcoholism. Satisfactory performance until just prior to discharge may express the patient's need for a simple, well-supervised environment like that of the Armed Forces, or may relate to a particularly stressful home environment which the returning soldier dreads. There may be an elementary problem of checking the patient's veracity. A striking instance of this occurred in the case of a pathological liar who presented an elaborate history of exposure to hazardous overseas duty. His service record showed that he was stationed comfortably in the United States throughout the time of alleged stress.

The patient's medical history in the service is of great importance. Was he on sick call frequently? Was he hospitalized? If so, for what reasons and how often? Repeated hospitalizations for physical complaints may have represented his way of coping with his anxieties at that time. If he was hospitalized for psychiatric reasons, it will be interesting to compare the diagnostic impression then with the current one. Not uncommonly patients who had schizophrenic episodes in the service present themselves as veterans with nonpsychotic reactions. The problem of why they reacted with psychosis in the service and with psychoneurosis in civilian life should engage the interest of all concerned from a theoretical as well as a practical point of view. Such data may clarify the current diagnosis and prognosis. Is the patient showing a more or less malignant clinical picture? Is he deteriorating? Thus many data of importance can be gleaned from a careful study of the patient's service record.

How to Obtain the Military History

If the veteran has received benefits of any kind from the V.A., then he has a claim file, which is sometimes referred to as his "C" file, or parent file. He is identified in V.A. records by his name and "C" number. The "C" file of the patient will often contain an abstract of his service record which is complete enough for the psychiatrist's needs. One ascertains from the veteran or his family which Regional V.A. Office has custody of his "C" file. The social worker of the mental hospital then writes to the chief social worker of that Regional Office. If his "C" file is not there, a letter to the Director of the Claims Division of the V.A. Central Office (Washington 25, D.C.), with the man's name and "C" number, or his serial number while in the service, will lead to the location of his file.

If the veteran does not have a "C" file, or the information in it about his previous military service does not fulfill the psychiatrist's needs, then a letter may be addressed to the Adjutant General's Office of the Army or the Air Force, or the Chief of the Bureau of Personnel of the Department of the Navy in the Pentagon Building, or to the Commandant of the United States Coast Guard in Washington, D.C., depending on the veteran's branch of service. It is well to secure the consent of the patient or the next of kin for the release of this information. If consent has not been obtained, the reason for this should be explained in the letter of request. However, if the patient is psychotic then current regulations permit release of these data to properly qualified authorities. Additional information may be obtained from the local Social Service Exchange (see Chapter VIII). Finally, the Regional V.A. Office may dispatch a social worker to the veteran's home if further information is requested.

What to Ask For

Inasmuch as the files on the veteran may be voluminous, it is important to ask specific questions in the letter of request. For example, one may ask for data concerning previous V.A. hospitalizations, diagnoses and treatments. Or, information may be desired about a specific relationship, the veteran's parents, siblings, or wife. For example, if the veteran states that his wife has been sexually promiscuous, information about her may help establish if this is delusional or a fact. In addition to the need for asking specific questions, it is also important to state the purpose for which the information will be used. The more clearly the psychiatrist makes known his needs in his request, the more adequately will they be fulfilled.

Outpatient Facilities for Veterans

Outpatient clinics for veterans are of four categories: a regional clinic which operates from the Regional Branch Office of the V.A. and which provides psychiatric services to fifty-one areas demarcated in this country by the V.A. for organizational and administrative purposes; a hospital clinic which operates in the outpatient department of a veteran's hospital, usually a neuropsychiatric specialty hospital; a travelling clinic; and contract clinics which are units associated with Regional Offices that operate in areas adjacent to these offices and are directed by qualified private psychiatrists who organize clinics which meet prescribed standards of the V.A. The contract clinic supplements the day service of the regional clinic by operating in the evening, a matter of immeasurable importance in planning the treatment of a patient who is well enough to hold down a full-time job by day. V.A. clinics are staffed by social workers and a psychologist who work under the direction of the psychiatrist. In many clinics they participate to a limited extent in administering psychotherapy in addition to their usual duties, an arrangement that can be satisfactory if their training is adequate and if the treatment follows a rational plan drawn up in consultation with the psychiatrist. Many actively psychotic patients are carried on an outpatient basis by such clinics. Thus, these outpatient facilities may in some instances eliminate the need for hospitalizing a veteran patient altogether, as well as expedite the point in hospital treatment at which the patient may be discharged into the community for outpatient care.

Special Problems in the Psychotherapy of Veterans

A veteran with mental illness often presents special emotional complications because of the disability compensation which he receives. If he is hospitalized the problem is intensified because he is not only the recipient of free hospital care but he receives his full compensation as well. This doubles the secondary gain from his illness. As a result, there is a tendency for the excessive mobilization of infantile attitudes of helpless dependency, either in the form of extreme passivity or in tantrum-like outbursts of aggressiveness. The receipt of the monthly compensation check often intensifies feelings of failure, guilt over continued infantile gratifications, and the need for face-saving mechanisms. Guilt over the death of friends in combat is not uncommonly encountered in the surviving veteran. The loss of prestige, of a sense of purpose, and of security often attend the return to civilian life. These are some of the special factors to be kept in mind in the proper conduct of his treatment.

Liaison Between the V.A. and Other Mental Hospitals

The V.A. has pioneered in the field of hospital care for the mentally ill. It has given a convincing demonstration of the place of a psychiatric service in every general hospital (see Chapter XXXIII). It has developed the resources of the voluntary worker to unprecedented effectiveness in the V.A. Voluntary Service (V.A.V.S.). Many of its hospitals take the lead in demonstrating the ideal of genuine teamwork between different disciplines and departments within the mental hospital. The utilization of social service and social service aides are also unusually effective (see Chapter VIII). Research and the training programs for residents and other personnel are similarly excellent. For these and other reasons liaison between V.A. hospitals and other mental hospitals should be encouraged. Joint meetings of staffs, co-ordinated research and training programs, exchange of ideas and clinical experiences, joint exploration for the fullest utilization of community resources are already in progress in some areas to the advantage of all participants.

The Role of Psychiatry in Selective Service

The mental hospital psychiatrist may be called upon to serve directly or to act in an advisory capacity to a Selective Service Board. Early in World War II, an attempt was made to eliminate all potential psychiatric casualties prior to induction. Notwithstanding high rejection rates at the induction level, large numbers of psychiatric casualties occurred. It became apparent that our present knowledge in this area is insufficient to justify high rejection rates for psychiatric reasons. In fact many psychiatrists came to believe that a trial of duty is the only reliable test. However, some psychiatric screening remains necessary and is aimed primarily at the exclusion of the obviously unfit or the grossly incapacitated.

The main reason why effective screening at the induction level does not seem possible is to be found in the unconscious or symbolic meanings with which the individual invests the military service. Separation from an unsatisfactory home is not in all instances a trauma, particularly if it is replaced by an Army assignment where leadership is excellent and morale is high. The latter factors are of critical importance and touch upon the whole problem of motivation which is impossible to assess at the induction level, precisely because it is related to the quality of the leadership to which the inductee will be exposed. As has already been mentioned, separation from the service is a far greater trauma for some individuals than was induction into the service in the first place. The problem is not one of finding a certain group of individuals but rather the more dynamic one of estimating how a given person will adapt to a multifaceted situation.

A dramatic example of the difficulties involved in estimating the future effectiveness of an inductee was seen in an alcoholic and a drug addict who had completed a sentence in Sing Sing because of difficulties arising from his addiction. At induction he showed grossly manifest evidences of anxiety. In spite of all of these negative features he was inducted into the Navy because he had certain naval skills that were in demand at that time. In the service he became transformed into a person with a keen sense of responsibility, patriotism and high self-esteem, and was able to fulfill all of his duties in a highly creditable manner.

SELECTED REFERENCES

ADLER, M. H.; GATES, P. H.: Veteran Status Complicating Psychotherapy. *J. Nerv. & Ment. Dis.*, 119:52, 1954.
BOND, D. D.: *The Love and Fear of Flying*. New York: International Universities Press, 1952.
    Demonstrates clearly and lucidly that selection is a continuous process.
BOONE, J. T.: The Medical and Hospital Program of the Veterans Administration. *J.A.M.A.*, 154:756, 1954.
    Facts and fallacies about V.A. medical care presented in question and answer form.
DRIBBEN, I. S.: Mental Hygiene Clinics of the Veterans Administration. *J.A.M.A.*, 155:331, 1954.
GINZBERG, E.; HERMAN, J. L.; GINSBURG, S. W.: *Psychiatry and Military Manpower Policy. A Reappraisal of the Experiences in World War II*. New York: King's Crown Press, 1953.
    One of the Columbia University Graduate School of Business "Human Resource Studies," based on a survey of the opinions of a group of distinguished psychiatrists with World War II military experience.

HAMBURG, D. A.; BASKIN, T. G.; TUCKER, A. C.: Prediction of Immediate Psychiatric Breakdown in Military Service. *U.S. Armed Forces Med. J.*, 5:625, 1954.

TOMPKINS. H. J.: State and Veterans Administration Cooperation Towards Better Mental Health. *Am. J. Psychiat.*, 111:172-176, 1954.

VETERANS ADMINISTRATION INFORMATION SERVICE FACT SHEETS:
August 13, 1952, Peace Time Fact Sheet.
August 13, 1952, World War I Fact Sheet.
September 15, 1953, Post Korea Fact Sheet.
October 1, 1953, World War II Fact Sheet.

Chapter XXIII

THE SEX DEVIATE

Dread of Deviant Sexuality

The fact that psychiatrically untrained people develop anxiety when exposed to the mentally ill has been referred to previously in these pages. The strangeness, the unpredictability and the potential violence that seems to reside in the behavior of the disturbed patient have been given as causes. One of the most frequently verbalized fears is that there is a contagion about mental illness as a result of which "normal" people will themselves become psychiatrically affected if they are exposed to people of unsound mind. Psychoanalytic studies have brought out that there is an important unconscious basis for this anxiety. In a dimly recognized way, people perceive in the manifestations of psychopathology, mental mechanisms of their own which were brought under control and repressed in early childhood; for example, the impulse to soil, to smear feces, to disrobe before company, to masturbate, to give expression to feelings of omnipotence and magical thinking. Paradoxically then it is not the strangeness of mental illness but the faintly recognized familiarity of it that makes it so terrifying. The lay person fears that the hard-won control of his infantile impulses will be lost by observing the example of these uncontrolled people. Hostile punitive attitudes toward the mentally ill often reflect similar attitudes toward these impulses in oneself. It is as if the observer were saying angrily, "I control myself! Why doesn't he?"

This irrational attitude obtains with particular force whenever sexual deviations constitute a feature of the clinical picture. Sex crimes give rise to a special atmosphere of horror. In the State of Massachusetts the statute on bestiality, for example, speaks of it as "the abominable and detestable crime against nature," adjectives which are not employed in the statutes governing murder or robbery. Even doctors are not immune to unscientific thinking when it comes to sexual symptomatology. Not uncommonly they display punitive and judgmental attitudes in sexual matters which would be foreign to them in any other medical situation. Even scientific investigators may react to sexual phenomena with psychic scotomata.

Sex crimes have not increased to any marked degree, but popular articles on the subject have. In articles written for their appeal to morbid curiosity the danger from this source has been magnified far beyond that which is warranted by the facts. A legend has been cultivated that the mentally abnormal sexual offender proceeds from the commission of trivial offenses such as exhibitionism or voyeurism to crimes of major seriousness, such as rape and murder, a conception which is rarely confirmed by clinical experience. As a result of irrational fears and hatreds unwise and ill-considered legislation may be passed. In courts of law accusations made by the mentally ill are apt to be taken uncritically when they concern sexual matters, even when these accusations represent an acting out on the part of the accuser of unconscious or psychotic fantasies. Thus, the psychiatrist has a particularly grave social responsibility when it comes to sex offenses. Standing firm against hysterical pressures from all sources, he must counteract widespread fear by inculcating the public with sound principles of mental hygiene.

Theory of Deviant Sexuality

A long time ago Freud pointed out that sexually deviant patterns of behavior in the adult are identical with patterns of behavior seen normally in certain stages in the emotional development of the child. Characteristic of these early patterns is a preoccupation with the mouth and anus, with pleasure in touching, with masturbation, with exhibitionism and peeping. Indeed, these patterns exist in the normal adult as part of the so-called "forepleasure" or sexual play that usually precedes sexual intercourse. When these preliminary patterns represent the exclusive expression of sexual pleasure, we may speak of an arrest in the sexual development of the individual. Such arrested development probably never occurs in isolation but rather as part of a more generalized arrest in emotional development, so that these people are almost invariably passive, dependent, and incapable of emotional gratification in normal sexual relationships. Typically they lack adult control over their impulses in general, as a result of which other antisocial acts may occur, such as alcoholism, stealing, or assault. However, a given pattern of sexual behavior tends to remain constant for an individual, so that an individual apprehended in a trivial sexual offense rarely progresses to crimes of major seriousness in the future.

Among individuals apprehended for sexual offenses a history of unfavorable childhood with severe emotional deprivation is the rule. Psychological studies tend to confirm the clinical impression of retarded emotional development.

In the normal course of events the young child experiences some anxiety as he proceeds to each new level of emotional development. If the satisfaction which he experiences during any given phase is particularly intense, or if the anxiety attending the transition to the next phase is, for some reason, particularly great, he tends to persist at that level of emotional development. He is then said to have developed an "infantile fixation." He may never proceed in his emotional development beyond the fixation point, and he remains permanently "stunted" in his patterns of sexual expression. Or he may advance to a more mature level only to return to this fixation point, episodically or permanently, in response to some particularly severe emotional stress later on in life. This process is called "regression." The infantile fixation point is the position of safety to which he will tend to retreat whenever he has difficulty in adapting throughout his life.

The pattern of sexual behavior characteristic of this fixation point is a source of intense pleasure. To an individual who experiences overwhelming anxiety in some or all aspects of his role as an adult, pleasures attending the infantile patterns of sexual expression become an additional reason for regression. It is this element of pleasure that makes it difficult for the patient to give up the infantile pattern even when he has been helped to understand, by psychotherapeutic means, that his original fears were unfounded.

Arrested emotional development in the male usually interferes with his ability to carry out normal sexual intercourse, since his capacity to achieve and maintain an erection during an adult heterosexual relationship is usually also impaired. The woman, on the other hand, is usually able to carry out sexual intercourse in spite of considerable emotional immaturity. For this reason the sexual act is more threatening to the immature male, by and large, than it is to the immature female. This fact is responsible for the considerably greater incidence of socially manifest aberrant sexual behavior in the male than in the female.

Some Clinical Observations

Very commonly the sexually deviate male marries a woman considerably older than himself, often with children of her own. His relationship with her is manifestly infantile, even to being supported by her wholly or in part. If he feels that she has withdrawn her love from him, he reacts to this rejection with sexually deviant behavior. This may happen because of a quarrel, because of the birth of a new baby, or because a physical ailment may prevent her from having sexual intercourse with him. Many such patients are deeply dependent upon a normal sexual outlet. Under circumstances of enforced abstinence (as for example during military service), regressive sexual patterns tend to emerge.

The adaptive function of deviate sexual behavior is well exemplified in certain patients with organic brain disease. Patients with such disease, in whom there exists a clouding of consciousness, will deal with the anxieties generated by their illness in a variety of patterns, all of which are calculated to diminish them. Among these patterns deviant sexual behavior can be found. A patient who is debilitated and impotent will deny these infirmities in exhibitionistic display of his sexual prowess, in words, in genital exposure, and in masturbation. In addition, these patients will sometimes attempt by means of sexual display to seduce doctors and nurses into giving them more attention.

A twenty-five-year-old unmarried man presented himself for treatment because of compulsive masturbation. He was also a "peeping tom." However, he conducted these activities in the privacy and safety of his own home, so he never got into trouble with the police. In the course of his psychoanalysis his infantile fixation on both parents became clearly evident. When one of his three younger sisters had a baby, he used to enjoy watching her bathe the infant. However, in this situation, he developed a strong urge to exhibit himself before other children and to play with their genitalia. Fortunately, he was able to control this urge. To reinforce his control he found that he had to avoid visiting his sister. Psychoanalysis showed that he was placing himself in the role of the little infant and enjoying what he believed was the baby's pleasure at being fondled by its mother. His urge to exhibit himself was part of his identification with the naked baby. His urge to fondle little children was in part related to his wish to be fondled by his mother.

The experiences of the patient described in the preceding paragraph were paralleled by those of another patient who was first seen in a state hospital where he had been referred for study by the local court. He was under arrest for exhibiting himself before a group of children in a public park. He was a thirty-year-old man, given periodically to alcoholic excesses, who married a woman five years his senior. They lived fairly congenially together for the next four years. During this time he worked steadily and supported her.

When she became pregnant during the fourth year of their marriage he resumed his drinking. After the baby was born his emotional state deteriorated. His alcoholism increased. The sexual exposure occurred during a period of alcoholic intoxication.

Psychological studies in the hospital richly documented the infantile conception that he had of himself. They also indicated that he reacted to the birth of his own son as if he were a sibling competing for the love of the mother. On the psychiatrist's recommendation sentence was suspended and the patient was referred to the outpatient clinic of the hospital for treatment. By means of the foregoing psychological insights it was possible to plan a course of supportive psychotherapy designed to increase his self-esteem. The social worker in conjunction with the psychiatrist helped the wife to understand and accept her husband's inordinate dependency needs.

Classification of Sexual Deviates

Sexual offenses rarely if ever occur in "normal" individuals. Clinical experience has shown that they usually occur in individuals who fall into one or another of the following psychiatric categories.

Mental Deficiency. A significantly higher per cent of sex offenders are mentally defective than are a corresponding group of general offenders. (This problem has been referred to in Chapter XIX.) Some people have tried to explain this by attributing to this group an abnormally intense sexual urge. This is a fallacy. Usually they trangress the law because they lack sufficient understanding of the need to control and conceal their impulses. In addition, because they are so suggestible, they are more prone to fall victim to delinquent influences if their environment is not carefully regulated.

Psychosis. Some sexually deviated offenders are found to be schizophrenic. This is relatively uncommon. The schizophrenic offender is most likely to be involved in homosexual offenses or in molesting women. Senile psychotic reactions are much more frequently encountered. Their sex offenses usually involve exhibitionism and the molesting of children (pedophilia).

Psychoneurotic reactions probably account for the bulk of the sexually deviated offenders. The deviate sexual act is likely to be a compulsive symptom. Unless the psychoneurosis is associated with mental deficiency or alcoholism these individuals are usually able to gratify their impulses under circumstances which do not give public offense. At times the sexually deviant act is intensely repugnant to them, is carried out only after a prolonged inner conflict and is followed by overwhelming feelings of guilt. Such people may cover up their tracks with striking ineptness as if to insure detection, punishment and confinement. When confined they often experience a great relief of tension. The need to exhibit (for example) may be entirely absent while in prison only to recur in response to the pressures of life outside. One such patient said to the policeman who arrested him, "It's about time you found me!"

Alcoholism plays an important role in sex offense. Many individuals who are able to control their pathological sexual impulses when sober may lose control when drunk. On recovering in jail from the intoxicated state of the previous night they often have a complete amnesia for the sexually deviant act for which they were arrested. They may protest their innocence in all sincerity (although conscious dissembling can also occur). In an overseas theater in World War II many minor deviant sex offenses were committed by soldiers under the influence of alcohol. It was found that harsh disciplinary measures resulted in unnecessary loss of man-power without in any way influencing the behavior of other soldiers when drunk. Milder disciplinary measures were accordingly instituted with no adverse effects.

Psychopathic personality is a term that has been employed with con-siderable inexactness. Cleckley applied it to a specific type of character disorder in which there occurred marked egocentricity, irresponsibility, unreliability, apparent lack of guilt feelings, poverty of emotional re-sponsiveness and an inability to follow a constructive life plan. This group of characteristics was often associated with good intelligence and superficial social charm. These people become involved in sexually devi-ant offenses relatively infrequently. More frequently this diagnostic term is applied to individuals inexactly as a term of opprobrium, and implies a judgmental and punitive attitude. From our present knowledge of char-acter disorders we know that many of these people who outrage our sense of justice and propriety without overt evidence of remorse or anxi-ety often experience much more suffering than they reveal. In any event these people are mentally ill, for the most part, and nothing constructive is achieved by neglecting that clinical fact.

Certain apparently nonsexual offenses turn out on deeper investiga-tion to have an underlying sexual basis. For example, larceny may be the result of kleptomania, arson the result of pyromania. Sexual excite-ment and gratification may occur as part of these acts, and can even occur in rare cases of murder. Reference has already been made to the tendency of some of these offenders to act in such a way as to insure arrest.

In the well known case of William Heirens the offender began steal-ing women's undergarments at the age of nine and would masturbate while wearing them. In time this pattern of sexual gratification was replaced by another in which he achieved a climax of sexual excitement at the moment of breaking and entering into a home for the purpose of stealing female undergarments. He gave up masturbation in favor of this new sexual pattern. In fact he felt very strongly that masturbation was worse than burglary. Breaking into and entering a home thus came to represent for him a substitute masturbatory pleasure at the same time that it was a defense against masturbation. Although he continued to have his orgasms, he could reassure himself that he was not masturbating. This psychological stratagem gradually failed him, however, since with time he found that it required an increasing number of burglarizing acts in a given night to produce relief of sexual tension. He fought a desperate battle against his perverse impulses without being able to master them. Before succumbing to an urge to burglarize he would suffer excruciating headaches and panic. He would take all his clothes off and hide them in a closet in an attempt to dissuade himself from going out. But in the end the urge would overpower him. He committed several murders to avoid capture. In the apartment of one of the women he murdered he scrawled in lipstick on a mirror, "Catch me before I kill again, I cannot help myself."

In this case the relation between deviant sexual impulses to apparently nonsexual crime was clearly evident.

Sociological Classification of Deviant Sexual Offenders.

Some sex offenders, as the one detailed in the preceding paragraph, inflict emotional and physical trauma upon those about them. Others, at worst, have only nuisance value to society. This purely sociologic consideration should be the basic frame of reference for the psychiatrist in advising the court. For example, a rapist may be less sick than a peeping tom from a clinical psychiatric point of view, yet sociologically the rapist is a menace and the peeping tom but a nuisance. Where public hysteria has pushed through harsh sex laws, the nuisance offender is more often caught than the genuine social menace. Prisons and state hospitals may become filled with a host of nontraumatizing offenders, some of whom may even be innocent.

A married man with two children was arrested for indecent exposure. One day he went to a corner of the basement of a house on which he was working as a carpenter and urinated. A seven-year-old girl saw him and reported this fact to her mother who became enraged and brought charges against him. Two psychiatrists expressed the opinion that this did not constitute an act of sexual psychopathy and that the man was not in any sense a danger to the community. A third psychiatrist in agreement with his colleagues included in his report the fact that this man had a history of masturbation as a youngster. The judge became so outraged at this latter fact that he overruled the opinions of the consulting psychiatrists and committed the man to a state hospital as a "criminal sexual psychopath."

Such instances can be multiplied throughout the country. The responsibility of the psychiatrist to educate the uninformed and to deal scientifically with public hysteria is apparent. The psychiatrist sometimes acquiesces to public pressure with the rationalization that he is unable, after all, to stand up to the "will of the people and the courts." If this "will" is based on unreason, then it is his duty as a physician to stand up to it. The nontraumatizing offender should be protected from unjust punishment. All sex offenders, traumatizing and nontraumatizing alike, should be treated in accordance with the best scientific knowledge and medical judgment.

When is a sexually deviant act traumatizing to the victim? Although this is readily answered in many cases, in many more cases the outcome of the experience is not so self-evident. An isolated minor sexual experience such as the usual act of exhibitionism rarely exerts a lasting traumatic effect upon the normal child, particularly if the parents are successful in hiding their own distress and if the child is not exposed to evidences of widespread indignation. In short, the hysteria of the "normal" adults represents, by and large, a greater emotional hazard than the sexual exhibitionism itself. The problem is complicated by the fact that some children are more prone to become involved in experiences with adult sex offenders than others. Very commonly there is a history of repeated experiences in a single child in a neighborhood where no other children have been similarly "traumatized." Such "trauma-prone" children often come from emotionally disturbed homes. A precocious interest in adult sexuality is often part of a psychopathological state which is of fundamental importance. Motivated by feelings of insecurity and loneliness such children may actively seek out such experiences and even play a seductive role. (An example of this is to be found in the case history described at the end of Chapter I.) Definite psychopathological states may be found to emerge on follow-up study of such children. However, these are more likely to be outgrowths of the emotional disorder which led to the sexual experience in the first place than of the experience per se. Naturally, not all children belong to this category. A dispassionate evaluation of each case is most likely to protect the mental health of the community.

Examination of the Deviant Sex Offender

Usually the sexually deviated offender will be seen by the psychiatrist at the request of the court. There will be a question concerning the capacity of the accused to co-operate mentally and emotionally in his

own defense; and whether he can be expected to assume responsibility
for his behavior at the time of the offense (see Chapter XXIV). The
psychiatrist may also be asked to make recommendations concerning the
disposition of the accused—will he benefit from penal incarceration,
should he receive treatment in a mental hospital, can he be returned to
the community without constituting a public menace, can he be helped
by outpatient psychotherapy? The examination and the report to the
court should aim to answer the following list of questions:

1. Present clinical psychiatric diagnosis.
2. Physical examination. This should cover evidences of alcoholism,
cerebral arteriosclerosis, drug addiction, encephalopathy, epilepsy, cir-
rhosis of the liver, senility, impaired visual or auditory acuity. The face-
hand test and the sodium amytal test for organic brain disease (see Chapter VII) are useful additional items.
3. Laboratory studies. These should include cerebrospinal fluid examination, blood chemistry, skull X-rays and electroencephalography.
4. Psychopathology at the time of the examination; psychopathology
at the time of the offense.
5. Psychological studies, including intelligence quotient, diagnostic
impression, data concerning the meaning of the sexually deviant behavior in terms of unconscious infantile motivations and psychological
mechanisms of defense, a statement concerning the accessibility of the patient's psychopathology to alteration by psychotherapy, and the prognosis.
6. Social service report. The social service department should investigate the home circumstances of the sex offender ascertaining the degree
to which environmental circumstances have contributed to his disordered
behavior, and the degree to which these can be corrected. The latter point
will enter into the recommendations concerning disposition and treatment.
7. Alcoholic history. Was he drunk at the time of the crime?
8. Drug addiction. Was he under the influence of drugs at the time of
the crime?
9. Specific inquiry concerning the attitude of the accused concerning
his crime, currently and at the time of the offense. Does he comprehend
the nature and quality of his act; does he know how the community views
his act and the seriousness of his predicament?
10. Is he capable mentally and emotionally of co-operating in his
own defense?
11. Could he form the proper degree of intent, that is, are there
mitigating circumstances?
12. Is there an irresistible impulse? If yes, elaborate.
13. Is there an amnesia? If yes, what kind (hysterical, psychotic, alcoholic, head injury, epilepsy, malingered)?
14. Prognosis for recovery.
15. Danger to society.

Further psychiatric considerations concerning criminal responsibility before the law are discussed in Chapter XXIV.

The Integration of Legal Processes and Medical Science

Medieval attitudes toward mental illness have given way to a more enlightened scientific point of view over most of the civilized world. However, when it comes to the sex offender or criminal behavior in general, indicated psychiatric procedures are often hampered by outmoded legislation. The futility of punitive, moralistic attitudes and severe prison sentences as devices for correcting pathological sexual behavior has been demonstrated time and again. In various states studies and legislative reforms are in progress to bring legal practices into line with modern scientific understanding. Because the psychiatrist's approach is based on a steadily growing body of scientific data he has the responsibility of leading the way for the lawmakers. M. S. Guttmacher, the distinguished authority on forensic psychiatry, has suggested an ideal plan which centers about the formation of a government-sponsored scientific legal institute for the social, psychological and medical study of the juvenile and adult offender. He recommends that such institutes be co-ordinated with universities so that research and continued scientific growth will be insured. The following is quoted from his article in the *Bulletin of the World Health Organization,* which outlines his plan:

This scientific legal institute should have three divisions: a social division directed by a sociologist or a professionally trained social worker, a psychiatric division directed by a psychiatrist who has had training and experience in criminal psychiatry, and a medical division directed by a physician who has sound clinical and pathological knowledge. These divisions should be administered by men whose intellectual attainments, professional training, and personal stature are equivalent to those of men of the legal profession who become judges, and they should be compensated accordingly.

The social division, in addition to making recommendations in regard to the granting of probation and being responsible for individuals placed on probation, should have as one of its major duties the obtaining of full and accurate socio-medical case histories in a high proportion of cases. They should be made a part of the permanent record and be filed and made accessible to the proper authorities. They should be kept current by contemporary notes and reinvestigations. Such investigations and current records would not only be of the greatest assistance to the court in sentencing, but would also serve as the basis for probation and parole work. They would, furthermore, be of the greatest value to the penal authorities in rehabilitation and proper prison administration.

In order to function most efficiently, the scientific legal institute should reach down to the magistrate or police court level for its base. Whenever possible, a specially trained psychiatric social worker representing the social division should be present at the sessions of these courts to spot psychiatric problems and to advise the magistrates in psychiatric matters. Furthermore, one can visualize such a social worker as an official agent, working informally in the cause of criminal justice by advising parents concerning predelinquent children, aiding individuals involved in serious marital discord and giving advice in regard to the handling of suspected cases of mental disorder. This service should act as a powerful force in the prevention of crime.

The psychiatric division of the institute would be staffed by one or more psychiatrists, psychiatric social workers, and clinical psychologists. This division should have its own psychiatric ward or ready access to psychiatric hospital beds for the observation of the more psychiatrically difficult cases among both juveniles and adults. Psychiatric examination of offenders should not be made before the socio-medical investigation has been completed by the social division.

The psychiatric division could not and should not examine all individuals charged with crime. Such routine examinations, even if practical, would have little value except from a research point of view. In juvenile cases, no radical treatment plan, such as commitment to an institution or to a boarding home, should be made without a medical and psychiatric examination. It is also believed highly desirable that a psychiatric examination be made before granting probation or parole to an adult.

This division should examine any defendant prior to trial or following conviction, when requested to do so by the court, the grand jury, the prosecutor or defense counsel (with the acquiescence of the court), and the medical and social divisions. Except in those cases in which the referrals specifically request psychiatric examination before trial because of the possibility of criminal irresponsibility, and in the cases referred to in the following paragraph, the psychiatric examination should be made after trial but prior to sentence.

It has been established through experience that, among individuals charged with certain types of crime, there is a high incidence of significant psychopathology. Consequently, in the cases of such defendants, a psychiatric examination should be made routinely prior to trial to make certain that no instances of legal irresponsibility are overlooked. In this category are individuals charged with capital offenses, those three times charged with the same crime, and those charged with sex offenses, homicide, arson, bigamy, abandonment of or cruelty to children, assault on wife, and turning in of false fire alarms.

The psychiatric examinations made prior to trial should be made available to the defense and the prosecution as well as to the court. These examinations, carried out by the professional staff of the psychiatric division of the institute, would in large measure eliminate ex parte testimony and the resultant spectacles that have so long redounded to the obloquy of both medicine and law.

In juvenile cases, the psychiatric examination should always be made prior to trial and the full report sent to the court, since such courts are not administered under the criminal rules of evidence.

Diagnosis is, however, merely a sound preliminary to treatment. Society can no longer restrict its focus to the understanding and the disposition of the offender; it must treat and rehabilitate him. Although psychiatry is only beginning to treat the nonpsychotic offender, significant progress has been made in many instances. There is great need for the analysis and evaluation of the varying therapeutic techniques that are now being employed in treating criminals. The psychiatric division of the institute should provide treatment facilities for certain selected probationers and parolees. Moreover, in co-operation with the other divisions it should serve as a powerful educative and inspirational force for the staffs of the penal institutions and the probation and parole offices, advising workers in regard to specific cases, holding case conferences, giving lecture courses, etc.

The medical division should act as the official, neutral, medical agency advising the court and its agents on all medical problems, including:

(1) whether witnesses or jurors should be excused from court appearance because of illness;

(2) whether individuals should be relieved of compliance with the court order to support, because of a physical condition;

(3) the examination of injuries of complainants in assault, rape cases, etc.;

(4) the presence of venereal infection in putative sex offenders, prostitutes, et al.;

(5) blood-grouping in bastardy cases, in criminal identification problems, etc.;

(6) analysis of stains for blood, semen, etc.;

(7) blood-alcohol determination in traffic offenders, murder suspects, et al.;

(8) post-mortem investigations.

After conviction, but prior to sentence, all three divisions should give definite recommendations in their reports to the court regarding disposition. In the past, judges have frequently been willing to accept advice from the prosecutor and the defense counsel in regard to sentence. Certainly there can be no valid reason why the court should be unwilling to have the advice of its own neutral, scientific experts in carrying out this very important function. These advisory reports should be made matters of record but would, of course, not be binding nor mandatory upon the court.

Treatment of the Sexual Offender

Castration has been employed for many years as a means of treating sexual offenders. This treatment is based on the idea that the sex drive in these people is abnormally intense and that castration diminishes this drive. Both of these contentions lack scientific validity. This procedure has had extensive trial in Europe over a period of years, and to a lesser extent in this country. Follow-up studies have confirmed its ineffectiveness. A patient reported by Guttmacher who committed a long series of crimes which were related to pathological patterns of sexual expression had bilateral testicular atrophy on physical examination. The use of castration as a punishment for sexual offenses is an entirely irrational procedure which has no place in a civilized community.

Shock therapy and psychosurgery has been employed in the treatment of sexual offenders and occasional favorable results have been reported. This may well have ocurred in instances in which the abnormal sexual behavior represented an attempt to reduce unbearable anxiety. Hormones have been employed without any established scientific rationale and with equivocal results.

On the basis of the understanding of abnormal sexual behavior as a meaningful although pathological attempt at emotional adaptation, a psychotherapeutic approach would seem to be the treatment method of choice. The therapeutically successful psychoanalysis of individual sexual deviates has been reported from time to time. In recent years experiments with group psychotherapy has been initiated with encouraging preliminary results.

The treatment of the sexual offender by any means currently available is admittedly difficult. In a recent analysis of 102 sexual offenders in Sing Sing prison in New York it was the opinion of the consulting psychiatrists that only 8 per cent of the entire group could be released on parole and safely treated on an outpatient basis; 49 per cent were, in their opinion, not treatable at all by present methods and were likely, after release, to continue as a danger to the public; 43 per cent had a good prospect of improvement if provided with proper inpatient treatment.

Until more effective treatment methods are available sexual offenders who constitute a public danger must be "institutionalized." This should be done, preferably, in a special center designed for their treatment and study. New York and other states provide a "one day to life" sentence for certain sexual offenses. The law governing sex offenders gives the State Board of Parole the authority to terminate the sentence absolutely or conditionally in accordance with the recommendations of examining psychiatrists. Thus, ideal legislation regards the sexual offender as suffering from a mental disorder and as such delegates to the psychiatrist the major responsibility for evaluating the case and estimating his danger to the community. The New York law requires the re-evaluation of such indeterminate sentences every two years. Since most sexual offenders are not commitable by existing legal criteria, special legislation is needed to provide for the defendant's involuntary admission to a state hospital.

SELECTED REFERENCES

ATCHESON, J. D.; WILLIAMS, D. C.: A Study of Juvenile Sex Offenders. *Am. J. Psychiat.*, 111:366, 1954.
  A statistical study which confirms the basic role of emotional and intellectual disorder in sexual offenses. Sociologic factors are also emphasized, particularly in girls. The need for inpatient diagnostic and treatment centers for children is pointed out.

DAVIDSON, H. A.: *Forensic Psychiatry*. New York: Ronald Press, 1953.
  A highly useful compendium of current legal practices as they apply to psychiatry.

FREUD, S.: Three Contributions to the Theory of Sex. In *The Basic Writings of Sigmund Freud*. New York: Modern Library, 1938.
  This classic monograph (written in 1905) details the relationship between deviant sexual behavior in the adult and normal development patterns of sexual expression in the child. The idea of sexually deviant behavior as a psychiatric disease is clearly documented.

GLUECK, B. C., JR.: Psychodynamic Patterns in the Sex Offender. *Psychiat. Quart.*, 28:1. 1954.
  A lucid presentation based on considerable personal experience.

GROUP FOR THE ADVANCEMENT OF PSYCHIATRY: *Psychiatrically Deviated Offenders*. Formulated by the Committee on Forensic Psychiatry of G.A.P., Report No. 9, 1949.
  Contains in brief outline a comparative study of current legal practices with recommendations for future reforms.

GUTTMACHER, M. S.: *Sex Offenses: The Problem, Causes and Prevention*. New York: W. W. Norton, 1951.
  The Jacob Gimbel Lectures on Sex Psychology, delivered in 1950 at Stanford University in California. A highly recommended summary.

—— Psychiatric Examination of Offenders. *Bull. World Health Org.*, 2:743, 1950.
  This presents in outline an ideal plan for bringing medical science directly into the criminal court process.

—— WEIHOFEN, H.: *Psychiatry and the Law*. New York: W. W. Norton, 1953.
  An expert psychiatric and legal partnership combine to make this a masterful critique of current forensic psychiatric practices.

KALINOWSKY, L. B.; HOCH, P. H.: *Shock Treatments, Psychosurgery and Other Somatic Treatments in Psychiatry*. New York: Grune & Stratton, 1952.
  Describes psychosurgical experiences in the treatment of sex offenders.

KARPMAN, B.: *The Sexual Offender and His Offenses*. New York: Julian Press, 1954.
  Contains a vast amount of clinical data and an extensive bibliography.

OVERHOLSER, W.: *The Psychiatrist and the Law*. New York: Harcourt, Brace, 1953.
> Based on the first Isaac Ray Lecture delivered at Harvard University in 1952, the book is rich in the special wisdom and experience of its distinguished author. Highly recommended.

Report on the Study of 102 Sex Offenders at Sing Sing Prison As Submitted to Governor Thomas E. Dewey. New York: State Hospitals Press, 1950 (1213 Court Street, Utica, N.Y.; 40¢).
> This well-known monograph deserves careful study by all interested in the field.

UNSIGNED: Towards Rehabilitation of Criminals: Appraisal of Statutory Treatment of Mentally disordered Recidivists. *Yale Law J.*, 57:1085, 1948.
> A scholarly survey of current legal practices and the need for a new, psychiatrically based orientation.

Chapter XXIV

THE CRIMINAL

Psychosis and Criminal Behavior

A schizophrenic woman working as a housekeeper for an elderly widower developed a delusional system involving her employer. One night while he slept she crushed his skull with an axe. Several days later she was found by neighbors kneeling in prayer before the now putrefying corpse. She showed no signs of remorse and made no attempt to escape. When questioned she explained that God had told her to do this as a sacrificial act to purify the world of its lustful desires. She said it would have been sinful not to obey "the voice of God." Because she expected public approval for what she did she felt no guilt and no need to conceal herself or the evidence of her violent deed. On the contrary, she had a feeling of exultation and fulfillment after months of unrelenting inner torment. This woman was not brought to trial. She was committed to a state hospital where she remained in a psychotic condition until her death from pneumonia fifteen years later.

The idea of bringing to trial a person in such a disordered state of mind and executing her for what she did is repugnant to the modern mind. A civilized society does not punish those who are ill. It treats them in accordance with the best medical knowledge. In addition, society takes steps to protect itself from the effects of illness, even isolating the sick individual from society at large, if necessary, until he no longer constitutes a menace. This is just as true for smallpox and tuberculosis as it is for mental disease. Not so long ago, however, countless hundreds of persons were tried and executed as witches because they displayed symptoms of mental derangement. Today we regard this period as a black chapter in human history. Although we have made advances on many social fronts since those days, these have not been uniform. In dealing with criminal behavior, for example, there has been a decided lag.

Sociologic Aspects of Criminal Behavior

Certain criminal acts are products of a social milieu. Under specific socioeconomic circumstances it actually requires an attitude of non-conformity to avoid a career of crime. It is possible (although by no means a proven scientific fact) that punishment will act as a deterrent for some people in such undesirable environments. Even in these instances, however, the mechanical application of punishment without regard for the social forces which give rise to crime is irrational and fruitless. Criminal behavior which has its primary origin in social forces has its own specific epidemiology, prophylaxis, treatment and aftercare requirements—problems of momentous importance but not relevant to the purposes of this book. This chapter will concern itself with criminal behavior which has its primary origin in psychiatric disturbances within the individual. Those who fall into this group present an entirely different problem in their relationship to the law and in regard to the likelihood that punishment or attempts at re-education will exert a deterrent or corrective influence upon them.

The Problem of Legal Responsibility

In some instances at least, these two categories of criminal behavior, sociologic and psychiatric, can be clearly differentiated. For example there would be little doubt concerning the primarily psychiatric basis for the murder described in the opening paragraph of this chapter. Similarly, in a murder committed during the armed robbery of a bank by a group of youngsters from an underprivileged neighborhood, sociologic factors would probably play a role of predominant importance. It is hardly necessary to add that in many instances both factors are involved, and the placing of a criminal act in one category or another poses a more difficult problem, one for which no definitive solution has been found after a century or more of study. In 1839 a book was published entitled *Medical Jurisprudence of Insanity*, the first systematic treatise devoted to this subject in any land. Its author was Isaac Ray, a distinguished American psychiatrist. He contrasted what he called "criminal homicide" and "homicidal insanity" as follows:

> In homicidal insanity, murder is without any motive strictly deserving the name; or, at most, with one totally inadequate to produce the act in a sane mind. On the contrary, murder is never criminally committed without some motive adequate to the purpose

in the mind that is actuated by it and with obvious reference to the ill-fated victim. Thus, the motive may be theft, or the advancement of any personal interest, in which case it will be found that the victim had or was supposed to have property, or was an obstacle to the designs or expectations of another. Or it may be revenge, and then the injury, real or imaginary, will be found to have been received by the murderer from the object of his wrath. In short, with the criminal, murder is always a means for accomplishing some selfish object, and is frequently accompanied by some other crime; whereas, with the homicidal monomaniac, murder is the only object in view, and is never accompanied by any other improper act.

The homicidal monomaniac, after gratifying his bloody desires, testifies neither to remorse, nor to repentance, nor to satisfaction, and if judicially condemned, perhaps acknowledges the justice of the sentence. The criminal either denies or confesses his guilt; if the latter, he either humbly sues for mercy, or glories in his crimes, and leaves the world cursing his judges and with his last breath exclaiming against the injustice of his fate.

The criminal never sheds more blood than is necessary for the attainment of his object; the homicidal monomaniac often sacrifices all within his reach to the cravings of his murderous propensity.

The criminal lays plans for the execution of his designs; time, place, and weapons are all suited to his purpose; and, when successful, he either flies from the scene of his enormities, or makes every effort to avoid discovery. The homicidal monomaniac, on the contrary, for the most part, consults none of the usual conveniences of crime; he falls upon the object of his fury, oftentimes without the most proper means for accomplishing his purpose; and perhaps in the presence of a multitude, as if expressly for court observation; and then voluntarily surrenders himself to the constituted authorities. When, as is sometimes the case, he does prepare the means, and calmly and deliberately executes his project, his subsequent conduct is still the same as in the former instance.

The criminal often has accomplices and always vicious associates; the homicidal monomaniac has neither.

The acts of homicidal insanity are generally, perhaps always, preceded by some striking peculiarities in the conduct or character of the individual, strongly contrasting with his natural manifestations; while those of the criminal are in correspondence with the tenor of his past history or character.

In homicidal insanity, a man murders his wife, children, or others to whom he is tenderly attached; this the criminal never does, unless to gratify some evil passion, or gain some other selfish end, too obvious to be overlooked in the slightest investigation.

A stronger contrast than is presented, in every respect, between the homicidal act of the real criminal and that of the monomaniac, can hardly be imagined; and yet we are obliged to acknowledge that men of learning and intelligence have often refused to acknowledge it. . . .

Although these words were written long ago this lucid pronouncement could, with certain modifications, be a useful guide in our day.

Contemporary medicolegal practices have been dominated by a point of view which is embodied in the well-known McNaghten Rule. Drawn up in 1843, its vintage is not less ancient than that of the foregoing formulation by Isaac Ray. To establish a defense on the ground of insanity it must be proved, according to this rule, that at the time of committing the act the party accused was laboring under such a defect of reason from disease of the mind as not to know the nature and quality of the act he was doing, or if he did know it, that he did not know what he was doing was wrong. If this rule is employed in accordance with modern psychiatric knowledge it provides a possibly useful formula for presenting the psychiatrist's opinion to the court. In actual practice, however, this rule is often an intellectual strait-jacket which interferes with the proper application of modern scientific knowledge in behalf of the accused and of society alike.

The basis for this difficulty is to be found in the opinion expressed by some judges and even concurred in by some psychiatrists that a person's mind may be deranged and unsound upon some subjects and yet function normally with respect to others. While this is admittedly true for certain intellectual processes which are relatively free from emotional involvements (as, for example, when one adds two and two to make four), the psychiatrist knows that a delusional system which is rooted deep in the emotional life of the individual is never watertight. Necessarily, it reflects a disorganization of thinking which, potentially at least, may contaminate all of the patient's thought processes. If the "fallacy of a compartmentalized psychotic disorder" is rejected, then a person who is overtly psychotic at the time of committing a criminal act cannot be said to know the nature, the quality and the wrongfulness of his act in the same sense that a nonpsychotic person knows these things; and in that sense cannot be regarded as fully responsible for his behavior before the law.

Before the psychiatrist is asked to express an opinion concerning the legal responsibility of the accused at the time of the criminal act he is asked to express an opinion whether the accused is capable, intellectually and emotionally, of co-operating in his own defense in a court of law. Once again, the opinion has been expressed by some judges, with the concurrence of some psychiatrists, that a person may be overtly psychotic and still be capable of understanding the nature and the object of the proceedings against him. If the "fallacy of a compartmentalized psychotic disorder" is rejected, then it must be concluded here, too, that a person who is overtly psychotic during a trial cannot possibly understand the nature and the object of the legal proceedings in the same sense that a nonpsychotic person knows these things.

The extent to which legal practices can depart from those dictated by available scientific knowledge is exemplified in the famous case of Albert Fish who was executed in 1934 for the murder of ten-year-old Grace Budd. Fish knew the parents of Grace Budd very casually. In 1928, when Fish was fifty-seven years old, he prevailed upon the child's parents to let him take her to a children's party. In spite of some misgivings they let Grace go with him. That was the last they saw of her. Fish and the little girl seemed to have disappeared from the face of the earth. Six years later the mother of the child received the following unsigned letter:

My dear Mrs. Budd:
    In 1894 a friend of mine shipped as a deckhand on the steamer Tacoma, Captain Davis. They sailed from San Francisco for Hong Kong, China. On arriving there he and two others went ashore and got drunk. When they returned the boat was gone. At that time, there was a famine in China. Meat of any kind [that is underscored] was from one dollar to three dollars a pound. So great was the suffering among the very poor that all children under twelve years were sold to the butchers to be cut up and sold for food in order to keep others from starving. A boy or girl under fourteen was not safe in the street. You could go in any shop and ask for steak, chops or stew meat. Part of the naked body of a boy or girl would be brought out and just what you wanted cut from it. A boy or girl's behind, which is the sweetest part of the body and sold as veal cutlet, brought the highest price. John stayed there so long he acquired a taste for human flesh. On his return to New York he stole two boys, one seven, one eleven, took them to his home, stripped them naked, tied them in a closet, then burned everything they had on. Several times every day and night he spanked them, tortured them, to make their meat good and tender. First he killed the eleven-year-old boy because he had the fattest [behind] and of course the most meat on it. Every part of his body was cooked and eaten, except head, bones and guts, he roasted in the oven. All of his [behind] boiled, broiled, fried, stewed. The little boy was next, went the same way. At this time I was living at 409 East 100th Street, rear right side. He told me so often how good flesh was, I made up my mind to taste it. On Sunday, June 3, 1928, I called on you at 406 West 15th Street, brought you pot cheese—strawberries. We had lunch. Grace sat on my lap and kissed me. I made up my mind to eat her, on the pretext of taking her to a party. You said yes she could go. I took her to an empty house in Westchester I had already picked out. When we got there I told her to remain outside. She picked wild flowers. I went upstairs and stripped all of my clothes off. I knew if I did not I would get her blood on them. When all was ready I went to the

window and called her. Then I hid in a closet until she was in the room. When she saw me all naked she began to cry and tried to run downstairs. I grabbed her, and she said she would tell her mamma. First I stripped her naked. How she did kick and bite and scratch. I choked her to death, then cut her in small pieces so I could take the meat to my rooms, cook it and eat it. Her sweet and tender little [behind] was roasted in the oven. It took me nine days to eat her entire body. I did not have [intercourse] with her although I could have had I wished. She died a virgin.

Through this letter the police were able to trace the whereabouts of Albert Fish. He made a full confession corroborating the description in the letter of the way he killed the child, and showed the police where he had hidden her bones. Psychiatric studies revealed a lifelong history of gross psychopathological aberrations. He had been arrested repeatedly for minor offenses, had entered repeatedly into illegal marriages. An examination in a mental hospital prior to the murder in 1928 revealed evidences of presenile dementia. He indulged in extremely painful self-lacerating masochistic rituals including sticking several dozen pins permanently into his body. He was subject to auditory and visual hallucinations with a hyperreligious content. The shocking irrationality of the crime was utilized not as evidence of his mental disorder but as the basis rather for an unreasoning vindictiveness which enveloped doctors, lawyers, judges and general public alike. He was declared legally responsible for his actions and capable of co-operating in his own defense. He was tried, found guilty and subsequently executed.

Examination of the Offender

If the human mind is viewed as a psychobiological unit, as all the available scientific data confirm, then a diagnosis of overt psychosis automatically postpones a trial until such a time as the mental disorder has subsided. A diagnosis of overt psychosis at the time of a crime would automatically eliminate legal responsibility for a criminal act. Such diagnoses call for a multidisciplined investigation of the accused, combining the data of the psychiatrist, psychologist, social worker and other trained observers on the treatment team of a mental hospital. In no sense can so complicated a decision be regarded as lying in the province of a lay jury to arrive at by means of a vote. This fact is receiving increasingly widespread recognition in the form of new legislation and modificiation in court practices.

As the law is now constituted in most states, the psychiatrist may become involved in a criminal case at any point after the accused is apprehended. The request for his help as an expert witness may be initiated by anyone concerned with the case, whether associated with the prosecution, the defense, or the court. In accepting this responsibility the psychiatrist makes it clear at the outset that his findings will not be influenced by the fact that one side or another engaged him. If the findings of the psychiatrist are contrary to the side which engaged him, he will not be asked to testify. The opposite side then may subpoena him as a witness. However, he can refuse to answer questions referring to confidential information from the defendant's file, since this is in the category of a privileged communication between a physician and his patient.

This is the procedure which used to give rise to widely publicized courtroom duels between opposing psychiatrists, a situation which is happily on the wane. A self-centered concern for personal victory often replaced a scientifically balanced concern for truth, justice and the welfare of the accused and the community. To circumvent such unfortunate occurrences legal reforms have been instituted. The Brigg's Law in Massachusetts is an outstanding example of such a legislative advance. According to this law, the following categories of defendants are subjected to special psychiatric scrutiny: a) persons indicted for a capital offense; b) persons known to have been indicted for any other offense more than one time; c) persons who have been previously convicted of a felony. If a defendant belongs to any of the foregoing categories, the court clerk notifies the Department of Mental Health of the fact. The Department then arranges for a psychiatric examination with a view to determining the defendant's mental condition and the existence of any mental disease or defect which would affect his criminal responsibility. The psychiatrist collects his data with the aid of various experts in allied disciplines, on the basis of which he advises the court. He submits a report with recommendations which are then accepted by the judge at his discretion. The proceedings are non-partisan in their entirety.

Another plan for providing the court with psychiatric guidance of the highest scientific validity is that suggested by Guttmacher which depends upon the establishment of a medicolegal institute. This has been discussed in Chapter XXIII in relation to the sex offender. In that same chapter is a checklist of items for the preparation of a report which should be followed in the examination of the general offender, too.

Theory of Criminal Behavior

In the discussion of the relationship between psychopathology and crime only psychosis has been specifically considered thus far. However, many criminals come to the attention of the psychiatrist who are not psychotic and who are yet unmistakably irrational in their patterns of criminal behavior. Some thieves have more than adequate means to buy the objects which they steal, as in most cases of kleptomania. To many criminals prison is a refuge. When free in the community they suffer intolerable anxiety. Often this anxiety stems from a fear that they will lose control of abnormal impulses, erotic, aggressive, or both (see Chapter XXIII for further discussion of this). For them a minor offense represents a mechanism of escape from a freedom which they cannot master to the well-ordered security of prison routine. These individuals are conspicuous in the speed with which they get themselves rearrested after serving a prison sentence. Typically, they are model prisoners during the period of incarceration and their recurrent criminal behavior is often baffling and angering to those who have put their "faith" in them to reform. Many criminals are obsessed by intense guilt feelings which they themselves do not understand. For them imprisonment satisfies a pathological need for punishment. Like the phobic criminals previously mentioned, they may actively seek out arrest. Psychoanalysis of such criminals sometimes reveals an unconscious patricidal wish as the basis for the pathological guilt feelings.

Important insights concerning the psychology of criminal behavior can be derived from the psychoanalytic study of kleptomania. The peculiarly intense pleasure from the enjoyment of a stolen article is a widespread human experience, occurring well within the limits of normal behavior. A transitory phase of petty pilfering in the form of "shop lifting" is not at all rare in adolescent girls. That unconscious sexual meanings may be invested symbolically in such acts is indicated by the fact that orgasms have been reported to occur in some cases at the moment of stealing. Patients in whom kleptomania is a presenting symptom regularly express feelings of emotional deprivation. Often they have experienced real deprivation as a result of maternal illness or death and broken home. Many times they fantasy that the stolen object is a gift from an ambivalently loved parent. At times the stolen object clearly symbolizes a baby, as for example in the case of a woman who developed kleptomania when she learned that she would never bear children. A schizophrenic patient with kleptomania would speak tenderly to his stolen objects as if he were a loving mother talking to her babies. Some patients have reported unaccountable feelings of anger against the proprietor whose shop they were pilfering, indicating an aggressive component in the urge to steal. To one female patient who used to steal fountain pens, the stolen object symbolized a penis and her wish to be a man.

At times one can demonstrate flare-ups in the intensity of the compulsion to steal in response to periods of emotional deprivation. The antisocial act becomes understandable as an attempt to diminish anxiety and to mitigate feelings of loneliness and depression.

A man with a long criminal record as a bank robber recently published his autobiography. He recalled having had a severe phobia for separation from his mother as a youngster. He experienced intolerable anxiety when he was first taken to school. Everyone around him seemed fearfully unfriendly. On successive days his panic mounted to an uncontrollable degree and he fled to his home. Nowadays we would permit the mother to stay in the classroom for days or even weeks until the child has become able to wean himself from the need for her presence. In those less enlightened days the frightened youngster was compelled to return to the classroom without her. He submitted to the school authorities for several months and then he developed a behavior disturbance. He became an "incorrigibly bad boy." This was the beginning of his antisocial career. As a result of it he was frequently sent home. One can observe with great clarity the phobic origins of this boy's criminality. The delinquent behavior served an adaptive function, in that it helped him to get back to his mother. Although his subsequent criminal career took him far away from her, he remained deeply attached to his mother all his life and in his book he makes frequent tender references to her. He became involved with other women who were mother figures to him. He speaks of them too with great tenderness, and to them too he brought much grief. References to his father are conspicuous in their paucity, almost as if he obliterated his father from his conscious mind. He prided himself, exhibitionistically, that he never carried a gun in the commission of his many robberies. The use of artful subterfuges was his stock in trade in outwitting bank authorities, just as his delinquent behavior in school was a subterfuge for outwitting the school authorities. In this sense, too, the forbidden treasures of his adult criminal career symbolized the treasured mother whose company he needed so desperately as a youngster. He escaped repeatedly from great prisons, as if to nullify the attempts of the authorities to coerce and confine him. Yet, for all of his rebellious display against the established order, he remained very much what he was as a youngster, a "mama's boy." The prison provided him with warmth, food and shelter, symbolically represented for him a protecting parent. He was not able to endure separations from this symbolic mother either, having spent, for all his cleverness, the largest part of his life in prison.

Psychotherapy of Criminal Behavior

In view of the unconscious psychological determinants of criminal behavior it is not surprising that simple punitive measures are so often without effect. It is becoming increasingly apparent that chronic incorrigible criminal behavior is symptomatic of mental disease, representing in common with other psychiatric symptom patterns an attempt to adapt to emotional stress. It follows that patients of this category should have the same type of work-up as other psychiatric patients. The psychologist, the social worker and other experts must combine forces with the psychiatrist to elucidate the meaning of the patient's criminal behavior in terms of his individual needs, his specific wishes and fears. Treatment should be planned rationally in accordance with these understandings in the form of individual and group psychotherapy, somatotherapy, environmental modifications through social service, recreational and occupational therapy and vocational rehabilitation. This approach to the management of incorrigible criminal behavior is largely untouched. It calls for considerable study in specially designated research centers.

The fear is sometimes expressed that such an approach will endanger society. As a matter of fact the contrary is true. If criminals were institutionalized for an indefinite period of one day to life, as has been the practice in some states with sex offenders, opportunities for controlling the unimproved offender would be greatly increased. This approach would eliminate crimes which we know with certainty will be committed each time we release criminals who are compulsive repeaters. In the discussion of sex offenders it was stated that they tend to retain a given pattern of deviant behavior and rarely progress from minor offenses to major ones. This is not true of the general offender. The man who burglarizes is much more likely to become involved subsequently in rape and murder than the man who exhibits himself. The principle of giving sentences of gradually increasing length for repeated offenses until the offender is "sent up" for life omits the fact that in many instances the drive toward criminal behavior loses its intensity as the criminal reaches his middle years. Thus, when he finally becomes capable of living successfully in the community his permanent incarceration may be required by law. A flexible approach to the rehabilitation of the so-called incorrigible criminal would parallel the current trend with respect to the sex offender. Although it is drastically out of keeping with current practices, a revolutionary change in our approach is nevertheless justified since punitive techniques have failed so completely as devices for correcting patterns of recurrent criminal behavior.

The Problem of Parole

Among the many complicated tasks that the mental hospital psychiatrist may be called upon to perform is that of advising prison parole boards concerning the release of prisoners. Most prisoners are given a so-called indeterminate sentence. That is to say, there is a minimum and a maximum sentence with additional time that may be deducted from the minimum sentence as a reward for good behavior. It is good criminologic practice to release all prisoners on parole as soon as they become eligible. This provides an incentive for self-control, as well as a vote of confidence in the prisoner's capacity to resume his place in the community, thereby enhancing his self-esteem. The psychiatrist will be asked to help decide if a prisoner is or is not ready for parole. In this decision he has a grave responsibility to society as well as to the prisoner, since the over-all incidence of parole violation is considerable (around 20 per cent).

The psychiatrist should implement his clinical observations with thorough psychological studies and social service data. He diagnoses the case and attempts to formulate the problem of the prisoner in terms of his motivations, defenses, intellectual and emotional endowments. Prisoners with grossly manifest psychiatric abnormalities are more apt to violate parole. A good pre-prison work record and a history of having assumed economic responsibility for one's dependents are also associated with a good parole record. Those with prior arrests and prior imprisonments and those whose crimes were serious are more apt to be parole violators. One might generalize and say that evidences of emotional immaturity correlate with poor parole records. The psychiatrist will take into account the environment to which the prisoner is returning, and the type of job available to him. It is an error to return a man to a known traumatic environment which will tend to foster a recurrence of his criminal behavior patterns. If possible, the psychiatrist should make specific recommendations as to aftercare, including measures for vocational rehabilitation, the use of sheltered residences and workshops (these are discussed elsewhere in this volume) and outpatient psychotherapy where indicated and where facilities are available.

The prisoner who is released on parole is supervised by a parole officer until his sentence is completed, unless the period of supervision is reduced on the advice of the parole officer. The parole officer should be a person with broad social work training who can implement the plan of aftercare as formulated by the psychiatrist in the prison.

Criminal Acts by Patients on Trial Visit

Each time a crime is committed by a person who was once a patient in a mental hospital this fact is emblazoned in newspaper headlines. As a result the public has a grossly exaggerated notion concerning the criminal tendencies of psychotic patients. Statistical studies in different states have proven that the rate of crime in the general population is many times higher than it is for patients on trial visit from mental hospitals. The released patient is far from being a menace to peace and good order, a fact in which the psychiatrist must instruct the general community if he hopes to secure its fullest co-operation in the rehabilitation of the mentally ill.

SELECTED REFERENCES*

AICHHORN, A.: *Wayward Youth.* New York: Viking Press, 1935.
 The first attempt to apply psychoanalytic psychology to the understanding and treatment of juvenile offenders. A classic text.

ALEXANDER, F.; STAUB, H.: *The Criminal, the Judge and the Public.* New York: Macmillan, 1931.
 A pioneer contribution to the psychoanalytic undertanding of the psychopathology of criminal behavior. Rich in case material.

BOVET, L.: *Psychiatric Aspects of Juvenile Delinquency.* New York: United Nations, 1951.
 A study prepared on behalf of the World Health Organization as a contribution to the United Nations program for the prevention of crime and treatment of offenders. A summary of worldwide experiences; a particularly valuable bibliography. Obtainable at the U.N. bookstore, New York City.

COHEN, L. H.; COFFIN, T. E.; FRANK, B.: *Murder, Madness and the Law.* New York: World Publ., 1952.
 Although written in popular style, this book presents a sound psychiatric orientation concerning the problem of legal responsibility in homicide. Excellent illustrative case histories.

GROUP FOR THE ADVANCEMENT OF PSYCHIATRY: *Criminal Responsibility and Psychiatric Expert Testimony.* Formulated by the Committee on Psychiatry and Law of the G.A.P., Report No. 26, 1954.
 This report considers the place of psychiatry in the determination of criminal responsibility and mental illness, the McNaghten rule, the ethical position of the psychiatric expert witness and recommendations for reform. A valuable summary.

EISSLER, K. R., ed.: *Searchlights on Delinquency: New Psychoanalytic Studies.* New York: International Universities Press, 1949.
 Contributions to the psychological and social understanding of delinquency, including therapeutic approaches in a great variety of settings.

ELLIOTT, M. E.: *Crime in Modern Society.* New York: Harper, 1952.
 A comprehensive summary of criminology in the United States; its history, current practices and theoretical points of view. Extensive bibliography.

FRIEDLANDER, K.: *The Psychoanalytical Approach to Juvenile Delinquency: Theory, Case Studies, Treatment.* New York: International Universities Press, 1947.

HUIE, W. B.: *The Execution of Private Slovik.* New York: Signet Books, 1954 (25¢).
 The story of the only American soldier executed as a deserter since 1864. The detailed case history is valuable from a psychiatric point of view, bringing out the intensity of overt anxiety which can occur in a so-called psychopathic personality, and the use of the prison as a refuge from neurotic suffering.

* References for Chapter XXIII are also relevant to the material of this chapter.

THE CRIMINAL

335

MATLIN, M., ed.: *National Probation and Parole Association Yearbook.* New York (1790 Broadway): National Probation and Parole Assn.

Current opinion on the treatment and prevention of delinquency and crime. Based on the papers delivered at the annual conferences of the National Probation and Parole Assn.

REYNOLDS, Q.: *I, Willie Sutton.* New York: Signet Books, 1953 (25¢).

The autobiography of a famous bank robber, as told to Quentin Reynolds. A detailed case history of considerable psychiatric interest, tracing a career of incorrigible criminal behavior from its orgins in a childhood phobia. The use of the prison as a refuge from neurotic suffering emerges here too, as it does in the case of Private Slovik.

SELLIN, T., ed.: *Prisons in Transformation.* New York: Ann. Am. Acad. Pol. & Soc. Sci., May, 1954.

A collection of essays concerning criminological practices in prisons by distinguished authorities in the United States and in Europe.

ZILBOORG, G.: *The Psychology of the Criminal Act and Punishment.* New York: Harcourt, Brace, 1954.

The Isaac Ray Award Book, based on the Isaac Ray lectures delivered at Yale University in 1953. A psychoanalytic critique of current legal practices based on an analysis of the unconscious aspects of aggression, guilt and punishment, with suggestions for reforms.

Chapter XXV

CARING FOR THE PHYSICALLY ILL

Introduction

Having spoken frequently of the mental hospital as a therapeutic community, it should be recalled that it is in itself a community in the literal sense of the word. Typically, it houses thousands of patients and hundreds of employees. A population of such magnitude living in the close quarters of a hospital inevitably poses all the problems of a general medical practice. There are medical and surgical emergencies to contend with, the chronically ill to be provided for, and a variety of preventive measures to be carried out. It has been estimated that a 2000 bed hospital with 500 new admissions a year and 600 employees will have about 350 operations per year. This will include major and minor surgical procedures, orthopedic surgery and possibly obstetrics. In addition to the medical and surgical problems usually found in the general community, there are a series of problems which are of special importance in a mental hospital. Epidemics of measles, acute upper respiratory infections and other infectious diseases occur. Food poisoning occurs from time to time. These present challenging problems in prophylaxis, calling for a knowledge of modern public health techniques, the use of preventive inoculations, and the maintenance of a high level of general health in the hospital community. The control of epidemics, which may erupt occasionally in spite of the best prophylaxis, may call for assistance from local public health authorities. Psychosurgical procedures pose formidable technical problems, calling for the co-ordinated discipline of a modern neurosurgical team in addition to special operating room facilities. Fractures occur relatively commonly in mental hospitals, some as complications of electroshock therapy, some from assaults by disturbed patients, and a sizable number as a result of falls among aged patients. As a result there is need for a fracture table, portable X-ray equipment and sufficient

336

space for plaster work as well as for the services of a competent ortho-
pedist.

Tuberculosis

Of greatest importance among the special medical problems of the
mental hospital is tuberculosis. Active tuberculois is probably more
prevalent in mental hospitals than anywhere else in the world outside of
a tuberculois hospital proper. Surveys in mental hospitals reveal twenty-
seven to forty active cases per thousand as compared to one per thousand
in the general population. That this spectacular difference is not simply
the result of institutional living but rather one which is in some way
related specifically to the problem of mental disease is indicated by the
fact that the case rate in prisons is twelve per thousand. The death rate
due to tuberculosis in mental hospitals is nineteen times as great as in the
general population. It has been estimated that at least 30,000 patients
in the United States hospitalized for mental illness are also afflicted with
tuberculosis, although not all have been definitely diagnosed.

Where a tuberculosis control program exists the percentage of patients
who develop the disease while in residence in a mental hospital is reduced
considerably. State hospitals with substandard control systems have a
4 per cent incidence of tuberculosis among their patients. This is ten
times as high as the incidence of tuberculosis in psychiatric sections of
Veterans Administration hospitals, in which tuberculosis control is
rigidly enforced. The state hospital system in Illinois started with a 2
per cent incidence of tuberculosis in 1945 when they instituted a tuberculosis control program. By 1951 the incidence had fallen to 1 per cent.

Work in the tuberculosis section of a mental hospital presents a major
occupational hazard, not only because psychotic patients are less likely
to observe prophylactic measures against contagion but also because
of inadequacies in physical equipment and trained personnel. The incidence of tuberculosis among employees working with tubercular psychotic patients is nine times as great as the incidence of tuberculosis
among those employed elsewhere in the hospital. For this reason several
states (New York and Wisconsin, for example) have laws that make
tuberculosis contracted by employees in mental hospitals compensable.
Some states with poor tuberculosis control programs have difficulty
getting insurance companies to write workmen's compensation policies
for them. The cost of caring for employees after they have contracted
tuberculosis greatly exceeds the cost of a tuberculosis control program
which will reduce the incidence among patients and employees.

The employee with tuberculosis presents a triple hazard. He endangers patients, other employees and the community outside the hospital. The infected patient who is sent out on trial visit presents a similar hazard. It must be clear from the foregoing facts that a mental hospital can ill afford to omit tuberculosis control from its total treatment program.

Tuberculosis control has three phases: (1) Case finding, (2) Segregation, and (3) Treatment.

Case finding requires that all patients be examined on admission and prior to visits to the community, that all new employees be similarly examined and periodically thereafter, particularly if they work in exposed positions. Modern X-ray equipment in the hands of a well-trained medical and technical staff is the item of major importance in case finding. In most states the Health Departments assist in case finding by lending mass radiographic equipment. Laboratory procedures involving culturing and animal inoculation of infected material must be done with technical perfection or they will become a further source of infection in the hospital. The autopsy room is another danger spot. The case in which tuberculosis is discovered accidentally presents an even greater hazard than the post-mortem examination of known cases of tuberculosis because of the general lack of concern about contagion in the former. Personnel involved in any of the foregoing procedures are therefore in exposed positions.

A valuable procedure that is omitted in most mental hospitals is tuberculin skin testing of all new patients and employees. Negative reacting employees should never be put to work in exposed positions. Some mental hospitals administer the BCG vaccine to all negative reactors. When the tuberculin reaction becomes positive after vaccination the employee may be placed in an exposed position with less danger of becoming ill.

Segregation is the second phase of tuberculosis control. Patients with known active tuberculosis should be placed in one area and those who are questionably active suspects should be placed in a separate area. Ideally this calls for a special tuberculosis building, constructed and equipped in accordance with accepted standards for the control of contagion. The most important aspect of the segregation phase of tuberculosis control is education. All employees must be taught the techniques that will prevent the spread of the disease. In spite of anticipations to the contrary, most psychotic patients are amenable to anticontagion discipline. The defeatist assumption that psychotic patients are not accessible to this instruction is dangerous as well as unwarranted. Communicable disease control techniques should be enforced for all visitors on the tuberculosis wards.

The third or treatment phase of the tuberculosis control program calls for a trained staff with special surgical facilities at its disposal. It has been suggested that specific mental hospitals be designated as tuberculosis centers. Preferably, these hospitals should be close enough to large population centers so that consultation facilities are more readily available. It has been recommended that the tuberculosis unit not exceed 300 beds, nor should its capacity be less than 150 beds in the interest of optimum care. The tuberculosis building should be a self-contained unit with respect to all aspects of treatment, including recreational and rehabilitation facilities.

Regardless of real or alleged deterioration in mental patients afflicted with tuberculosis, all the current therapies for tuberculosis must be made available to them. This includes chemotherapy, collapse therapy, and every other treatment device, medical and surgical, which is available. Apart from the obvious humanitarian motives are the important public health considerations already mentioned as well as administrative reasons, in terms of dollars saved and of making bed space available for new cases.

It is advisable that one physician be designated as the tuberculosis control officer. Ideally he should be a specialist trained in chest diseases and capable of administering a staff of competent nurses and technicians. Practically speaking, this is often impossible. A member of the mental hospital staff may be sent out to a tuberculosis center for intensive training in phthisiology. The mental hospital may be able to affiliate itself with an existing tuberculosis hospital and secure personnel and direction for its own control program in that way. In some hospitals part-time service of specialists is obtained on a fee basis. In one mental hospital visiting chest surgeons even had to bring their own sterilized packs because of inadequate operating room facilities. Even with such makeshift procedures useful work could be done.

Proper treatment of the mental illness is of major importance in the tuberculosis control program since the mental accessibility of the patient may determine his capacity for proper treatment co-operation.

Electroconvulsive therapy is hazardous. When the treatment does not result in improvement of the mental disorder, there is a better than 50 per cent chance that the tuberculosis will get worse. However, if the mental disorder does improve in response to ECT, then it becomes possible to treat the tuberculosis more successfully. Improvement in general nutrition and an increased capacity for physical relaxation contribute to this result. The tuberculosis death rate is appallingly high for patients in mental hospitals. Ninety-four per cent of psychotic patients whose chest X-rays show advanced tuberculosis at the time of diagnosis will be dead within five years. For this reason a trial of ECT is warranted, in spite of the hazards, in any patient whose mental disorder prevents proper treatment of the infection. The recently introduced drug, Thorazine, may provide a more satisfactory means for bringing about a co-operative mental state in psychotic patients with tuberculosis. It is generally felt that insulin coma therapy is too drastic for patients thus afflicted. However, insulin in subshock doses may exert a valuable sedative effect as well as improve the patient's food intake. Psychotherapy in all its forms is no less important for tubercular patients than it is for other victims of mental illness. However, added to the usual difficulties encountered in these procedures are new ones related to the problem of contagion. The necessity for wearing a mask may interfere with the establishment of a suitable working relationship with a patient. Once the patient has become acquainted with his therapist the mask becomes less of an obstacle. For this reason it has been suggested that in the first few sessions, at least, the psychiatrist not wear a mask unless the patients are heavily infected or entirely unco-operative.

Group-psychotherapeutic approaches to these patients are very effective. For example, in response to group pressure by fellow patients, even highly disturbed psychotics will go to bed willingly each afternoon for the prescribed rest period. When the rest period comes to an end, curiously enough, this controlled behavior often comes to an end as well, and previously overactive behavior is thereupon resumed. Formal group psychotherapy sessions have been well received by these psychotic patients, the common bond of physical illness contributing one more factor toward group formation. Sessions may be conducted in an informal circle on the open wards, with patients free to join or leave at their own pleasure. A more rationally co-operative attitude concerning treatment of the infection can be achieved in this way as well as improvement in the primary psychotic process itself. As full a program of activities as can be arranged should be provided for the tuberculosis unit, including recreational and occupational therapy, vocational rehabilitation, motion pictures, television, theater and bibliotherapy.

Because the phthisiologist and the psychiatrist have, by and large, widely divergent interests, it is preferable that a separate physician be in charge of each aspect of treatment in the tuberculosis unit. However, close liaison between the two departments must be maintained. That the patient's improved mental health can facilitate the task of the phthisiologist has already been indicated. However, the observations made by the phthisiologist may be no less important for the psychiatrist. For example, isoniazid and other hydrazine derivatives which benefit tuberculosis also affect the psychiatric picture, frequently beneficially. As a result of such observations these drugs have been used to some advantage in the treatment of depressed patients who do not have tuberculosis. In studying the central nervous system effect of these drugs psychiatrists have found that they produce abnormal slow waves in the electroencephalogram and that in large doses they can produce toxic psychoses. Thus we see two apparently divergent branches of medicine interact and enrich each other.

Rehabilitation is the final stage in the care of the patient in the tuberculosis unit. To the difficulties involved in restoring the mentally ill to their families and the general community are added the special problems which result from the tuberculous infection. The patient will have to accept a permanent physical handicap in addition to his emotional limitations. He will also have to overcome a double prejudice in the community, that against mental disease and that against tuberculosis.

The Patients' Infirmary

Many of the details of the tuberculosis control program can be applied to the general medical and surgical program of the mental hospital. The need for a tuberculosis unit is paralleled by the need for a general hospital unit. The need for a close liaison between the phthisiologist and the psychiatrist is paralleled by the necessity for a similar liaison between the psychiatrist and his medical and surgical colleagues. To state that there is a relationship between mental health and physical health is to repeat the obvious in these days of psychosomatic medicine. The latter has been defined as an approach to the theory and practice of medicine in which emotional changes are dealt with as a factor in health and disease just as are physiological changes, chemical changes and anatomical changes. The emotions make their contribution to the clinical picture of every physical ailment. What is more, they play a role in every phase of the illness from its onset to its final stages, whether it eventuates in convalescence and recovery or invalidism and death. The specific role that the emotions play is determined by many factors not all of which are known or understood.

The infirmary of a mental hospital provides a unique opportunity to study psychosomatic relationships. Which physical illnesses occur more frequently in psychotic patients, which less frequently or not at all?

What changes take place in the mental disorder as the physical illness changes? What are the responses of psychotic patients to painful stimuli? Along with the latter question goes another one, namely, what are the special difficulties in clinical diagnosis of physical disorders in psychotic patients? For example, a schizophrenic patient may have a perforating peptic ulcer or an impacted calculus in the ureter or cystic duct without complaining of pain. Many who have worked in the infirmary of mental hospitals have commented on the improved mental function which may occur during periods of grave physical illness in previously disturbed psychotic patients. The readiness of psychotic patients to accept the discipline of enforced bed rest has been commented on in the discussion of the tubercular patient. Systematic study of these facts may uncover principles of theoretical and practical importance in psychopathology and treatment.

The statement is sometimes made that the physical ailments of mental hospital patients should always be taken care of by one group of physicians and their mental disorders by another. Apart from the impracticality of such an arrangement it is also inadvisable. In the foregoing paragraphs the importance of psychiatrically oriented medical care has been emphasized. The role of heart failure or toxic metabolic states in the psychotic reactions of older people has been referred to elsewhere (Chapter XV). Mention has also been made of the capacity of acute organic brain syndromes to simulate schizophrenia (Chapter VII). The psychologic changes associated with various recent drugs like the corticosteroids and hydrazine derivatives which are merely side effects to the internist may be of central importance to the psychiatrist. In short, the psychiatrist dares not lose contact with the main body of medicine. He must view every patient as a physical and psychological continuum. Nevertheless, the mental hospital psychiatrist cannot hope to master all of medical practice. For that reason he will have frequent recourse to consultants. If the location of the hospital makes it possible, a large volunteer staff of consultants should be recruited and utilized with enthusiasm and professional cordiality. When as a result of geographical isolation a regular visiting service is not available, part-time consultant services should be obtained on a fee basis. By organizing the clinical material so as to make the most effective use of the consultant's time, the long-term expense of such an arrangement can be kept down. For example, if a dermatologic consultant is expected, the fact should be known well in advance so that all the patients that can be benefited by his advice can be assembled in a single area. Medical students can make a valuable contribution during vacations or on clerkships doing routine physical examination. They, in turn, will have an opportunity to see a wide range of interesting problems in physical diagnosis as well as to become acquainted with a most important, if not the most important, phase of modern psychiatry, namely mental hospital psychiatry. By means of affiliation with neighboring hospitals the aid of resident physicians can be obtained for the various specialized medical and surgical problems.

The full-time services of at least one physician should be available for every fifty patients in the infirmary as well as one nurse for every five patients. All the physical requirements of a good general hospital should be met, including fully equipped operating rooms and laboratory facilities. Careful records should be kept with particular reference to psychiatric detail, as these change during the course of the physical illness. The hospital should have a well-stocked pharmacy and a standard formulary of useful medical preparations drawn up with the advice of the visiting staff.

Other Medical Services

An outpatient clinic for the management of medical and surgical emergencies should be maintained on a twenty-four hour basis, with responsible personnel on duty and with proper equipment kept in readiness for such occasions. In addition, there should be regular clinics for eye, ear, nose, and throat, gynecology, medicine, orthopedics, skin, and allergy, which should be serviced, ideally, by a visiting staff.

The dental department should be of sufficient size to provide complete dental care for patients. This should include preliminary examination and treatment, follow-up examinations and replacement care. Dental care for patients on trial visit provides a device for maintaining a psychotherapeutically useful liaison with patients. The dentist may give lectures to patients concerning proper dental hygiene. Although much research has been done on the relationship of dental infection to mental illness (with negative results), there is room for further study concerning changes in oral health with changes in the mental condition of the patient. It has been estimated that a 2000 bed hospital requires a full-time chief dentist with two staff dentists, one oral hygienist, two dental assistants and one dental technician.

Every new patient should be inoculated routinely against smallpox and typhoid. A Dick and Schick test should be done, with appropriate immunizations if positive. Blood serology should also be done routinely. Chest X-rays should be obtained on admission and repeated twice a year thereafter.

Stool examinations should be done on patients assigned as food handlers, as well as careful inspection of the hands before each meal. Other public health measures should include regular examinations of the milk and water supply, periodic inspection of plumbing, an insect control program with adequate screening and the use of insecticides, inspection of the sewage disposal plant, the laundry, the farm and the cannery. In the event of ten or more cases of diarrhea or any other infectious condition a public health team should be brought into action at once to trace the origin of the infection and to institute appropriate control measures.

A parallel set of services should be available for employees. New employees should be carefully examined, and this examination should be repeated at regular intervals thereafter. Evidence of genuine concern for the physical welfare of employees improves morale. It can compensate for the physical and monetary limitations of an attendant's job, for example, by providing him and the members of his family with a priceless sense of security from a health standpoint. Social service assistance should also be made available to employees when indicated. Employees who feel that they are treated with dignity and friendliness will be more inclined to display similar attitudes toward patients.

Accidents in Mental Hospitals

Accidents present an important problem in mental hospitals. They are of two main categories; those due to falls, which occur primarily in senile patients, and those due to physical overactivity and assaultiveness, in younger schizophrenic patients. The latter group not uncommonly results in injuries to employees. Most accidents occur on the wards. Those due to overactivity are most likely to occur before mealtime with a peak incidence prior to breakfast. (This fact has already been discussed in Chapter VI in relation to "orality.") Female patients are more frequently assaultive than males and are more apt to utilize a weapon, with the shoe being most frequently employed. However, assaultive behavior in female patients is less likely to result in serious accidents than it is in male patients. A small group of assaultive patients tends to be involved repeatedly in accidents. It is worth noting that another small group of patients tends to be involved repeatedly in accidents as the victims of assaults.

These generalizations suggest means for preventing accidents. Special architectural requirements for the protection of the aged have already been mentioned in Chapter XV. Women patients should be equipped with shoes that cannot be used as dangerous weapons. Nourishment on the ward between meals will decrease tensions due to hunger. Other aspects of controlling disturbed behavior are discussed in Chapter X.

Physical Illness and the Patient's Family

Written consent for all surgical procedures should be obtained from a responsible relative or friend of the patient. If this was not obtained on admission in the form of a general treatment consent, then it should be secured prior to an operation. It is well to obtain an additional specific consent in any event, if possible. If the family lives far away and the patient presents a surgical emergency, then an attempt should be made to secure consent by telephone with the hospital operator listening in as a witness.

If the patient is critically ill, the family should be apprised of this fact by telegram and accorded every courtesy when they make inquiry or come to visit. If death seem imminent, or if the patient asks for religious consolation, the chaplain of the appropriate denomination should be notified.

When the patient dies the family should be notified by telegram. The remains of the deceased should be treated with respect. Post-mortem examination for external evidences of mistreatment or violence should be carried out meticulously and officially recorded. Autopsy permission should be requested, of course. The autopsy percentage is a measure of the general level of work in the hospital. A high autopsy rate is expressive of intense scientific interest as well as good relations with the families of patients, both of which tend to be associated with a superior treatment program.

Notifying the Coroner

The coroner or medical examiner should be notified in the case of any death which has occurred in circumstances which are even remotely suspicious. These include:

All cases of patients who die within forty-eight hours after admission to the hospital;

Those having had a fracture within a period of twelve months preceding the death;

Cases of unexpected death;

Cases of suicide, accidental death, or death of obscure origin;

Any death following an accident or altercation in which employees have been involved.

SELECTED REFERENCES

BONNER, C. A.; TAYLOR, L. E.: A Study of Accidents in a Mental Hospital. *Am. J. Psychiat.*, 96:283, 1939.
  An excellent analysis of the epidemiology of accidents in mental hospitals.
BRYAN, W. A.: *Administrative Psychiatry.* New York: Norton, 1936.
  Contains data of considerable importance for the proper administration of the medical and surgical services of a mental hospital.
FELDMAN, P. E.: A Public Health Program in a State Hospital. *Ment. Health Bull.*, 30:1, 1952.
  Outlines the essentials of a mental hospital public health program.
GROUP FOR THE ADVANCEMENT OF PSYCHIATRY: *Control and Treatment of Tuberculosis in Mental Hospitals.* Committee on Hospitals of the G.A.P., Report No. 24, 1954.
  An extremely valuable and thorough summary of this vitally important subject.
GRUBER, T. R. K.; GOULD, S. E.: Control of Communicable Disease in a Large Mental Hospital. *Am. J. Psychiat.*, 104:122, 1947.
  An excellent summary of preventive techniques.
HECKER, A. O.: Medical and Surgical Services in the Neuropsychiatric Hospital. *Am. J. Psychiat.*, 107:450, 1950.
  Based on experiences in a Veterans Administration psychiatric hospital with 2000 patents; quantitative estimates are drawn up concerning personnel requirements in the various medical and surgical specialties.
JETTER, W. W. E.; HADLEY, R. V.: A Study of Casualties Occurring in Institutions Under the Supervision of the Mass. Dept. of Mental Health. *Am. J. Psychiat.*, 100:506, 1944.
  A useful statistical survey.
LEHRMAN, S. R.; ALPERT, H. S.: The Management of Epidemics in State Institutions. *Psychiat. Quart. Supplement*, 15:27, 1941.
  A summary of experiences with a measles epidemic and an influenza epidemic in two State institutions.
PLEASURE, H.: 233 Patients with Mental Illness Treated with Electroconvulsive Therapy in the Presence of Tuberculosis. *Am. J. Psychiat.*, 111:177, 1954.
  A summary of extensive clinical experience documenting the hazards of ECT with patients suffering from active tuberculosis.
SPERBER, I. J.: Coordinated and Standardized Dentistry for State Hospitals. *Psychiat. Quart.*, 6:30, 1932.
  An outline of a thorough dental program for mental hospitals.

Part Four

THE HOSPITAL

Chapter XXVI

ARCHITECTURE AS THERAPY

Security versus Therapy

Early in the North African campaign in World War II, a medical officer related the following incident.

He was assigned as a psychiatrist to a station hospital in Algeria. An ancient maternity hospital was requisitioned and he was directed to set up a psychiatric division in one part of it. Approached by the Army engineers, he was asked what installations he needed for his department. In his first reaction one thought dominated his mind—"Maximal security for violent patients!" His first impulse was to surround his area with barbed wire, cover the windows with iron bars, and to reinforce flimsy doors. Fortunately, events moved more quickly than the engineers did and he was soon filled up with psychiatric casualties from the battle of the Kasserine Pass. The behavior of his patients and the methods of treatment employed soon demonstrated the absurdity of the restrictive and coercive devices that he had planned for them initially. What they needed was rest, access to outdoor recreational facilities, and an opportunity to discuss some of their problems in privacy. Thus, his architectural plans were based not at all on realistic therapeutic considerations but rather on his own anxiety. He was concerned about his ability to control a group of patients with whose problems he was not yet acquainted.

The principle that emerges from the foregoing experience is basic to all forms of treatment in psychiatry: plans or decisions made for psychiatric patients which stem from the therapist's anxiety are most likely to be wrong. This is true whether the problem under consideration exists in a psychotherapeutic session or in therapeutic influences mediated through architecture. And as far as the architecture of a psychiatric hospital is concerned, it is just as true here at home as it was then in North Africa. A hospital that is constructed with the idea that patients are dangerous or obsessed with a determination to escape, omits the elementary facts about the vast majority of the mentally ill. It also neglects the primary psychiatric consideration which is that of treat-

349

ment. Every detail of hospital construction should be referred back to this question: How does it serve to further the rehabilitation of the psychiatric patient?

Paul Haun of the Bowman-Gray School of Medicine, an authority on psychiatric architecture, has given this problem much thought. He summarizes his ideas in a series of propositions which will be included in this chapter.

Location

First, the hospital should be located where it can be staffed. It must be close to a large community from which a full-time staff of competent physicians can be assembled. It is obvious that most physicians will want to work close to the community where they have their social and family roots. Any appointment which takes them far from home will be accepted ambivalently and usually as a temporary expediency. A matter of no less importance is the fact that most hospitals could not be run without the help of a visiting staff, either for expert consultative services or to do much of the spade work of the hospital in operating its clinics and in maintaining its teaching and research program. A visiting staff provides much more than working personnel to a hospital, however. It also helps integrate the intramural medical services with the medical needs of the community. For a psychiatric hospital, this means that the treatment program within the hospital is more likely to be regarded as an emergency phase of a larger treatment program which should take place primarily in the community. In addition, a visiting staff contributes enthusiasm. Often it brings a special interest or love for the work, which is less likely to settle into uncreative routine. In the Mount Sinai Hospital in New York City, almost a hundred psychiatrists in private practice contribute freely of their time to the department of psychiatry. Although it is true that this is a general hospital, a similarly located psychiatric hospital could probably attract just as large a volunteer staff if its program were sufficiently stimulating.

Staffing a hospital involves more than doctors alone. The shortage of nurses and attendants which chronically harrasses remotely situated hospitals is more readily overcome by those situated near large population centers. With the possibility of continuing normal family life in the community, the attendant is less likely to become a member of an inbred group whose rigid cultural structure inadvertently contributes to the patient's sense of social isolation. The volunteer program (see Chapter XIII) also depends to a considerable degree on the hospital's accessibility to the community. Proximity to a large city, preferably one with a medical school, alone, can answer the requirements for a mental hospital site.

Size

The hospital must be the "right" size, that is, neither too small for efficient operation nor too large for effective medical care. If the hospital is to support and re-create the sense of individuality in patients, it must not dwarf them by its size or by herding them together in thousands in great monoblock buildings. It is becoming accepted that new psychiatric hospitals should not exceed 1000 beds. This figure is not suggested as an optimum but rather as a maximum which should not be exceeded. It is often argued that hospitals of smaller size encounter unbearable economic hardships. The Expert Committee on Mental Health of the World Health Organization, on the other hand, has estimated that the optimal capacity for a mental hospital from the point of view of financial economy probably lies between 250 and 400 beds. Above 400 beds the cost per bed begins to rise slowly and reaches rather high figures above 800 beds. The reason is probably to be found in uncontrollable waste, lack of a sense of individual responsibility among the members of an oversized staff, unnecessary buying, and a tendency toward procedural inflexibility. The director of a mammoth hospital cannot hope to have any kind of sustained personal contact with the hundreds of people who work with him.

It is true that heating, general stores, repair and maintenance shops, laundry and purchasing can be more economically arranged when thousands of beds are involved. However, if a new psychiatric hospital is constructed as a part of a hospital group and co-ordinates its economy with that of several other hospitals, psychiatric and nonpsychiatric, then this problem can be overcome.

In keeping with the trend away from overwhelming massiveness, it has been recommended that the mental hospital be composed of a group of small buildings rather than a single block. The therapeutic community should take the village as its model. Each unit should be planned for a small group of patients, preferably about twenty-five or thirty. It should be assumed that the majority of patients will sleep, eat and work in small groups of up to ten patients. An attempt should be made to plan for separate sleeping accommodations for a high percentage of patients, and much of the remainder should be in small dormitories. It has been the custom in the past to place the more seriously ill patients in single rooms and to move them into wards as they improve. The modern and more logical trend is in the opposite direction. Patients requiring intense supervision should be placed in small dormitories. When their capacity for self-control returns, they should be given single rooms.

A large group of patients were once queried concerning their reactions on admission to a mental hospital. Almost invariably they spoke of feelings of panic, isolation, defeat and humiliation at being placed unceremoniously on a large ward filled with patients. At that time what they wanted most desperately was privacy to collect their thoughts and to gather the resolution to face the strange new world of the mental hospital. The lack of privacy at this time was the most intensely traumatic item in their hospital experience. The resulting impairment in their receptivity to subsequent therapeutic measures can well be imagined. To overcome this, the use of movable partitions has been suggested, as a flexible device for providing privacy for patients as needed and varying degrees of increasing community living as the patient's needs alter.

Along with the question of the size and internal arrangement of new buildings is that of durability. Most existing mental hospitals have been built to last too long. Many countries will be burdened for a long time to come with large obsolete structures built years ago to fit a conception of the role of the mental hospital which is now completely rejected. It should be assumed that any new hospital will be obsolete in many respects in twenty to thirty years. Prefabricated structures like those used for military hospitals in wartime may provide a practical and readily available answer to this problem. Such structures would also lend themselves most readily to experiments in the arrangement of individual hospital units in their physical relationship to each other and to outdoor recreational spaces.

Relation to Treatment Program

Construction must take into account the actual treatment program and provide facilities for every phase of it, whether it be an up-to-date operating unit for psychosurgery or a garden where patients may grow flowers.

The nurse's station should be located so that it has a commanding view of the ward and an adjoining recreational space. In addition, the nurse's station should be equipped for maintaining patients' records, for the storage and preparation of medications and for the sterilization of light medical equipment. Since most patients will be ambulatory and physically sound, a full-sized utility room equipped with the usual elaborate paraphernalia of bedside nursing may be omitted. There should be a conveniently located laundry chute, as well as equipment for washing soiled linen and cleaning the rarely used bedpans and urinals.

A nourishment kitchen should be located near the nurse's station with space for a hot plate and a refrigerator, so that the nurse may prepare extra nourishment and bedtime snacks without leaving the nursing unit. Facilities for serving coffee on the ward before breakfast may decrease accidents due to assaultive episodes (see Chapters VI and XXV).

A ward linen closet should contain ample supplies for bed linen changes, extra blankets, mattress covers, pillows, rubber sheets, bath robes, fabric slippers, towels and face cloths. The routine issue of towels to psychiatric patients is not a customary practice because of the danger of suicide.

A ward supply closet should afford storage space for paper cups, toilet tissues, rubber goods, reserve medications, flashlight batteries and hypodermic needles.

Toilet facilities for male and female personnel should be available on the ward.

For the patients a large recreational space should adjoin the ward. Paul Haun suggests that thirty-two square feet of floor space be provided for each patient. It should be recalled that the number of disturbed episodes on a ward increases geometrically with crowding (see Chapter X).

The ward should be attractively furnished. For thousands of years man has tried to influence fellow men with inscriptions and pictures on walls. This was true of the ancient temples of the Middle East uncovered by archaeologists, the walls of our churches and public buildings, and in the advertisements in public conveyances and billboards. In contrast to all these speaking walls are the blank surfaces of our hospital interiors. Here is an opportunity for exercising psychotherapeutic influence that has been left practically untouched and that has in any event never been studied systematically. Familiar quotations from the Bible and maxims from great national and spiritual leaders which emphasize positive living values may exercise a special power because of the emotional overtones of the sources of this wisdom. Beautifully phrased, decoratively inscribed, and authoritatively signed, they can by their continued presence contribute to the formation of a stronger and healthier ego ideal.

Colored murals which can be applied like wallpaper and illuminated by backlighting provide a relatively inexpensive device for achieving realistic scenic effects. It has been observed that even withdrawn patients will respond to such decorations, selecting seats or moving chairs to a position where favorite scenes can be viewed more readily. Scenes often stir comments and conversational exchanges between patients, including discussions of geography and recollections of previous pleasant experiences which can be made the basis for therapeutically useful group discussions. The use of rich colors and tasteful decorations arouses impulses to self-control in patients who act destructively in less attractive surroundings.

For patients unable to leave the ward this space should be fully equipped for all phases of the activities program (see Chapter IV and V). Traditionally the sexes are segregated in mental hospitals in an unspoken fear of what these uncontrolled people might do in each others' company. Clinical experience has shown that the free mingling of the sexes in commonly adjoining day rooms is a therapeutically effective maneuver which tends to mobilize personal controls and improved social behavior.

In a mental hospital it is necessary to be vigilant against impulsive acts of self-destruction or elopement. The necessary security measures should be provided unobstrusively. There should be no overhead pipes. Nooks and niches should be avoided on the ward, in the rooms and corridors. All rooms should be surveyable at a glance from the door. Partitions should be slightly rounded at all corridor junctions. Windows should be protected by screening and operated with a portable crank by an attendant. Coat hooks and railings should be avoided. Radiators should be recessed and covered. In the washrooms, hot water should never reach scalding temperatures. Showers are turned on and off by attendants. The nurse's station should be panelled with shatter-proof glass. Stairways should be constructed without stair wells.

Security provisions not only protect patients but have direct therapeutic implications as well.

I saw a paranoid schizophrenic woman recently on the locked ward of a sanitarium who pleaded endlessly her request to be released from the hospital. When this same patient was placed in an open cottage, however, her fear of sexual attack from prowling strangers became so intense that she herself requested the "safety" of the locked ward, in which she resumed her request to be released. This is a common experience; that is, the dread of the unsupervised freedom of the open community, on the one hand, and the dread of the locked ward, on the other. It is clear that a compromise is needed. Buildings for disturbed patients can be so designed as to permit them free access to an outdoor recreational space all through the day when the weather is not inclement, and in some instances free access to recreational buildings which adjoin the open space. A solution such as this strives for a middle road between the agoraphobic and claustrophobic tendencies of the patient.

Toilet facilities for patients should also avoid crowding. Like the recreational space, they should be located so that they can be freely observed from the nurse's station, but with due regard for the patient's need for privacy. The use of partitions between toilet stalls that are not over shoulder height is a way of achieving this. Electric shavers make it possible for more patients to be given the responsibility, with safety, for their own grooming. Bathing facilities should include showers for co-operative patients and tubs for those who are helpless or unco-operative. In so far as possible, the need for privacy should be respected here too.

A clothing locker room should be provided with individual locker space for each patient where his street clothes, linen, extra shoes, and personal treasures, can be stored. Patients should be given access to their lockers only when supervised by attendants. Individual lockers prevent pilfering, improve the appearance of the bed rooms and simplify the duties of the ward personnel. Most important of all are their effect on the patient's self-esteem, and sense of individuality. The latter are pathologically traumatized in mental patients to start with, and are further shattered by the routines ordinarily followed in mental hospitals. If the locker room is properly situated, patients may readily obtain their overcoats and hats on their way to the out-of-doors. In the interest of convenience, the locker room should be located close to the nurse's station.

A pleasantly decorated visitors' room helps to involve the family in constructive rehabilitation procedures. In addition, this space can be used at other times for group psychotherapy, socials and selected enter-tainment.

A luxury closet should be available for the patients' tobacco and candy to be distributed by the nurse in suitable amounts on appropriate occasions.

The facilities for the doctor should include an examining room with space and equipment for complete neurological and physical examination, for diagnostic tests such as lumbar puncture and intravenous amytal (see Chapter VII), for examinations by medical and surgical consultants, for psychotherapy, and for emergency electroconvulsive therapy. Additional interview rooms should also be available with relatively simple equip-ment for individual and group psychotherapy. The doctor will also require an office in which he can interview patients and their relatives and in which he can store personal professional equipment. Secretarial services should also be conveniently available, preferably with dictaphone or similar facilities.

Other specific facilities will include a social service office, a conference room, record room, serving kitchens and dining rooms (see Chapter VI), hydrotherapy room, with swimming pool and ultraviolet radiation, barber shop, beauty parlor, wheel chair and stretcher room and a janitor's closet.

Regularly scheduled ECT should be given in a room equipped with emergency restoratives and recovery rooms properly placed so that patients are spared unnecessary exposure to the physical details of the treatment. An insulin treatment room, a psychosurgery unit, psychiatric outpatient facilities, a recreational and occupational therapy unit, a theater and a chapel are other treatment facilities with special architectural requirements.

In addition to these general considerations it is necessary to take into account the individual needs of specific patient categories. Some of these problems have been touched upon in Chapters XV and XVI as they relate to the aged patients and the very young. The chronic patient who may never again be able to adjust in the community should also be provided for. One should not dismiss all such cases as therapeutic failures. In the words of Paul Haun, "His case is rather to be regarded as a brilliant therapeutic success if, by treatment, he lives out his life on an open rather than on a disturbed ward, if he can nurture a bed of flowers in the greenhouse rather than lie stuporous in a corner of the day room, if he can smile occasionally at a moving picture performance rather than know the unguessed anguish of uninterrupted mental torment."

Building Arrangement

The parts of the hospital should be arranged with regard to the most effective utilization of the staff's time. A properly designed institution can accomplish a given task with 30 per cent fewer employees in every service capacity than a hospital which is badly planned. Modest sums spent on careful planning are often saved many times over through unexpected economies in the proposed construction investment covered by the planning itself. They are certainly liquidated a thousandfold when a permanent lowering of the hospital's operational expenses can be obtained by more efficient design.

Total Medical Care

The mental hospital should be prepared to offer total medical care. Mental illness does not immunize the patient against infection, injury, or metabolic disorder. Up-to-date laboratories, air-conditioned operating rooms, special diet kitchens, surgical nursing units, and all the other resources of the progressive general hospital are today essential parts of the modern mental institution.

Aesthetic Considerations

Beauty is a potent therapeutic instrument just as ugliness is the reverse. Strange, forbidding exteriors, long bleak corridors, that echo footsteps and the metallic jangle of attendants' keys, the challenging sentry at the hospital gate, unscalable walls and barred windows combine to drive the patient more deeply into his psychotic retreat and to repel the surrounding community from reaching out a rescuing hand.

Training and Research

Finally, the modern psychiatric hospital should be built as a center for training and research. We must set aside the work rooms, the lecture halls, the laboratories, the libraries, and the record room facilities and regard them as instruments of psychiatric progress, no less important than the most recent treatment facility, inasmuch as the treatments of the future will come from them.

Miscellaneous Considerations

In addition to these broad principles there are details without number that the therapeutically oriented psychiatrist can and should record not only for revisions in his own hospital but for the guidance of others who are building today. Curiously, in the very milieu where every detail should be therapeutically planned with the major emphasis placed on enticing the patient back to reality, I have seen the strangest aberrations. In one hospital I saw a two-storied building with a gabled roof that slanted not to the second story, as would be expected, but incongruously downward, so that it terminated just one foot from the ground, giving a weird Daliesque effect to the landscape. I was never able to discover the reason for this particular design. In another hospital all the patients are awakened in the morning by a fearful raucous blast from a giant klaxon horn. In the main lobby of one hospital I saw a large grand-father's clock with its pendulum hanging immobile in dead center. Never-theless, the clock invariably showed the exact time! The reason? It had been electrified. The effect of this on the newcomer was truly disconcert-ing. A justly renowned skyscraper institution was built on the side of a cliff with its main entrance on the plateau, so that one walks off the street into the main lobby and finds himself on the tenth floor, gets into an elevator and asks for the fifth floor and finds himself shooting rapidly downwards. Although this last example has its humorous aspects and cannot be altered, we must not lose sight of the effect of such bizarre details, however, on a patient for whom so much of the world has become strange.

SELECTED REFERENCES

AMERICAN PSYCHIATRIC ASSOCIATION: *Design for Therapy*. Conference held at Mayflower Hotel, Washington, D.C., April 6, 7. Available through the APA., 1785 Massachusetts Avenue, N.W., Wash. 6, D.C. 1953.
> An investigation into the possibilities of collaboration between psychiatrists and architects in developing basic information for mental hospital design, construction and equipment. Based on a series of presentations by distinguished specialists in psychiatry and architecture.

EXPERT COMMITTEE ON MENTAL HEALTH OF THE WORLD HEALTH ORGANIZATION: *Third Report*. Available through the U.N. book store in New York City (25¢).
> Contains an informative section on architecture.

HAUN, P.: New Trends in Hospital Design. *Am. J. Psychiat.*, 104:555, 1948.
—— Psychiatric Facilities for the General Hospital. *Architectural Record*, 105:128, 1949.
—— Food Service in Psychiatric Hospitals of the Veterans Administration. *Mod. Hosp.*, 74:104, 1950.
—— A Program for a Psychiatric Hospital. *Psychiat. Quart. Supplement*, 24:148, 1950.
—— *Psychiatric Sections in General Hospitals*. Garden City, N.Y.: Country Life Press, 1950.
> The foregoing list of references by Paul Haun represents a summary of the contributions of a distinguished pioneer in psychiatric architecture.

MERRILL, B. R.: A Note on the Architecture of the Psychiatric Ward. *Am. J. Psychiat.*, 105:691, 1949.
> Contains some interesting suggestions for the arrangement of the wards in a mental hospital.

MILLER, T. K.: Color is Good Medicine for Mental Patients. *Mod. Hosp.*, 77:81, 1951.
> Interesting observations showing that patients do respond favorably to changes in decoration of the wards.

Chapter XXVII

ADMINISTRATIVE PSYCHIATRY

Definition

Mental hospital administration has been defined by Baganz of the Veterans Administration as "a branch of medicine and a branch of psychiatry that deals with the human relationships, the human resources, the hospital community and its total resources in such a manner as to produce optimal results in terms of patient care." He goes on to add that if this definition of administrative psychiatry is correct, then "only an individual adequately trained in the field of human relations and motivations can competently direct a modern mental hospital. This complex hospital with its manifold disciplines and many professions demands of the mental hospital administrator that he be not only an able and mature psychiatrist, but also well trained in personnel administration, budget planning and control, public relations, maintenance and repair procedures, forensic medicine, mental hospital construction, post-graduate psychiatric education, employee-training, food service and cost, the operation of an outpatient department, program planning and analysis, logistics, and methods for departmental audits of a mental hospital."

The Standards for Psychiatric Hospitals and Clinics drawn up by the Mental Hospital Service of the American Psychiatric Association define the mental hospital administrator as the one who is chief of both the professional and administrative departments of the hospitals. Ideally, he should be appointed by a single integrated state agency which has as its exclusive function the development of the mental health program of the State, as for example the Department of Mental Hygiene in New York. He should have authority commensurate with his great responsibility. And, of course, he should be free from partisan political interference, and responsible only to the authority which appointed him. The Mental Hospital Service recommends further that he should be (1) a graduate of a medical school approved by the American Medical Association, (2) a diplomate of the American Board of Psychiatry and Neurology, or similarly qualified, (3) licensed to practice medicine, (4) and that he should have not less than five years experience in a mental hospital, of which not less than three years were in a responsible position involving administrative duties. Recently a board has been established which passes upon the qualifications of applicants for certification as specialists in administrative psychiatry.

The Mental Hospital Service has recommended in addition that the director have a first assistant who serves in his absence, with a background similar to the administrator's, except that he need have only one year's experience in responsible administrative duties; and that there should be, in addition, one or more clinical directors whose primary function is the integration and co-ordination of the treatment program. The clinical director's task is to encourage and assist the physicians and the other members of the professional treatment team to maintain high standards of patient care and to improve their skills and their training. His qualifications are essentially the same as the administrator's, except that his experience (minimum of five years) should be primarily in the diagnosis and treatment of mental illness and in the teaching of psychiatry.

In hospitals of less than 500 patients, the duties of the clinical director and assistant superintendent may be combined. In hospitals of more than 2500 patients, there should be at least two clinical directors.

Finally, the director should have immediately under him a business manager who is responsible for the nonmedical administrative and maintenance functions of the hospital. The Mental Hospital Service strongly opposes a dual control system under which one administrator has final authority over business matters while another has responsibility for the care and treatment of patients.

Within the limitations set by the administrator, the business manager supervises the following activities: engineering and general maintenance, personnel office, purchase and supply, finance, disbursement and budget, and office of the registrar. He should be well trained in modern business methods and in the details of hospital administration. Not less than three years of responsible executive experience in the broad phases of hospital administration and management are required for this position.

It has been argued that the business problems of a mental hospital are too complex to be handled by a physician. Indeed, many medical men are perversely proud of the legend of their business incompetence. There has been a tendency to disdain administrative problems and those physicians who try to solve them. Out of this attitude has come a readiness to surrender the field of administration entirely to nonmedical administrators. Such a trend would run counter to the historical fact that mental hospitals were in the words of Baganz "born of physicians, nurtured and developed by physicians." It is rarely possible to draw a sharp line between treatment and maintenance responsibilities. It has become apparent, for example, that new constructions and alterations of buildings cannot be planned by one who is ignorant of the problems of psychiatric treatment. It is quite natural, therefore, that a distinguished psychiatrist, Paul Haun, should also become an authority on mental hospital construction. The way a gate watchman greets a newcomer, the way a switchboard operator answers a telephone, the behavior of the receptionist at the information desk, the very availability of her desk to bewildered patients and their families are all part of treatment. The business department has much to do with the purchase and preparation of food, but everyone accepts the fact that the way in which the food is served can be therapeutic or disintegrative to the mentally ill. Dirt, foul odors, overcrowding, poorly kept clothing, all these details can contribute to what the psychiatrist refers to as deterioration, yet are in the province of the maintenance services. Maintenance workers should learn enough about psychiatry so that they can work constructively with patients assigned to them in the vocational rehabilitation program. These are some of the reasons why it is easier by far to teach a psychiatrist the elements of business than it is to instruct a business man in the amount of psychiatric information necessary to utilize his facilities in the therapeutic community properly.

Group Psychotherapy as an Administrative Technique

In addition to the previous definitions one can also describe an administrator as one who performs all or part of his work by influencing the behavior of other workers. By this token all the physicians in a mental hospital function in an administrative capacity as well as all other chiefs of departments and wards, professional and nonprofessional alike. At every echelon in the mental hospital there are key people who should be trained so that administrative responsibility can be delegated. Leaders at all levels should be given a sense of participation in policy making and a feeling of sharing in achievement.

To a considerable degree the hospital administrator can achieve these effects most satisfactorily in group therapy sessions with personnel in administrative positions. They in turn should be trained and encouraged to utilize similar group techniques in working with the personnel of their own departments. The effectiveness of group psychotherapy techniques thus applied in nonclinical settings has been proved in mental hospitals, government, and private industry (see references at the end of this chapter). In these sessions the goal is to uncover personality difficulties and individual problems that interfere with satisfaction, personal and professional, and with good patient care. Stated differently, the aim is to get to the nub of reality in every situation. Paranoid attitudes and other distorting psychological mechanisms of defense should be sought out in group discussion and eliminated. At first it may be necessary to begin group discussions by using unsigned cards on which workers raise questions, register complaints and criticisms, or make suggestions. As mutual trust and respect develop, and as the group structures itself increasingly around the needs of the therapeutic community, discussion will become more free and general participation will grow.

Basic Principles of Administration

The preceding paragraphs have attempted to emphasize the fact that administration should concern itself with people not with paper. It is not enough for an administrator simply to give an order. He should keep in mind that a person accepts an administrative communication under certain limited circumstances only, a) if he can and does understand the communication; b) if he believes that it is consistent with the purpose of the mental hospital; c) if he believes it is consistent with his own welfare; d) and if he is physically and mentally able to comply with it.

The duties and responsibilities of each individual should be clearly defined. Organizational charts should be used freely to promote understanding of the role of each individual in terms of the total task. Administrators should observe how members of their departments get along with each other, who their effective workers are, which ones are unable to fulfill their work goals, and why they are failing. They should be sensitive to tensions and devise techniques for bringing them out in group discussion.

The administrator should seek to conserve the energy of his group. There are few things more demoralizing than the feeling that one is exerting himself unnecessarily or to no purpose.

Effective channels of communication are of great administrative importance. Group meetings, conferences, posters, special bulletins, memos, suggestion boxes with rewards, and an employees' newspaper should all be used.

Training personnel for leadership is another great administrative responsibility. Ability should be given proper recognition. Administrators should work actively to secure promotions for deserving individuals. On the other hand, recommendations for promotion should be carefully evaluated in terms of the motivation involved in the person making the recommendation and the one seeking the promotion. It should also be recognized that many excellent workers are characterologically unsuited for positions of leadership.

The administrator should concern himself with the living accommodations and the physical working conditions of employees. Social affairs for employees should be a regular part of hospital life.

It is desirable to have a personnel director, preferably one with social service training, who will interview applicants for positions, provide personal counseling when needed, and who will arrange for social service assistance with problems arising within the employee's family. Employees who are leaving the hospital should also be interviewed by the personnel director. He can insure this termination interview by being the one to give the departing worker his severance check. This provides an opportunity to learn why good workers are leaving, and to decrease the resentments of those who are discharged. The latter measure may be of importance from a public relations point of view.

The Clinical Staff Conference

Of the many administrative gatherings which take place in a mental hospital none is more important than the daily clinical conference. Traditionally it is run by the clinical director. However, it should occasionally be conducted by the hospital administrator, attended by him at other times and always guided by his basic philosophy. Before a patient is presented he should be worked up in detail, with data gleaned from all possible sources. The presentation should provide the basis for a preliminary formulation of the clinical diagnosis, the motivations and defenses, the plans for treatment and aftercare. After the presentation by the staff psychiatrist, the conference leader should summarize the case and then open it for general discussion. The administrator should strive for standardized definitions of all terms used in hospital records and conference discussions, and the use of the new nomenclature and statistical classification of mental disorder should be insisted upon (see Chapter XXVIII and Appendix E).

Although conscientiousness in statistical classification is of utmost scientific importance, the clinical conference should not be allowed to degenerate into a stereotyped roll call of diagnostic opinions. A given

diagnosis refers to a given pathological pattern of adaptation. A patient
may avoid a sexually threatening situation, for example, by means of a
loss of motor power in his lower extremities, which we then call conversion hysteria; or he may accomplish the same avoidance of sexual
danger through dread of going out-of-doors for fear of a heart attack,
and we then call it a phobia, or anxiety hysteria; or he may develop
hallucinations which warn him to barricade himself inside his house, in
which case we say he shows an acute schizophrenic reaction. Human
beings rarely employ a single fixed pattern of adaptation. They try one,
and when that fails, they try another, and when that fails, they try still
a third. This is repeated until the best adaptation possible under the
circumstances is obtained. And then if the circumstances change, the
pattern of adaptation may change once again. In short, it is often difficult if not impossible to assign a precise psychiatric diagnosis to a
patient. One pattern of adaptation does tend to predominate and ultimately to become fixed in most patients. But if we see many different
patterns, we must understand why this is so and not exhaust ourselves
in the futile quest for a static name for a fluid situation. It is one of the
virtues of the new statistical classification that it takes these dynamic
facts into account. What is most important of all, the understanding of
the dynamic interplay of forces which have resulted in emotional maladaptation must be utilized in planning a rational program of treatment
for patients and not simply for the purpose of pigeon-holing them. This
is the philosophy with which the administrator should seek to imbue his
staff in their daily clinical conference.

The patient should be prepared psychologically for his personal
appearance at "staff" in meetings with his psychiatrist. It is sometimes
forgotten that this occasion is a highly momentous one for the patient.
Soon after the conference the psychiatrist should meet with the patient
again to discuss the recommendations that have been made and to attempt to utilize the entire experience psychotherapeutically.

In the interest of stimulating the professional growth of staff psychiatrists, different members of the staff should be permitted to conduct the
conference. To counter the intellectual inbreeding which almost inevitably develops in a mental hospital, outside psychiatrists should be
invited at frequent intervals to conduct staff conferences. For the purpose of saving time many clinical conferences can be reduced to a meeting
between the individual staff psychiatrist and his supervisor. The assembled conference can then confine itself to matters of special interest.

The Hospital Administrator and His Relationships with Patients

Many hospital administrators look back wistfully to the time when they were not encumbered with administrative responsibilities and were free to work directly with patients. One device that administrators have used for maintaining contact with their patients is the personal letter. In some hospitals every new patient receives a personally signed letter from the administrator welcoming him and orienting him as to the hospital's plans for him. Many recovered patients have described with gratitude and pleasure the comfort they derived from that communication, even though they may have appeared indifferent to it at the time. Some hospital administrators send a letter to every patient after presentation at "staff," giving some reassuring explanation of the findings, or offering good wishes if the staff's decision was to send the patient out on trial visit. The following material is reprinted from W. A. Bryan's well-known book on administrative psychiatry because it illustrates so well the way such material can be utilized.

Dear ——

I am sending you this letter in the hope that it may help you to get your bearings in this new and unusual situation. I know how confused anyone must be in coming to this hospital for the first time. The place is so large, there are so many people about, and there are so many different ways of doing things that it is hard to get matters straight.

Because of this, I am sending you, together with this letter, some information about the way of doing things here that I hope will help you. It is hard to think in advance of all the questions you may want to ask, but I am sure that everyone in the hospital will be glad to give you information that is not given in this leaflet. Do not hesitate to ask questions about things you do not understand.

As the Superintendent of the hospital I extend to you my greetings. I want you to know that we are interested in your comfort and well-being while you are here. But more than this—we are most anxious to help you in every way to make your time in the hospital as short as possible. I hope you will profit by your stay here and that you will leave with feelings of friendship towards the institution.

There are 2200 patients in this hospital. I cannot, therefore, know each one as intimately as I should like, but there are many doctors, nurses, and other assistants, who are as anxious to help you as I am.

I hope you will have full confidence in them. You may also write a
personal letter to me if you think there is any special thing I can do
for your comfort and well-being.

Cordially yours,
Superintendent

Information About Hospital

The questions in this leaflet have been asked by patients admitted
to this hospital over a period of many years. If you will read the pamphlet carefully the information in it will help you understand why
you are here. The nurse will tell you in greater detail about those
matters upon which you wish further explanation.

1. *What is this place?* It is a hospital maintained by the state for
the cure of people who have mental or nervous illness. It is located
in the city of Worcester and is the largest of eleven state hospitals.
There are 2200 patients here, and 500 employees.

2. *Why are people brought here?* People are usually brought here
because someone in the community thought that their ideas and actions were very strange and reasoned from this that their mind must
be sick. It may have been friends, relatives, or even a stranger. People
are sent here to find out whether or not they are ill.

3. *How long do people stay here?* That depends entirely upon what
the doctors find. If they do not believe that you have any sickness
that should cause you trouble, you may leave just as soon as they decide. But if they find you are ill, then you must remain until you are
better. Your doctor will be glad to talk it over with you.

4. *Can one write letters?* Certainly. Ask the nurse for paper, en-
velopes, and pencil. Please leave your letters unsealed. The law says
that the doctor must read all mail leaving the hospital, but we always
send the letters if they are not indecent or threatening. Of course, all
letters sent to you will be given to you unopened.

5. *How can patients take care of their affairs outside the hospital?*
There are special trained social workers in the hospital who will see
the people outside of the hospital about business that patients may
have. They may also be helpful to patients in making all necessary
arrangements for the time when they leave the hospital.

6. *When can relatives and friends come to see patients?* The regular visiting days are Tuesday, Saturday, and Sunday of each week.
All holidays are also visiting days. The hours are from 9 to 11 in the
morning, and from 1:30 to 4:30 in the afternoon.

7. *Why are new patients kept in bathrobes?* For two reasons. First
—to enable the doctor to carry out a careful physical examination and
to do certain tests. Second—to give the office a chance to list and mark
your clothes so they will not be lost. They are usually returned after
two or three days.

8. *What happens to the patient's money?* Any money that the patients bring to the hospital or any that is sent by their relatives is

deposited in the Treasurer's office, where it is kept safe for the use of the patient.

9. *Can one buy things in the hospital?* Yes, there is a store in the hospital, and patients can buy what they want with their money, if the doctor approves the order. The nurse will prepare a list of store orders every once in a while, usually on Saturday or Sunday. Tell her what you want, and she will put in an order for the Treasurer to pay for it out of your money.

10. *Can one smoke?* Certainly, if one wants to and if one's health permits. Ask the nurse to take you to a place where smoking is permitted and give you a light.

11. *Are there any entertainments in the hospital?* During the fall and the winter time there are picture shows on Wednesdays and dances every once in a while. Ask the nurse to take you to them. In the summer there are games and concerts.

12. *Can one go out for walks?* There are seven wards on the men's side and six on the women's side that have no locked doors. Patients on these open wards have ground privileges, which means that they are free to come and go on the grounds as are the employees. They are permitted to go to the city at certain times, and frequently go home to spend a few days. Ground privileges are given to patients only if they behave in a normal and sensible way, and consent to follow certain rules. Your doctor can tell you about these rules. To be placed on an open ward is a step towards home.

13. *How does one get books to read?* Ask the nurse to take you to the library or get a book for you. We have an excellent library which we hope you will use.

14. *Does one have a chance to go to church?* Yes. We have Catholic services each Sunday morning at 9, Protestant services at 10:15, Jewish service twice each month on Sunday afternoon, and Episcopal service once each month. We have both a Catholic and Protestant chaplain attached to the hospital.

15. *What is going to happen during the next few days?* Your doctor will have long talks with you and ask you many questions about yourself and your family. You will also be given a thorough physical examination. Your eyes, nose, and throat will be examined; some blood will be taken from your arm for analysis, and your teeth will be examined in the dental office. After all the examinations have been completed, the doctors will discuss in a staff meeting whether something should be done for you in the hospital, or whether you are well enough to go home.

16. *How can one spend one's time in the hospital?* Ask the nurse if she can find any occupation for you on the ward. If you want any other occupation, ask for the O.T. girl. We say O.T. for Occupational Therapist. They are specially trained people who can teach you new and interesting occupations. You can tell them by their dress: they wear bright blue uniforms, and no caps.

17. *What good does one get from occupation?* Occupation keeps the troublesome thoughts away, keeps you interested in useful things,

and gives the necessary exercise to your mind and body. Work for your own sake and peace of mind if your doctor finds that you are physically able. To take an interest in some occupation is the best and quickest way to convince the doctors that you are well enough to go home.

18. *Do many patients leave this hospital?* Each year about 500 patients are discharged from the hospital. We need room for so many new patients coming in all the time that we are only too glad to send a patient home as soon as we can. Listen to the radio on the ward, and once each month you will hear the names of the patients who have been discharged from the hospital during the month.

It was found from a study that 69 out of 100 patients read and understood the letter, either wholly or in part. The effect in the great majority of cases was a positive one. It was appreciated mainly as a source of information about the basic facts of hospitalization and life in the hospital. By enabling the patient to orient himself in his new situation, it helped in relieving his uncertainty and apprehension. Other but not less valuable functions were those of giving him practical directions for his behavior and of restoring his self-respect. The latter was produced less by the contents of the letter than by the fact that the general tone was one of consideration for him.

Other letters can be sent to the newly admitted patient at intervals of several days to a week, each one reinforcing the original but presenting the material in a different way. The second communication might contain more detailed information regarding legal methods of commitment. Patients are always interested in this subject, and I know of nothing on which they show greater confusion. A third letter giving details about the different departments of the hospital would be helpful. The number of tons of coal used, the number of loaves of bread baked, etc., would show that the patient was in a large institution. In this country we are impressed by bigness. One of the points noted in the study was that most patients were overwhelmed, impressed, and even pleased by the size of the hospital to which they had come, though involuntarily.

Most patients are more or less apprehensive about the staff conference where their case is to be considered. They think of the proceeding as a court. A letter can be delivered before the patient has this experience, giving information about the meeting and telling what will occur. There are many variations of this plan. Naturally, the information given will change with the individual hospital. The questions and answers can be put into an attractively illustrated booklet. A freshly written communication actually signed by the superintendent would be excellent if the admission rate were not too large. The more personal these are, the more powerful they become in building morale.

Other communications can be sent to the patient from the office of the superintendent. Frequently letters come from relatives stating that the patient does not write. A note of reminder to the patient may stimulate him to do so and it will certainly give him considerable satisfaction to receive it.

It would be excellent therapy for the administrative office to notify the patient every time an inquiry is received from his home. Such a letter can be a regular form but always freshly written.

The following are indicative of the kind of communications that bring rich returns in the form of better hospital-patient rapport:

My dear Mr. Doe,

We have today received a letter from your (Relative) asking about your mental and physical health. Why not write and tell her about yourself? I know she will appreciate hearing from you.

Sincerely,
Superintendent.

A letter should be sent to the patient when money is received, informing him of the fact.

My dear Mr. Doe,

We have today received (Amount) from your (Relative), which is to be used for (Purpose). The money has been placed to your credit in the Treasurer's office.

Please write your (Relative) and thank her for this money.

Sincerely,
Superintendent.

It is an excellent practice for the superintendent to answer the communications of patients. Most of them find their way into the waste basket. Psychotic patients get many delusions about their letters, and great care is needed to prevent these ideas from having a real foundation in fact. Every ward in the mental hospital should have a locked mail box where a patient may drop his letters. These boxes should be made as nearly like the official United States mail receptacles as possible. Putting a letter into such a box gives the patient a sense of security about his mail that he cannot have when he has to coax a supervisor to take it. There is much carelessness in many mental hospitals about taking care of out-going letters written by patients. If a letter is not sent it should be returned to the writer with a written explanation giving the reasons why it has not been mailed. Absolute honesty with patients is an excellent builder of morale.

When the superintendent answers the patient by correspondence his answer should be noncommittal. Any attempt to particularize may lead to difficulty.

Such a form letter would be:

Dear Mrs. Doe,

I have received your note of (Date). Thanks for writing me. I shall be glad to go over the matter with you the next time I visit your ward.

Sincerely,
Superintendent.

And he must be sure to see her when he does visit the ward, or the letter will do more harm than good.

Another way in which the administrator can maintain contact with patients was devised by B. A. Cruvant when he was clinical director of St. Elizabeth's Hospital in Washington, D. C., and which he called administrative group psychotherapy. Patients in group psychotherapy often bring up complaints about food, mistreatment by personnel, discomforts or inconveniences on the ward which may contain a considerable element of reality but which carry the group discussion far afield from that which is most therapeutically advantageous. What happens is that the group therapy session degenerates into a "gripe session" which is essentially unproductive as far as promoting the personal emotional growth of the patient. Cruvant conceived the idea of having patients save all their gripes for a special group session with the hospital administrator. In this way, he clears the path for more effective use of the regular group therapy time. However, additional benefits result. Cruvant was impressed with the high percentage of patients in his hospital population who had never belonged to any mass action group in their lives and who were devoid of any knowledge of parliamentary procedure. He felt that this was expressive of a lifelong impairment in their capacity to relate normally to fellow human beings. These sessions provided much needed experience in human relationships and self-government. Realistic discussions about the physical limitations of hospital care added an incentive toward personal improvement. Thus, these sessions represented a therapeutic contribution in their own right as well as an adjuvant to the remainder of the group therapy program.

The Administrator in the Research and Training Program

Research in mental hospitals is complicated by many obstacles. By and large, remuneration is insufficient to attract the best research talent. Budgetary allowances are so skimpy that in some instances research projects designed to improve the welfare of patients have been financed out of the personal salaries of the research workers themselves. The pressure of other duties, mainly in relation to the needs of patients, prevents workers in mental hospitals from accomplishing more research than they are now doing. The administrator plays an important role in all these matters. He can fight for increased research allowances from the state legislature, he can allot more time for research even though this may complicate other aspects of the hospital program. The complaint of lack of time is occasionally less valid than it seems. The psychiatrist who makes this complaint may often find many hours to devote to a favorite hobby. There is certainly no objection to the enthusiastic pursuit of favorite hobbies. However, the administrator can promote a spirit in which research becomes a favorite hobby, by fostering research seminars, offering prizes for original work, providing time off for the presentation of papers at meetings, by helping to get needed materials, and by securing the co-operation of other departments. The idea that only specially gifted people can do research is not always true. Many men do not know how to do research, yet would be capable of very useful work if given proper direction. Such men should be assigned a project, guided in carrying it out and in writing it up, and assisted in getting it published.

The hospital administrator should appoint a physician, preferably full time, to direct the research and training program of the hospital. With such a program in operation, grants may be applied for under the auspices of the National Mental Health Act (see Chapters XXIX and XXX) or from private funds. The director of research and training can co-ordinate the projects in his hospital with those in hospitals and institutions elsewhere. He can bring in consultants to stimulate, initiate and supervise research and to participate in the training program as well. Joint conferences with other hospitals can be arranged. These matters are given more detailed consideration in Chapters XXIX and XXX.

The Lay Board

Every mental hospital should have a board of visitors or trustees who represent the public. It is their responsibility to visit the hospital to see that patients are humanely treated, and to insure efficient and economical management. The extent to which they become involved in hospital activities is determined by the administrator. He should invite their criticism and solicit their help. They may be most useful in providing access to a legislator's ear, or in starting a volunteer program, or in extending the family care program. Such a board should play a purely advisory role.

Actual executive decisions should be left to the authority of the hospital administrator.

The Medical Executive Committee

The administrator should foster the growth of a large visiting staff representing all specialties by forming a committee of prominent physicians in the community, to be called the medical executive committee. This committee should be assigned the responsibility for surveying the hospital's medical and surgical needs and for recruiting a competent professional volunteer staff to meet them, also to see that the hospital has adequate facilities and equipment, to draw up a hospital formulary, to provide consultation in all specialties, to enforce good ethical practices, and to provide training for the staff. This demands that the administrator participate in his local medical society, and have as many professional meetings at the mental hospital as possible, including the local dental society, laboratory technicians, hospital administrators, tuberculosis experts, nurses and social workers.

Public Relations

This subject is discussed in some detail in Chapter XXXVII. Without the administrator's express encouragement and co-operation, it is impossible to establish a volunteer program (see Chapter XIII). The administrator should encourage his staff to take on community assignments in clinics and in the mental hygiene program. Proper recognition for such contributions should be forthcoming. Good relations with the press, radio and television should be fostered and utilized in the community's mental hygiene program in which the mental hospital is directly concerned. The hospital administrator should delegate the actual responsibility for these matters to a public relations officer who, ideally, has special training and ability in this field.

The Budget

In 1888, the average per diem cost for a patient in a general hospital was $1.40. In 1948, the corresponding figure was $14.61. In 1888, the Boston State Hospital per diem cost for a patient was 70¢; in 1948, it was $1.70. In these cost figures is to be found a principal reason for the difference in the standards for care of patients in mental hospitals as compared to those in general hospitals. By themselves, however, these figures do not tell the whole story. Although more money must doubtlessly be allotted for the care of mental patients, other changes are called for, too. Part of the problem arises from the mechanical application of general hospital principles to the mental hospital. The idea, for example, that a hospital is a place where sick people stay in bed is obviously not true of the mental hospital. Mental patients go to bed at night like anyone else, but bed is not the place where treatment is carried out. In addition, the mental hospital is an emergency device called into play when the patient can no longer remain in the community. Ideally, treatment should take place in the community where the patient remains in contact with as much of his real world as is possible for him. These ideas were embodied by Cameron and his colleagues at the Allan Memorial Institute in Montreal in what they called the "Day Hospital" (see Chapter XXXV for details). It has been reported that day care units like the Day Hospital can be operated at one third to one fourth of full hospitalization costs. Thus, when viewed in terms of the Day Hospital plan, the financial deficit is not as formidable as it first seems to be.

Whether a day hospital plan is instituted or not, the administrator should have a specific treatment program for his hospital. His estimated budget should be based not on what was spent last year, but what his specific program calls for. That is, it should be a "program" budget rather than the antiquated "line" budget. For example, a proper food ration is planned and then its cost is calculated. One should not name a sum of money and then try to feed the patients on that sum without regard to price rises, or nutritional and aesthetic needs. The Mental Hospital Service of the American Psychiatric Association provides assistance to administrators in calculating their budgets.

Legislators must be reminded of the fact that 75 per cent of all the mental hospitals of our land are overcrowded, that the majority of mental hospitals are now omitting or restricting the use of known successful methods of treatment due to lack of staff or facilities, or both. For example, insulin coma therapy is now omitted completely by 40 per cent of our mental hospitals because of lack of funds for adequate staffing. Budgeting based on such false economies is financially wasteful.

Training in Administrative Psychiatry

With the growing appreciation of the vital role which the administrator plays in the therapeutic community of the mental hospital, administrative psychiatry is being included routinely in the training schedules of psychiatric residents today. The Mental Hospital Service of the American Psychiatric Association has set up the machinery for board examinations in administrative psychiatry. As training in this area is perfected and more mental hospital administrators come to this gigantic task adequately prepared for it, every aspect of the therapeutic community will be benefited.

Research in Administrative Psychiatry

A variety of research problems are of special concern to the administrative psychiatrist; for example, psychological techniques for the selection of hospital personnel, the effect of staff tensions on patients' behavior, the resolution of staff tensions by group therapy, experimentation with day care and night care arrangements, the effect of mixing of the sexes in hospital activities for patients, experiments in low cost hospital design with army type hutments. The manifold research problems in administrative psychiatry emphasize all over again that the administrator must be a psychiatrist, and a very special one at that, capable of boldness and imagination in devising new administrative approaches in addition to his skill in handling the old ones.

SELECTED REFERENCES

AMERICAN PSYCHIATRIC ASSOCIATION: *Better Care in Mental Hospitals.* Proceedings of the First Mental Hospital Institute of the APA., held at the Institute of the Pennsylvania Hospital, Philadelphia, Pa., April 11-15, 1949.
—— *Mental Hospitals.* Proceedings of the Second Mental Hospital Institute, held at the Medical Society Auditorium, St. Louis, Mo., October 16-19, 1950.
—— *Working Programs in Mental Hospitals.* Proceedings of the Third Mental Hospital Institute, held at Kentucky Hotel, Louisville, Ky., October 15-18, 1951.
—— *Steps Forward in Mental Hospitals.* Proceedings of the Fourth Mental Hospital Institute held at Deshler-Wallick Hotel, Columbus, Ohio, October 20-23, 1952.
    The published proceedings of the Mental Hospital Institutes are available through the Office of the Medical Director, APA. Mental Hospital Service, 1785 Massachusetts Ave., N.W., Wash. 6, D.C. They provide an unequaled source of information concerning administrative psychiatry based on the pooled experiences of our greatest experts.
—— *Standards for Psychiatric Hospitals and Clinics.* Mental Hospital Service, Washington 6, D.C. Revised, 1954.
    Contains the APA recommended standards for administrative qualifications and hospital organization.
BAGANZ, C. N.: Psychiatric Aspects of Hospital Administration. *Am. J. Psychiat.,* 108:277, 1951.
—— The Growing Science of Mental Hospital Administration. *Am. J. Psychiat.,* 110:161, 1953.
    C. N. Baganz is a leader in the field of administrative psychiatry. These articles are based on his vast personal experience.

BLUM, M. L.: Group Dynamics in Industry. *Int. J. Group Psychother.*, 4:172, 1954.
The application of group psychotherapy techniques to administrative problems in industry.

BRYAN, W. A.: *Administrative Psychiatry.* New York: W. W. Norton, 1936.
This well-known book contains many useful data. Unfortunately it is out of print.

Conference of Mental Hospital Administrators and Statisticians, April 15-17, 1953. Washington, D.C., Gov. Printing Office, 1954, 133 pages. U.S. Public Health Service Pub., No. 348 (40¢).
The responsibilities of the administrator with respect to nomenclature and statistical classification.

DUVAL, A.: The Clinical Director Looks at the Hospital Superintendent. *Am. J. Psychiat.*, 107:173, 1950.
Part of a useful symposium (see also Fitzsimmons and Perkins).

FITZSIMMONS, L. W.: What the Nurse Looks for in the Administrator. *Am. J. Psychiat.*, 107:173, 1950.
Part of a symposium (see also Duval, Perkins).

FULLER, R. G.: A Study of Administration of State Psychiatric Services. *Ment. Hyg.*, 38:177, 1954. Also available as a reprint through the National Association for Mental Health, 1790 Broadway, New York 19, N.Y.
A scholarly study, analyzing existing defects with recommendations for improvements.

KOHL, R. N.: Administrative Aspects of a Teaching Hospital. *Am. J. Psychiat.*, 107:481, 1951.
Some of the special administrative problems associated with a teaching hospital are considered.

LAUGHLIN, H. P.: A Group Approach to Management Improvement. *Int. J. Group Psychother.*, 4:165, 1954.
The use of group-psychotherapeutic techniques for the solution of administrative problems.

PERKINS, C. T.: Why State Hospital Superintendents Fail. *Am. J. Psychiat.*, 107-170, 1950.
Part of a symposium (see also Duval and Fitzsimmons).

READ, C. F.: Clinical Staff Conference. *Am. J. Psychiat.*, 93:1391, 1937.
A thoughtful presentation which remains fresh and pertinent in spite of the fact that it was published several years ago.

RINKER, C. D.: A State Mental Hospital Activates Its Department of Personnel: Better Patient Results. *Hospitals*, 26:67, 1952.
An excellent report of experiences in setting up a personnel department with a full-time director.

RUSSELL, W. L.: The Role of Medical Administration in Psychiatric Hospital Treatment. *Am. J. Psychiat.*, 105:721, 1949.
Contains important recommendations for the continued development of administrative psychiatry.

SHEFFEL, I.: Administration—A Point of View for Psychiatrists. *Bull. Menninger Clin.*, 15:131, 1951.
An extremely valuable presentation of basic administrative principles.

STEVENSON, G. S.: Ideals and Principles for Proper Management of the Mentally Ill. National Association for Mental Health, New York. Reprinted from *Ment. Hyg.*, 1942.
A highly recommended summary by a leader in administrative psychiatry.

Chapter XXVIII

STATISTICAL PROBLEMS IN PSYCHIATRY

The Importance of Statistics

The mental hospitals of our day are quite different from what they were half a century ago. They have grown in patient population at a pace which outstrips by far the rate at which the general population has grown. The character of the population has changed, too. Diagnostic categories formerly of major importance have become clinical curiosities in our time, whereas new diagnostic categories have soared into positions of predominant importance. Overcrowding has resulted in the deterioration of certain human aspects of treatment in mental hospitals. On the other hand, a variety of physical methods of treatment have been introduced in recent years. What can we learn about the significance of these changes? Which segments of the population have contributed most to the rising admission rates? Can we identify the areas of the country which are contributing the largest part of this increased case load and locate new treatment facilities which are more rationally based? In other words, can we learn to do something about mental health from a logistical point of view? How effective are the new physical methods of treatment and how harmful the effects of overcrowding? If we spend more money on patient care, is this reflected in better treatment results or does it imply simply an investment in decency and humanity? Or is this extra money only expended on poor administration? When a patient is discharged into the community, what happens to him? Does he stay well? Or does he enter a mental hospital elsewhere and remain erroneously on our books as a cure? If he returns to his family, what is the effect of his presence on family life and on the surrounding community? Does he become involved in antisocial behavior more often than those who were not patients? What outpatient psychiatric care does he get, and how effective is it?

These and many more questions are of interest and practical importance to every psychiatrist and to every member of the community for that matter. The answers can be found only in statistical analyses of the activities of each mental hospital. Until recently, statistical studies were very limited, and served primarily to emphasize the staggering magnitude of the problem of mental disorder and the woeful shortages in meeting that situation. These figures are available in many places, and their greatest value is to be found in their shock effect upon the public mind. By dramatizing them sufficiently for our legislators and in our public educational activities, we may succeed in arousing an interest in the problem consonant with its importance. However, there are more important uses to which statistics can be put. A more significant utilization of the facts and figures about mental disease demands drastic alteration in the statistical reporting techniques of most states and in each individual mental hospital.

Mental Hospitals Are "Big Business"

Large manufacturing plants employ elaborate systems of inspection and reporting. By the techniques of industrial engineering they learn to spot defects in the production lines or any other part of the total operation. Business men lose no time in following this information up with research and corrective action to overcome deficiencies uncovered by the reporting system. Although every mental hospital has a reporting system, in most instances it has not been modernized for decades. Data are collected routinely which often deal with questions no longer relevant to current problems and which in any case may not be available for practical use for half a decade. By that time the data are likely to be obsolete. Often the data are collected by clerks without special training for the job, and without any appreciation of their practical importance. Routinely, they fill in blank spaces on statistical cards and then send them on to a central office to be filed or, more accurately, to be buried. There is a kind of "functional schizophrenia" in the split between what is done statistically in most states and what the actual needs are. No business managed in this way could survive very long. Yet mental hospitals are in some measure big business.

All told, the forty-eight states and the District of Columbia spend more than $300,000,000 each year for the care and maintenance of patients with mental disorders. Despite the fact that many states are conducting multi-million dollar organizations, relatively little information is available to demonstrate what this expenditure means in terms of patient care. M. Kramer, Chief of the Biometrics Division of the National Institute of Mental Health, has said,

> Many of the reporting systems are using records and producing tabulations that were at one time important and may still be of value for certain purposes but which provide relatively little insight into the actual accomplishments of the mental hospital system. For example, there are many tabulations and historical series on the distribution of first admissions by ages, sex, mental disorder, use of alcohol, degree of education, occupation, citizenship, nativity, economic conditions, etc. However, there is a dearth of information on such pertinent questions as these: What is the age distribution of *resident* patients by mental disorder? How long have the patients resident in the hospital as of July first in any year been on the books of the hospital? Of the patients admitted in a given year what proportion of patients are released, or have deceased within one, two, three or four years following admission? How do these discharge and death rates vary by type of therapy or by age of the patient at the time of admission?

One of the severest criticisms that can be made of published statistics on the mental hospital population is that although much has been published there is little to show what effect the new advances in treatment and in hospital care have exerted on the chances of returning patients to the community. Ironically enough, much of the basic data needed to answer such questions as raised above are already on the records waiting merely for the appropriate analysis. I believe, therefore, that the time has come when we must reorient our thinking as to the kind of information that should be collected on our mental hospital populations and make a concerted effort to put this information to good use.

Asking the Right Questions

Any system of collecting data will answer those questions primarily for which it was designed. In other words, a good statistical system for mental hospitals begins with a clear understanding of the problems of the mental hospital. The statistician, by himself, can no more design a suitable system than can an architect design a suitable mental hospital, unless he is well grounded in the basic principles of treatment and care of mental hospital patients. In Kramer of the National Institute of Mental Health, psychiatry has a man who combines an understanding of these two widely separated disciplines, and under his leadership a new era of psychiatric statistics can be envisaged.

Apart from the questions which concern psychiatrists directly are administrative questions which impinge indirectly on the welfare of patients. Dollars sometimes spent on inefficient administration could have been used to better purpose for patient care. Malzberg, Director of the Bureau of Statistics of the Department of Mental Hygiene in New York State, has emphasized that every administrator should constantly compare his own hospital with others of similar type, not necessarily invidiously but to focus attention upon differences, if they exist, and the reasons for such variations. Do relative costs of maintenance differ, for example? If so, are they due to differences beyond the control of the hospital? Do they result from differences in types of care given to several classes and grades of patients? Do they arise from geographical and environmental factors? Is the hospital so isolated that costs of transportation are high? Or is the climate so rigorous that it necessitates larger expenditures for coal and oil?

The differences due to natural causes cannot be avoided; but if, after due allowance, variations in per capita costs still exist, they leave room for reasonable speculation as to efficiency, and should stimulate the search for legitimate economies. A hospital need not only compare itself with others. It may act as its own yardstick in order to see how it varies from year to year. Are there definite trends? Is the cost of maintenance changing? If there is an upward trend, to what is this due? Is it the result of changes in price levels? Is it possible, therefore, to use judgment with respect to purchases, and to substitute cheaper commodities when no harm results from such substitution? The values of such comparisons cannot be overestimated. They serve as a constant reminder to the administrator to manage his hospital as economically as is consistent with efficiency and with justice to the patient and to those who meet the costs.

Statistics are an essential aid in administrative matters in still another way. No budget can be planned without them. The utilization of growth trends with respect to population is the foundation stone for this structure. Since budgets are usually planned at least a year in advance, one must have an adequate idea of the size of the expected population. Forecasting by means of population trends is the basis of such prediction.

In addition to assistance on budgets, these forecasts may indicate a need for expansion and for the construction of new hospitals. Without some idea of how large the hospital population may grow in five or ten years, it is impossible to plan properly for new construction.

Furthermore, when state hospitals are integrated so as to function within an appropriate department, the population estimate serves two other purposes. They enable the administrative head to achieve a more balanced use of available facilities by shifting and transferring patients from crowded hospitals to those with unused bed facilities. They also make possible a more rational planning of new construction by indicating the territory which is in greatest need of additional facilities.

Concerning the evaluation of treatment methods, Malzberg says,

> It is now established that raising the body temperature of the patient
> halts the progress of general paresis. But in the early years how was
> one to determine the value of such treatment? Only through the com-
> parison of the outcome of treatment in two groups, identical (or prac-
> tically so) in all respects except that one group received the new ex-
> perimental form of treatment, and the other did not. If the results
> showed differences in recovery rates, improvement rates, and mortality
> rates, were these differences significant in the sense that they could
> not be attributed to chance variations?
> The technics that answer such questions are now basic in the
> theory of applied statistics and in scientific logic. The same proced-
> ures must be applied to other forms of treatment, to insulin shock,
> metrazol, electric shock and psychosurgical procedures. There is no
> reason why the results of psychoanalytic therapy should not be put to
> the same tests.

As a matter of fact, the American Psychoanalytic Association has undertaken, during the past few years, to evaluate the results of psychoanalytic therapy. This study deals largely with patients treated on an
outpatient basis. All methods of treatment should be put to the same
test in a mental hospital, including individual and group psychotherapy,
the effect of the activities program, the effect of social service interventions in the patient's extramural problems, and other therapeutic devices.

Special Difficulties in Mental Hospital Statistics

Perhaps the greatest difficulty in collecting an ideal set of mental
hospital statistics derives from the fact that psychiatrists work in a field
where, for the most part, the etiologies of the basic disorders they are
attempting to measure are unknown. There are no standard methods for
diagnosing quantitatively the disorders with which they are attempting
to deal, nor are there generally accepted methods of determining when
a patient is cured. This makes the problem of obtaining quantitative
measurements on comparable diagnostic groups a difficult one. The difficulties can perhaps be sharpened by referring again to the problem of
general paresis. Here is a disease whose cause is known. Based on the
characteristic changes produced in the body by the spirochaete of syphilis, one can diagnose the condition by standard clinical and laboratory
criteria, and it is largely possible to evaluate qualitatively the criteria
of cure. All of this can be done without referring to the manifestations
of the mental disorder which accompany the disease. In fact, we know

now that there is no specific mental disorder characteristic of this disease and that the patterns of psychological change are probably determined as much by the premorbid personality characteristics of the patient as by the changes due to the syphilitic process proper.

In other words, if one still had to diagnose general paresis on the basis of the psychiatric symptoms alone, the old confusion would continue to exist. Yet this is pretty much what psychiatrists are called upon to do in the diagnosis of the so-called functional psychoses which make up the great bulk of the mental hospital population. Add to this the fact that the diagnostic labels were themselves, until recently, quite unsatisfactory, and it becomes apparent how confusion was aggravated. Statistics can be no better than the nomenclature system on which they are based. And yet, in 1948 the status of psychiatric nomenclature had deteriorated so badly that it had reached a point of confusion which existed throughout medical nomenclature in the twenties. At least three nomenclatures (Standard, Armed Forces, and Veterans Administration) were in general use, and none of them fell accurately into line with the International Statistical Classification. One agency found itself in the uncomfortable position of using one nomenclature for clinical use, a different one for disability rating, and the International for statistical work. In addition, practically every teaching center had made modifications of the Standard for its own use, and assorted modifications of the Armed Forces nomenclature were introduced into many clinics and hospitals by psychiatrists returning from military duty. This is the situation with which the Committee on Nomenclature and Statistics of the American Psychiatric Association had to deal when asked to produce a revision in 1950.

A nomenclature to be really useful should be flexible. It should have as many categories as are necessary to cover the entire clinical field. There must be some room for overlapping diagnoses in cases that are not clear-cut clinically and which seem at times to fall into two or three different categories. It was pointed out in Chapter XXVII that the syndromes used today in psychiatry as diagnostic entities represent essentially patterns of adaptation to emotional stress. Human beings rarely employ a single fixed pattern of adaptation. They experiment, as it were, with different patterns until the best adaptation possible under a given set of circumstances is obtained. If the circumstances change, the pattern of adaptation may change once again; therefore, it is not at all rare to find representations of almost every possible diagnostic label in a single case, waxing and waning in importance at different stages of the illness.

On the other hand, a statistical classification should be relatively rigid.

In order to set up a system of statistics the number of diagnostic categories must be limited, and the categories should be mutually exclusive. Here, then, is a real conflict between the requirements for a good nomenclature system and those of a good statistical system. Nevertheless, practically useful compromises are possible. The new *Diagnostic and Statistical Manual: Mental Disorders* of the American Psychiatric Association's Mental Hospital Service is the product of years of serious labor, involving the practical experiences and wisdom of many people. Psychiatric progress by means of statistical studies depends to an important extent upon the universal adoption of this system, until such a time as a better system, preferably one rooted more firmly in etiology, becomes available.

The New Nomenclature

In the new nomenclature all patients are divided into those who are known to have organic brain disease and those without diagnosable brain disease. Patients with organic brain diseases are given a psychiatric classification if they show a basic syndrome consisting of:

1. Impairment of orientation
2. Impairment of memory
3. Impairment of all intellectual functions (comprehension, calculation, knowledge, learning, etc.)
4. Impairment of judgment
5. Lability and shallowness of affect.

This syndrome of organic brain disorder is a basic mental condition characteristic of diffuse impairment of brain function from any organic cause. The severity of this basic syndrome generally parallels the severity of the impairment of brain tissue function. If organic brain disease is focal and lacks the foregoing psychological evidences of diffuse brain impairment, then the disease is not given a psychiatric classification at all, but is categorized in exclusively neurologic terms.

The foregoing syndrome may be the only mental disturbance present in patients with organic brain disease, in which event the illness is simply classified further into acute and chronic syndromes depending upon its prognosis, treatment, and general course. On the other hand, the acute and chronic organic brain syndromes may or may not be associated with psychotic or neurotic manifestations, or with behavioral disturbances. If present, the latter reactions are determined not so much by the organic process proper but rather by inherent personality patterns, current emotional conflicts, and the immediate environmental situation, including the social forces to which the patient is exposed. In short, these reactions represent psychopathological attempts by the brain-injured patient at continued emotional adaptation. When these reactions are present to a significant degree, they are recognized in the diagnosis by the addition of the appropriate qualifying phrases. The organic brain syndromes are classified finally in terms of the underlying etiology. All diagnostic components may be categorized as mild, moderate or severe. Each component of the diagnosis—the acute or chronic organic brain syndrome, its etiology, its severity, disturbance—are all given individual code numbers which can be found in the official *Diagnostic and Statistical Manual: Mental Disorders* of the American Psychiatric Association (see also Appendix E). This makes possible precision in classification which is essential for statistical purposes.

The disorders of "psychogenic origin," that is, without clearly defined physical cause or structural change in the brain, are classified by and large into categories which are familiar to the mental hospital psychiatrist, although precise definitions of each of these diagnostic categories are to be found in the *Manual*. The new statistical *Manual* makes it possible to define psychosomatic reactions and behavioral disorders with increased precision; most of all, however, it facilitates the combination of different reaction patterns in a given diagnosis in a way which helps statistical analysis. This, as in the previous instance, is accomplished by assigning to each component of the diagnosis a specific code number which can be found in the official *Manual* (see also Appendix E).

In addition to a lack of uniformity in diagnostic categories, there has been a lack of uniformity in the definition of terms used to describe the movements of patients into and out of the hospital. The term, "first admission," for example, is variously used to mean first admission to a particular institution, first admission to any public institution of the state in question, first admission to any mental hospital, first admission to any mental hospital in the last five years, and so on. Discharge is variously used to designate a release because of recovery, any separation from the institution, final separation following a trial period at home, and so on. Uniform definitions of terms relating to movements of patients are obviously necessary. The following definitions are proposed for general use in the official *Manual:*

First admission: A patient admitted for the first time to any hospital for the treatment of mental disease, except institutions for temporary care only.

Readmission: A patient admitted who has previously been under treatment in a hospital for mental disease, excepting transfers and those who have been hospitalized only in institutions for temporary care.

Transfer: A patient brought directly from one hospital to another without a break in custody and without being formally discharged from the first hospital and formally admitted by the second.

Trial visit (conditional discharge, convalescent status, convalescent care, indefinite leave): Status of patients absent from the hospital but still on the books or in its custody. This is a type of care for patients, usually in their homes, in which the ability of the patient to adjust to normal community life is tested. He might be returned to the hospital at any time before discharge for his own protection or that of the community.

Family care: Status of patients who have been placed in the community in private families other than their own, under state supervision (see Chapter XXXVI). The expense of maintenance may be borne by the state, the patient's estate, relatives, Old Age Assistance or some other person or agency.

Temporary visit (leave of absence): Status of patients temporarily absent from the hospital for short periods of time with the understanding that the patient will return to the hospital within a specified time.

Otherwise absent: Status of patients leaving the hospital without permission (escape or elopement) or remaining away without leave and who are not discharged from the hospital books.

Discharge: Status of patients removed from the hospital books (except by death).

Death: Patients who die while on the hospital books.

The data collected in mental hospitals must be standardized also in terms of the actual items collected. Kramer has pointed out that the greatest defect in mental hospital statistics up to now has been the failure to study what happens to a group of patients followed over a long period of time. This has resulted in a situation in which data are available on patients who are discharged or who die but very little that relate to the patients that *remain* in residence or on extramural care. He emphasizes the need for following a group of annual admissions through the hospital and computing separation and death rates for this single group (which group is referred to as a "cohort") rather than a preoccupation with the crude discharge rates that are commonly used in mental hospital statistics, such as annual discharges per 100 admissions or annual discharges per 1000 average daily resident population.

A Simple Reporting System

An efficient reporting system can be designed to provide basic facts concerning the admissions, patients under treatment, discharges and deaths by having a limited number of basic variables reported to a central office for every patient admitted to the hospital system. For example,

Kramer has suggested that the following items be reported at the time of admission:

1. Patient's name
2. Residence (street address, city or town, county, state)
3. Serial number assigned to patient
4. Hospital to which admitted
5. Date of current admission
6. Birth date (month, day, year)
7. Age (last birthday) on admission
8. Sex (male, female)
9. Race (white, Negro, American Indian, Chinese, Japanese, etc.)
10. Marital status (single, married, widowed, divorced, separated)
11. Admission status (first, readmission, transfer)
12. Type of commitment (voluntary, medical, certification, standard nonjudicial procedure; medical certification, emergency procedure; without medical certification, emergency procedure; court order, judicial procedure)
13. Mental disorder (diagnosis)

The following facts should be reported subsequent to admission at the time each event occurs:

1. Changes in diagnosis
2. Dates of placement on trial visit, family care or temporary visit and return from such leave
3. Dates of escape and return from escape
4. Dates of transfer
5. Date of discharge and whether discharge is from hospital direct, trial visit, family care, temporary visit or while otherwise absent
6. Date of death and whether death occurred in hospital, on trial visit, family care, temporary visit or while otherwise absent
7. Causes of death

These items should be collated on a single card. From these few items an extraordinary amount of practical information can be gleaned, the nature of which is outlined in the statistical *Manual*.

As an example of the way in which the foregoing data can be useful, Kramer presented a series of tables at the Fourth Mental Hospital Institute designed to answer the following question: What is the current experience of patients during the first year following admission in terms of the per cent remaining in the hospital, out of the hospital, or dead within the twelve-month period following admission? How does the current experience compare with that of some earlier period? For purposes of comparison he used data which had been collected in New York State for the year 1914. He compared the 1914 data to similar data collected under his direction in seven states in 1948.

He was able to show, for example, in a group of first-admission schizophrenics that 33 per cent were out by the end of the first year, and 65 per cent were still hospitalized in 1914. In 1948, on the other hand, discharge rates for this same group ranged between 46 and 70 per cent in various states.

Of a group of patients with involutional psychoses only 35 per cent were out of the hospital within one year in 1914, 22½ per cent had died, and 42½ per cent remained in residence. The 1948 experience indicated a considerable decrease in the death rate ranging from zero in two states to a high of 8 per cent in two others. The per cent of involutional patients out of the hospital after one year, in 1948, ranged from 58 to over 80 in various hospitals.

In a group of patients with mental disorders of old age 56 per cent were dead at the end of one year in 1914 compared to 30 to 46 per cent in 1948. There was no increase in the number of patients out of the hospital at the end of the first year in 1948; actually the per cent remaining in the hospital after one year increased from 27 in 1914 to between 38 and 50 in 1948. Translated into dollars it seems as though modern methods of treatment have resulted in a considerable saving to the states in the care of schizophrenics. However, this saving is more than offset by the expenditure of additional sums for care for senile patients who are surviving but are not being rehabilitated.

Kramer summarizes these and other data of the two eras, as follows:

There are data available that suggest that the mental hospitals of the nation have made some striking accomplishments in the treatment of their patients. If it is true that savings are being made now by getting schizophrenics back into the community more quickly than before, I think that it is a major accomplishment. But, unless you look at your data realistically and use methods for analysis that are appropriate to the problem you are studying, you will not be able to show convincingly such differences. One may argue that getting schizophrenics out of the hospital more rapidly may not be progress. Perhaps they are relapsing more rapidly. I do not know the answer to that question. We have very little data on the follow-up of patients, once they go back into the community. Additional follow-up data collected and analyzed appropriately are needed. But the point I wish to make is that there are data available which, if analyzed properly, document a very impressive case for the mental hospitals.

Outpatient Psychiatric Clinics

Kramer's reference to the need for follow-up data after patients return to the community brings up the fact that however inadequate reporting systems for mental hospitals may have been up to now, reporting by outpatient psychiatric clinics has been even more primitive. It has been suggested that outpatient clinics desiring help in setting up a statistical system get in touch with the Biometrics Branch of the National Institute of Mental Health in Bethesda, Maryland, where current experiences in a few more progressive States are being collected for use in the guidance of others (see also Chapter XXXV).

Compiling the Data

The mental hygiene program of every State must include the full-time services of a statistician. More and more States are installing IBM equipment which at a nominal yearly rental makes statistical tabulation possible that would otherwise occupy a staff of ten or more experts. A single statistician can direct activities in each mental hospital, designating the hospital librarian for example, so that collection of data will proceed satisfactorily in each locale. With IBM equipment at his disposal it becomes possible for the statistician to make his calculations and to draw his conclusions with unprecedented completeness and speed.

The study of the epidemiology of mental disorder opens up new hope for significant psychiatric progress in the future, advances which improved statistical methods are making possible. Every member of the hospital therapeutic community must be alerted to the significance of good reporting in promoting the scientific development of his own special field of endeavor, as well as the welfare of the patients under his care.

SELECTED REFERENCES*

COMMITTEE ON NOMENCLATURE AND STATISTICS OF THE AMERICAN PSYCHIATRIC ASSOCIATION: *Diagnostic and Statistical Manual—Mental Disorders*. APA Mental Hospital Service, 1785 Massachusetts Avenue, N.W., Washington 6, D.C.
    An invaluable reference, providing standard definitions of terms, a description of the basic principles of statistical reporting, and tables with the official statistical classifications of mental disorder, old and revised. Reprinted in part in Appendix E.

* See also references to Chapter XXXV.

CONFERENCE (THIRD) OF MENTAL HOSPITAL ADMINISTRATORS AND STATISTICIANS: *Proceedings.*
Public Health Service Publication No. 348, U.S. Gov. Printing Office, Washington
25, D.C. (65¢).
A report on early experiences with the new nomenclature and statistical classification of mental disorder. Rich in factual data.

FELIX, R. H.; KRAMER, M.: Extent of the Problem of Mental Disorders. *Ann. Am. Acad.*
Pol. & Soc. Sci., 286:5, 1953.
Factual data are presented with a critique of existing practices for collecting
data and recommendations for reforms.

GROUP FOR THE ADVANCEMENT OF PSYCHIATRY: *Statistics Pertinent to Psychiatry in the*
United States. G.A.P. Report No. 7, March, 1949.
A fact sheet which may be useful in educating the public about the magnitude
of the problem of mental disorder.

MENTAL HOSPITAL INSTITUTE (Second): *Mental Hospitals,* 1950.
—— (Fourth): *Steps Forward in Mental Hospitals,* 1952.
APA Mental Hospital Service, 1785 Massachusetts Avenue, N.W., Washington
6, D.C.
The proceedings of these two institutes have particularly informative sections
on statistics.

NATIONAL ASSOCIATION FOR MENTAL HEALTH: *Facts and Figures about Mental Illness*
and Other Personality Disturbances, 1952. National Association for Mental
Health, 1790 Broadway, New York 19, N.Y.
An unusually readable presentation for the laity of basic facts concerning
mental disorder.

Chapter XXIX

EDUCATING THE STAFF

Introduction

It is generally agreed that the higher the teaching standards are in a mental hospital, the better will be the treatment for each patient, and the higher the caliber of research. This is not only because teaching inevitably improves the work of the beginner but also because a good teaching program attracts superior personnel, a matter of no small concern in these times of staff shortages. The teaching program should include every detail of the hospital work and should involve every worker who has anything to do with patients. Dedication to learning must be a dominant philosophy in the hospital. Some will come with previous psychiatric training—the doctors, social workers, psychologists, and some of the activities' therapists. Many more will come with no psychiatric background at all. Yet all will share the common task of learning how his specific contribution fits into the total treatment plan. They will have to understand each other's skills. This means that all must learn and all must prepare to teach if the therapeutic program of the hospital is to proceed.

A teaching program requires adequate physical facilities—an auditorium for lectures and motion pictures, classrooms for smaller discussion groups, treatment rooms with one-way screens where beginners may learn by watching skilled instructors at work, an adequate medical library with an up-to-date collection of relevant periodicals, recordings of interviews for teaching purposes, contrasting the problems in patients of different diagnostic categories, as well as the technique of the experienced interviewer and the beginner. There should be easy access to a psychiatric film library. In addition, there should be a liberal policy toward educational leaves, giving personnel the opportunity to attend important scientific meetings and courses while still on salary.

Background for Psychiatric Training

Because the psychiatrist's role in the mental hospital is basically that of the co-ordinator of all activities carried out in the patient's behalf, his training will be discussed first.

The Council on Medical Education of the American Medical Association in collaboration with the American Board of Psychiatry and Neurology inspects and judges institutions which seek recognition of their psychiatric training program. Approval may be given for one year, two years, or three years of full-time residency training, depending on the teaching facilities which are available. As of May, 1953, a total of 257 hospitals were approved for some degree of resident training.

The physician who applies for a residency has already travelled a long educational road. His first contact with psychiatric concepts may occur during his undergraduate work in elementary courses in psychology. Most medical curricula today start psychiatric training during the first year. The medical student is taught from the outset to think of the patient as a total human being with psychological and sociological aspects as well as physical ones. "The clinical picture is not just a photograph of a man sick in bed; it is an impressionistic painting of the patient surrounded by his home, his work, his relations, his friends, his joys, his sorrows, hopes and fears" (Francis Peabody). The medical student is also taught the team concept of treatment; he has learned something about the role of the social worker, the public health nurse and the courts in administering the health of the community. If taught recently, he will have some conception of psychodynamics as well as the general problem of classifying the categories of mental illness. Many internships now include a period of psychiatric training. Thus, the physician who applies for a residency usually comes moderately well equipped to deal with the work ahead of him.

In addition to his educational background, the resident should be possessed of a reasonable amount of emotional stability inasmuch as intensive work with psychotic patients can be very taxing. Outgoing qualities and warmth will make it easier for patients to relate to him. Attempts to select residents with the proper emotional and characterological qualifications by means of formal psychological testing have not worked out so far, although continued research along these lines may lead to more successful predicting devices in the future. At the moment, this problem is unfortunately academic in most hospitals, because the number of applicants for psychiatric residencies has fallen steadily in recent years.

In 1952, twenty-one accredited state hospitals were unable to get residents to fill their vacancies. The reason for this is not entirely clear, although the loss of young physicians to the armed forces is regarded as an important cause.

Board Certification

Most men who begin a psychiatric residency plan to become diplomates of the American Board of Psychiatry and Neurology at the conclusion of their training. The following is a summary of the procedure and requirements for securing board certification:

Application for Certificates: An application, in order to be considered at any meeting of the board, must be in the hands of the secretary of the board not less than 90 days before the date of such meeting (David A. Boyd, Jr., Secretary-Treasurer, 102-110 Second Avenue, S.W., Rochester, Minn.). A proper application form may be obtained from the secretary. Application may be made for certification in psychiatry or in neurology or in both fields. Applications will be formally considered only when made on the official application blank in such form as may be adopted from time to time by the board and when accompanied by an application fee in such amount as may be fixed by the board.

The secretary of the board, on receipt of an application, shall forthwith make inquiries from those to whom the candidate refers and from such other persons as the secretary may deem desirable and shall verify the candidate's record from the biographical records of the American Medical Association, after which he shall forward the application to the Committee on Credentials. This committee shall consider the application and other information available and notify the secretary whether the application is accepted. The certification of a candidate in either psychiatry or neurology, or both, shall be approved by a majority of the members of the entire board at any meeting held for such certification.

Form of Certification: There shall be separate certification in psychiatry and in neurology and two certifications or a combined certification for those qualified in both fields. The certifications shall be in such form as is approved by the Board of Directors.

General Requirements for Applicants: Each applicant for a certificate must establish that:

(a) He is a physician duly licensed by law to practice medicine.

(b) He is of acceptable ethical and professional standing.

(c) He is now a member of the American Medical Association or a member of such medical societies as are recognized for purposes of certification by the Council on Medical Education and Hospitals of the American Medical Association. Exceptions to the foregoing may be made at the discretion of the board for good and sufficient reasons.

(d) He has received adequate training in psychiatry or neurology, or both, as a specialty.

Classes of Applicants: Class A.—Applicants who graduated from an approved medical school before the foundation of the board (1934) will not be held to the strict interpretation of the published requirements in formal graduate training. Under such circumstances the board will consider the training and experience of the applicant and decide whether or not he will be admitted to the examinations. After Jan. 1, 1954, for such graduates the board will consider 10 years of full-time acceptable experience in psychiatry or neurology in lieu of the formal training requirements. Should the candidate then apply for supplementary certification, the Credentials Committee will require five years of additional acceptable experience in the supplementary field.

Class B.—Applicants who graduated from an approved medical school after 1934 shall fulfill the following requirements.

Professional Education: 1. Graduation from a medical school in the United States or Canada approved by the Council on Medical Education and Hospitals of the American Medical Association. In the case of an applicant whose medical training has been received outside the United States and Canada, such training must be satisfactory to the aforementioned Council.

2. Completion of a year's internship approved by the same Council in general medicine, general surgery, pediatrics, or a rotating service.

3. The nine-month wartime internships will be accepted as an equivalent of one year.

Specialized Training: Admission to the examination for certification in psychiatry or neurology requires a total of five calendar years of training and experience, three years of which must be specialized training obtained in approved training centers, plus two years of experience. Admission to the examination for certification in both psychiatry and neurology requires a total of six calendar years of training and experience, five years of which must be specialized training obtained in approved training centers, plus one year of experience. The specialized training may be subdivided into two and a half years each in psychiatry and neurology or three years in one subject and two years in the other. The required years of experience should be spent in clinical practice with major responsibility for the care of patients.

This training for psychiatrists should include clinical work with psychoneurotic and psychotic patients, combined with the study of basic psychiatric sciences, medical and social psychology, psychopathology, psychotherapy and the physiological therapies, including a basic knowledge of the form, function and pertinent pathology of the nervous system. This training should be supervised and guided by teachers competent to develop skill and understanding in the utilization of such basic knowledge in dealing with patients. Mere factual knowledge is not sufficient. This training period should include instruction in the psychiatric aspects of general medical and surgical conditions and the behavior disorders of children and adolescents sufficient to develop practical ability to direct the treatment of such conditions. It should also include collaborative work with social agencies. The training program of the candidate for certification in psychiatry should include sufficient training in neurology to enable him to recognize and to evaluate the evidences of organic neurological disease.

The training for neurologists should be based on clinical work with adults and children with neurological disorders, including the neurological complications of medical and surgical conditions. This should be combined with study of basic neurological sciences, neuroanatomy, neurophysiology, neuropathology, and neuroroentgenology. This training should be supervised and guided by teachers competent to develop skill and understanding in the utilization of such basic knowledge in dealing with patients. Mere factual knowledge is not sufficient. This training should include sufficient training in psychiatry to enable the candidate to recognize and to evaluate the common psychiatric reactions.

The board offers the foregoing two paragraphs as an outline of desirable training. If, however, the candidate has evidence of equivalent qualifications of training and experience not in the pattern here formulated, this evidence with appropriate documentary support may be included in his application for evaluation and possible approval by the board.

Candidates seeking certification in both neurology and psychiatry or supplementary certification in one after being certified in the other must submit evidence satisfactory to the board of an additional two years of full-time basic training in the supplementary specialty.

Thus, no candidate is eligible for examination by the board until he has completed at least five years of special training and experience in neurology or psychiatry for a single certificate, or at least six years of special training and experience in neurology and psychiatry for certification in both neurology and psychiatry.

The board will give not more than six months of credit for not less than six months of training in an approved training center for internal medicine or pediatrics in lieu of six months of experience to candidates for the certificate in psychiatry or neurology, but not to candidates for certification in both psychiatry and neurology.

The board will give credit for one year of training in child psychiatry providing it is the third year of the required three years of special training and providing it is taken in a center approved by the board for training in child psychiatry. After July 1, 1956, training credit for work in the field of child psychiatry may be gained only by participation in a hospital residency training program that is regularly approved. After that date, all independent training approval of psychiatric clinics for children is discontinued.

The list of training programs approved by this board and by the Council on Medical Education and Hospitals of the American Medical Association may be found in the most recent issue of the Internship and Residency Number of *The Journal of the American Medical Association.*

Training in the Armed Forces: Credit will be granted for one year of wartime military service in the Army, Navy, Public Health Service, and Veterans Administration. Wartime to this board means Dec. 7, 1941, to Feb. 15, 1946. Further credit for specialized training will be granted only if the candidate has received training in an institution recognized by the Council on Medical Education and Hospitals of the American Medical Association and approved by this board. Time beyond one year spent in the above government agencies may be credited to experience providing the candidate has been regularly assigned to a service in neurology or psychiatry.

Training and experience credit toward requirements for examination will be granted for military duty under certain conditions. One year of training credit will be granted for one year spent in full-time psychiatric and/or neurological duties. Additional training credit will be granted for that amount of time spent in approved training programs. Experience credit will be granted for any remaining time spent in full-time psychiatric and/or neurological assignments. Double credit will not be granted for any single period of time. For military duty after Jan. 1, 1954, only experience credit will be granted for full-time psychiatric and/or neurological duties. Training credit will be granted for residency assignments in regularly approved training programs.

Examinations: Dates and places of examinations are set by the board at its discretion and shall be announced in *The Journal of the A.M.A.,* in the *American Journal of Psychiatry,* in the *Journal of Nervous and Mental Diseases,* and in the *Archives of Neurology and Psychiatry.*

Though the purpose of the examination is to test the competence of the candidate in psychiatry or neurology or both, it must not be forgotten that both these medical disciplines constitute part of the broad field of general medicine. The board requires some proficiency in neurology on the part of those it certifies in psychiatry, and vice versa, but examines the candidate in accordance with the certificate he seeks. The examinations will be of such type that no adequately trained person will fail and yet they will be sufficiently searching so that the specialist in fact may be separated from the specialist in name. The practical examination will include the examination of patients under the supervision of the examiner. The manner of examining patients, and the reasoning and deductions therefrom, will constitute an important part of the examination. Oral and practical examinations will be given in the basic sciences with special regard to their clinical implications. Written examinations may be given at the discretion of the board. The examination for certification in psychiatry will differ from the examination for certification in neurology.

Payment of Fees: The candidate on filing his application shall accompany it with an application fee of $35 which is not returnable. If a preliminary written examination has been decreed, an additional $25 fee will be required at the time of the applicant's acceptance. When notified by the secretary that he is eligible for the oral and practical examination, the candidate shall send to the secretary an examination fee of $65. A candidate who has been certified in either psychiatry or neurology and who has been admitted to supplementary examination for the other certificate shall pay an additional examination fee of $65.

A candidate who has failed in one examination is eligible for re-examination within one year on payment of a re-examination fee of

$50. After the year has elapsed he must submit a new application and pay new application and examination fees. If he fails the re-examination, he may, after two years have elapsed, submit a new application and $35 fee, present evidence of further training and pay an examination fee of $65.

A candidate who fails in one or two subjects is eligible for re-examination in those subjects within one year on payment of a re-examination fee of $50. After the year has elapsed he must submit a new application and pay new application and examination fees and repeat the entire examination. If he fails the re-examination, he may apply again for the complete examination after two years on submission of evidence of further training and on payment of an application fee of $35. If admitted to the examination, he must pay a new examination fee of $65.

Any candidate who finds himself unable to attend an examination to which he has been admitted and does not notify the secretary at least six weeks before the date of the examination will forfeit half of his examination fee. Any candidate who fails to appear for examination within a period of three years following the date of notification of eligibility for examination shall be required to submit a new application and pay the attendant fee. If a candidate dies before his certificate is issued, all fees will be returned to his estate.

The following outline was prepared by F. G. Ebaugh for the 1952 Conference on Psychiatric Education, held at Cornell University in Ithaca, New York. It presents a plan for a three-year program of psychiatric training calculated to meet the board requirements.

The first year. A program in this year is based on the care, diagnosis, and treatment of patients in a psychiatric hospital or on the psychiatric ward of a general hospital. The hospital ideally should be a diagnostic and a treatment center receiving a wide variety of patients, including the neurotic, the alcoholic, the psychotic (organic as well as psychogenic types), drug addicts, court cases, etc. If possible, the resident serves as psychiatric consultant to a general hospital emergency service at some time during the year, since this gives him firsthand experience in handling acute hysterical, drug, alcoholic and psychotic reactions.

The first two weeks can profitably be spent in orientation in the hospital's procedure and the general care of mental patients. Very active and close supervision during this period helps the resident to overcome the rather hopeless and impotent feelings that commonly overwhelm him as a result of the sudden change from internship in a general hospital to a new and strange position of responsibility with psychiatric patients.

At general teaching rounds for senior and junior staffs, the resident presents current cases for diagnosis and therapeutic suggestions. As the year progresses, more emphasis is put on the dynamics involved in a case in distinction to descriptive aspects. This shift of emphasis is necessarily a gradual process in which each resident is allowed to progress at the rate commensurate with his own learning abilities and his resistances. More psychological data—Rorschach, Thematic Apperception Test, etc.—are progressively presented. A weekly treatment conference of residents, senior staff, and social service staff is very useful from the administrative and educational points of view. At this conference the specific treatment procedures to be carried out on each patient are discussed. As the resident becomes more sure of his psychotherapeutic abilities, relatively less emphasis is placed on somatic therapies and more on psychotherapeutic ones.

An extensive didactic program is probably inadvisable at this stage because the harried resident cannot digest a large amount of descriptive and dynamic material. Nevertheless, a series of weekly lectures covering some of the basic descriptive concepts of clinical intramural psychiatry is useful.

To aid the resident in acquiring techniques of interviewing and psychotherapy, at least one hour per week is spent in observing, through a one-way screen, an interview of a hospitalized patient by a staff member. As the year progresses, a simple type of nondirective psychotherapy in process is demonstrated to the resident by having him observe weekly therapeutic sessions through the one-way screen. In some sessions, the resident becomes the interviewer and the resident group may later discuss the techniques observed.

The backbone of the teaching program in the first year—and also in the second and third years of residency—is counseling. In the first year, the resident spends at least one hour per week discussing problem cases with his counselor, who is a member of the full-time senior house staff. Because of the type of cases handled by the resident and the preliminary status of his training, counseling in the first year differs somewhat from that in the following years. Less emphasis is put on process recordings and psychotherapeutic interviews and more on the problems of management, somatic therapy and surface dynamics. The resident's feelings of hopelessness, insufficiency and anxiety in the face of seemingly insurmountable therapeutic problems can be allayed by counseling. This aspect of counseling is important.

An attempt is made to lay the groundwork for the understanding and utilization of the contributions of clinical psychology. The resident works directly with psychologists and regularly administers Rorschach and Thematic Apperception Tests under supervision. The aim is not to make the resident a clinical psychologist but to enable him to evaluate these various psychological tools.

The resident is also given experience in the special clinical services. For example, he observes and administers the various types of electroshock therapy and handles the insulin service. The necessity for careful supervision and instruction in these fields is obvious.

Finally, the resident learns how to work closely with the psychiatric nurse and to appreciate her problems through discussion of academic and current ward problems at regular meetings of the head nurses and residents. Lectures to nursing students and supervision of their work is valuable experience. The practical problems of forensic psychiatry may be approached through presentation of cases in lunacy commissions and court evaluations, and through appearing in court as an expert witness.

The second year. The program in the second year continues to be chiefly intramural, with assignments to the various general hospital services: surgery, obstetrics, gynecology, general medicine, tuberculosis, physical medicine, rehabilitation, etc. This clinical experience adds up to training in psychosomatic medicine. The resident is also introduced to outpatient psychiatry. Many of these cases in the medical and surgical outpatient departments present problems that are referred to the psychiatric division for evaluation and possible treatment. These cases are used as an outpatient case load.

Teaching by seminars and case conferences continues. More time can now profitably be spent in didactic lectures on psychosomatic problems, with residents themselves reporting on topics in which they are especially interested. During this year work in clinical neurology is undertaken.

As in the first year, counseling is the chief and most important method of training. Counseling is adjusted to the progressive development of the resident and for this reason differs somewhat from that of the first year. The resident is beginning to comprehend dynamic factors, and to utilize some of this understanding in psychotherapy. His own learning is enriched by working closely with residents in training in other specialties and also by teaching and counseling medical students.

The third year is devoted entirely to extramural psychiatry, preferably centered in a community or university mental hygiene clinic offering outpatient care to both adults and children. The resident learns to work more closely than in the previous years with clinical psychologists and social workers. He is given an opportunity to do evaluation work for schools, courts, state institutions, and other referring agencies. The major part of his time, however, is spent in actual therapy.

The chief teaching method, as in the previous years, is personal supervision through counseling. An attempt is made to teach the resident a consistent type of therapeutic approach, and to help him develop a technique in which he becomes skilled. Essentially, the therapy is the short-term, interpretative type, oriented by psychodynamic principles.

During this year, the resident starts to learn his potential role in the community—what the community may expect of him, and how he can meet these expectations. By working in community agencies he learns how to deal in a consultative capacity with social workers, public health nurses, teachers and members of other professions concerned with community welfare. He learns how to address public groups on mental hygiene problems by talking before parent-teacher associations, social work, church, school and other groups.

There is a continuation of seminars and rounds. If social work and psychology staffs as well as psychiatrists participate in some of these, the resident broadens his understanding of how members of these professions use psychotherapeutic tools, and how they contribute to the psychiatric team. The seminars exclusively for residents can to good advantage be devoted to a systematic study of psychodynamics. If this type of data is presented too soon, the resident is not equipped to appreciate the validity of the material. As with the premature presentation of interpretations to patients in psychotherapy, the premature presentation of psychodynamics to residents may mobilize hostilities and resistance.

General. In addition to the program outlined above by years, basic courses in neurophysiology, neuropathology, etc., are offered at some time during the training period: special courses, conferences and seminars, and also journal clubs on current problems are fitted into the over-all plan. Residents are encouraged and guided in undertaking research in accordance with their interests and capacities.

The foregoing outline has the advantage of completeness as far as meeting the requirements of the specialty board are concerned, although one may choose not to follow it in detail, or precisely in that order. However, it does bring out quite clearly that the full training of psychiatric residents can rarely if ever take place within the walls of a single institution. More frequently, training must be conducted through the co-ordinated facilities of several different hospitals and clinics. A mental hospital located in a metropolitan area usually has little difficulty in making the necessary arrangements. If it is part of a vast medical center, it may have all of these facilities available within a few steps. Sometimes the program necessitates traveling to widely separated institutions for what amounts to essentially separate residencies, except that the program of each institution complements the other to give a rounded-out training to the resident. When the training program is carried out in conjunction with a medical school, the teaching possibilities are naturally enriched.

Psychological Problems of a Psychiatric Residency

The strange environment and the many responsibilities of a new residency are sufficient to arouse anxiety in any young physician. If one adds to this the fact that intimate and prolonged contacts with psychotic patients are particularly anxiety-provoking to untrained persons, one gets some measure of the emotional stress under which the new resident labors. Where a physician in another specialty might carry on with relatively unimpaired efficiency in spite of his anxiety, this symptom is grossly disrupting in the work of a psychiatrist. The basis of psychotherapy is to be found in the effective manipulation of the relationship which the patient develops with the physician. Anxiety on the part of the physician interferes with the development of a proper relationship and disrupts the possibility of utilizing it flexibly in a therapeutically meaningful interaction. As a result, educators have emphasized the importance of recognizing that residents have anxieties and that these must be dealt with properly. Usually the recognition of the anxiety and reassuring discussions with an understanding supervisor are enough to reduce it to less complicating levels. However, there are instances where anxiety remains high and where continued training does not seem to reduce it. In these instances, the resident does not work at the peak of his potential capacity. He may be compelled to confine himself to certain limited areas of psychiatric work, to the somatotherapies for example. Inhibitions in a resident may interfere not only with his therapy with patients but with the learning process as well. Ideas which arouse anxiety are less easily comprehended, or may give rise to unreasonable hostility or disbelief. Hence when one speaks of "teaching," it is well not to forget the other half of that process which consists of "learning." A failure to take into account the mental state of the resident, his motivations, his fears, his ambitions, may nullify the best of training programs.

Psychoanalysis and Psychiatric Training

As a result of work difficulties, the resident may decide to undergo a personal psychoanalysis. If successful, this would not only make him more comfortable but would considerably broaden his professional usefulness.

This raises the question: Is a personal analysis and psychoanalytic training an indispensible part of psychiatric training? The fact that many of our great psychiatrists contribute brilliantly to almost all phases of mental hospital work without the benefit of a personal analysis provides a simple answer in the negative. Many such men do not have personal difficulties of sufficient intensity to interfere with their work with patients. Many develop great diagnostic acumen and clinical judgment which permits them to formulate cases and supervise treatment with great skill, or to utilize the various forms of shock therapy with maximal effectiveness. There are many instances in which analysis is inadvisable, where as a result of age and personal circumstances, it can be anticipated that more harm can come from it than good. It is fortunate that psychoanalytic training is not essential, because for many people analytic training is impossible, either because of lack of available training facilities or lack of sufficient funds. However, if a young resident has the means, and analytic training is available, it is certainly to be recommended. Such training will equip him with a new instrument for observing the patient and himself which will contribute significantly to his effectiveness as a therapist and as a psychiatric research worker. In fact, I would like to regard it as part of the basic training of a psychiatrist, even though, like the electroencephalograph for example, it is not absolutely essential for useful and even brilliant clinical work.

Training for the Senior Staff

We have spoken thus far of the resident. But what if he has already been certified by the specialty board and is a permanent member of the senior staff? Certainly his training should continue, too. Attending meetings, organizing a journal club—these are the traditional ways that specialists adopt to maintain their professional growth. For men working in mental hospitals, it is almost a necessity to have psychiatrists from the community participate in their teaching program. Without a doubt, the psychiatrist from the community will learn as much from the hospital staff as they will learn from him, but it is only in such exchanges of ideas that psychiatry will grow. Electroshock therapy, which is an indispensable part of the armamentarium of the psychiatrist in the community, is available to him only because the details of its use were worked out in mental hospitals. The science of psychodynamics, on the other hand, including human motivation, mechanisms of defense and the general problem of emotional adaptation, was worked out to a considerable degree by psychoanalytically oriented psychiatrists in the community. The application of these principles in mental hospitals in the individual and group psychotherapy of psychotic patients has opened up a new and fruitful therapeutic approach. On the other hand, experiences with these techniques in mental hospitals have recently given the psychiatrist in the community the courage and inspiration to utilize them on ambulatory psychotic patients in the community. The use of psychiatric social workers, which is so routine in the work of the psychiatrist in the community, had its origin in psychiatric practice in the mental hospital. Other examples of this mutual interacting influence could be given.

Over a period of several years the author has conducted week-end seminars at various state hospitals in New York, with the assistance of Robert L. Kahn, psychologist at the Mount Sinai Hospital in New York City. Staff members of neighboring mental hospitals would also attend these seminars. Sometimes guests had to travel long distances and arrived at the hospital on the preceding night. The host hospital would provide food and lodging for all guests. Classes would be held Saturday morning with a recess for lunch and would be resumed Saturday afternoon. A final session would be held Sunday morning, and the seminar would conclude with Sunday lunch. Initially, sessions were held Sunday afternoon as well, but this proved to be too exhausting.

The seminars were based primarily on case presentations. Formal didactic lectures were reduced to a minimum, although cases were selected in accordance with the practical needs of the group. Original work was always encouraged and emphasized in the presentations.

Perhaps the most fruitful part of the seminar would take place Saturday evening during an open house. Food and liquid refreshments were a feature of these gatherings. Although a spirit of informality and sociability prevailed, much psychiatry would be discussed, including theory, questions concerning specific patients, advanced psychiatric training, psychoanalysis and research. At times such discussions even had a group psychotherapeutic "flavor," in that personal problems interfering with treatment and research would also be discussed.

This exchange involves not only psychiatrists but other medical colleagues in the community as well. The idea of psychosurgery had its origin outside of the mental hospital, but our clinical understanding of it has grown as a result of its application in mental hospitals. Medical colleagues treating arthritis with cortisone and tuberculosis with isoniazid observed mental changes in the patients. They reported these changes to psychiatrists in mental hospitals. They in turn checked their observations and the possible applications of these drugs to psychiatry. Psychosomatic studies on the wards of general hospitals are giving us new insights concerning mental mechanisms. In recent years several patients with organic brain disease have been seen on the neurology service of the Mount Sinai Hospital in New York City that were clinically indistinguishable from schizophrenics to competent observers in the community. The following case dramatizes one way in which general medicine and psychiatry have become related:

A twenty-eight-year-old married woman developed acute generalized lupus erythematosis following the birth of a child. She was given cortisone and ACTH after which the lupus subsided, but there emerged instead a state of acute catatonic excitement in which she rapidly exhausted herself. As a life-saving measure the cortical steroids were stopped. The psychosis stopped promptly, but concomitant with her psychiatric improvement the lupus returned. Her fever mounted, she became critically ill, and as a life-saving measure the drugs were resumed. Once again the lupus subsided and the psychosis emerged. This cycle was repeated two more times. During her fourth catatonic attack, she was given electroshock therapy. This produced a mild improvement in the psychosis, but she had to be transferred to a mental hospital.

This case poses many problems, practical and theoretical, the answers to which we do not know, touching upon the relationship between somatic disease and disturbances in the emotional life of the individual. Through a free exchange of experiences and ideas between the psychiatrist in the mental hospital and his colleagues in the community, these and other answers will be found. The mental hospital's educational program, through lectures and seminars, provides the opportunity for implementing this exchange.

Lectures versus Seminars

There is a common tendency to use lectures in teaching programs to excess. Although the formal lecture can be very informative and at times even stirring, more often it is not an effective device for teaching psychiatry. It is in the abstract nature of the subject that one quickly loses the audience unless ideas are heavily documented with clinical facts. This experience has resulted in a general trend in psychiatric teaching away from lectures and toward the use of small case seminars.

The Use of Motion Pictures in Training

The use of motion pictures with sound track for psychiatric training has become an increasingly popular practice, particularly with the growth of a vast library of excellent films which are available on rental. The film catalogues listed as references at the end of this chapter should be studied. Useful titles will be found for the training of all personnel, non-medical as well as medical.

All film showings should be introduced by a discussion leader and followed by a period for questions and general discussion. This discussion period is always the most important part of the presentation. Many psychiatric films arouse anxiety in the audience based on personal and popular misconceptions. A competently directed discussion provides an opportunity to correct these errors, thereby relieving anxiety and improving the quality of the work with patients.

Additional Areas for Study

In addition to topics already touched upon, there are other special fields which concern a mental hospital teaching program. For example, administrative psychiatry is a field that has only recently been accorded the recognition which is its due. Forensic psychiatry is a difficult and highly specialized field to which continued thought and study should be given. Industrial psychiatry, an area which in many ways is largely unexplored, is a field of proven importance. Liaison with industry through this area of common interest could also further the vocational rehabilitation program of the hospital.

Teaching the Rest of the Staff

One of the most effective methods of learning is by teaching others. In preparing material for classes, the teacher is compelled to organize his information and to clarify his basic concepts. Teaching student nurses, attendants, volunteers, and members of the various activities departments should be part of the resident's duties. If he has done his work well, he will have trained cadres of teachers who can go out into the hospital and provide instruction to personnel in all departments on a ward level. In other words, the teaching program sets off a chain reaction which is capable of revolutionizing the caliber of psychiatric practice at every echelon in the hospital. In the chapters on recreational therapy, occupational therapy, dietetics, the attendant, the social worker, the psychologist, the nurse, the chaplain and the volunteer worker, the psychiatrist's responsibility for their instruction was emphasized. The resident physician who is usually assigned the task of instructing these groups must not forget the anxiety which besets those who are now his students. The resolution of this anxiety is the most important part of his work. Unless this is adequately dealt with, the rest of the program will fail, for their anxiety can harm the atmosphere of the therapeutic community no less than the anxiety of the physician. These specialists will not only receive instruction from the psychiatrist but will in turn instruct each other concerning their own fields, until that state of mutual professional understanding is achieved which is prerequisite for the proper functioning of a mental hospital.

Administrative Aspects of the Training Program

The organizational needs of a training program call for the services of a director. In Chapter XXVII it was recommended that this be a physician assigned full time to the task, which should also include the hospital's research activities. He will draw up the curriculum after proper study and consultation, making teaching assignments and arrange classes to co-ordinate with work schedules. In addition, he will bring in outside teachers, if possible affiliating his teaching program and faculty with that of a nearby university. In some places it has been possible to obtain one year of college credit for properly qualified hospital workers attending classes (see Chapter X). This not only improved the level of teaching but attracted a higher quality group to apply for work in the hospital. The director also encourages his staff to attend scientific meetings and conferences off the grounds and invites scientific groups to hold meetings at his hospital. The Council of State Governments has recommended that the official in charge of the state mental health program have an assistant specifically assigned to direct the training and research program for the state. His activities are discussed in more detail in Chapter XXX. He will include among his responsibilities the co-ordination of the training programs in the separate mental hospitals throughout the state.

Training Opportunities Under the National Mental Health Act

One of the most serious handicaps in combating mental illness is the shortage of trained personnel. There are only about 7,200 trained psychiatrists in the entire United States. It has been estaimated that we need at least three times that number. We also need many times the present number of clinical psychologists, psychiatric social workers, and psychiatric nurses. Other mental health personnel are equally scarce.

Before any real progress can be made in conquering mental illness and improving mental health, we must have trained personnel to provide mental health services throughout the country. The National Mental Health Act, which was passed in 1946 to "improve the mental health of the people of the United States," provides, among other things, for the training of increased numbers of persons in the field of mental health.

Training Grants to Institutions

Under the National Mental Health Act, the Public Health Service of the Department of Health, Education, and Welfare, upon recommendation of the National Advisory Mental Health Council,[1] may make grants to public and other nonprofit institutions "to provide training and instruction in matters relating to psychiatric disorders." In this way

---

1 The Advisory Mental Health Council consists of the Surgeon General, the Chief Medical Officer of the Veterans Administration, and a medical officer designated by the Secretary of Defense, who are ex-officio members; and twelve members appointed by the Surgeon General. These members "shall be leaders in the fields of fundamental sciences, medical sciences, or public affairs; and six of such twelve shall be selected from among leading medical or scientific authorities who . . . are outstanding in the study, diagnosis, or treatment of . . . psychiatric disorders . . ."

institutions that already offer training in the mental health fields may improve and expand their teaching staffs to instruct a greater number of students, and potential training centers in universities, hospitals, medical and other schools may be developed.

At the present time, grants are being awarded to institutions offering graduate training in psychiatry, clinical psychology, psychiatric social work, psychiatric nursing, and public health mental health. It is anticipated that grants for training other types of mental health personnel may be awarded in the future.

Grants may be used by such training institutions to pay the salaries, in whole or in part, of additional instructors, other teaching personnel, and nonprofessional help; to acquire permanent and expendable training materials; and to provide special lectures and demonstrations for training purposes. No funds may be used for the construction, alteration, or rental of buildings.

Further information on training grants to institutions may be obtained by writing to the Training and Standards Branch, National Institute of Mental Health, Public Health Service, Bethesda 14, Md.

Traineeships

The Public Health Service also provides funds to institutions to pay traineeships for a limited number of graduate students in psychiatry, clinical psychology, psychiatric social work, psychiatric nursing, and public health mental health. A list of these institutions can be obtained from the National Institute of Mental Health, Bethesda 14, Md., upon request.

As the program expands, additional teaching institutions will be allocated funds for traineeships. The names of additional institutions selected to award such traineeships will be announced periodically in professional journals.

Traineeships are usually awarded for an academic year of training.

Who Is Eligible for Training?

General Requirements: An applicant must be a citizen of the United States or have declared his intention to become one.

Persons receiving educational benefits from another Federal agency cannot at the same time receive traineeship payments under the National Mental Health Act.

An applicant must meet the requirements of the training institution awarding Public Health Service traineeships. Training institutions collaborating in the training program under the National Mental Health Act give preference to students who manifest a genuine interest in teaching, research or public service.

Specific Requirements and Traineeship Levels

Psychiatry. An applicant for a traineeship in psychiatry must be a graduate of an approved medical school, or its equivalent outside the

United States, and have completed at least one year of clinical internship.

Traineeships are awarded at the following levels: First graduate year, $2,000; second graduate year, $2,400; third graduate year, $3,000; fourth graduate year, $3,600.

Clinical Psychology. An applicant for a traineeship in clinical psychology must be a graduate of an accredited college or university and be a candidate for a doctorate in psychology with specialization in clinical psychology in an approved clinical psychology training program. An applicant for a traineeship at an institution providing internship training only shall have completed successfully at least two years of graduate work as a candidate for the Ph.D. in psychology in an approved clinical psychology training program.

Traineeships are awarded at the following levels: First graduate year, $1,200; second graduate year, $1,600; third graduate year, $2,000; fourth graduate year, $2,400.

Postdoctoral clinical psychology traineeships are available at a number of institutions, primarily for advanced training in clinical research, clinical teaching, and clinical supervision. Traineeships are awarded at the following levels: first postdoctoral year, $3,000; second postdoctoral year, $3,600. Applicants for these traineeships shall have received a Ph.D. in psychology, with specialization in clinical psychology.

Psychiatric Social Work. An applicant for traineeship in psychiatric social work must be a graduate of an accredited college or university and have had at least one year of graduate training in an approved school of social work.

Traineeships are not awarded to students in their first year of graduate social work training at this time. Traineeships at the $1,600 level are awarded for second-year graduate training, and at the $2,400 level for advanced third-year graduate training.

Applicants for advanced third-year graduate training must have a Master's degree in social work followed by at least three years of successful professional experience. Recipients of third-year traineeships may take some training outside the school of social work administering the traineeships provided that the student's entire training program is approved by the school of social work concerned.

Traineeships ranging from $2,700 to $3,000 for fourth-year graduate training are available for accepted doctoral degree candidates who have completed the third advanced year in psychiatric social work or who have previously qualified in psychiatric social work.

Psychiatric Nursing. An applicant for a traineeship in psychiatric nursing must be a graduate of an accredited school of nursing and be registered in at least one state. In addition, the applicant must be eligible for matriculation in an approved school offering an advanced program in psychiatric nursing or in mental health and psychiatric nursing.

To meet the most important needs at this time, traineeships are awarded for the training of clinical specialists, teachers, supervisors, administrators, and consultants. Traineeships at the $1,600 level are awarded for undergraduate school training programs.

Public Health Mental Health. Some traineeships are available in schools of public health for special programs in public health mental health. An applicant must have:

Psychiatrist—Completed residency training in psychiatry.

Clinical Psychologist—A Ph.D. in psychology with specialization in clinical psychology and at least two years of experience as a clinical psychologist.

Psychiatric Social Work—A Master's degree in social work with specialization in psychiatric social work followed by at least three years experience in social work which will include one year in a psychiatric setting, and one year in administration, supervision, or consultation, or a Master's degree in social work followed by three years of experience in social work which will include two years in a psychiatric setting with a minimum of six months under the supervision of a psychiatric social worker and one year with work in administration, supervision, or consultation.

Public Health Officer—A Master's degree in public health, or its equivalent in training and experience, and be engaged in a public health mental health program.

Nurses—A B.A. or B.S. degree from a recognized college or university and must have completed an approved undergraduate or postgraduate program of study in public health nursing or its equivalent and give evidence of satisfactory experience in public health nursing.

Traineeships are awarded at $3,600 for psychiatrists, clinical psychologists and public health officers, at $3,000 for psychiatric social workers, and at $2,000 for nurses for the first graduate year of mental health study and $2,400 for the second and third graduate years.

How Traineeships Are Administered

When an applicant has been approved for a traineeship, payment will be made to him directly by the training institution where he will take his training. Payment is made to the student by the training institution when he is officially registered and while he is in good standing.

How to Apply: Applications for traineeships *should be addressed to the institution of one's choice.* Lists of these institutions are issued periodically by the Public Health Service. Closing dates for application vary with the training institution and may be ascertained by writing directly to the institution. Applications should not be submitted to the Public Health Service.

Reapplication. Recipients of traineeships must reapply annually to the training institution for reappointment. The institution will review the request for reappointment and decide whether the trainee shall receive a traineeship for an additional year.

Responsibilities of Traineeship Recipients

Recipients of traineeships are subject to the rules and regulations of the training institution at which they are enrolled. They will receive no supervision from the Public Health Service. Each training institution will maintain the records of traineeship recipients in its own files.

Students who receive traineeships are not obligated to work for the Public Health Service at the conclusion of their training; conversely, the Public Health Service assumes no obligation for employing them. However, it is hoped that recipients of traineeships will go into teaching, research, or public service.

Training Under the Grants-to-States Program

In addition to the opportunities described, training in mental health may be obtained in some States and Territories through Federal grant-in-aid or State funds. To obtain information on training of this kind, write to the director of the agency designated as the State Mental Health Authority of your state. A list of these is issued by the U.S. Public Health Service.

SELECTED REFERENCES

COUNCIL OF STATE GOVERNMENTS: *Training and Research in State Mental Health Programs.* Council of State Governments, 1313 East 60 Street, Chicago 37, Ill., 1953.
> An authoritative and comprehensive summary of existing practices and needs, with recommendations for reforms.

FEDERAL SECURITY ASSOCIATION, PUBLIC HEALTH SERVICE: *Mental Health Motion Pictures. A Selective Guide,* 1952. Public Health Service Publication No. 218, U.S. Gov. Printing Office, Washington 25, D.C. (35¢).
> A large group of films are described briefly; the audience for whom each film is particularly suitable is mentioned; the distributing agencies through whom the films can be obtained are given; information concerning the use of each film on television is also given. The manual also includes a list of particularly useful sources of films on psychiatry, psychology, neurology and neurosurgery.

LEIGHTON, A. H.; LIDZ, T.: The Talking Pictures in Psychiatric Teaching and Research. *Am. J. Psychiat.,* 98:740, 1942.
> A pioneer article in a now well-established practice.

MENTAL HEALTH FILM BOARD:
> Has produced an excellent group of films which are available for sale directly from the International Film Bureau, Inc., 57 E. Jackson Blvd., Chicago 4, Ill., or for rent from the nearest educational film library. *Man to Man* is particularly valuable for the recruitment and training of attendants. *Broken Appointments* is useful in demonstrating the role of the nurse as a mental health consultant in an outpatient setting. Write to Mental Health Film Board, 166 East 38 Street, New York 16, N.Y., for literature describing other films.

NATIONAL ASSOCIATION FOR MENTAL HEALTH: *Mental Health Publications and Audio-Visual Aids,* 1953. National Association for Mental Health, 1790 Broadway, New York 19, N.Y.
> A catalogue of literature, films, film strips and plays of great importance in a mental hospital training program.

NICHTENHAUSER, A.; COLEMAN, M. L.; RUHE, D. S.: *Films in Psychiatry, Psychology and Mental Health.* Minneapolis, New York: Health Education Institute, 1953.
> A large group of films are reviewed by a board of experts. Content of each film is described, followed by an appraisal and recommendations as to most effective usefulness. Highly recommended.

PERKINS, G. L.: A Plan for Training in Dynamic Psychiatry for State Hospitals. *Illinois Med. J.*, 101:261, 1952.

Emphasizes need to deal with the anxieties of those being taught. Recommends residencies for State hospital personnel in centers specializing in the psychotherapy of schizophrenics.

REISER, M. F.; ROSENBAUM, M.: Supervision of Residents in Psychotherapy: A Comparison of the Problems of Residents in Psychiatry and Medicine. *Am. J. Psychiat.*, 111:835, 1954.

Emphasizes need to individualize didactic approach in accordance with needs and motivations of different groups.

WHITEHORN, J. C., chairman: *Psychiatry and Medical Education*. American Psychiatric Association, 1785 Massachusetts Ave., N.W., Washington 25, D.C.

Report of the 1951 Conference on Psychiatric Education held at Cornell University, Ithaca, N.Y., in June, 1951. Organized and conducted by the American Psychiatric Association and the Association of American Medical Colleges.

Chapter XXX

RESEARCH

Who Can Do Research?

The mention of a research program to the overworked staff member of a mental hospital usually calls forth vehement protestations concerning its impracticality. In a fundamental sense this attitude is justified. A research program runs headlong into many of the familiar problems of the mental hospital—lack of funds, lack of personnel, time and equipment. In addition, many members of the hospital staff will protest that the scientific investigator is a special breed, and not every one can do research. There is some truth to this contention. Nevertheless, it is a fallacy to write off the regular member of the hospital staff as a research worker. A creative element can be added to many of his ordinary duties by the simple expedient of keeping careful records. The proper organization of the facts of the mental hospital worker's daily experiences with patients can lead to important original contributions. Research does not have to be esoteric or grim to be significant. On the contrary, there is a spirit of fun in the work attitudes of the greatest researchers. And while the average person may need guidance from an experienced research director to obtain the best results, research can be a gratifying as well as scientifically useful hobby for many members of the mental hospital staff. One need only observe how a research tradition in an institution impels the staff as a whole to become research-minded, or how certain great teachers inspire their students to go beyond rote mastery of lessons to make original contributions of their own, however modest, in order to know that a research program depends on a proper spirit in the therapeutic community no less than on special talent among the individual members of the staff.

Administrative Aspects of Research

It has been recommended by the Council of State Governments that the authority for the entire mental health program in a state be invested

410

in a single commissioner and that he in turn have a properly trained assistant who will take charge of training and research. This assistant commissioner in charge of research, the recommendation continues, is to organize two committees, one of which is composed of department heads of all agencies whose activities relate in any way to mental health, including general health, mental health, welfare, education and correction. This committee will meet to discuss whatever aspects of their own research programs involve psychiatry. It, in turn, is to draw freely on the advice of a second committee which they themselves will select and which will consist of prominent scientists and educators chosen for their knowledge of the problem of training mental health personnel and in the design of research experiments. With the assistance of these two committees the director of training and research will review the major proposals which are submitted to him by the various state institutions and make recommendations concerning the allocation of funds, as well as arrangements between hospitals for a co-ordinated training program. In addition, he will maintain a research clearing house and arrange for cooperation with other states on specific projects. He will submit to the commissioner of mental health a recommended budget based on actual research plans which is to be included as a specific item in the department's total budget request before each legislative session. Each institution should delegate to one man the responsibility for directing the training and research program in his hospital, preferably on a full-time basis.

A major administrative task is to publicize the need for funds for psychiatric research and to mobilize state, national and private campaigns for additional financial support. Good administration can coordinate the facilities of hospitals, schools and laboratories in an economical manner. By offering desirable conditions for scientific work it becomes easier to attract properly qualified personnel. By providing opportunities for the publication of scientific work, by making available good scientific library facilities, by arranging for scientific meetings, seminars and workshops, it is possible to keep staff members abreast of developments elsewhere and intensifies interest in scholarship. It can prevent unnecessary duplication of effort, and set up confirmatory studies when necessary.

Special Difficulties of Psychiatric Research

It has been observed frequently that new therapies destined to be discarded as ineffective seem to produce a favorable response in patients when first tried. The reason for this is not hard to find. Patients seldom receive an adequate amount of attention from the staff after the initial workup and the acute treatment period are over. After months or years of the dull routine of even good hospital custody, a patient's interest and his desire for cure decline. If, however, he is now taken from his monotonous existence and is placed on an active treatment ward where he is made the subject of increased nursing attention, testing procedures, staff conferences, and in addition receives a better diet and is exposed to all the enthusiasm that accompanies a research study, then he may very well show improvement regardless of the therapeutic value of the specific treatment itself. Such improvement may last for weeks or months before the effects wear off. This nonspecific therapeutic effect of a research program introduces the first difficulty characteristic of psychiatric research in mental hospitals.

A second complication results from the absence of an etiologic nosology. Observations on patients with organic brain disease emphasize that the psychiatric manifestations are determined to a considerable degree by the premorbid personality of the patient and the quantitative extent of the pathology rather than by qualitative etiologic factors. For example, identical psychiatric manifestations may occur in a patient with a brain tumor, general paresis or a virus encephalitis. The treatment in each case is vastly different. The fact that the patient shows a paranoid, a manic or a depressive reaction is entirely irrelevant in deciding on proper therapy. And yet, for the bulk of our mental hospital patients we have no other course for the present but to classify them in terms of their psychiatric manifestations. When one adds to this the fact that the very terms that have been used to describe these ambiguous categories have been inconsistently applied from hospital to hospital then the confusion is compounded.

The recently adopted system of nomenclature (see Chapter XXVIII and Appendix E) will clarify the situation somewhat. However, the ideal of an etiologic classification awaits further fundamental research. One approach to this problem has been suggested by N. S. Kline, Director of the Rockland (New York) State Hospital Research Facility. He addressed himself to the task of selecting for the research ward a homogeneous group of patients with so-called functional schizophrenia. He began by confining the experimental population to a group of male patients who were at least sixteen years of age at the time of admission to the hospital and were between the ages of twenty and thirty-five at the time of the investigation. The clinical diagnosis of schizophrenia had to be agreed upon unanimously by all the members of the research team and the patient must have been continuously in residence in the hospital for at least three years prior to the period of study. They were able to find 350 such patients out of a total hospital population of 7500. Then they eliminated patients with grossly manifest physical illness. The remaining patients were subjected to further sampling and screening until they arrived at a group of twenty-five to thirty patients who were selected in a maximally random fashion from a maximally homogeneous population of male schizophrenics. By such rigorous selection procedures they hope to overcome the research handicap of modern nosological ambiguity.

A third problem is the difficulty of evaluating long-term results. In most of the so-called functional psychoses "spontaneous" remissions are common, as are relapses after remissions of many years. There are indications that many therapeutic techniques yield relatively good immediate results but fail to demonstrate any long-term advantages over other methods. The long-term follow-up studies which this situation calls for are hampered by the shortage of social workers and by difficulties in securing patient co-operation.

A fourth problem is to be found in the difficulty of measuring or defining "improvement" or "cure." In general medicine it is not too difficult to determine how much a fever has subsided, when a wound has healed or when an infection has been eliminated. In psychiatry, however, the terms "cured," "recovered," "improved" are not so easily defined. Is a patient "cured" when he has been returned to his level of behavior prior to illness, to the level which he is now capable of attaining when one takes into account the effects of the disease, or to the average level of people who never had the illness? Shall his recovery be judged by his increased productivity, capacity to withstand frustration and conflict, absence of compulsive behavior, general freedom from symptoms, insight into his own problems (and how shall we define insight?) good social relations, capacity to derive pleasure from his social and personal life? Certainly the criteria upon which a given designation is based must be clearly stated. However, even when this has been done, it is difficult to translate these standards into objective quantities with which scientists prefer to work.

While there are no universally satisfactory solutions to these difficulties at the moment, it is possible nevertheless, by taking them into account, to plan experiments which can expand the frontiers of basic psychiatric knowledge.

What Projects Are Important?

When the great British physicist, Michael Faraday, once gave a public demonstration of the fact that a loop of wire in a magnetic field moves when it is electrified, a lady in the audience asked, "What good is it?" Faraday's rejoinder on that occasion is said to have been, "Madame, what good is a newborn baby?" We all know that human beings love babies for their own sake. We also know that as a result of the loving care which is given to babies the human race is blessed with a few extraordinary people from time to time. Faraday surely could not have dreamed of the full potential of the baby which he named "electromagnetic induction," of the vast development of electrical machinery which would stem from it and the way it would transform our world. Similarly, no man can tell beforehand what weighty and important discoveries may come from the investigation of seemingly trivial problems, nor the trivia which will be turned up in the investigation of apparently important ones. How then should an administrator decide about the allocation of a limited quantity of money and resources for research? James B. Conant, the former president of Harvard University and the co-ordinator of much governmental research, has said of this dilemma, "Don't appraise the project but the proposed investigator; don't bet on the subject but on the man. And like all successful gamblers play your hunches heavily; don't distribute your money over a wide field."

Research Opportunities Under the National Mental Health Act

Research in mental illness is steadily increasing in volume, scope, and diversity of approach. Today it presents one of the greatest challenges which scientists in medicine and related fields may select as an area of investigation. In the past many scientists, hampered by the complexity of the problem of mental illness and by the lack of tools and techniques with which to study it, turned to more hopeful fields of research. Recent developments not only in psychiatric concepts and practice, but in the biological and behavioral sciences, have opened up whole new areas for exploration, and men and women from many disciplines are turning their attention to the study of mental illness and mental health.

Recognizing the importance of research on a health problem for which the mental hospitals of the United States provide diagnostic, treatment and follow-up services for nearly a million people a year, Congress passed the National Mental Health Act in 1946, authorizing the Public Health Service to conduct research on this problem, to make grants to nongovernmental scientists interested in research in this field and to award fellowships to scientists for training in research techniques.

Research Grants

Research grant funds may be used for the support not only of applied and developmental research but also of fundamental studies in the related biological and behavioral sciences. The National Mental Health Act provides for "the conducting of researches, investigations, experiments, and demonstrations relating to . . . psychiatric disorders, assisting and fostering such research activities by public and private agencies, and promoting the co-ordination of all such researches and activities and the useful application of their results." Broadly speaking, grants can be made for the support of research on any problem directly or indirectly related to the mental illnesses and mental health.

The range of research appropriate to the problem is indicated by studies currently receiving grants-in-aid from the National Institute of Mental Health. The etiology and epidemiology of mental illnesses, diagnostic techniques and treatment methods, child development, the aging process, personality and behavior, genetics, learning and perception, endocrinology, biochemistry, neurophysiology, and pharmacology are representative of these studies. Clinical research in the psychoses, neuroses, behavior disorders, mental subnormalities, and other mental health problems are also receiving support.

Objectives of Research Grants Program: The long-range objective of the mental health research grants and fellowships program is to assist scientists in research centers to solve the pressing problem of mental illness and to build better mental health.

The immediate objectives of the program are: (1) to expand research in mental illness and related problems in universities, hospitals, clinics, and other institutions where programs now exist; (2) to stimulate the initiation of research in mental health problems in centers where previous research programs have been limited or nonexistent; (3) to encourage investigators to undertake research in neglected problem areas; (4) to provide opportunities for younger scientific personnel to learn research methods and techniques.

In summary, the program is designed to support and encourage the widest possible participation of scientists in bringing their specialized knowledge and interests to bear upon the problem of mental health. Policies and procedures governing the program have been carefully developed with these objectives in mind.

Scientific Freedom: Basic to the success of the program is the complete independence and autonomy of the research investigator. The granting of funds does not imply Federal control, direction, or supervision in any way, and the investigator is free to follow any leads which may develop in the course of his work. In addition, he may publish the results of any work aided by research grant funds without review by the National Institute of Mental Health.

Use of Grant Funds: Grant funds can be used to support most of the expenditures which are necessary in carrying out a research project or program. They may be used to provide salaries of the principal investigator and other professional personnel who are not considered by the institution to be holding permanent positions from which the application is submitted. If any portion of the salary of permanent personnel engaged in the research project has been previously paid from funds other than normal institution funds, such as those provided by a grant from a foundation, that portion of the salary may be provided from the research grant. Grant funds may also be used to employ substitutes to relieve permanent personnel of normal teaching, clinical, or administrative duties, in order that they may devote more time to the research project.

Funds may be used for travel incidental to the successful prosecution of the research project, except for foreign travel to international meetings.

At the present time, grant funds may not be used for the construction of buildings.

There is no statutory limit on the size of individual grants. They may be made in small amounts to cover supplies and equipment, or to provide a research assistant, or they may be made in larger amounts for more extensive support. They may be used to support a current research project or to initiate a new one; they may be used to supplement funds obtained elsewhere or to support the entire cost of a project. There is no limitation on the number of grants that may be made to any one investigator or any one institution, and the matching of grant funds is not required.

Projects Usually Not Recommended: Some of the types of projects usually not recommended for support are: (1) requests from full-time Federal Government employees;[1] (2) research conducted outside the territorial limits of the United States unless satisfactory evidence is provided that the research, for scientific reasons, can best be conducted outside the United States and is of general importance to the health and medical sciences; (3) clinical work of a nonresearch character; (4) requests for support for the sole purpose of equipping a laboratory; (5) problems of exclusively or predominantly local importance.

Duration of Grants: Research grants are awarded on an annual basis but commitments may be approved for up to four years of additional support. Projects may begin at any time during the year and usually cover a period of twelve months. Because of a delay in effecting payment immediately after the beginning of a new fiscal year (July 1), it is undesirable to activate new projects during the months of July and August.

For research projects which are planned to cover a period of several years, the application form provides for estimates of financial requirements to operate the project during the first, second, third, and fourth years immediately succeeding the initial year covered by the application. Notification to the grantees concerning initial support will include a statement as to the moral commitment for future years which is necessarily contingent upon congressional appropriations.

[1] Grants may be made to medical schools on behalf of full-time or part-time Veterans Administration investigators whose research proposals represent the collaborative effort of a local V.A. facility and a local medical school.

Progress Report: Brief progress reports are required annually.

Procedures: Universities, hospitals, laboratories and other public or private institutions, and individual investigators may apply for research grants from the National Institute of Mental Health. It is preferred that anyone named as a principal investigator on an application be the person who is to be actively responsible for conduct of the research. This does not preclude more than one person being named as a principal investigator.

Requests for application forms, inquiries concerning deadline dates for receipt of applications, and for further information about grants in the field of mental health should be directed to the Division of Research Grants, National Institutes of Health, Bethesda 14, Md.

The deadline dates for receipt of applications are July 1, November 1, and March 1 in each year. Announcement of final action on the application is forwarded to the applicant four to five months following the deadline date.

Review of Applications: The National Advisory Mental Health Council (see footnote 1, Chapter XXIX) is responsible for the review of all applications for research grants in the field of mental health, and for making a recommendation on each application to the Surgeon General of the Public Health Service. The primary considerations in the review of each application are the scientific merit of the proposal, the ability or promise of the investigator or investigators, and the adequacy of the facilities available to him for carrying out the proposed project.

To assist this and other advisory councils in obtaining the fullest possible information on each application, preliminary review is provided by one of seventeen scientific advisory committees called study sections, composed of outstanding authorities in each of the major fields of research. The study sections meet prior to the regularly scheduled conferences of the advisory council in order to submit their recommendations to the Council at its next session. Before a grant can be paid it must be recommended favorably by the advisory council.

Research Fellowships

Postdoctorate Research Fellowship: To assist young scientists to obtain training and experience in research techniques and methodology for work in the field of mental health, Postdoctorate Research Fellowships are awarded annually to qualified persons holding a doctor's degree in any of the fields of science or medicine already mentioned.

This fellowship carries a stipend of $3,400 a year; dependency allowances are available for a dependent spouse and children at the rate of $350 each annually. Postdoctorate fellowships which are renewed for a second year are increased $300 over the first year.

Special Research Fellowship: A special fellowship is awarded to qualified applicants who have a doctor's degree in any of the fields of science or medicine already indicated, and in addition have demonstrated unusual competence for research or require specialized training for study of a specific problem. The stipend for this fellowship is determined by the Surgeon General at the time of the award.

Renewal of Fellowships: Postdoctorate fellows are supported for not more than two years, renewal for a third year being made only in the most unusual circumstances. Special fellows may be supported for a second year only when evidence presented clearly justifies the need for additional training.

Citizenship Requirement: Public Health Service Fellowships are available only to citizens of the United States.

Location of Work: Research fellows may undertake their studies at any qualified institution in the United States, including governmental research laboratories, where interests and facilities are appropriate for the specific type of training elected by the fellow. Studies may be undertaken in institutions outside the United States only when satisfactory evidence is provided that the type or quality of training sought cannot be obtained in the United States. It is the responsibility of the applicant to make all necessary arrangements for the execution of his proposed research fellowship task, both with the institution where the job will be done and with the investigator under whom he will work.

Limitations on Nonresearch Work: Fellows are permitted to accept teaching or lecturing assignments if they wish. However, they may not devote more than 10 per cent of the working time available during the fellowship term to these activities (including preparation), or to laboratory assisting.

Care and observation of patients directly involved in the research problem undertaken are considered to fall within research duties, but it is expected that fellows engaged in clinical research will spend not more than 10 per cent of their time in receiving clinical training.

Applications: Forms for use in applying for a postdoctorate or special research fellowship may be obtained from the Research Fellowships Branch of the Division of Research Grants, National Institutes of Health, Bethesda 14, Md., and should be submitted to that branch when completed.

Applications may be submitted at any time. However, three to four months must be allowed for processing and review, before final notification. Applications should not be submitted more than twelve months prior to the intended activation date of an award.

Applications for research fellowships are reviewed and acted upon by Public Health Service Fellowship Boards.

Supply Grants: Research grants up to $500 may be made to institutions for the support of postdoctorate research fellows as reimbursement to the institution for expenses incurred in making the fellowship possible.

SELECTED REFERENCES

BROSIN, H. W.: On Discovery and Experiment in Psychiatry. *Am. J. Psychiat.,* 112:561, 1955.

A thoughtful analysis of theoretical and practical problems related to research in psychiatry. The paper is brilliantly discussed by J. Romano and J. E. Finesinger.

COUNCIL OF STATE GOVERNMENTS: *Training and Research in State Mental Health Programs* (see references Chapter XXIX).

DRINKER, C. K.; POLCH, J.; COBB, S.; GASSER, H. S.; PENFIELD, W.; STRECKER, E. A.: *Psychiatric Research*. Cambridge: Harvard University Press, 1947.

Papers read at the Dedication of the Laboratory for Biochemical Research, MacLean Hospital, Waverly, Mass.

MALAMUD, W.: The Present Status of Research in Dementia Praecox. *Ment. Hyg.*, 34:554, 1950. Available as a reprint through the National Association for Mental Health, 1790 Broadway, New York 19, N.Y.

A summary of work done under grants from the Scottish Rites Masons fund to support research into the causes of dementia praecox.

TANNER, J. M., ed.: *Prospects in Psychiatric Research*. Springfield, Ill.: C. C. Thomas, 1953.

Based on the Proceedings of the Oxford Conference of the Mental Health Research Fund, in March, 1952. Brilliant presentations and discussions make this a most stimulating document. A "must" for anyone interested in psychiatric research.

WHITEHORN, J. C.: A Century of Psychiatric Research in America. In: *One Hundred Years of American Psychiatry*. New York: Columbia University Press, 1944.

A summary of great researches, traditions and future prospects.

Chapter XXXI

FORENSIC PSYCHIATRY

Mental Illness and Loss of Personal Liberty

The law impinges at many points upon the work of the mental hospital psychiatrist. The major reason for this stems from the fact that individuals often lose many of their legal rights when they become patients in a mental hospital. These rights are taken from them in the words of the Iowa Supreme Court "to aid and assist the individual, to provide means whereby the state may protect its unfortunate citizens, to furnish hospitalization so that the insane will have an opportunity for rehabilitation and readjustment into useful and happy citizens. It is not a criminal proceeding in any way. The restraint placed upon them is only until they have recovered so that they may again take their places in the communities from which they came. The confinement is not intended as a punishment but solely and only to provide the mentally sick with that environment which may possibly cure the disease and return them to society as useful citizens." One might wish to add that we also take into consideration the dangers to society which sometimes ensue from the actions of the mentally sick, although admittedly the importance of this factor has often been exaggerated, and it may certainly be given second place in our thoughts. Most of us would want to mention, unhappily, that the environment which we provide for the mentally ill is not always as therapeutic as we would like it to be. However, with these provisos in mind, this quotation contains what is doubtless the dominant philosophy which motivates modern society in placing restraints upon the mentally ill. Notwithstanding this fact, there is a widespread and unwarranted suspicion in the public mind about the dangers of so-called "railroading"—i.e., the illegal confinement of a mentally sound person as part of a nefarious scheme. The public has no reluctance whatever about the confinement of patients with tuberculosis, smallpox, plague or leprosy on the

advice of doctors. But when a similar group of doctors advise confinement of people for mental disease, great anxiety is aroused.

The well-known author, Albert Deutsch, wrote of this in his excellent
book, *The Mentally Ill in America*, as follows:

> Of all the social problems arising out of the phenomenon of
> mental illness, perhaps none has captured the popular imagination
> during the past century as the possibility of confining sane persons in
> "insane asylums." Let thousands of mental patients in the public
> hospitals of a state exist under terrible conditions of overcrowding;
> let them be fed bad food; let them be placed under all sorts of
> unnecessary restraints; let them lack adequate medical care due to
> poor therapeutic equipment or an understaffed personnel; let them
> be housed in dangerous fire-traps; let them suffer a thousand and one
> unnecessary indignities and humiliations, and more likely than not
> their plight will attract but little attention. The newspapers will
> maintain a respectful silence; the public will remain ignorant and
> indifferent. But once let rumor spread about a man or a woman
> illegally committed to a mental hospital, newspaper headlines will
> scream; the public will seethe with indignation; investigations and
> punitive expeditions will be demanded. Now, it is indubitably true
> that there have been instances where sane persons have been com-
> mitted to institutions for the insane, sometimes through honest error,
> sometimes through the machinations of intriguing relatives, "friends"
> or unscrupulous owners of proprietory hospitals. This state of affairs
> must have been particularly true during the first century of our
> nation's existence, when safeguards against illegal commitment (espe-
> cially in private hospitals) were either entirely absent or inadequate.
> But that this aspect of the history of the mentally ill in America has
> been greatly exaggerated is no less true.

Psychopathological aberrations of thought and behavior seem uncanny
to the general public. They arouse primitive attitudes of dread which are
strikingly out of keeping with the rational attitudes toward other disease entities which prevail in our times. The reasons for this are discussed
in Chapter XXIII. Psychiatrists must recognize this widespread tendency and reckon with it in their dealings with the public. There are
now laws in all of the states which are designed to protect the rights of
patients. It is perhaps ironic that commitment laws which were originated
to prevent "railroading" function primarily in our day to forestall the
ill-advised removal of patients from mental hospitals by disturbed relatives. In any event, what survives, or what should survive in these laws, is
a dedication to the welfare of the patient. The laws vary widely from
state to state, and it behooves each psychiatrist to familiarize himself in
detail with the mental hygiene laws of his own state. In New York, for

example, they are available in two volumes, *Mental Hygiene Law and General Orders,* and *Laws relating to Mental Hygiene* (see references).

Commitment Proceedings

In general, proceedings to commit a patient are initiated at the request of relatives or other responsible individuals in the form of a petition. The patient is then examined by one or two doctors to ascertain if he is a danger to himself or those about him. If so, they complete a certificate which endeavors to explain to a court of law why it is necessary to deprive the patient of his liberty. The patient is then brought to a court hearing at which time judicial approval may be given or withheld at the judge's discretion. If the doctors feel that the appearance of the patient in court may be detrimental to his health, this appearance may be waived in many states. In fact, court approval is usually given as a matter of routine on the basis of the considered opinions of properly qualified physicians.

The responsibility for a psychiatric patient's treatment begins in the psychiatrist's initial contact with him, even when this takes place during a commitment proceeding. Any semblance of a punitive attitude should be avoided. The existence of quasi-criminal proceedings for the hospitalization of the mentally ill is a holdover from the dark ages when thousands of innocent people were burned at the stake because of symptoms clearly recognizable today as manifestations of mental illness. The anachronistic use of sheriffs with warrants, detention in prison, and hearings before open courts should arouse the deepest feelings of revulsion in the psychiatrist. Often, such maneuvers seem to confirm to the patient the most irrational of his delusions. If our task is to help the patient re-establish normal contact with reality, then such proceedings must be immeasurably traumatic. From a psychotherapeutic point of view it is most important that emergency commitment procedures be available by means of which the acutely disturbed patient may be taken directly to the hospital where he may be detained until regular commitment proceedings can be instituted if this becomes necessary. The patient who is intact enough to request hospitalization should be able to enter a mental hospital voluntarily. It is wrong to deny him this easiest method of securing help. Even where commitment proceedings have been humanized, a traumatic terminology has continued to exist as an unfortunate heritage from our less enlightened past. Psychiatrists no longer refer to the mentally ill as lunatics and do not speak of hospitals as asylums. We speak of admission certification rather than commitment, and send a patient out on a trial visit, not on parole. In short, mental illness is in the province of the physician. It is his duty to see that the maximal opportunity for prompt care is provided, and that above all, we do not add insult to minds that are already injured.

The Patient and Legal Transactions

It often happens that a patient has property. The law is interested in seeing that this property is protected until the patient recovers his health. A major contract, signed by a committed patient without proper court approval is not valid. An individual who is adjudged by a court of law to be incapable of entering into legal contracts because of mental illness is said to be incompetent. In most states the fact that a patient has been committed to a hospital does not necessarily mean that he is incompetent. The basic principle is that a patient may be in need of mental hospital care without suffering incompetence; and vice versa, a patient may be incompetent even though he does not require commitment to a state hospital. For example, with respect to the problem of drawing up a will, we speak of a patient's testamentary capacity. All that the court requires of a patient is that he know: a) that he is making a will; b) the nature and extent of his property; c) the natural objects of his bounty. It is generally contended that the presence of a psychosis by itself does not necessarily invalidate a will. It must be proved that the psychosis impaired one of the three essential elements in the testamentary capacity. The presence of a delusion of infidelity, for example, could interfere with the patient's capacity to recognize the proper object of his bounty. Similar tests apply in all other contractual arrangements. In a business transaction it must be ascertained if the patient understands clearly all the reality factors involved. If a patient is psychotic or mentally defective at the time of a marriage, it may be annulled if it is proven that the patient was incapable of comprehending fully the meaning of the marriage contract. In the case of a mother surrendering a baby for adoption, the surrender document has been held valid if a psychotic mother "knew" what she was doing when she signed the surrender document (see Chapter XXI). In spite of this legalism, a psychiatrist would be inclined to shudder at a surrender document secured under such circumstances inasmuch as rejection of the newborn child is so regularly a part of a postpartum psychotic reaction and is so frequently replaced by an intense maternal attachment when the psychosis has lifted.

The obviously questionable ability of a psychotic mother to "know" what she is doing when she signs an adoption surrender document raises a question concerning the ability of any psychotic person to "know" what he is doing when he signs a legal document. It has been said previously (Chapters XXI, XXIII, XXIV) that a delusional system is never watertight and that it reflects a disorganization of thinking that may, potentially at least, contaminate all of the patient's thought processes. That is, the mind functions as a unit and the conception that it can be "insane" in one part and "sane" in another is not consonant with present psychiatric knowledge. As a result many authorities have contended that a person who is committable because of mental illness is automatically incompetent. The law, however, usually provides for separate proceedings for commitment and for declaration of incompetence. That there is wisdom in this arrangement will become evident from the following.

Although the actual procedure varies in different areas, a declaration of incompetency typically involves a formal judicial proceeding. If the court rules that a person is incompetent, it then assigns a group of people, usually referred to as the patient's committee, who will conduct whatever legal negotiations are to the patient's best interest. In some states the court assigns two committees to supervise an incompetent person, a "committee of the person" charged with the care and treatment of the insane person and a "committee of the property" charged with looking after his financial affairs. The committee is usually paid for its services and must render accountings to the court for its various actions. A declaration of incompetence not only takes away a patient's right to enter upon various contracts, it also deprives him of his right to vote or hold office; it vacates his license to practice a profession. What is most important, recovery from his mental illness and release from the hospital may neutralize the commitment but leaves, in many areas, the incompetency status unchanged and may call for further legal action to neutralize that. Inasmuch as the ego of the recovered patient is comparatively fragile, embroiling him in such proceedings may be psychologically traumatic. Because of the far-reaching legal and psychological consequences of a declaration of incompetence, this step should not be taken unless unavoidable. In many instances it will be to the best interest of the committed patient to let him enter a contractual agreement provided that the transaction receives the approval of the appropriate court.

The Psychiatrist as Witness

In the course of competency hearings, and other legal proceedings the psychiatrist may be requested to testify in court. The doctor must keep before him his obligations to the patient. He should give the information that is legally required and no more. He should endeavor to protect the patient's good name. If he feels that a given line of questioning is not in his patient's best interest, he should tell this to the judge. If directed to answer anyway, he should indicate that he is giving the information under protest. If the patient's records are called for, these are surrendered only when there is a proper subpoena for them. The psychiatrist may feel free to demand respectful treatment from the attorneys who question him. He should be prepared to describe his professional qualifications.

The psychiatrist may be called upon to testify in one of two capacities: a witness as to fact, and a witness as to opinion. The ordinary witness is required to testify concerning those facts involved in a given case which are directly within the province of his knowledge. Thus, a psychiatrist may be subpoenaed to give certain facts from the patient's clinical records. In his capacity as a witness as to fact his professional opinions regarding the significance of these facts are irrelevant and out of order. However, the psychiatrist may be called as an expert witness. He must be prepared to state in court what his qualifications are as an expert. He will then be asked to express his opinion concerning the clinical significance of a given set of facts which are usually presented to him in the form of a hypothetical question. Whereas he is compelled to testify in court when subpoenaed as a witness as to fact, his decision to appear as an expert witness is always a purely voluntary matter. As a result of legislative reforms (see Chapters XXIII and XXIV) the use of the testimony of the expert psychiatric witness and the hypothetical questions have been largely superseded by new procedures. In general, the defendant whose mental competence has been questioned is examined by an objective board of inquiry. After a multidisciplinary study of the accused, the board submits a report to the court with opinions and recommendations.

Mail

Very often the letters of psychotic patients have potential nuisance value for the community, particularly if they are obscene, threatening, or litigious. The patient's psychiatrist is ordinarily permitted to exercise his professional judgment as to whether a letter should be mailed, or destroyed. However, certain letters, particularly those addressed to the District Attorney or to the County Judge, must be transmitted uncensored.

Writ of Habeas Corpus

Anyone in custody as a mentally ill person, a mental defective, or an epileptic, may make a written appeal to the District Attorney for his release. When a patient writes such an appeal, the psychiatrist must have it notarized and transmitted to the court. Any relative or friend of the patient may initiate such an action for him. Hearings will then be held and appropriate action taken in the patient's behalf.

Insanity as a Basis for Divorce

In many states, so-called "incurable insanity" is grounds for divorce. Most of the states that permit this do so only where the insane spouse has been committed to an institution for a period of years and where testimony by experts certifies that recovery is not reasonably probable.

Personal Injury as a Cause of Mental Illness

The psychiatrist may be called upon in a litigation to help decide if a given mental illness was the result of physical injury. Psychotic reactions can occur after injury, particularly when associated with physical damage to the brain. In that case, one may see acute delirium, posttraumatic personality disorders, and chronic deteriorating psychotic reactions. Cases of paresis have been known to become clinically manifest following head injury. The argument that syphilis was present prior to the injury is not regarded as relevant. The psychiatrist must only decide if the disease process was accelerated by the injury to such an extent as to impair the claimant's mental condition and earning capacity.

Posttraumatic epilepsy is, of course, well known. Manic-depressive psychosis and schizophrenia have been judged to follow trauma in rare instances, although in these cases it was felt that the illness was the outcome of the emotional, not the mechanical effects of the injury.

Psychoneurotic reactions following injury are exceedingly common. However, these are rarely within the province of the mental hospital psychiatrist.

Malpractice Suit

In spite of the fact that the state hospital psychiatrist is an employee of the state, he is not immune from suit for malpractice. If, for example, a patient dies after a shock treatment, the family can sue the doctor who administered the treatment individually, as well as the state for which he works. The state will doubtless provide for his defense or even finance an appeal if necessary, and will assemble experts to testify in his defense. However, according to Davidson, if there is a judgment against him, the state will not pay it. It is Davidson's recommendation, accordingly, that every doctor on the full-time staff of a private or public hospital or agency should have malpractice insurance. Inasmuch as such insurance is now extremely expensive, this recommendation works a hardship on the state hospital physician. However, in view of Davidson's considerable personal knowledge, it would certainly seem wise for a state hospital psychiatrist to ascertain how he is covered in his particular area.

In a relatively new field like psychiatry one is constantly on the alert for new methods of treatment. Certainly the future of this specialty depends upon such a progressive attitude. However, what if a patient dies after an experimental treatment and the family brings suit? The fact that the family signed a waiver is regarded as immaterial. The main question which will interest the court is whether or not the treatment in question represented a departure from generally accepted knowledge and method. The court may decide by that standard that the doctor has been negligent. And since no one can sign permission for a doctor to be negligent, the family waiver becomes invalid. In short, says Davidson, the doctor who departs from generally accepted methods does so at his own legal risk. The principle that a family cannot sign permission for a doctor to be negligent is relevant, naturally, to nonexperimental methods, too, and serves as a possibly unnecessary reminder that all procedures on patients must be carried out with regard for the highest possible standards of medical practice. (See Chapter III for American Psychiatric Association standards governing shock therapy.)

Competence of a Witness

Davidson has recently discussed the problem of evaluating the competence of a witness from a psychiatric point of view (testimonial capacity). The major clinical conditions affecting testimonial capacity are the psychoses, mental deficiency, drug addiction, alcoholism, personality disorders, certain organic involvements of the brain, and sometimes certain forms of psychoneurosis. The psychiatrist forms his opinion concerning testimonial capacity on the basis of four questions: (1) Is the patient capable of observing the event intelligently? (2) Can he remember it clearly? (3) Is he free of any emotional drive to suppress or distort the truth? (4) Is he articulate enough to communicate what he observed? Each of the foregoing diagnostic categories present their own special problems which must be searched out and evaluated in terms of the basic criteria for testimonial capacity. These criteria inevitably raise the question of "partial insanity." It is necessary to recall again that a delusional system can contaminate all of a patient's thought processes. For this reason it would surely be unwise to base a judgment or a verdict entirely upon the unsupported testimony of an actively psychotic individual. On the other hand, injustices might result from a policy of rejecting all testimony by psychotics. In short, each case will have to be considered individually with the expectation that instances will occur in which decision will be difficult.

Credibility of Testimony

A psychotic person may lodge false accusations based on unconscious drives expressed as delusions, hallucinatory experiences or other distortions of perception. These are the situations, essentially, that have been covered in the preceding section. However, there are cases where legally responsible individuals consciously falsify testimony for personal gain or to evade deserved punishment. Psychological means are sometimes employed in an attempt to decide whether or not an individual is lying. By and large such devices are unreliable and do not deserve legal status in our courts.

One device, for example, is the lie detector. There is nothing magical about the instrument, and to trade on the fear and the ignorance of suspects by assuring them that the lie detector never lies because it is some mysterious and infallible invention of science is a reprehensible way of dealing with a person whose guilt is in doubt. All that one can say definitely is that an emotional reaction is a physiological event. It is a nonspecific event: there is no special reaction peculiar to guilt. The very term lie detector is a misnomer, perhaps a deliberate misnomer to further the purposes of the police. A better term would be stress detector—and to detect stress is all that the "lie" detector can honestly claim to do.

Narcoanalysis is another such device. The popular term "truth serum" for intravenously administered barbiturates or similar substances is also a potentially dangerous misnomer. "Truth serum" tests are occasionally effective on persons who would have told the truth in any case, if they had been properly interrogated, while they are commonly ineffective in those who are determined to lie. In addition, it has been demonstrated repeatedly that some innocent people will produce self-incriminating confabulations under the influence of such drugs, confessing to crimes they never committed. The latter phenomenon is possibly a result of abnormally strong masochistic drives in these subjects. The verbal productions of a narcotized subject are no more likely to be truthful than those obtained in the fully conscious state.

The only circumstance under which a psychiatrist should consent to perform a narcoanalytic examination on a defendant who has entered a plea of not guilty by reason of insanity is when this examination is part of a complete psychiatric evaluation of the subject's mental status. The information so obtained is not to be used under any circumstances in evidence at the trial to determine the suspect's guilt or innocence unless the defendant or his attorney specifically request its use. Narcoanalysis may be used to restore speech in a mute suspect or in an attempt to lift an amnesia. Here, too, the aim of the psychiatrist is to evaluate the mental status, not to secure evidence. In all cases the examination should not be carried out unless the written consent of the defendant has been obtained after he has consulted with his attorney.

Medicolegal Problems in Psychosurgery

Any operation performed by a surgeon without the consent of the patient or someone authorized to give consent constitutes an assault and battery upon the patient for which the surgeon will be liable in damages. When the operation is a psychosurgical procedure carried out for mental illness, the problem of operative consent may be somewhat complicated. The psychiatrist and neurosurgeon must decide whether or not the patient is legally competent and capable of understanding and appreciating the consequences of the operation. If they decide in the affirmative, then the consent of the patient alone is sufficient. In doubtful cases the conservative procedure is to have the court decide concerning the patient's competence. Where incompetency is declared to exist, consent must be obtained from the committee.

A patient who has been overtly psychotic for years may improve so much after psychosurgery that complete control of his personal affairs may be restored to him at his request or that of his committee and by order of the court. Patients who have had psychosurgery are sometimes involved in antisocial acts. Legal responsibility is determined in such cases exactly as in patients who have not had psychosurgery. Considering the number of patients upon whom psychosurgery has been performed, the incidence of major crimes committed following operation is surprisingly low.

Privileged Communications

Medical ethics dating back to the time of Hippocrates have sealed the doctor's lips concerning the secrets of patients which become known to him in the course of treating their illnesses. There is one exception to this rule and that is when the law of the land requires disclosure. For example, the physician is usually expected to report injuries due to violence or industrial accident, contagious diseases, narcotic addiction and previously unrecorded births and deaths. It is in the nature of the psychotherapeutic relationship that the psychiatrist is privy to an unusually large number of personal secrets. He has sometimes been subpoenaed and asked to reveal these secrets in court. In general, the refusal to reveal his patient's secrets in civil cases is respected by the court. In criminal cases he may be expected to testify. If a psychiatrist claims the privilege of protecting his patient's communication and is overruled by the court, there would not seem to be a basis for any further liability to the patient if he decided to testify. The law governing privileged communications is in many respects uncertain. In particular instances special study of all the facts and circumstances by legal counsel may be in order.

SELECTED REFERENCES

AMES, F. R.: Objective Detections of Lying. *J. Forensic Med.*, 1:94, 1953.
A clarifying discussion of this popularly controversial subject.
DAVIDSON, H. A.: *Forensic Psychiatry*. New York: Ronald Press, 1953.
A highly useful compendium of current legal practices.
—— Appraisal of the Witness. *Am. J. Psychiat.*, 111:481, 1954.
An excellent discussion of "testimonial capacity."
DEUTSCH, A.: *The Mentally Ill in America*. New York: Columbia University Press, 1946.
A brilliant history of American psychiatry including an account of legislative developments.
GROUP FOR THE ADVANCEMENT OF PSYCHIATRY: *Commitment Procedures*. Report No. 4, 1948.
A brief summary of existing practices and suggestions for reform.
GUTTMACHER, M. S.; WEIHOFEN, H.: *Psychiatry and the Law*. New York: W. W. Norton, 1953.
A masterful critique of current forensic psychiatric practices.
KELLEY, D. M.: Summary of Symposium on Privileged Communications. *Am. J. Psychiat.*, 111:13, 1954.
A review of basic principles and current practices.
MACDONALD, J. M.: Narcoanalysis and Criminal Law. *Am. J. Psychiat.*, 111:283, 1954.
A lucid summary of the legal status of this occasionally abused or misunderstood procedure.
NATIONAL INSTITUTE OF MENTAL HEALTH: *Draft Act Governing Hospitalization of the Mentally Ill*. U.S. Public Health Service Publication No. 51, 1951, U.S. Gov. Printing Office, Washington 25, D.C.
A model law to guide those deliberating about legislative reforms.
NEW YORK STATE DEPARTMENT OF MENTAL HYGIENE: *Mental Hygiene Law and General Orders; Laws Relating to Mental Hygiene*. Utica: State Hospital Press, 1952.
The laws of New York State, worth studying as an example of progressive legislation.

OVERHOLSER, W.: *The Psychiatrist and the Law*. New York: Harcourt, Brace, 1953.
The first Isaac Ray Lectures. A rewarding critique of forensic psychiatry.
SILBERMANN, M.; RANSOHOFF, J.: Medico-Legal Problems in Psychosurgery. *Am. J. Psychiat.*, 111:801, 1954.
A provocative discussion pointing out the need for reforms.

Chapter XXXII

UTILIZING THE HOSPITAL LABORATORY

Needs versus Available Facilities

In discussing the laboratory facilities in a mental hospital, it is well to distinguish between the need for such facilities and the extent to which they are practically available. When one learns, for example, that there are only forty full-time pathologists in all the state hospitals in the United States, or that the services of only one laboratory technician are available for every 1100 state hospital patients, it is necessary to set modest goals for a hospital laboratory program at this time. The laboratory needs of a mental hospital present a special problem. One may be able to recruit a volunteer force to augment the activities program, utilize money and hospital space more effectively by means of a day-hospital arrangement, meet medical and surgical emergencies by means of a staff of visiting consultants; but a laboratory needs expensive equipment and much space, and most of all trained personnel, physicians to direct the laboratory facilities and technicians to carry out the routines. The practical problems of meeting these needs do not properly concern us in this chapter. An effective public relations program can make such needs known to the community, and proper legislative action can be initiated by local mental health groups. However, it may be well to discuss this problem from an ideal point of view, as a practical medical necessity even if not yet as an attainable goal.

Pathology

The pathology laboratory is in many ways the heart of a hospital. In autopsy studies or in the study of tissues removed at operation, the clinician puts his diagnosis and clinical judgment to the test. In the correction of his errors the physician grows, and in the development of individual physicians in pathology laboratories all over the world medi-

432

cine has risen to its present great stature. The same situation should obtain in a mental hospital. Even though autopsy findings by present methods of study are usually only remotely related to the mental illness of the patient, they provide, nevertheless, a check on the general medical competence of the staff. This, in turn, is a measure of the caliber of its scientific thinking. It is unlikely, for example, that good psychiatry will be practiced in a hospital where all other branches of medicine are practiced poorly as proven at the autopsy table.

It is pertinent in this connection to recall that the first pathology laboratory in an American mental hospital was established in 1893 in the Illinois Eastern Hospital for the Insane at Kankakee. Its director was Adolph Meyer. The great tradition which he inaugurated in American psychiatry was preceded by his distinguished work as a neuropathologist and neuroanatomist. In that same year August Hoch was appointed pathologist at the MacLean Hospital in Waverly, Massachusetts. There can be little doubt that the disciplined approach to data which characterized their work in the laboratory set the stage for their great psychiatric contributions. In the laboratories of the MacLean Hospital monumental biochemical investigations were carried out by Otto Folin. Although his exhaustive researches led to the negative conclusion that it was "impossible to identify any one metabolism peculiarity with any particular form of mental disorder," he succeeded in developing his well-known micro-methods of chemical analysis, a by-product of this work of such great importance as to amply reward his efforts.

These examples from America can be multiplied many times over in work concomitantly in progress in Europe. Meynert, Wernicke, Flechsig, Forel and Monakow made major contributions to neurology, neuroanatomy and neuropathology as by-products of their psychiatric interests. Freud, too, made contributions of permanent significance to neuropathology in the early stages of his interest in the mind.

It is true that these discoveries were self-limiting as far as the development of psychiatry was concerned. It was soon noted, for example, that severe, far-advanced mental illness, associated with all degrees of deterioration and dilapidation, could occur in patients with anatomically normal brains at autopsy—normal at least by all methods of examination then available. In addition, disturbing inconsistencies were found. Far-advanced senile dementia sometimes occurred in patients with relatively minimal organic brain changes. On the other hand, a well-integrated personality was found to be compatible with relatively advanced arteriosclerotic changes in the brain. It seemed quite clear that organic factors by themselves could never account for the clinical psychiatric picture.

As a result there developed an appreciation of the importance of psychological factors in mental illness. Freud and Adolph Meyer contributed most significantly to what has been called the "psychogenic concept" in medicine, which holds that certain emotional experiences can be traumatic or pathogenic, and can give rise to mental illness not associated with demonstrable structural changes in the brain; and that emotional traumata can give rise to a variety of physical illnesses as well. The "psychogenic concept" has been emphasized in these chapters.

However, with the advent of the shock therapies, psychosurgery and new chemical substances, an interest in the brain as a physical organ has been rekindled. Psychosurgery in particular has opened up a new era in neuropathology, anatomy and physiology. Neurone degeneration studies after the different forms of psychosurgery (lobotomy, gyrectomy, topectomy and thalamotomy) have increased our understanding of neuroanatomical pathways. The living brain tissue which is removed from a mentally ill patient in a psychosurgical procedure presents a challenge to the experimental neuropathologist. Grossly normal in appearance, what micropathological secret is locked within it? New techniques of tissue study are just coming into existence. Even the possibilities of the old techniques have not yet been exhausted. To a considerable extent, much of the old fruitless search for neuropathologic changes in the mentally ill has been carried out in the wrong parts of the brain. Only recently have we come to understand that deeper, older structures, particularly those of the so-called rhinencephalon, are closer to the heart of the problem of mental illness than the more intensively studied higher centers.

There has also been a revival of interest in the relationship between emotional disturbances in the individual and the appearance of somatic abnormalities. For example, it has been known for a long time that the incidence of rheumatoid arthritis is much lower in the mental hospital population than it is in the general population of corresponding age. This curious fact assumes renewed interest in the light of the action of cortisone and ACTH which can diminish the intensity of rheumatoid arthritis, on one hand, and bring about a psychotic reaction, on the other. Although these facts may be unrelated, there is a suggestive parallelism. Other organic illnesses seem to have a reciprocal relationship with abnormal mental states. On the psychosomatic ward of the Mount Sinai Hospital in New York City, several cases of ulcerative colitis were observed in which a schizophrenic process emerged as the colitis improved. A case of generalized atopic dermatitis was reported by E. Joseph and M. R. Kaufman in which the relief of the associated pruritis under hypnotism resulted in healing of the skin lesions and in the simultaneous efflorescence of an acute schizophrenic reaction. A similar reciprocal relationship has been seen in some asthmatic patients, between episodes of depression and episodes of status asthmaticus.

A reciprocal relationship does not occur invariably. In some instances, the physical pathology and the psychopathology parallel each other. That there is some kind of relationship between the two processes does seem quite clear, although the nature of this relationship remains equivocal. This is an area in which the pathologist's observations, if correlated with an adequate clinical record, can make an important contribution. It used to be said that peptic ulcer did not occur among mental hospital patients, and some tried to draw theoretical conclusions from this. Careful post-mortem studies revealed, however, that the incidence of peptic ulcer in mental hospital patients was exactly the same as that of the general population. The apparent clinical difference was the result of the failure of psychotic patients to complain about their pain.

The reaction of schizophrenic patients to pain is a matter of considerable theoretical interest in its own right. Pathologists have reported finding perforated peptic ulcers, impacted calculi in the cystic duct of the gall bladder, or in the ureter at the post-mortem table without any history of complaints of pain ante-mortem. This raises questions about the relationship between somatic pain and psychic pain. It would seem, for example, that the same pathologic process which obtunds the schizophrenic's emotional suffering impairs his response to painful stimuli of somatic origin as well.

The chemistry laboratory is usually under the direction of the pathologist. Its facilities are particularly important in the diagnosis of psychoses of toxic origin. Hematologic and blood chemistry studies, including blood bromide and barbiturate determinations, may clarify a diagnosis and contribute to a more rational plan of treatment. For example, a toxic psychosis due to barbiturates can be perpetuated by the use of barbiturates in an attempt to sedate the patient. An increased sedimentation rate may reveal an infectious process underlying a toxic psychosis. A spinal fluid examination very soon after the onset of a psychosis may show inflammatory changes which will disappear in a few weeks.

A patient developed an acute schizophrenic reaction while sick with influenza. On admission to the state hospital, the psychosis soon subsided and she was discharged to her home, apparently recovered. A few years later, she had a second psychotic episode which resembled her first, except that there was no associated infectious process. This time she did not recover. She is in a state of marked deterioration after many years of mental illness.

Acute schizophrenic reactions which are part of a toxic process are sometimes clinically indistinguishable from so-called functional schizophrenia. Such patients tend to recover when the toxic process has subsided. They are then often found to have a "prepsychotic" personality. That is to say, they show severe deep-seated psychopathology apart from the toxic state which brought out the psychosis. Under ordinary circumstances, they are able to maintain a marginal adaptation in the community until a generalized toxic state, usually the result of an infection, further impairs their hold on reality and a psychotic reaction results. When the infectious process subsides, they are able to resume their marginal adaptation in the community. It is not surprising that these basically psychopathological individuals may show psychotic reactions in response to emotional stress alone, or that under certain circumstances, the psychotic reaction may crystallize into a chronic form. Prompt, detailed laboratory studies which are not ordinarily carried out in mental hospitals today may make it possible to demonstrate toxic factors in the onset of many more acute schizophrenic reactions.

The use of blood transfusions in the treatment of irreversible insulin coma is mentioned in Chapter III. It has even been suggested that all patients who are to undergo insulin coma therapy should be blood typed in preparation for such an emergency. In any event, blood typing and access to a blood bank should be part of the laboratory facilities of a mental hospital.

Electrocardiography

At one time, it used to be recommended that every patient have an electrocardiogram prior to electroconvulsive therapy. This has not proved to be necessary. Cardiac complications have occurred following ECT in patients whose ECG had been reported normal only a few hours previously. On the other hand, ECT has been life-saving in patients with known heart disease who were exhausting themselves in an agitated psychotic state.

Psychotic reactions in elderly patients are sometimes activated by heart failure. ECG studies along with clinical evidence of heart failure may result in more effective treatment.

Patients operated for senile cataracts not infrequently become psychotic during the postoperative period when both eyes are bandaged. Typically, the psychosis subsides when the unoperated eye is uncovered, unless some physical complication exists.

An elderly patient who showed an acute paranoid reaction following cataract extraction remained psychotic when the unoperated eye was uncovered. Clinical and laboratory studies showed the presence of auricular fibrillation with myocardial failure. Heart function improved promptly on digitalization. With that his psychosis subsided. If the heart failure had not been treated, he might have remained psychotic until his death.

X-Ray

Adequate X-ray facilities are an urgent necessity in every mental hospital. Schizophrenic patients have a much higher incidence of active tuberculosis than is present in the general population. Senile patients to a lesser extent are also a reservoir of tuberculous infection. Such patients on an open ward can infect others on the ward, as well as in the community at large when they are discharged from the hospital. Patients with tuberculous lesions tolerate insulin coma therapy poorly. For these reasons, chest X-rays for all patients and personnel should be part of hospital routine.

X-rays of the spine are sometimes done routinely prior to ECT. There is no necessity for this unless a patient has complaints referrable to the spine. X-ray facilities must be available for the diagnosis and proper treatment of the orthopedic complications which may occur with ECT.

Where there is reason to suspect brain tumor, chest X-rays for metastatic lesions may give a clue to the nature of the intracranial neoplasm. Plain X-rays of the skull may show a fracture, shift of a calcified pineal gland, exostoses which may or may not be associated with a meningioma, erosion of the sella turcica or the internal auditory meatus, congenital or acquired abnormalities of the bony structure of the skull and pathological calcifications in the brain. Air studies may be desired not only for the diagnosis of intracranial lesions, but to verify the position of a lobotomy incision by means of instilled pantopaque. Arteriography may give information about the nature of an intracranial lesion. All of these procedures should be done in a setting where adequate clinical neurological evaluation of the findings is available as well as neurosurgical intervention if indicated.

Electroencephalography

The newest laboratory procedure of special interest to the mental hospital is electroencephalography. Interpretation of the EEG requires considerable training and experience. There is a tendency for inexperienced electroencephalographers to see abnormalities in records which would be normal by the criteria of more experienced workers. Thus, the usefulness of this device to a mental hospital depends entirely upon the proficiency of the physician in charge of this department.

When consciousness is obtunded by any organic disease process, the EEG becomes abnormally slow. The degree of slowing, the amplitude and regularity of the slow activity all increase with greater and more acute obtundation of the state of general awareness. In this setting, dreamlike states tend to become clinically manifest and are occasionally indistinguishable from acute schizophrenic reactions. (The way in which a generalized impairment of awareness affects psychological functioning is discussed in Chapter III.) The cause of the pathological mental state may be a drug intoxication, any organic brain disease which exerts a diffusely disrupting effect on brain function, and a variety of toxic metabolic states. Because these processes are often self-limited, particularly if acute infection is the cause, EEG abnormalities may subside quickly, and in a few weeks it may no longer be possible to say whether a given schizophrenic reaction was part of an organic disturbance in brain function or a so-called functional schizophrenic state. For this reason it is important that EEG studies be carried out as soon after the onset of an acute psychosis as possible. It is in the diagnosis of this group of patients that the EEG is probably of greatest value in a mental hospital. The finding of diffuse hypersynchronic fourteen to twenty per second wave activity is considered almost pathognomonic of barbiturate intoxication if present. However, chronic long-standing barbiturate intoxication can also be associated with diffuse slow activity.

Reports concerning the EEG in patients with schizophrenia are conflicting. Most often the EEG is normal. However, the variations from the norm are greater in a schizophrenic population than they are in the general population. This is not surprising in view of the previously mentioned fact that schizophrenic reactions which occur in a setting of organic brain disfunction are at times indistinguishable from "functional" schizophrenia. If schizophrenic patients with abnormal EEGs were investigated routinely with the face-hand test, the amytal test for organic brain disease (see Chapter VII), cerebrospinal fluid studies and other laboratory procedures, it might be possible to sort out an organic group from the larger group of schizophrenic reactions without evidence of organic brain disease. The same general facts obtain with respect to the affective psychoses.

Epileptic patients show a variety of psychological abnormalities (see also Chapter XX). The following classification is by Penfield and Erickson:

1. Dreamy states.
   a) Illusional: for example, visual or auditory illusions; illusions of memory (*déjà vu*); illusions of reality.
   b) Hallucinatory: a brief seizure lasting seconds to minutes, with a clearly marked beginning and end, accompanied by spikes and sharp waves over the temporal lobes.
2. Petit mal: a clearly recognizable brief seizure, invariably accompanied by spike and wave activity.
3. Automatism (ictal and postictal): the automatism is a brief period of uncritical inappropriate behavior, associated with mental obtundation. It may occur as a seizure phenomenon, in which case it is constantly accompanied by paroxysmal three to six per second activity, or it may occur during a period of postictal confusion in which case it lasts no longer than the period of confusion and is accompanied by diffuse slow one to five per second activity.
4. Psychotic states: these are not seizure manifestations. Epileptics are subject to psychotic episodes, usually brief, sudden in onset, characterized by much confusion and turmoil. They are frequently (though not always) accompanied by generalized or localized delta activity.

Putnam and Merritt described periods of dullness, mental retardation, apathy and confusion persisting for hours or days in epileptics associated with serial or paroxysmal slow EEG activity.

Strauss, Ostow and Greenstein, in their textbook on *Diagnostic Electroencephalography*, comment that a specific behavior pattern must occur concurrently with an electroencephalographic seizure discharge before it can be considered an epileptic manifestation. The mere fact that it is episodic, violent, aggressive, impulsive or repetitive by itself does not make it epileptic. Abnormal EEG patterns are found in many children and adults with behavioral abnormalities characterized by difficulty in the control of aggression. Strauss, et al., make the point that this relationship does not establish the behavior abnormality as an epileptic phenomenon unless an actual concurrence between behavioral paroxysms and EEG paroxysms can be established. This problem has medico-legal implications. Is a patient with abnormal slow waves over the frontal lobes legally responsible for his behavior if he is being held for some violent act? It is obviously impossible to generalize. The electroencephalographer will have to weigh the EEG findings in the light of all the clinical facts.

Probably the most interesting aspect of electroencephalography in a mental hospital is its usefulness in research. Good examples of the possibilities in this field are recent papers by Ostow in which he was able to demonstrate that the temporal lobe plays a role in the repression of unwelcome thoughts. The ingenious experimenter will find limitless possibilities for electroencephalographic research in a mental hospital, perhaps in connection with the newer pharmacological agents, in association with psychotherapeutic procedures and following the newer psychosurgical techniques. The use of various devices to provoke the appearance of abnormal rhythm in a manifestly normal record has been studied with increasing intensity in recent years. Flickered light, hypnotic and convulsant drugs have all been found to be effective. This, too, is an area which warrants further research.

SELECTED REFERENCES

BUNKER, H. A.: American Psychiatric Literature During the Past One Hundred Years. In: *American Psychiatry, 1844-1944*. New York: Columbia University Press, 1944.
　　A scholarly summary of the literature which includes references to laboratory work during this period.
FERRARO, A.: Laboratory Work in the State Hospitals and Its Relation to the Teaching and Research Program of the N.Y. Psychiatric Institute. *Psychiat. Quart.*, 3:180, 1929.
　　An outline of the role of the laboratory in a mental hospital.
JOSEPH, E. D.; PECK, S. M.; KAUFMAN, M. R.: Psychological Study of Neurodermatitis; with a Case Report. *J. Mt. Sinai Hosp.*, 15:360, 1949.
　　A dramatic example of the reciprocal relationship which can exist between a somatic disease process and schizophrenia.
OSTOW, M.: Fluctuations of Temporal Lobe Activity During Psychic Function. *Am. J. Psychiat.*, 110:55, 1953.
——— Psychodynamic Disturbances in Patients with Temporal Lobe Disorder. *J. Mt. Sinai Hosp.*, 20:293, 1954.
　　These two papers by Ostow are good examples of the use of the electroencephalogram in psychiatric research.
STRAUSS, H.; OSTOW, M.; GREENSTEIN, L.: *Diagnostic Electroencephalography*. New York: Grune & Stratton, 1952.
　　This highly recommended textbook contains an excellent summary of the relationships of electroencephalography to psychiatry as well as an extensive bibliography.

Chapter XXXIII

A PSYCHIATRIC SERVICE IN A GENERAL HOSPITAL

Hospitalization: Therapy or Trauma

It has often been stated in these pages that the most important phase of psychiatric treatment is that which takes place in the community. In many instances hospitalization augments the rift with reality in patients whose primary problem involves a pathological tendency to retreat from reality. The drawbacks of hospitalization notwithstanding, this step is often unavoidable. When hospitalization means many miles of travel to strange surroundings which are inaccessible to friends and relatives, then poignant realities are added to the patient's growing psychological estrangement. These purely geographical factors also make it impossible to staff the hospital adequately, thereby ruling out an adequate treatment program. This further contributes to the patient's deterioration. In these terms hospitalization may represent a major psychic trauma rather than a step on the road to mental health. Paul Haun, whose ideas about mental hospital architecture (see Chapter XXVI) command great respect, has said that proximity to a large city, preferably one with a medical school, alone can answer the requirements for a mental hospital site. But this is a requirement for a good general hospital as well. If that is the case, it would seem logical to ask why not combine the two and make a psychiatric service part of every general hospital?

A General Hospital Should Include Psychiatry

If a general hospital is to fulfill the meaning of its name, it should accept patients suffering from all categories of illness. In an ideal sense the general hospital should be a center in which the community health needs are met realistically, and in a way that promotes the general well-being of the people as well as their confidence in the medical profession.

441

It has been estimated that emotional disturbances account for at least
25 per cent of all admissions to a general hospital, even though the vast
majority of general hospitals are supposedly not allowed to accept psychiatric patients as a matter of policy. These patients gain admission by
means of diagnostic subterfuges or because the referring physician himself
does not appreciate the psychiatric nature of the patient's problem. Less
than 6 per cent of all the general hospitals in the United States maintain
a full or partial psychiatric service. Together they account for less than
4 per cent of all the psychiatric beds in the country. So that in terms of
arithmetic, too, it would seem logical to ask why general hospitals do not
extend their facilities to include psychiatric patients.

Various objections have been raised concerning a psychiatric service
in a general hospital. For example, it has been said that psychiatric
patients will be too noisy for a general hospital ward. Yet practical experience has shown that there is more noise on the average obstetrical,
pediatric or surgical ward than there is on a well-run psychiatric ward.
It has been said that psychiatric patients represent a suicidal hazard
which is unsupportably great in a general hospital, yet T. J. Heldt has
reported that there were three suicides on the general wards of the Henry
Ford Hospital in Detroit over a period of four years, which was one more
suicide than that which occurred on the psychiatric service itself during
that same time. The opinion has also been expressed that the retention of
psychiatric patients in a general hospital presents too complicated a
series of legal problems. As a matter of fact it has been found that not
more than 3 per cent of the patients found on the psychiatric service of
a general hospital will require a court order to make adequate treatment
possible. The rare patient who requires further care and who demands
his release can be detained in most states by means of legal devices that
are relatively uncomplicated. Fears that the cost of running a psychiatric
service in a general hospital would be prohibitive have also proved unfounded. On the contrary, it has proved, in many instances, to be advantageous from a financial point of view, since, for one thing, otherwise
vacant beds become occupied.

As a matter of fact the idea of including a psychiatric service in a
general hospital is an old one. The Pennsylvania Hospital, which was
opened in 1755, included in its charter the fact that it was to function,
among other purposes, for the "cure and treatment of lunaticks." The
New York Hospital made provision for a psychiatric service as far back
as 1808, and in 1932 this arrangement was continued in the form of the
renowned Payne Whitney Clinic. Bellevue Hospital and the Albany Hospital in New York established psychiatric services in 1902. One can list

further sporadic instances; the Henry Ford Hospital established a psychiatric service in 1923, the Strong Memorial Hospital in Rochester, N. Y., did likewise in 1926. In 1934 a psychiatric service was started at the Massachusetts General Hospital under the direction of Stanley Cobb. By and large this development was slow. In World War II, the general military hospitals included psychiatric services as a matter of practical necessity and in the process demonstrated the simple practicality of this arrangement. The Veterans Administration hospitals established after World War II continued this trend. The increased use of somatic forms of treatment, particularly ECT, led to an influx of psychiatric patients into general hospitals. Starting primarily in medical experiences during World War II, the knowledge that emotional factors operate in every phase of physical illness has become widespread. Psychoanalytically oriented medical education has added an additional dimension of understanding to this relationship and as a result physicians have become more eager for help from their psychiatric colleagues in handling the so-called psychosomatic aspects of their practice. All of these factors together have contributed to the growing interest in the expansion of psychiatric services in a general hospital.

The Advantages of a Psychiatric Service in a General Hospital

Many advantages can be listed for a psychiatric service in a general hospital. The possibilities for early treatment in a setting which is most advantageous to the patient from a psychological point of view are maximalized. Many patients will be spared the necessity of admission to a mental hospital where overcrowding and inadequate treatment may make for progression, chronicity and deterioration in mental illness.

The presence of a psychiatric service in a general hospital opens up an entirely new series of treatment possibilities. Day hospital and night hospital arrangements are made more practical. A patient can be admitted briefly, as an emergency device, to protect him from an untenable home situation or to tide him over an emotional storm. A hospitalized patient can continue treatment under the direct supervision of the psychiatrist or his family doctor who treated him in the community. The possibilities for the development of an effective volunteer service in the hospital's activities program is enhanced. In a home situation where good relationships exist it becomes possible to utilize members of the family in the treatment of the hospitalized patient.

A twenty-six-year-old nurse developed a catatonic schizophrenic reaction as part of an acute encephalitis of unknown etiology. She was admitted to the Neurologic Service of the Mount Sinai Hospital in New York City. As the inflammatory process subsided, the psychotic reaction improved. Eight weeks after admission she was transferred to a convalescent home, in a remission from her psychosis and considerably improved as far as her encephalitis was concerned. However, when she arrived at the convalescent home she seemed confused. In a few hours she displayed an excited reaction in which she gesticulated bizarrely in front of a mirror and spoke as if in response to hallucinations. Because she was unmanageable there she was returned to the Mount Sinai Hospital where she was admitted to the Psychiatric Service. A sister, toward whom the patient felt very close, was summoned and permitted to remain with her all that day, helping to feed her and reassure her. She spent the night in the room with the patient. The next morning the psychosis had subsided again. At the patient's request she was discharged into the custody of this sister in whose home she had an uneventful convalescence and was able to return to work.

A major consequence of including psychiatry in a general hospital is that of overcoming its isolation from the main body of general medicine. Formerly psychiatrists were consulted in general hospitals only to diagnose an acute psychotic reaction and to arrange transfer of the patient to a mental hospital. Now we are learning how to do something about these psychotic reactions within the general hospital itself, and how to prevent some of them by the more judicious use of sedatives. We are promoting the awareness among physicians that acute disorientation in older patients is not rare and usually subsides in a day or two with proper treatment, if the hospital's facilities make it possible to keep the patient there until the psychotic storm has been weathered. By means of Thorazine we can now control patients in acute excited states with the relatively simple facilities available in the average general hospital (see Chapter III). A suicidal depression of so-called functional origin, or even one starting in the course of corticosteroid therapy, can sometimes be quickly interrupted with a few electroconvulsive treatments and make possible the continuation of urgently needed medical treatments in the hospital. The corticosteroids and other new drugs have shown a propensity to elicit mental disturbances which have increased the number of calls of medical colleagues for psychiatric help, particularly to elucidate the nature of these psychotic reactions and the way in which they can best be controlled.

Once a psychiatric service is established in a general hospital, its influence is felt in every aspect of medical practice. The psychiatrist may be called upon to help a surgeon decide whether or not to proceed with an elective operation, or to prepare an apprehensive patient for a major procedure, or to deal with a reactive depression following a mutilating operation. The internist may request the psychiatrist's help in the treatment of asthma, peptic ulcer, ulcerative colitis, or eczema, in cases which are not responding as expected to medical treatment and in whom an emotional disturbance seems to play a major contributing role in the over-all clinical picture.

An obese patient in the Mount Sinai Hospital in New York City with nonunion of a fracture of the femur was so noisily and insistently demanding of attention from the nurses, that she interfered seriously with the routines on the orthopedic ward. She was transferred to the psychosomatic ward where she was able to learn, in psychotherapy, that her demanding attitude toward the nurses was a repetition of an infantile demanding relationship with her mother. Armed with this insight she became much more co-operative and even undertook a much needed weight-reducing regimen which she had previously refused. Without the co-ordinated help from psychiatry it would not have been possible to continue the orthopedic treatments of the patient in the hospital.

Medical colleagues tend to compel the psychiatrist to be more scientifically rigorous in his use of psychological concepts. At the same time, they learn from the psychiatrist the practical usefulness of concepts like transference, countertransference and other manifestations of the unconscious in the doctor-patient relationship and in the general behavior of the patient. For years the psychiatrist drifted further and further from neuropathology, neuroanatomy and neurophysiology in his daily work with patients. It could be said in all honesty that the patient's head might just as well be stuffed with sawdust for all the reference that the analytically oriented psychiatrist made to its physical contents. However, there is a growing rapprochement between the psychiatrist and the neurologist. The dynamic concepts of analytical psychology have made some aspects of the behavior of brain-injured patients more comprehensible to the neurologist. At the same time, neurophysiologic concepts coming from animal experimentation, neurosurgery in general and psychosurgery in particular are shedding light on psychologic mechanisms.

It has become almost universally accepted that dynamic psychiatry should be considered as a basic science in the curriculum of the medical student. Instead of the perfunctory clinical demonstrations of a few years ago psychiatry is now integrated with the medical curriculum in all four years of the students' training in one third of our medical schools, and the percentage of schools in which this is true is rising. It is similarly recognized that psychiatric training should continue during the internship and residency. However, only 4 per cent of the internships in the

United States include psychiatry. Little can be done about this unfortunate situation until psychiatric services are more universally included in our general hospitals. It was pointed out in Chapter XI that a satisfactory course for student nurses demands that it, too, be integrated with psychiatry at all levels of training, exactly as in the case of the medical student. This approach to nursing education will not only improve the level of nursing in general but represents the only way of overcoming the vast shortage of psychiatrically trained nurses throughout the land. A psychiatric service in a general hospital would vastly enhance the possibilities of meeting this need.

Opportunities for co-ordinated research are naturally enhanced in a general hospital with a psychiatric service.

Although psychiatric disturbances following cataract extraction have been known for many years, the problem was not studied systematically. In 1952 the psychiatry service of the Mount Sinai Hospital in New York City in conjunction with the departments of opthalmology, neurology, electroencephalography, social service and nursing studied twenty-one consecutive admissions for cataract extraction in an attempt to evaluate factors in the total picture. Twenty of the twenty-one patients showed evidence of organic brain damage, indicating that cataract is simply one external evidence of a widespread degenerative process, which affects the brain as well as the eye and probably other parts of the body. So that what started as a psychiatric study contributed inadvertently to our understanding of the pathology of cataract. The eyes of these patients were covered for a twelve-hour period preoperatively. Several patients reacted to this procedure with intense anxiety. They tended to show the most marked psychiatric disturbances postoperatively. It became possible by this means to anticipate which patients would require special nursing care postoperatively. It was repeatedly possible to demonstrate that uncovering the eyes had a dramatic anxiety-relieving effect, as did removal of side rails from the beds, early ambulation, and early return to their own homes, all matters of considerable importance from a prophylactic point of view. In addition, the material was instructive from a theoretical psychiatric viewpoint, shedding light on the psychological mechanisms of defense against anxiety and how these defenses were modified by organic brain disease.

Many of the contributions to the field of psychosomatic medicine in recent years have come from general hospitals with a department of psychiatry.

The psychiatric service of a general hospital plays a mental hygiene role in the community too. It does much to remove the stigma from the diagnosis of mental illness, and encourages the community to seek psychiatric help early when it can do the most good. In addition it opens up unparalleled opportunities for work with children both in prophylactic measures and in treatment early in life when serious mental disturbances begin.

The discrimination which is expressed in general hospital policies concerning psychiatric patients has reflected itself in the insurance plans for hospitalization and medical care. Voluntary health insurance plans seldom include psychiatric treatment in their benefits. The present general policy of excluding all psychiatric disorders is unrealistic and definitely harmful. A few plans do cover psychiatric diagnosis and some aspects of psychiatric treatment, largely as they relate to electroconvulsive therapy. They have been set up by a few big corporations and unions (see references at the end of this Chapter). They seem to have worked out well from the standpoint of cost and the patient's satisfaction. It is doubtful at this time whether a practical way to cover long-term outpatient psychotherapy can be found.

The Organization of a Psychiatric Department in a General Hospital

The following checklist is suggested by Ebaugh in his book on *The Care of the Psychiatric Patient in General Hospitals* (see references). It states average physical and personnel requirements which have worked out successfully in Ebaugh's rich experience with this problem.

Requirements for a Twenty-Five Bed Psychiatric Unit in a General Hospital for Both Men and Women

Construction Details—
1. Sound-proof, and air conditioned (preferable).
2. Four isolation rooms.
3. Five private rooms with lavatory—some with bath; six two-bed semiprivate rooms.
4. Two four-bed wards with cubicles, private clothes closets and one lavatory.
5. Solarium, recreation room with closets adjoining for recreational and occupational equipment and dining room.
6. Kitchen—Equipment depends on use. At least stove, ice box, sink and cupboard space.
7. Nurse's station equipped with built-in medicine closet, locked cupboards for valuables, office stationery, supplies, etc. Chart table, desk and table, telephone, lavatory.
8. Utility room equipped with bed pan and basin sterilizer, rack for pans, sink and drainboard, shelves for equipment, laundry chute and rods for hanging rubber sheets.

9. Treatment room equipped with examination table, small instrument sterilizer, lavatory, built-in cupboards for sterile supplies. Isolation rooms, when not otherwise needed, can be used as treatment rooms, pack room, etc.
10. Interview rooms (which can also be used as treatment rooms).
11. Linen cupboard ⎱ Two small ones if ward is not compact in
12. Blanket cupboard ⎰ arrangement.
13. Small classroom for ward teaching, with desks, chairs and blackboard, and locked cupboards for books.
14. Two tub rooms, each with two tubs and a drying closet.
15. Two bathrooms with showers.
16. Two lavatories with toilets.
17. Lavatory and toilet for nurses and closet for nurses' wraps.
18. Provision for bringing music from selected records to ward.
19. Drinking fountains.
20. Janitor's closet and hopper.
21. Electric connections wherever necessary, for radio, etc.

Personnel Required for a 25-Bed Psychiatric Ward in a General Hospital

Medical—
Director
Visiting Staff
Resident
Two internes from Medical Service

Nursing—
1. A charge nurse—who has had postgraduate work in psychiatry plus a superior record in administering a ward and in teaching.
2. An assistant charge nurse with postgraduate training and demonstrated ability.
3. An afternoon nurse (3:30-12).
4. Two night nurses (11:30—7:30).
5. Two general duty nurses—
   Preparation for these five nurses: Postgraduate course and one year of satisfactory experience in psychiatric nursing. Rotate the night and afternoon nurses with the other two every two or three weeks.
6. Men and women attendants—
   5 women ⎱ Working 8-hour shifts and relieving each other for
   4 men ⎰ days off, vacations and illness.
7. An occupational and recreational therapist.
8. A ward maid for cleaning plus part-time help from hospital janitor for mopping and sweeping.
9. Students and affiliates, 5 being the maximum that should be taken each quarter.
10. Psychologist.
11. Social—One or more psychiatrically trained social workers.
12. Stenographic—Secretarial, record, and stenographic staff.

More architectural details considered from the point of view of the patient's emotional needs are taken up in Chapter XXVI. Paul Haun's book on *Psychiatric Sections in General Hospitals* (see references) is the most important source of information on this subject currently available.

Although one cannot predict exactly the changes in the over-all psychiatric picture if psychiatric services become universally available in our general hospitals, it seems quite certain that they would exert a profound and beneficial effect on the mental health of the nation. The mental hospital psychiatrist, with his special experience, will have to play an important role in this development.

SELECTED REFERENCES

BENNETT, A. E.: Biological Psychiatry. *Am. J. Psychiat.*, 110:244, 1953.

—— HARGROVE, E. A.; ENGLE, B. S.: Psychiatric Treatment in General Hospitals. *J.A.M.A.*, 147:1019, 1951.

These two articles survey current practices relating to psychiatric treatment in general hospitals with recommendations for future developments.

—— —— —— Voluntary Health Insurance and Nervous and Mental Disease. *J.A.M.A.*, 151:202, 1953.

An important survey of current insurance practices pointing the way to practical reforms which may revolutionize modern psychiatric care in hospitals.

BRILL, N. Q.: Army Experience Proves That Psychiatric Patients Belong in a General Hospital. *Mod. Hosp.*. 68:56, 1947.

CONFERENCE OF MENTAL HOSPITAL ADMINISTRATORS AND STATISTICIANS (First): *Proceedings.* U.S. Public Health Service Publication No. 295, U.S. Gov. Printing Office, Washington 25, D.C.

Surveys the advantages of a psychiatric service in a general hospital.

EBAUGH, F. G.: *The Care of the Psychiatric Patient in General Hospitals.* American Hospital Association, Official Bull., No. 207, Chicago, Ill., 1940.

A survey of the problem covering history, current trends, advantages and disadvantages, organizational requirements and management principles. In addition there is an excellent bibliography.

HAUN, P.: *Psychiatric Sections in General Hospitals.* Garden City, N.Y.: Country Life Press, 1950.

This book states the architectural problem in dynamic psychiatric terms. It includes a critical study of several blueprints for psychiatric sections in general hospitals and a good bibliography. A text of fundamental importance.

KAUFMAN, M. R.: The Role of the Psychiatrist in a General Hospital. *Psychiat. Quart.*, 27:367, 1953.

A survey of the types of psychiatric problems presented by patients on the medical and surgical wards of a general hospital. Several illustrative case histories enhance the value of this paper.

LINN, L.; KAHN, R. L.; COLES, R.; COHEN, J.; MARSHALL, D.; WEINSTEIN, E. A.: Patterns of Behavior Disturbances Following Cataract Extraction. *Am. J. Psychiat.*, 110:281, 1953.

An example of a multidisciplinary psychiatric research in a general hospital.

OSBORNE, L. A.: Psychiatric Services in General Hospitals, *J.A.M.A.*, 153:259, 1953.

This paper considers the advantages of a psychiatric service for children in a general hospital.

Part Five

THE COMMUNITY

Chapter XXXIV

THE RELATIVES OF PATIENTS

The Hostile Psychiatrist

Psychiatrists in mental hospitals often develop unfriendly attitudes toward the families of patients. They tend to see them as enemies who take away precious moments from patient care. They become irritated by nagging importunations, exasperated by impossible demands and irrational beliefs, and outraged by unjust accusations. It is no wonder that the psychiatrist comes to dread visiting day and speaks of his encounters with relatives as the most difficult of all his duties. "I have so much work to do for my patients; why must I waste all this time with relatives?" "Can't these people see how earnestly I try to help my patients?" "How can they be so stupid as to take those delusional utterances literally?" "How can they possibly believe that I prefer to keep the patient imprisoned?" All psychiatrists in mental hospitals wrestle with these and similar questions in their contacts with relatives. Successful therapy of the hospitalized patient depends to an important degree upon the way these questions are answered.

The Patient and His Family: A Unit

The family is indissolubly a part of the patient. They are the people to whom the patient related as a child. They frustrated some of his infantile desires and seductively enhanced others. They are the people with whom he first identified. They provided him with his earliest adult aspirations. This brother and that sister were his first rivals. This mother cannot bear to see him grow up as an independent adult. That father cannot control his disappointment that the patient did not have the qualities he wanted for him. It is impossible to understand the patient's problems unless one makes a serious attempt to understand the family from which he came.

Although much of this information will come from the social worker (see Chapter VIII), the importance of the psychiatrist's contacts with the family cannot be minimized. Often relatives will present him with a completely different facet of themselves than that which they give the social worker. In addition, pronouncements from the psychiatrist possess a special authoritative weight that communications from other sources do not have. As a result, his opportunities for effecting therapeutically favorable changes in the family milieu are often enhanced. Since the plan of treatment inevitably hinges upon the return of the patient to the community, the family cannot be excluded from the deliberations. The relatives may be capable of understanding how the family milieu contributed to the patient's illness and be motivated to make appropriate changes. If the home environment is hopelessly unsuitable and cannot be modified, then the doctor must be apprised of this fact, must plan other living arrangements and must help the family to accept the change. Thus, for diagnosis, formulation of the plan of treatment, for trial visits, for work and permanent living arrangements, whether for good or evil, the family of the patient is involved. The psychiatrist can no more afford to be unhappy about the patient's family than he can about his illness.

Families Have Anxieties

As a result of his familiarity with the manifestations of mental disease, the psychiatrist may forget the horrifying impact that the eruption of a psychosis can have upon a family, tiny children and adults alike. Few things in life have a more demoralizing effect upon the laity than the seemingly senseless actions and remarks of the mentally ill. The psychiatrist must stand prepared to deal with uncanny feelings which are thus aroused. In addition, hospitalization may represent the first separation from a loved one, an experience sometimes rendered particularly unbearable by unprecedented hostility or indifference on the part of the patient. Depending on the psychiatric facilities which are available in the community, the family may have undergone nightmarish experiences before securing help. Inevitably, families have a variety of misconceptions about mental illness. They may feel that the loved one is irretrievably lost, that mental illness is perforce incurable. They may fear for their own sanity and for that of their children. Prejudices against mental hospitals are almost universal. Starting with the fact that there are genuine short-comings in the available treatment facilities, they may have, in addition, unwarranted fears of brutality or callousness on the part of hospital personnel, and fears that the patient will not be released when he has recovered. All these factors contribute to the mental suffering of families. These matters have been considered in more detail in Chapter VIII.

Families Have Guilt Feelings

Guilt feelings play an important role in the behavior of relatives. Sometimes this guilt is based on grossly evident facts, as for example, where actual neglect or mistreatment of the patient has occurred prior to hospitalization. More often this guilt is related to unconscious factors, to a subliminal awareness of aggressive controlling family influences that have contributed to the patient's illness, also to ambivalent attitudes toward the patient, as when a manifest attitude of loving concern conceals unconscious feelings of disappointment, resentment and even wishes that the patient would die.

Psychological Defenses Employed by Families

In the face of such painful emotions, it is inevitable that attempts at adaptation should be manifest in the behavior of relatives. This takes many familiar forms, all of which represent in one way or another attempts to deny the reality of the patient's mental illness. For example, a family that has gone through fearful trials to get the patient into the hospital may suddenly decide that it has been the victim of an unfortunate series of errors, that nothing is really wrong with the patient and that the patient should be released at once. Or the family may insist that "the entire problem is physical; what he needs is a doctor, not a psychiatrist." Or the family may accept the patient's delusions uncritically and, forgetting the picture which preceded hospitalization, believe that the patient's troubles are all the result of mistreatment in the hospital. Contained in this is often a deeply rooted paranoid defense in the family —"We are not hostile to the patient; you are the ones who are guilty."

The Psychological Defenses of the Physician

The psychiatrist labors under a triple burden compared to his non-psychiatric medical colleagues. He must try to cure the patient, the patient's family, and last but by no means least, he must cure himself. For the psychiatrist above all other physicians does the ancient admonition hold: "Physician, heal thyself!" When the family accuses the psychiatrist of mistreating the patient, oftentimes there may be just enough of a grain of truth in it to make the accusation hurt. The fact is that not a single public hospital in the United States meets the minimal requirements of the American Psychiatric Association. There is probably no psychiatrist who is fully satisfied with his treatment of the hospitalized patient. If the psychiatrist is in addition a neurotically ambitious person who has a compulsive need to cure everyone (as contrasted simply to doing his best), he may suffer guilt because of unsatisfactory results with many of his patients. Underpaid and overworked, he may have a human enough desire for some evidence from the family that they appreciate his efforts. When, instead, they attack him, his fury may be unbounded. Thus, in his contacts with families, the psychiatrist must stand guard over his own emotional needs lest they interfere with the proper treatment of the patient. A personal psychoanalysis will tend to diminish the destructive influence of such emotional pressures, as will to a lesser extent supervision by a psychoanalytically oriented supervisor.

Relations with the Average Family

Certain general questions beset all families. Every hospital should make available to the family suitable literature providing answers to those questions (see references at the end of this Chapter). Many times they will want to hear the answers directly, from the social worker (see Chapter VIII) or from the psychiatrist himself. However accomplished, the questions should be anticipated and the answers provided.

Mental illness should be explained to families as a failure to achieve a satisfactory resolution of conflicting impulses. A man's attachment to his wife may conflict with his attachment to his mother; his ambitions on the job to be a top executive may conflict with the comfort and security of a minor post where others make decisions for him; his wish to have children may conflict with his wish to be "babied" by his wife; his wish to succeed may conflict with his wish to be liked by those who will resent his success. Such a dynamic presentation of the nature of mental illness will prepare the family to accept the fact that the home milieu plays a role in the illness and that some alterations in that milieu will be necessary to achieve a definitive cure.

Families will be comforted to know that not all mental illness is alike; that patients are placed in one of many possible psychiatric diagnostic categories after a period of intensive study; that the prognostic estimate and the treatments are individualized on the basis of these diagnostic studies. They may derive some comfort from the statistical fact that they share their plight with every fifth family in the land. Fears based upon a mechanical conception of mental illness as an inherited "taint" must be allayed, as must be the notion that mental illness is a social disgrace. When families react with horror to the idea of being confined, they must be cautioned not to ascribe their own feelings to the patient. More often than families realize, the hospital represents a refuge for these frightened defeated people. Here patients feel safe from imagined persecutors. The simplicity of the hospital routines is less overwhelming. The security of the hospital is in itself a form of treatment.

Many families, in their eagerness to get the best possible treatment for the patient, will want to know about private sanitariums. If the family can afford it and suitable treatment facilities are available, they should certainly be encouraged to make use of them, not only to provide possibly (but not necessarily) better care for the patient but also to make room for another patient who cannot afford private care. The psychiatrist's greatest responsibility in this regard is to protect the family against ill-advised financial sacrifices based upon guilt and anxiety. Families will sometimes pauperize themselves for a few weeks' private sanitarium care for an illness that will require months and years of treatment. The futility of such a move is further underscored when the private treatment facility is in no way better than the public one.

Do's and Don't's for Families

The following list of "commandments" has been suggested by Kathleen Doyle (see references) for the guidance of families:

Do recognize mental and emotional illness for what it is; a sickness of mind and spirit as real as a broken leg; more common than heart disease and cancer combined. Don't brood about the "stigma" or resent the patient's behavior or doubt his need for professional care.

Do let the patient know you understand his illness and love him as much as ever. Don't abandon the patient, no matter how hopelessly ill he may seem.

Do observe the hospital rules. They are made for one reason: to insure the least possible distraction from the treatment of the patient. Don't plague the staff with requests for special privileges. Such requests upset the patient and make it difficult for the hospital personnel.

Do visit as often as the doctor considers it wise. Don't be hurt if the patient refuses to see you. The desire to escape from his former environment may be part of his illness.

Do remember that the patient's uncertainty and sense of defeat are greater than yours; his inner resources weaker. Don't break down or talk about him in his presence. Out of contact though he may seem to be, he is probably as sensitive to what is going on as when he was well.

Do be courteous to the other patients. Don't engage in conversation with them or accept notes to be mailed outside.

Do listen to the patient without arguing, no matter how fantastic some of his statements may be. The greater your patience and self-control, the more he will benefit from your visits. Don't give him any indication you think he is "crazy." If you find his ideas too disturbing, discuss them with the doctor. They may be typical of his particular illness.

Do take his complaints with a grain of salt. If the staff seems efficient and pleasant to deal with, if the patient is reasonably happy, if the hospital is clean and well-run, he is exaggerating. Don't be overly sympathetic or promise to "get him out" as soon as possible. This makes it harder for everyone, including the patient.

Do talk to him about what is going on in the world and at home: who won the World Series, where Susan visited over the weekend. Don't discuss his illness with him or comment on his appearance.

Do write often—casual, chatty letters that keep him in touch with the life from which he is cut off temporarily. Don't take family decisions to him or burden him with your problems. He has enough of his own.

Do keep him supplied with small luxuries, cosmetics, cigarettes, favorite magazines. Don't send useless gifts. The nurse may be able to tell you what he wishes for or needs particularly.

Do see that he keeps as well groomed as his condition warrants. The clothes you give him are a symbol of your faith in his recovery. Don't expect the hospital to mend his clothes or have them cleaned. The average institution has no such facilities.

Do be frank with the doctor and the social worker. The more detailed their study of the patient, the better equipped they are to start him on the path to recovery. Don't take the attitude that the hospital is prying into your private affairs. They are interested in you only in so far as you can help them uncover the root of the patient's trouble.

Do consult the hospital superintendent about having an outside psychiatrist or your family doctor check the patient's progress from time to time, if he is in a state or private hospital. The effect on everyone's morale—the patient's, the staff's, your own—will be well worth the expense. Don't be unrealistic about how much overworked personnel can do. In an understaffed overcrowded hospital, it is your sympathetic unflagging interest in the patient's welfare that will determine how much individual attention he gets.

A Positive Program for Families

It is a well-known fact that people are more apt to retain their mental health in times of disaster if given something to do toward mastering the problem. This principle is also applicable to the families of the mentally ill. We should strive to channel their anxieties and guilts into constructive activities. Urge them to join the National Association for Mental Health, either directly or through the local mental health association. Urge them to be honestly critical of the hospital's work and the entire state program for the care of the mentally ill. When they are unhappy about the admission procedure or the treatment facilities and get angry at you, urge them to take their anger to the state legislators through appropriate community organizations. Express an interest in meeting with the family doctor, the minister or any other significant member of the community who is concerned with the patient's welfare. Counter their attack on you with a call to public action from them. Tell the families about the mental health activities which are conducted in the community by staff psychiatrists, before parent-teacher association groups, and churches. Post notices of such activities conspicuously in the hospital and encourage families to attend, and to publicize them.

If there is an active volunteer program in your hospital, relatives may want to become involved. This is certainly out of the question at the particular institution where the relative-patient is hospitalized. Though they may understand the hospital and the mental illness, their approach cannot possibly have the prerequisite objectivity. They might wish to visit the patient or be assigned to that particular ward on their day of service. For these and other reasons, experience has shown that such use of relatives as volunteer workers does not work out. In addition, relatives may have severe emotional disturbances which, as has been indicated, are part of the milieu which gave rise to the patient's illness. Such workers, if used in other institutions or in mental hygiene clinics in the community, should be screened with particular care (see Chapter XIII).

One hospital has recently reported the use of family members to provide continuous nursing care for patients in need of special attention. A member of the family is permitted to sleep in the hospital in a bed adjoining the patient's, to minister to the various physical and emotional needs of the patient. Many more patients become willing to enter the hospital voluntarily when accompanied by a family member. When the proper member of the family is thus employed, it is sometimes possible to shorten episodes of panic or acute agitation. An example of this was described in Chapter XXXIII. Naturally, not all members of the family are equally suitable for this role. Some specifically intensify the patient's emotional distress. Where bed space permits, the use of the family in this way may provide a striking new approach to treatment.

Treatment of the "Hostile" Family

Many times suggestions based on common sense are of no avail. Families may persist in hostile attitudes and unreasonable demands in spite of all efforts to instruct them. This is the group that is most likely to elicit irrational counterattack from the psychiatrist. More important, this is the group that needs help most, if the patient is to be returned to that family. This is the type of family from which flight into mental illness is often a refuge for the patient, a fact which may contribute to the perpetuation of a psychosis if not overcome, and which may call for foster family care if not remediable.

Colonel Inwood studied this problem in the Walter Reed Army Medical Center in Washington, D.C., and concluded that persistent hostility toward the hospital was usually rooted in unconscious hostility toward the patient. In individual psychotherapy with family members, Inwood was often able to make this hostility conscious and to motivate families to make therapeutic modifications in their relationships with the patient. He describes as an example an interview with the father of a schizophrenic boy. The father began with the angry assertion that nothing was being done for the patient and that he, the father, was a man of action and expected just one of two things from the army hospital, either complete recovery or discharge from the army on a full pension. It was pointed out to him that the patient had had trouble for a long time and that he must have caused considerable difficulty to the father in growing up. The father replied, "He was always a disappointment to me. He has failed at everything." He revealed in considerable detail how he had repeatedly intervened to help his son, but, he said bitterly, it had never worked out. He eventually raised the question of whether or not he had erred in trying to help the boy too much. The explanation was given that his son had resented this overintense supervision and had kept on trying only because of his love for his father. For the first time the father became aware of his interference in his son's life. His initial hostility was replaced by an eagerness to co-operate. He saw that he had made his son excessively dependent upon him and that this dependence had crippled the boy emotionally and had aroused hostility which he could not express. The father left the interview to discuss with the son how he could help him to become independent. Son and father went on to work out a more satisfactory relationship which was mutually helpful and contributed materially to the recovery of the patient.

In addition to individual psychotherapy, group approaches to the emotional disturbances of relatives have been suggested and give promise of considerable usefulness (see Chapter II).

The group psychotherapist, Joseph Abrahams and his social worker collaborator, Edith Varon, working at the St. Elizabeth's Hospital in Washington, D.C., treated a group of schizophrenic female patients and their mothers in simultaneous sessions. The complex intertwining of the psychopathology of the mother with that of the schizophrenic daughter was quite clearly brought out. In their study, the schizophrenic process emerged as the end stage of a continuously unsuccessful attempt to achieve independence from a mother whose own inferiority feelings and pathologically intense dependence needs stifled the daughter's own strivings at every stage in her development. An experiment like this raises the question as to whether one can ever hope to treat a patient psychiatrically without simultaneously treating the family. In any case, it underscores the fact that the conception of the patient's family as a "nuisance" is incompatible with a rational program of treatment.

SELECTED REFERENCES

ABRAHAMS, J.; VARON, E.: *Maternal Dependency and Schizophrenia. Mothers and Daughters in a Therapeutic Group.* New York: International Universities Press, 1953.

COTE, F.; DANCEY, T. E.; SAUCIER, J.: Participation in Institutional Treatment by Selected Relatives. *Am. J. Psychiat.*, 111:831, 1954.
   This paper demonstrates the value of a simple plan whereby a selected relative accompanies a patient to a private voluntary hospital. The advantages are economic, educational, and in some instances, therapeutic. The only significant disadvantages arise from the improper choice of the participating family member. Brief case reports are included.

DOYLE, K.: When Mental Illness Strikes Your Family. *Public Affairs Pamphlet*, No. 172, 1951. Public Affairs Committee, 22 East 38 Street, New York 16, N.Y.
   An excellent pamphlet to orient the family of newly admitted patients.

GOODALE, E.: Intake Interviews with Relatives of Psychotic Patients. *Smith College Stud. Soc. Work*, 15:15, 1944.
   A fine group of illustrative case histories bring out typical family problems and satisfactory ways of handling them.

INWOOD, E. R.: The Problem of the Hostile Relative. *U. S. Armed Forces Med. J.*, 4:1734, 1953.
   The thesis is demonstrated that irrational hostility against the hospital on the part of relatives is the result of unconscious hostility against the patient. Excellent illustrative case material.

NATIONAL ASSOCIATION FOR MENTAL HEALTH: *A Visit to Your Mental Hospital.* National Association for Mental Health, 1790 Broadway, New York 19, N.Y.
   A pamphlet for orienting families, whose particular value lies in the use of cartoons for presenting the material.

PRATT, D.; NEHER, J.: Mental Health is a Family Affair. *Public Affairs Pamphlet* No. 155, 1949. Public Affairs Committee, 22 East 38 Street, New York 16, N. Y.
   A useful pamphlet to prepare relatives for a more constructive role in the aftercare of patients.

SELWYN, A.: Don't Let Mental Illness Scare You. *Reader's Digest,* February, 1954, p. 126. Available as a reprint through the National Association of Mental Health, 1790 Broadway, New York 19, N.Y.

A highly readable, informative and reassuring statement of basic facts about mental illness.

STERN, E. M.; HAMILTON, S. W.: *Mental Illness: A Guide for the Family,* 1951. National Association for Mental Health, 1790 Broadway, New York 19, N.Y.

This is a thorough, comprehensive and authoritative guide for the families of the mentally ill. Highly recommended.

Chapter XXXV

OUTPATIENT CARE

Importance of Outpatient Care

As a result of the woeful disparity in most mental hospitals between the patient's therapeutic needs and the treatment facilities actually available, a powerful force is set up which intensifies pathological tendencies in the patient to withdraw from reality. This has been discussed in Chapter XIV, where it was pointed out that deterioration is not an inevitable outcome of psychosis but rather a manifestation of the psychotic patient's attempts to adapt to a highly traumatic environment. In the average mental hospital self-perpetuating psychotic mechanisms tend to appear which render treatment more difficult, and a successful outcome less likely. When, on the other hand, treatment is instituted early and is carried out in the community, deterioration may be prevented and in any case rarely achieves the severity which is possible in a hospital.

Even the most effectively run mental hospital fosters passive dependent attitudes. The patient's needs are all provided for and his day is regimented. In spite of the finest activities program, the hospital environment can never be as challenging as any ordinary day in the community. Like the phobic who must face the situations he fears and the addict who must meet his problems without the help of drugs, so the hospitalized patient must resume extramural reality contacts before truly effective psychotherapy can take place. In this sense outpatient facilities represent logical and indispensable extensions of intramural care.

It has been estimated that fully a quarter of all the psychotic patients in our country never enter a hospital. Many are able to maintain a precarious adaptation to a fortuitously well-protected home and job situation. Many more psychotic people would be able to continue in the community with the help of outpatient care. By keeping such people at work, supporting their dependents, providing for the education of their

463

children, and in other ways contributing to family life, a destructive psychosocial trend can be reversed. During periods of emotional crisis outpatient emergency care may forestall the total disorganization of adaptation which makes hospitalization unavoidable, either by direct treatment of the patient or by easing an intolerable home situation.

A program of outpatient aftercare liberalizes the discharge policy of a hospital, making it possible to send patients home at an earlier date and to keep them in remission for much longer periods of time.

When outpatient facilities are available, popular prejudices tend to decrease, and the people apply for treatment earlier in the course of a mental illness at a time when the prognosis is better. The outpatient clinic helps overcome the traditional isolation of the mental hospital from the surrounding community, and as a result better liaison is maintained with colleagues in the community. In addition the lay public becomes more ready to volunteer its help in the treatment program. The clinic can become the community center for the distribution of authoritative mental health information and play an important role in preventive medicine.

Finally, the economic aspects of a good outpatient program must be mentioned. It has been estimated that the prevention of as few as two or three commitments a year would save as much money as is spent on the entire clinic budget. Similarly, a liberalized discharge policy will lead to economies. Surveys have shown that for every dollar spent on outpatient care, six to seven dollars are saved elsewhere in the mental hygiene budget.

The National Mental Health Act and Other Sources of Funds

In view of the foregoing facts, the enactment of the National Mental Health Act in 1946 represented a particularly wise and far-sighted contribution to the mental health of our nation. Funds available through this Act have been the most important single source for new mental health clinic facilities. A measure of its contribution to national welfare is the fact that almost 500 new clinics have been established in the United States with funds available through this Act. The intention of the Act is to provide the means for starting new clinics or for expanding old ones. Once the new facilities are well established, federal funds are withdrawn and made similarly available to other installations. In starting a clinic the federal government provides half the money and expects the state and the local community to provide the other half. Implicit in the program is the hope that local governments will raise sufficient funds to run the clinics on their own once the value of such facilities have been demonstrated. In short, it is the main function of the federal government to act as a catalyzer.

It was anticipated by the framers of the Act that expanded clinic facilities would intensify existing personnel shortages. The Act attempts to meet this by providing for the training of new specialists. Funds for the training of new psychiatric personnel, whether in nursing, psychology, social work, psychiatry or any of the ancillary fields, are available to eligible people directly on application. In addition, the Act makes funds available for approved research projects (see Chapters XXIX and XXX).

Individual states are now following the lead of the Federal government and in some areas are establishing similar and independent programs to expand existing outpatient facilities. Information concerning the availability of such funds can be obtained by writing to the Commissioner of Mental Hygiene or to the Governor of the State.

The public-spirited mental hospital psychiatrist can activate local service organizations to aid in expanding outpatient facilities. An example of the way in which a service organization can help is provided by the National Council of Jewish Women. In Asheville, North Carolina, they took the initiative in bringing together the city planning council, the Asheville Mental Hygiene Society and the State Department of Mental Health to draw up plans for a clinic which was finally established with funds from the National Mental Health Act. They then sponsored a community-wide forum which opened the campaign of the city planning council to secure additional funds to match the federal contribution. As a result of similar experiences in other communities, the National Council of Jewish Women has prepared a comprehensive procedure guide which is adaptable for use in communities of any size in estimating the community needs for mental health clinics and in initiating a program to meet those needs. Elsewhere we have discussed at length the contribution of volunteer workers in the mental hospital (Chapter XIII). Here, in outpatient psychiatry, is an entirely different area of volunteer work in which contributions of major importance to the mental health of our nation can be made.

Organizing a Clinic

Practical assistance with the details of initiating a new outpatient psychiatric clinic can be obtained from the National Association for

Mental Health which has had considerable experience with this problem (see references).

Most psychiatric outpatient facilities have their origin in the aftercare program for discharged mental hospital patients. The team charged with the care of the patient in the hospital—the psychiatrist, social worker, psychologist and the various special therapists—are often assigned to the clinic as part of their hospital duties. Although the ideal is the ultimate establishment of separate clinic facilities to serve the community, the mental hospital remains, nevertheless, in a particularly strategic position to initiate and expand this program.

The clinic should be established in light attractive quarters, preferably in the principal general hospital which serves the community. If it aspires to become a community mental health center, it should have surroundings of corresponding dignity. All too often the clinic is relegated to a dingy basement, the morbid appearance of which engenders discouragement and pessimism. Many patients have described their visit to the aftercare clinic as a bore and an indignity consisting of hours of uncomfortable waiting followed by a perfunctory examination by an overworked psychiatrist.

The clinic is a natural setting for group formation. The waiting room should be attractively decorated, recreational facilities made available, and simple refreshments served. Careful scheduling should seek to eliminate unnecessary waiting. In this way the entire visit can be transformed into a therapeutically beneficial social experience. The services of volunteer workers can be employed in creating the proper social atmosphere. The formation of self-governing social clubs should be encouraged. Provisions should be made for leisure time and evening activities (see discussion of Day Hospital, this Chapter). Sexes should be mixed at clinic sessions, although it is preferable not to mix age extremes.

The clerical staff is very important. However, nonprofessional personnel should be selected not simply for their work efficiency but for their capacity to relate in a warm friendly fashion to the patients.

All patients should be seen by a social worker who takes care of as many of the patient's problems as are within her province. She will refer selected patients for direct study by the psychiatrist. He in turn will request psychological test studies on some who have been referred to him. The psychiatrist will carry a few patients for brief periods of individual psychotherapy. He will organize group psychotherapy, assigning some groups to social workers and psychologists at his discretion to work under his direct supervision.

To the greatest extent possible a full activities program should be set up in the clinic with the assistance of occupational and recreational therapists, vocational counselors, the chaplain, and others.

Consultations between the psychiatrist and other members of his treatment team should take place regularly. Joint conferences to plan the management of each case and to consider special problems play a role of central importance in the clinic program.

The various functional needs of a clinic should be kept in mind in the architectural design.

Referral of Patients

If no other clinic facilities are available, the mental hospital clinic may be called upon to serve the community at large as well as its own ex-patient population. Such patients may be referred from schools, the department of welfare, general practitioners in the community, the courts and the churches. In addition, patients may refer themselves. With such a broad source of referrals a mental health clinic tends to become quickly overcrowded. It becomes a diagnostic facility primarily where disposition for extreme cases is recommended but where actual treatment is minimal. Notwithstanding the importance of diagnosis and disposition, active treatment for patients in the community and aftercare for the discharged inpatient represent the most important aspects of clinic function.

Fees

It has often been observed that patients work more earnestly in psychotherapy if they are compelled to pay for their treatment. Even though the fee be nominal, if the patient has to make some sacrifice to obtain therapy, his relationship to the clinic becomes more realistic. Dependent attitudes and other expressions of regression are reduced, and in general therapy tends to proceed more satisfactorily.

Children and Adolescents

Separate outpatient facilities for young patients are a necessity. In psychotherapy with children much less reliance is placed upon verbal production and more attention paid to their play, their drawings and their responses on psychological tests. This requires special physical facilities—play rooms, and play materials, as well as personnel specially trained to work with children. The entire relationship between a child and his therapist differs from that which exists between an adult patient and the psychiatrist. Reality factors are much more important in the relationship with the child. The role of the social worker in correcting poor home conditions is even more important in child therapy than with the adult because the child is more helpless in his capacity to deal with his environment.

Adolescents provide still another set of problems. Usually special clinic facilities are recommended for them. Certainly this is necessary if they are to be treated in groups. Withdrawn, autistic adolescents who seem to be on the fringe of a psychotic reaction are particularly responsive to group therapy, even though they are generally unresponsive when treated individually (see also Chapter XVI).

Where the case load becomes very great, the psychiatrist may be compelled to use part of his time for patients and part in a consultative capacity with teachers, social workers, psychologists, or truancy officers, attempting to guide them in their work with individuals and groups, seeing only selected cases which cannot be handled adequately by an indirect approach.

Night Clinics

An invaluable outpatient facility is a clinic that meets at night. This permits people who hold full-time jobs to come for treatment without losing time from work. The Veterans Administration has pioneered in this approach. Their facilities are, of course, open to eligible veterans, but similar opportunities should be available for nonveterans. A situation in which night clinics are particularly valuable is one in conjunction with child guidance clinics where night facilities makes it possible also for the father to enter the treatment situation. Ordinarily, because he cannot afford to lose time from work, he is omitted from the treatment plan for the child even though he may be the more mature parent and capable of contributing more significantly to the child's welfare.

Traveling Clinics

Another important outpatient facility is the traveling clinic. Areas which are unable to maintain the full-time services of a clinic staff sometimes maintain a mental health center run by a social worker and a clerk who assists her. A psychiatrist and a psychologist are engaged to visit the clinic once or twice a month. It is preferable if the social worker and the psychologist have some training in therapy. The psychiatrist and the psychologist stagger their visits. The psychologist does testing and participates to a limited degree in therapy at the discretion and under the direction of the psychiatrist. The social worker sees all patients who apply to the clinic for help and accepts certain cases for psychotherapy, also under the direction of the psychiatrist. The psychiatrist sees patients at the request of the other two members of the team and in consultation with them directs the activities of the clinic.

The Aftercare Clinic

In spite of the universal recognition that aftercare represents the most important phase of the mental hospital treatment program, this has been administered in a haphazard way heretofore. Traditionally the same doctors and social workers responsible for the patient's intramural care attempted to supervise him after his return to the community. This was wasteful and ineffective for several reasons. For example, two social workers might start out from widely separated hospitals and travel great distances to the same building in a community because each hospital had discharged patients living in that building. The social worker usually came to the home visit without a planned approach and without a base of operations in the patient's own community. The aftercare clinic rarely maintained a permanent professional staff but was manned rather by shifts of personnel from different hospitals on different days. Former patients could apply to the clinic for help only on those days when the staff of their particular hospital was on duty. A rueful patient once remarked about this arrangement, "You have to get upset on the right day in order to get help." Individual hospitals varied widely in other aspects of their outpatient practice. Some hospitals compelled all their patients to report to aftercare clinic even when they were receiving competent psychiatric help privately. Some hospitals assigned a specific doctor to clinic duty, others rotated this assignment, using it as a "day off in the city." Community agencies seeking to establish liaison with a mental hospital through its aftercare clinic found these varying practices highly confusing.

Because of the obvious disadvantages of such an arrangement the New York State Department of Mental Hygiene recently inaugurated a new type of aftercare service. This will be described in detail because it represents an important forward step in psychiatric care:

A group of independent aftercare clinics were established in the geographic areas in which professional services were actually to be dispensed. In this way great quantities of time and energy for patient care were saved which were previously consumed in nonproductive travel. This arrangement also made it possible for patients and their families to enjoy psychiatric supervision of unprecedented continuity and intensity in the community in which the patient resided.

This program is currently under the direction of D. M. Carmichael, who is in turn responsible to the Assistant Commissioner of Mental Health in charge of the division of Community Mental Health Services. Each clinic is directed by a chief psychiatrist and a supervising psychiatric social worker. Each state hospital with patients attending the clinic assigns two or three staff psychiatrists to work in the clinic on specified days. In this way a patient can maintain continuity with the staff of his own hospital and yet have interim help in emergencies through the services of the clinic chief. The supervising psychiatric social worker directs a large social service department consisting of four teams or units. Each unit consists of a senior psychiatric social worker and five or six staff workers. And finally, a clerical department completes the clinic staff. Evening clinic hours are maintained for patients who work. Emergency social service help is available at times when the clinic is closed, through a social worker on call.

When a patient is being considered for release, the state hospital issues a request to the aftercare clinic in his community for a preconvalescent study. The request is assigned to a clinic staff social worker who will be responsible for that patient from then on.

The request is made on a form which provides the clinic with detailed information about the patient. The following data are included: diagnosis, prognosis, intelligence, occupation, marital and family status. The clinic is also told who initiated the request for the patient's release, where and with whom the patient will live on release, the names and addresses of other significant relatives or friends.

If other social agencies in the community have previously worked with the patient, these are mentioned along with the names of the specific social workers involved.

The personal history of the patient includes his educational background, employment history, history of antisocial behavior, whether there is a court record or any court action pending. Precipitating factors in the patient's breakdown are indicated such as death, business reverses, unemployment, marital or sexual difficulties. The social factors which led to hospitalization are included, whether the patient was suicidal, assaultive, and seclusive.

The request also includes a summary of the patient's course in the hospital, including the presence of medical or physical disability, particularly if these require follow-up care. The results of special laboratory tests, including psychological studies, are included. The psychiatrist indicates clearly special problems for consideration in carrying out the preconvalescent study or in planning the clinic follow-up.

A description of the patient includes his present condition, the existence of residual symptoms, his physical appearance, and the general social impression he makes. Characteristic behavior patterns in response to emotional stress are described.

A vocational survey estimates his employability, describes his skills, interests, job prospects, and the presence of special factors to be considered in employment referral. There should also be a statement concerning his need for supervision, his financial status, his committee, and his need for special living arrangements. The report also gives the patient's estimate of himself, his living arrangements, his employment plans, his specific requests for help. If the patient is under seventeen, suggested educational plans should be mentioned.

Although this is a formidable amount of information to assemble in a single report, it is only in this way that the specific needs of the patient can be pinpointed and his aftercare individualized.

On receipt of this report the social worker visits the patient's family and discusses the plans as they have been formulated at the hospital. This preliminary contact, before the patient's return, is invaluable not only in creating a more wholesome and receptive family attitude toward the patient but in establishing a co-operative relationship with the clinic. If the social worker's report confirms the practicality of the hospital's plan, the patient is released.

On the first Friday after the patient has been discharged from the hospital he reports to the aftercare clinic. Approximately fifty new cases are seen each Friday at each clinic. Patients are seen by a social worker in groups of fifteen with their accompanying relatives. At this meeting the patients learn what the clinic is prepared to do for them. They are encouraged to express their fears, criticisms and hopes. Patients almost always respond to this approach appreciatively and with eagerness to co-operate.

After the group meeting each patient sees his own social worker who assists him with immediate problems. If necessary the patient is seen by a psychiatrist at once. Otherwise he is given an appointment two weeks later by which time his completed records will have been received from the state hospital. In almost all cases, but particularly if the home situation is tense, the social worker visits the home in the interim and provides supportive help or gives the patient an earlier appointment if relapse seems imminent.

After the first regular appointment with the psychiatrist, the patient is discussed by the clinic team. The case is formulated and the aftercare program planned. It may be decided that the social worker will carry the patient in a supportive relationship, or that the problem calls for more intensive individual psychotherapy. The patient may be assigned for group therapy or specifically excluded from group therapy because of suicidal or "acting-out" tendencies. Community family agencies may be brought into the picture to deal with specific family problems. The patient may be assigned to the clinic sheltered workshop to train for a job. He may be referred to state employment and rehabilitation services for vocational help (see Chapter V).

Inasmuch as most relapses and returns to mental hospitals occur within the first three months after discharge, it is the plan of the aftercare clinic to provide support of maximal intensity during this period, tapering off thereafter as the patient's condition permits. Previously patients were routinely placed on convalescent status for one year and discharged at the end of that time if they were still in the community. In keeping with the new program of individualized aftercare, patients are placed on convalescent status indeterminately. This can be prolonged or terminated at the discretion of the clinic team.

In addition to the main function of the aftercare clinic as outlined in the preceding paragraphs, it may be of assistance to state hospitals in other ways, for obtaining anamneses, lobotomy permits, or data for the determination of legal competence. Requests for such help are always given second priority and are never permitted to interfere with the main task of the clinic, which is aftercare. Statistical studies currently in progress have been designed to ascertain whether the foregoing program actually leads to better therapeutic results. This is an experiment of major importance in modern psychiatry.

The Day Hospital

A most ingenious and valuable development in outpatient therapy was that devised by Cameron and his colleagues at the Allan Memorial Institute in Montreal, which they called the Day Hospital. The following description is Cameron's own as he presented it before the Second Mental Hospital Institute in 1950:

> Back in the war years when we were setting up a new hospital we began to realize a tendency on our part to take over certain ideas from the general hospital of which we were a part. These ideas, on close examination, had validity for the general hospital, but did not necessarily apply to a psychiatric department.
>
> Among these was the idea that a hospital is a place where you go to bed. Now obviously, this is not true of the psychiatric division. Of course, mental patients go to bed at night like everyone else, but the bed isn't the place where treatment is carried out. The treatment area is the ward space, the recreational areas, and the occupational therapy areas.
>
> A second idea whose validity was questioned is that the patient goes to the hospital to get well. I do not think that this is literally true even in a general hospital. It certainly is not true in the psychiatric hospital. The patient stays in the hospital as long as necessary to get well enough to go home where treatment continues. If you keep people too long, you create an additional problem of dependence.
>
> Third, we are apt to take over the idea from the general hospital that the hospital is a place where patients and only patients are treated. Actually, we are all aware that the patient is only part of the problem. We have also to consider his whole setting, and family unit.

Hence, in our hospital, we decided to see if we could give expression to the facts that the patient is not treated in bed, that he does not stay in the hospital until he is well, and that the family has to be treated as well as the patient.

Part of this expression crystallized in the form of a day hospital to which the patient came from nine AM to five PM. It has been eminently successful. We have been able to take care of all kinds of patients, except acute suicidals, patients from disturbed homes, or patients who are themselves intensely disturbed, and these, I want to emphasize, are a small minority.

Among the values derived from the day hospital is that the patient throughout his stay remains in touch with his family and community. It is not a matter of some ill person coming to the psychiatric hospital and then going home better. It is a matter of the patient getting well step by step, seeing his family every night, a means of giving his family insight into his recovery, step by step as he goes along.

The day hospital prevents the retreat of the patient into the hospital, the escape into the private room. The system does not allow him to lose touch with his problem. It is a sound way of preventing psychological escape. The patients are more likely to enter into therapy which reveals what the real problem is. The day hospital makes it possible to treat men and women together. And I want to voice my agreement with whoever says that, after all, we are trying to prepare people for daily living and for taking up the threads of their life again. Clearly they are going to live in a bisexual world.

There is a very important economic value in the day hospital. With patients coming from nine to five, we are able to get along with one shift of nurses instead of two. We have one major meal and two snacks. We have a tremendous amount of space that otherwise we would use for beds, housing and clothing.

I looked over some of our figures since 1946 when the Day Hospital was set up. Of course, the cost in Canada is less than in the United States, but according to my figures, the daily cost to the hospital is $2.16 per patient. . . .

The patients sign a statement testifying to the fact that they want treatment. That is to protect the hospital. They do not even sign a form stating that they are voluntary patients. It seems to me that they go into this wholeheartedly. The matter of what they might do to themselves is more an apprehension than a reality. One patient committed suicide at home. He did not come in when we told him to and committed suicide two days later. We did not get into any trouble over that incident and we do not anticipate any. We put the responsibility onto the patient. The patient is not committed: therefore, he is a responsible person, and his relatives also share the responsibility.

In regard to financing, again the situation is like that of the rest of the general hospital. We have private and semiprivate patients. We have patients who are paid for by the city and province. The Blue Cross does not recognize the day hospital, however. The city does recognize it on the same basis as the others. . . .

Most patients are accompanied to the hospital and most patients do go home. We do give electric shock treatments. Where necessary, we give insulin. . . . People discharged after ECT are given follow-up treatment if necessary. . . .

We have developed techniques of emergency treatment. Anybody who shows suicidal trends or becomes overexcited presents an emergency and we get the resident staff and the nurses to act in the same way as they act when you have a ruptured appendix. I think a lot of our trouble with that kind of behavior is that we let it go on for hours or days before we act on it. If a person is treated in a few hours, the disorganization is often brought to an end. But if you allow it to go on for days or weeks, it becomes integrated and organized. If we couldn't clear it up in the day hospital, we would recommend to the relatives that the patient be entered in the hospital proper. We would probably clear it up there. But if that failed, or if the patient would not come in, we would recommend to the relative that the patient be committed. . . .

As you perhaps know, Canada was partially settled by Scotchmen, and it wasn't very long before a number of them said, "Now you have a day hospital, what do you do with it at night to earn money?" We have made provisions for night patients, and for people who work during the day. They participate in the evening program, and have the advantages of being in the group. In actual practice, we find these night patients are closer to being outside the hospital and on their own than the day patients.

Whenever this procedure has been tried the enthusiastic claims of Cameron's group have been confirmed. The importance of continued contact with family and friends has been stressed as well as the greater ease of social service liaison with the family. The Menninger Foundation in Topeka, Kansas, and the New Jersey State Hospital in Trenton, New Jersey, report that their day-care units operate at one third to one fourth of full hospitalization costs.

J. Bierer, the director of a day hospital in England (see references), has reported the successful treatment of a case load of 500 adults and 150 children per year with a staff of psychiatrists only 10 per cent of that which would be required by traditional clinic techniques and a non-professional staff of only 20 per cent the expected size. Among his patients were many chronic psychotics, some of whom had received psychosurgery and other major treatment procedures without improvement. He also provided aftercare for psychotic patients in remission, and for ambulatory schizophrenics who were maintaining a marginal adjustment in the community. Chronic neurotic reactions of all degrees of severity were treated, as well as delinquents and offenders who had been referred to the day hospital with suspended sentences, or who were discharged from prison or were on probation. The psychopathological states of childhood were treated in a program which included the family of the disturbed child as a unit. The day hospital facilities included individual and group psychotherapy, somatotherapy, occupational and recreational therapy, social club therapy, art therapy and psychodrama.

An interesting variant of the day hospital was described in a personal communication by P. H. Brauer, former director of the psychiatric program of the University Settlement House in New York City. This is a large recreational and educational center for families in an underprivileged neighborhood. Very often children and adults were thought to be in need of psychiatric help which they refused because they resented being singled out for special attention due to peculiarities of behavior. To circumvent this, all new applicants for membership in the center were interviewed routinely by a psychiatrically trained social worker. In this way no one could complain that he was being singled out for psychiatric attention. Program leaders were then alerted to individuals who gave evidence of psychopathology and attempted to individualize their approach in accordance with the psychiatric formulation. This did much to remove the stigma of the psychiatric evaluation, and as a result many who were in need of more intensive psychiatric treatment became more accessible. This is a promising device for providing psychiatric help to a large population with a relatively small professional staff.

The Netherlands' Plan

The mental health service in Holland, which is currently administered by N. A. Querido, is based on the proposition that acute emotional disorders which ordinarily require hospitalization are the product, by and large, of disturbances within the family and should be treated as such in the home. Psychiatric and social service help is made continuously available on a twenty-four hour basis through an outpatient center. Disturbed patients are seen in the home by psychiatrists and social workers, and an attempt is made to diminish stresses and to mobilize more adequate ego controls. If the home situation is untenable, foster home placement (see Chapter XXXVI) is arranged directly, and the mental hospital is by-passed completely in the process. All other aspects of treatment, including the liberal use of sheltered workshops, are similarly arranged.

This program has had brilliant results as measured by a lower suicide rate, a lower incidence of first admissions and a fall in the mental hospital population. This family-centered outpatient program has dramatized the fact that mechanical construction of more and more mental hospitals is not necessarily the solution to our growing psychiatric problems.

Outpatient Electroconvulsive Therapy

When applied to properly selected cases, ECT is an invaluable therapeutic device in an outpatient setting. Proper facilities for its application should be available, including preliminary physical clearance by an internist, qualified assistants, oxygen, airways, restorative drugs, and a recovery room where the patient may remain until he has reacted fully from the treatment. Because of the ease with which the treatment can be given one always hears cautions against its abuse. It is probably entirely unnecessary to repeat this caution, but naturally it should be given only where the proper psychiatric indications exist and as part of a total treatment plan, including whatever psychotherapeutic measures can be made available to the patient.

Any patient with a depression or an acute schizophrenia of sufficient severity to justify hospitalization should have a trial of outpatient shock therapy if the home situation makes this at all possible. Many acute psychotic reactions can be interrupted in this way and hospitalization averted. Such patients should be studied with all the detail of a hospital workup, including social service and psychological reports. Long-term treatment plans should be based on all the data. There are some patients to whom the home situation is so intolerable that ECT does not help in spite of an anticipated good result. Such patients may respond very quickly if treated in a hospital. When these patients are ready to return to the community, however, they relapse, or their improvement is very shortlived. Foster home care, a sheltered residence in the community or some similar living arrangement may have to be made in order to sustain an improvement.

A valuable outpatient procedure was suggested by Stevenson and Geoghegan (see references) called prophylactic electroshock. They observed that many patients who tend to relapse frequently can be maintained in remission for long intervals, up to several years in some instances, by the simple expedient of giving them an electroshock treatment at monthly intervals. Others have confirmed the usefulness of this procedure. Patients do not always want to keep their monthly appointments. The social service department can assist by explaining the importance of maintaining the schedule. In those instances in which it was maintained, the results were most rewarding.

Statistical Problems

It was mentioned in Chapter XXVIII that outpatient statistics in psychiatry are even more unsatisfactory than those available for inpatients. And yet, if outpatient care is the most important phase of treatment then statistical studies of outpatient methods must be of corresponding importance.

There are many reasons why clinical statistics are necessary. Public and nonprofessional groups want to know the extent of the community's mental health needs, and how adequately existing clinic facilities meet them. Groups providing funds—public and private, local, state and federal—want to know how the clinic's operating funds are being spent and whether the most effective use is being made of the clinic's resources. Professional organizations will want a scientific evaluation of their role in the clinic program, the extent to which recommended professional standards are being maintained, and the effectiveness of the professional training program. Research workers will want information about socioeconomic and other ecologic factors in mental illness, and the effectiveness of new treatment procedures. In order to obtain valid results, research projects of this nature must be designed in advance of the actual recording or collecting of data. Other information will be needed to plan the most effective co-ordination of the clinic and other resources in the community.

Types of Clinic Data. Enumeration of some of the types of clinic data which can be collected may be helpful in determining how factual information is needed in the broad review and planning of mental health programs.

1. Data on the availability of clinic services would include number and location of clinics, geographic areas served, and special groups of persons served. Indexes on the availability of clinic services in the community can be computed by determining the number of clinics and the number of clinic hours for each 100,000 persons, and also, the number of clinic professional man-hours for each 100,000 persons. Much more service is available to the community, for example, from clinic A, in which there are 500 professional man-hours of service each week, than from clinic B, which provides only 100 man-hours, although both may be full-time clinics.

2. Data on the services provided by clinics are among the most important clinic statistics. Among the ways in which clinic services to patients can be measured is the count which can be made of the number of services provided over a given time period; that is, so many interviews— so many psychological interviews, so many treatment interviews—in one month, in six months. This service count can be broken down into as

much detail by type of service and by type of personnel performing the service as is needed.

For example, before establishing a routine record system that would burden each professional worker with the task of reporting daily auxiliary patient services such as telephone calls and the writing of letters, it should first be decided whether this minute and often "defensive" kind of reporting is worth while. Where it is necessary for management analysis to know how much time is spent on such activities, it may be more economical to obtain this information through occasional time or workload studies.

3. How many patients of each age and sex group in the population visit a clinic during a year? In other words, are services for different segments of the population keeping up with evidences of needs in these groups?

How much service do patients receive? The amount of service received by individual patients can vary from one interview to well over 200 interviews. Because of differences in types of clinics, one clinic may see annually 1,000 patients for one or two visits each, whereas another clinic may see 100 patients from five to seventy-five visits each. It is important, therefore, to have some factual information on the amount of services received as well as on the number of patients.

For different age groups represented at the clinic, what are the problems uncovered or diagnoses made?

How many patients does the clinic treat?

What is the average amount and duration of the therapy?

Who gives treatment to various kinds of patients?

How does the outcome of therapy relate to diagnosis and to type, duration, and amount of therapy?

How many cases are terminated before planned services have been completed?

What are the reasons for the unsatisfactory termination of the case?

What is the probability of readmission?

In the area of patient services, the kinds of useful statistical questions that can be asked are almost limitless. So also are the kinds of useful cross-tabulations that can be made from data such as age, sex, amount of service, and outcome of therapy, particularly if punchcards pertaining to a large number of patients are available.

4. Data on the extent to which clinic activities are directed to the general community and community agencies rather than to registered clinic patients are valuable because of the increasing emphasis on community-oriented services, such as public mental health education, inservice mental health training of professional groups, and consultation services to other community agencies, in public mental health programs. Here again, there may be interest in several facets of the subject:

What community agencies make use of this type of clinic service?

What kinds of services are given?

Who in the clinic provides the services?

Is there any way of determining whether these services are of value other than from the fact that they are in demand?

In counting community services, either the number of different kinds of activities or the number of man-hours used for such activities might be recorded. The latter method is preferable because it provides a valid method for adding up different kinds of activities.

5. Or, the clinic might be looked at from a different focus, and questions might be asked about its administration—utilization of staff time, workload, or cost, such as:

How many professional persons are employed in mental health clinics?

What were the employment trends during the last five years?

To what extent are clinic staffs interdiscipline groups or composed of the basic clinic team?

Given the most desirable interdiscipline ratios of psychiatrists, psychologists, and psychiatric social workers for clinic teams in different types of clinics, how many additional persons of each profession would be needed to complete the staff of existing clinics or to staff clinics that may be planned for the next few years?

What training activities for the various professions are under way in the different clinics?

During a given month, how much professional time is used for patient services, community services, training, staff conferences, dictation, and other administrative work?

How many patients are there in active status on a given day?

How many of these patients are undergoing long-term treatment on a weekly basis? Semiweekly basis?

How many patients are on the treatment waiting list for one month? Six months?

Information is needed which shows how professional man-hours for different disciplines are distributed by activity and by case. Comparable, and perhaps nationwide, data are needed in this area so that clinics can review their experience with that of similar clinics and determine whether their staffs are being used in the most efficient manner. However, this workload information is of less interest to public, community, and supporting agencies than are data that will indicate the kinds of services provided, who are the recipients of such services, and how much the services cost.

There appears to be an increasing interest on the part of appropriation agencies in obtaining data on the cost of clinic services:

What is the mental health clinic cost per capita population in the country and in different communities?

What is the clinic cost for each interview hour? For each community service hour? For each professional man-hour? For each type of patient?

6. Data on the referral source of patients are another type of information which may be quite valuable to the clinic or local council of clinics. These data may indicate the extent to which different community agencies are being served by the clinic or are cognizant of the mental health clinic as a resource. These data may also indicate patient or family awareness of a psychiatric problem.

In the collection and interpretation of referral data on a national scale, however, there are some difficulties. Knowledge of the local machinery for referral and of clinic policy is essential for interpretation of referral data. Some clinics connected with schools, for example, do not accept patients without school referral. Families are therefore automatically referred through the school and counted as school referrals, although their attendance at the clinic is actually self-motivated. Several other types of clinics accept patients only through agency referrals. Also, where there is both self- and agency-direction to the clinic, "self-referral" and "agency-referral" are not defined in the same way by different clinics.

7. Data on applications pending or waiting lists can also be useful to the clinic and community, as indications of immediate demand for services. However, here again, knowledge of the local situation is necessary for careful interpretation of the data, particularly if they are to be used as indices of the community's unmet needs.

The community's referral mechanism and the clinic's application policy will have a marked influence on the number of applications pending at a clinic. Some clinics may not accept applications for temporary periods of time. Also, where the clinic has a long waiting list of applicants, this becomes known to referral agencies and persons who are seeking clinic services, and applications are not made. Some other method must be found, therefore, to obtain reliable data on the need for clinic services, if this information is desired.

Collecting Uniform Data. Several methods that may be used for collecting comparable clinic information on a national or wide geographic basis are: a) the use of a national report form for collecting minimum basic data from all clinics; b) the development of a model reporting area in clinic statistics; and c) the use of sample surveys for the collection of more extensive information. These methods can be used to supplement each other to get meaningful clinic information.

1. The use of a national summary report form is geared primarily to the routine collection of a minimum of basic information from all clinics. Such is the annual report from four psychiatric outpatient clinics proposed at the Second Conference of Mental Hospital Administrators and Statisticians in 1952 (see references) and subsequently developed by the National Institute of Mental Health of the Public Health Service in cooperation with State mental health authorities and professional organizations. Now that the preliminary revisions and some trial experiences have been completed, the report form was to be used voluntarily on a nationwide basis beginning July 1, 1954.[1]

The principal advantage of a uniform summary report for all clinics is that it can provide a nucleus of comparable basic information on nation-wide clinic services.

As a result of experience with the uniform report form or because of changes in clinic emphasis or policy, new items can be added to the form, and other items can be deleted, or classifications can be changed.

Data on terminated patients requested in the new national form may be prepared in a number of ways—from punchcards which are tabulated mechanically, from cards tabulated manually, or from listings and work-

[1]Copies of the new summary report form are available on request. Write to the Biometrics Branch of the National Institute of Mental Health, Bethesda 14, Md.

sheets. When more clinics, clinic councils, and state mental health authorities are cognizant of the advantages of punchcards, attempts will undoubtedly be made to explore all possible resources in order to utilize punchcard equipment which may be readily available.

2. Experience with a model reporting area in the field of mental hospital statistics may be cited as an example of how more extensive information can be obtained in a large-scale collection of clinic data, particularly through punchcard methods. A model reporting area of the mental hospitals in fifteen states has developed as a result of the three recent Conferences of Mental Hospital Administrators and Statisticians (see references). The fifteen states composing the area are Arkansas, California, Illinois, Indiana, Kansas, Louisiana, Michigan, Nebraska, New Jersey, New York, Ohio, Pennsylvania, Texas, Virginia, and Wisconsin. Representatives of the States meet annually, and have since 1951, to arrive at uniform definitions, minimum number of basic tabulations, and appropriate methods of statistical analyses. By mutual agreement, these states collect and tabulate data in addition to those requested in connection with the mental hospital census conducted by the National Institute of Mental Health of the Public Health Service. The use of machine tabulation methods in these states has made feasible such additional tabulations.

A model reporting area in the field of mental health clinic statistics, composed of State mental health authorities and possibly community councils, which utilizes punchcard procedures for tabulating patient reports, could operate in a similar fashion. For example, additional items of information could be collected on terminated patients if desired, or the group might decide to co-operate in a one- or two-year special study on a subject in which there is mutual interest. If a definitive study were desired on some particular type of patient or disorder presented at the clinic, it might be more readily accomplished as a co-operative project among all clinics represented in a model reporting area in a one-year study than if an attempt were made to collect this information in a single clinic or single state. In order to have enough cases for valid deductions, a small clinic might find it necessary to collect this information over a number of years.

3. The use of sampling techniques is another method of collecting clinic information on a broad scale. The obvious advantage of sample surveys is that only a relatively small proportion of the clinics are called on to supply the extra data. Yet, sample data, if properly collected, weighted, and interpreted, yield inferences applicable to the universe sampled. For each new study, samples of clinics can be reselected so that no single clinic would tend to be overburdened with supplying special data. However, it is desirable first to have basic data which describes the universe of clinics so that a sample can be properly selected.

Any data that would be available in a national file of punchcards, as the result of the collection of information on the new national report form, would certainly be made available to any accredited agency for the selection of clinics for sample or other studies. For example, if it were desired to study psychiatric social work services in mental health clinics throughout the United States, it would be possible to select a representative sample of clinics for query instead of querying all clinics in the country, and there would be a resultant saving of time and money to the clinics and to the group making the study. Thus, the use of sampling techniques makes accessible, in an economical manner, a rich reservoir of clinic information.

SELECTED REFERENCES

BAHN, A. K.: *Mental Health Clinic Statistics: Needs—Sources—Methods*. Public Health Reports, 69:619, 1954. Reprint No. 3234, U.S. Gov. Printing Office, Washington 25, D.C.

A concise summary of this vast new field.

BARHASH, A. Z.; BENTLEY, M. C.; KIRKPATRICK, M. E.; SANDERS, H. A.: *The Organization and Function of the Community Psychiatric Clinic*. National Association for Mental Health, 1790 Broadway, New York 19, N.Y.

A practical guide which should be studied by anyone associated with a psychiatric clinic in an administrative capacity.

BIERER, J.: *The Day Hospital: An Experiment in Social Psychiatry and Syntho-Analytic Psychotherapy*. London: H. K. Lewis & Co., 1951.

A useful report of a Day Hospital experience, containing many valuable case histories.

CAMERON, D. E.: The Day Hospital: An Approach to Expanding Hospital Facilities. In: *Mental Hospitals, 1950*. Proceedings of the Second Mental Hospital Institute, 1951. American Psychiatric Association, 1624 Eye St., N.W., Washington 6, D.C.

EDITORIAL: Mental Care: A Different Patient. *Lancet*, 266:1117, 1954 (see also Ling).

EXPERT COMMITTEE ON MENTAL HEALTH: *Third Report*. World Health Organization, Palais des Nations, Geneva, 1953. (Available through the U.N. Book Store in New York City.)

Contains useful recommendations concerning outpatient facilities.

LING, T. M.: The Prevention of Mental Illness: Some Lessons from Holland. *Lancet,* 266:1127, 1954. See also Editorial (same issue).

An excellent description of the Netherlands Mental Health Service as it is functioning under the direction of A. Querido. An important document on outpatient psychiatric care.

MEZER, R. R.; SOLOMON, H. C.: Value of Electro-Shock Treatment of Outpatients. *New England J. Med.*, 250:721, 1954.

A study which confirms the value of outpatient ECT.

NATIONAL ASSOCIATION FOR MENTAL HEALTH: *Psychiatric Clinics and Other Resources in the United States. Directory, 1952*. National Association for Mental Health, 1790 Broadway, New York 19, N.Y.

This directory lists psychiatric clinics, mental health associations, State institutions, State Governmental Departments, Veterans Administration and other Federal mental hospitals. Contains many useful facts about existing psychiatric clinics—their location, nature of staff personnel, case load, and schedule.

Public Health Service Proceedings of Conference of Mental Hospital Administrators and Statisticians (First conference, 1951; second conference, 1952; third conference, 1953). U.S. Gov. Printing Office, Washington 25, D.C.

These proceedings contain preliminary reports on outpatient psychiatric statistical studies currently in progress.

ROND, P. C.: The Day Hospital Unit—Milieu Therapy, Its Place in the Treatment of the Mentally Ill. *Ohio Med. J.*, 49:1093, 1953.

A useful description of a day hospital experience at the Columbus (Ohio) Receiving Hospital.

SMITH, L. H.: The Development of a Mental Health Center in a Private Non-Profit Hospital. *Ment. Health Bull.* (Pensylvania Dept. of Welfare), 25:3, 1948.

A "day-hospital-like" program is described, including a nursery school for well children which provided opportunities to study normal behavior, outpatient facilities for disturbed children and adults, a speech and reading disability clinic, vocational and marital counseling, adult education, occupational therapy, social and recreational opportunities for patients, and training opportunities for doctors, nurses, psychologists, social workers and students of occupational therapy.

STEVENSON, G. H.; GEOGHEGAN, J. J.: Prophylactic Electroshock. *Am. J. Psychiat.*, 107:743, 1951.

The technique and usefulness of maintenance outpatient ECT is described.

Chapter XXXVI

FAMILY CARE

The Role of Family Care

There are a great many patients in mental hospitals who are capable of adapting to a protected environment outside the hospital, but whose own home environment is unsatisfactory. Frequently family stresses which broke down the patient's emotional adaptation in the first place cannot be eliminated, and to return the already traumatized patient to that unfortunate situation is to court relapse. At times an overprotective environment can be even more disorganizing in its effect than an overtly rejecting one, generating unreasoning resentment in the patient who is fighting desperately for emotional independence. Many patients have no family to which they can return. In all these instances, placement in a foster home provides a practical answer. This form of continued treatment of the mentally ill is referred to as family care or foster home care. It is suitable not only for convalescing patients who are expected to recover, but for chronic patients, too, in whom a permanent emotional disability is expected.

The Gheel Colony

Family care of mental patients calls to mind the Belgian town of Gheel. Although this community pioneered in family care for a number of centuries, it is only in recent decades that this extraordinary treatment plan has fired the psychiatric imagination of this country. The pivotal point of the Gheel plan is a centrally situated building with room for a few hundred patients for purposes of observation, diagnosis and classification. New patients remain at this center until suitable arrangements can be made for their placement in private homes in the town. Patients who run into any kind of difficulty after placement may be returned to the center for further study, treatment and placement elsewhere.

The vast majority of the patients are boarded out with families in the surrounding town of Gheel. The standard practice is to place two patients of the same sex, age and general classification with a family. Families are all carefully investigated. At times their status is known from association with the Gheel colony for many generations. Placement is made with due regard for the social and cultural level of the patient and the foster family, as well as their mutual occupational interests. Close but informal contact is maintained between the families and the central institution. There are no walls or fences. The central institution is provided with various recreational facilities. Patients can circulate freely between the latter and their family homes. Families at all socio-economic levels receive patients. Although the income which is paid to them by the State plays an important motivating role in many instances, the principal factor is to be found in a tradition of sympathy and social responsibility going back many hundred years.

An interesting legend is told about the origins of this community. In the sixth century there was an Irish king. He was a pagan but his wife and only daughter became Christians. After the death of the queen, the king decided that the one person who could take her place was his daughter Dymphne. Horrified by his incestuous demands, Dymphne fled to Belgium with her Christian Father-Confessor. At Gheel the king caught up with them and when his daughter once again refused his incestuous importunations, he beheaded her with his own hands and also killed the priest. Her tomb became a shrine, and she became the patron saint of the mentally ill. Certain rituals had to be observed by suppliants at the shrine for nine days and nine nights, following which miraculous cures were sometimes said to occur. As the possessed and the persecuted continued to come from far and near to visit the shrine for refuge or for cure, the obscure village of Gheel gradually became a well-known refuge for the mentally disordered.

The content of the legend strongly suggests its origin in a psychotic episode which may have caused Dymphne's panic-stricken flight from her home in response to her delusions. In it there are death wishes toward the mother; incestuous wishes, which she then projected onto her father; and her own death as the fantasied punishment for her impulses, but which was simultaneously the incestuous fulfillment. The fantasy of a flight with the Father-Confessor may have been an expression of her attempt to use religious devotions to repress the "pagan" incestuous impulses which were overwhelming her. The mystic observances at the shrine for nine days and nine nights which were then to be followed by a miracle is suggestive of a pregnancy fantasy. Other psychoanalytically familiar symbolic usages may be recognized in the legend which will not be discussed further at this time. If this legend was indeed the product of Dymphne's disordered mind, it suggests that her mental illness led in some way to her becoming the patron saint of the mentally ill. The foregoing pregnancy fantasy, for example, may have also been a rebirth fantasy symbolizing her emergence from the psychosis with a sense of personal mission in behalf of other psychotic persons, just as happened to Clifford Beers many centuries later.

As the mentally ill were drawn to this shrine in increasing numbers, public accommodations within the church were soon overtaxed and the hospitable townsfolk started accepting the pilgrims into their own homes. Subsequently a hospital was established under state auspices. As the work grew, it became subject to local governmental regulations and in the middle of the nineteenth century the religious and communal facilities were officially transformed into a state colony for the care of mental patients.

Many thousands of people have been successfully treated in this colony. Patients are received fiom all over the world. The program now commands international attention by its extraordinary success and is a model to be studied for inspiration and inexhaustible experience in the problems of setting up a family care program.

The Growth of Family Care Elsewhere

The momentum of tradition and religious inspiration has given the Gheel program a special vitality which is probably not exactly reproducible elsewhere in the world. However, it has been utilized fairly extensively throughout Europe for many years. It was slower in taking hold in the United States, in spite of experiments with this technique in Massachusetts as early as 1885. However, the rate of growth of family care is definitely on the increase. In 1936, there were 426 patients on family care in New York State, and in 1953, there were 2,317. In 1951, there were 4,937 patients on family care throughout the United States. In 1952, this number had increased to 5,617, and in 1953, to 6,201.

Types of Family Care

Family care which is concentrated in a community located in the neighborhood of a hospital has been called Family Care, Community Type. This is the plan modeled more or less on the familiar one at Gheel. From many points of view it represents the ideal plan. Family Care, Individual Type, represents placement in a suitable home wherever it may be located. This necessitates much more traveling for the supervising psychiatrist and social worker. It may also result in a patient's having no access to recreational facilities and may complicate the problem of returning the patient to the hospital for emergency care.

Family Care, School Type, concerns itself primarily with the placement of children of school age and relates to the fact that in such instances placement is often determined by specific educational and training needs.

A patient may be placed in a work setting, a farm, for example, in which he earns wages in addition to his maintenance; or the patient may earn his maintenance or part of it. Most foster families, however, are paid an officially agreed upon weekly fee in return for which the patient is cared for. He has no obligation to work, although he is usually encouraged to work around the house for therapeutic reasons.

Selection of Foster Families

The Social Service Department is usually given the responsibility for publicizing the need for foster families in the community. Lectures are given before parent-teacher associations, nurses organizations, farm associations, and other social agencies. These groups are given a general description of the plan and its aims and are informed as to the total number of patients that are suitable for custody with families in the community. The opportunities offered to carry out altruistic and humanitarian pursuits and the benefits to be derived by both patients and families are also explained. Most families that apply for participation in the program do so initially for financial reasons. However, where a proper placement has been made, genuine human values enter into the relationship very quickly, and foster families tend to make contributions far beyond that required by the formal arrangements with the hospital.

Thus, one family had to take a trip. While they were gone they hired a housekeeper to look after the patient even though they could have returned her to the hospital. In another instance, the patient worked in a filling station owned by the family. The patient enjoyed this work so much that the family stipulated in an agreement selling the station that the new owners had to permit the patient to continue working there.

When a family files an application to receive patients into their home, the social worker ascertains if the physical accommodations are satisfactory and if the possibilities exist for wholesome family life. If these are suitable, the social worker explains to the family as much as is necessary about the patient's condition. In community family care, it is often possible to have a responsible member of the foster family come with the patient periodically to the hospital, not only for psychiatric examination of the patient but also for group instruction for foster families. The more understanding that the foster family has of mental illness, the more certain of success will a given placement be.

Instructions to Foster Families

The following set of general instructions addressed to foster families embodies many of the basic principles of family care.

1. Home care. The patients placed in your home are wards of the state and are entrusted to you with the expectation that you will give them good care and make them feel at home in your family.

2. Meals. Patients should be given three meals a day. The food should be wholesome and of sufficient variety and quantity to maintain health and vigor. Marked changes in weight of patients should be reported to the social worker of the institution. If a patient refuses to eat for more than a single day, the matter should be reported to the institution.

3. Bed. Each patient must be provided with a separate, comfortable bed in a well-ventilated room. In rooms of sufficient size, two or three beds may be placed.

4. Clothing. Patient's clothing is furnished by the institution or by relatives. Foster families are required to see that it is kept clean and in good repair. Patients when able may assist in care of clothing.

5. Work. Patients when physically able should be encouraged to do some work each day. Women patients may assist in housework and light outdoor occupations. Men patients may do chores, care for farm animals and assist in other farm and garden work. In addition, work projects may be furnished patients by the occupational therapist of the institution. No patient should be permitted to work beyond his strength or endurance, or to work for other families except by permission of the institution.

6. Play and Other Diversion. Some form of diversion should be provided for patients. Books and papers should be made available to those who wish to read. Outdoor activities should be encouraged in suitable weather. Games such as cards, checkers and dominoes should be furnished. Occasional social parties, movies and free access to television, if possible, are highly desirable.

7. Bath. Bathing facilities must be provided for patients. Every patient must have free access to a lavatory and have a thorough bath at least once a week.

8. Supervision. Patients must be carefully supervised and a responsible person must be in charge of them at all times.

9. Discipline. Patients must never be punished or locked in their rooms. Kind treatment and gentle persuasion will accomplish much more than harsh measures.

10. Illness. If a patient becomes sick or is injured, the institution should be notified at once. In an emergency a local physician should be called.

11. Absence. If a patient wanders away from your home a search for him should be made. If he cannot be found the institution should be notified.

12. Troublesome patients. If a patient becomes too troublesome for you to manage, the institution should be notified at once.

13. Visits. Patients must not leave your home to visit relatives or friends without written permission from an officer of the institution. A record should be kept of all visits to patients in your home.

14. Official visits. Official visitors from the institution when calling on patients in your home may desire to talk privately with each patient and to inspect the patient's clothing and rooms. Such inspection is required by the institution and is in no sense a reflection on you or on your care of the patient.

15. Peculiarities of patients. Foster families should discourage undesirable habits or tendencies of patients but should not laugh at their peculiarities or discuss them with others.

16. Co-operation. Foster families are expected to co-operate with the institution in promoting the well-being, happiness and recovery of patients. It is believed that much may be accomplished toward this end by making the home life of the patient as comfortable and congenial as possible.

It is made clear to the family at the outset that they will not and cannot be compelled to keep a patient who is uncongenial to them. Conversely, a patient who is unhappy will be free to return to the institution whenever he so desires.

Therapeutic Advantages of Family Care

By and large, patients are very happy in foster families. For many chronic patients, it is a release to the outer world that they had long given up as impossible. They are quickly transformed by the more natural environment of the home. Social workers will comment with pleased astonishment at the fact that the patient has become "so much more human." Opportunities for individualized attention in the home naturally exceed anything possible in an institution. The food and the way it is served are sources of great satisfaction to the patient. The environment of children, animal pets and normal family life exert a powerful psychotherapeutic effect. Occupational activities which are varied, interesting and most of all socially useful, exert a therapeutic influence which is superior to the more stereotyped occupational activities of the hospital. Family care often represents a "half-way house" for the patient, leading to discharge into the community as a fully recovered patient. It also makes it possible to send patients out on trial visits much earlier, since the foster home environment to which he goes is selected from a mental hygiene point of view and is generally more satisfactory than his own home.

Family care exerts a salutary effect on the community, broadening the general level of understanding of mental illness and laying the groundwork for a more effective program of prevention.

A socially prominent woman once bitterly opposed the construction of a nearby state hospital, and later resented the presence of patients in the community. She was induced to accept a patient for family care. She liked him so well that she asked for another to be placed on her son's farm. Her previous unfriendly attitude was replaced by one of enthusiastic support of the family care program.

Another was moved by the satisfaction she derived from her role in the family care program to remark in a letter, "It is the duty of all citizens to aid in the rehabilitation of patients."

Results of Family Care

Family care is effective treatment. Unmistakable improvements are noted in many chronic psychotic patients. Paranoid trends may decrease in their intensity. Catatonic patients may become more alert.

One chronic patient on family care wrote to the director of her hospital, "I think it only right that I should thank you for making it possible to come to live with kindly people, where I could regain myself, and again do the things that I felt I could do well before my sickness. I enjoy the home life here and all that goes with a home, as homemaking was what I always liked and worked for, and being deprived of that, suffered much. I think this was a happy way of solving the problem of my helplessness and to help me by showing me the way to help others."

During the year 1952, 305 patients from twenty-four Veterans Administration Mental Hospitals were placed in foster homes. Sixty-six per cent of them had been ill for five years or more. In spite of this fact, only 24 patients had to be returned to the hospital; 67 improved enough to be discharged from further supervision; 31 were able to make the transition from the foster home to their own homes where they continued on trial visit. The remainder showed improvement in behavior and general health. It was estimated by Roger Cummings of the Veterans Administration that there was a $500,000 saving to the taxpayer as a result of this treatment plan. In addition, much needed beds were released for patients on the waiting list.

Patient Returns from Foster Families

Although it is generally stated that the problem of matching the proper patient to the proper family is a difficult one, the actual percent-

age of unsuccessful placements is small. Most patients react gratefully to
the many positive aspects of family care, and the families in turn have
been quite content with the arrangement. As a matter of fact, most returns
from family care have been the result of physical illness in the patient or
some major change in the foster family, like the death of one of the prin-
cipals. Returns for psychiatric reasons do of course occur. Occasionally
a patient has become so attached to a member of the hospital staff that
separation from the hospital results in depression. Unsuccessful placement should not be a cause for discouragement even when it occurs
repeatedly.

The case of a young schizophrenic woman is described who was placed
first in a physician's home. She left him for an unauthorized visit to her
family, following which it became necessary to return her to the hospital.
Next she was placed as a laundress near her home. She visited her family
again, became disturbed and had to be rehospitalized. Her next placement was as a domestic in a family with three grown children. She became
very competitive with them for the parents' attention, became disturbed
and was again returned to the hospital. After improvement, she was
placed with an elderly couple of humble means. This couple's deceased
daughter would have been about the patient's age if she had lived, and
therefore they welcomed the patient with open arms. They treated her as
a daughter and took her wherever they went. This fourth placement
worked out successfully.
An elderly arteriosclerotic woman adjusted well in a foster home
until a younger patient, a schizophrenic girl, was placed there, too, after
which she became disturbed and had to be hospitalized. (As a rule, it is
best not to place old patients with young patients in the same household.)

In instances of unsuccessful placement, it is a great advantage to have
a community center or a "half-way house" where the patient can remain,
pending a more satisfactory placement. The patient is thereby spared the
highly traumatic feeling of failure attending a return to the hospital.

Popular Misconceptions Concerning Family Care

It used to be predicted that foster families would overwork their patients and otherwise mistreat them. Instances of this were not uncovered.
It was predicted that patients would become nuisances in the communities in which they were placed, and that patients would commit acts of
violence or indecency. All of these forebodings have not been substan-
tiated by the facts. Dangers and inconveniences to the community are
rare complications of family care. Benefits to the mental health of the
community, on the other hand, are great indeed.

The Transition to Unsupervised Care

Patients on family care are maintained on a committed status. That is, they remain under the direct supervision and control of the mental hospital from which they were placed. The ideal of family care is the restitution of the patient as a free and independent citizen in the community. This calls for continued teamwork with the patient, the foster family and his own family. The social worker will play a role of preeminent importance in modifying the home environment so that it becomes less distressing to the patient. The involvement of family social service agencies in the patient's own community and in an aftercare program like that described in Chapter XXXV represent particularly effective means for accomplishing this transition.

SELECTED REFERENCES

CUMMINGS, R.: *Dept. Med. and Surg., V.A. Information Bulletin* (IB-40). Psychiat. & Neurol. Div., April, 1953.
     A statistical study confirming the value of family care as treatment.
DEWITT, H. B.: Family Care as the Focus for Social Casework in a State Mental Hospital. *Ment. Hyg.,* 28:602, 1944.
     The role of social service in family care is well brought out in this paper. Excellent illustrative clinical material.
POLLOCK, H. M., ed.: *Family Care of Mental Patients. A Review of Systems of Family Care in America and Europe.* Utica: State Hospitals Press, 1936.
     This book is an invaluable introduction and practical guide to the field of family care. Highly recommended.

Chapter XXXVII

EDUCATING THE PUBLIC

The Mechanism of Denial

After World War II, many German civilians insisted that they had no knowledge of the extermination camps. Although this seemed incredible to on-the-scene observers, the fact is that man's capacity for deluding himself is remarkable. Denial is a psychological mechanism of defense in which an individual behaves and thinks as if some manifest reality did not indeed exist. The expression, "There are none so blind as those who will not see," actively embodies the idea of denial. The apparent failure to see or to hear which characterizes the mechanism of denial is purposeful. It protects the individual from anxiety, and it operates quite unconsciously.

For example, an individual who develops intolerable anxiety on seeing physical defects in others, often fails to "see" a physical abnormality which is obvious to his companions. Another example is the patient who comes to the psychoanalyst's office for months in the grip of an inhibition against looking. He is not aware of his inhibition until one day, when analysis has relieved his anxiety to a sufficient degree, he observes suddenly that the analyst has a moustache, or is bald, or that he has a lamp on his desk. On first observing the lamp, for example, he may express bewildered disbelief when told that it was present all the time.

A person given to denial may quickly forget or repress a painful detail which an outsider has compelled him to observe, and when placed in the self-same situation on another occasion, he fails to observe the painful detail all over again. The individual is inclined to cling to the "capacity" not to observe until his anxiety has been reduced to a tolerable degree, then suddenly his perceptual horizon becomes expanded.

In many ways, the attitude of the public toward mental hospitals is reminiscent of that of the German civilians toward their camps, or of patients in the grip of an inhibition against looking. They do not let themselves learn about conditions in hospitals at their own doorstep and when, from time to time, shocking accounts of hospital conditions appear in the press, their bewildered disbelief is like that of the previously mentioned analytic patients. There may be a brief reaction of disgust and indignation, but this is quickly repressed. The articles in the press are forgotten, and life goes on as before.

To rail against public indifference is to fail to take into account this common psychological mechanism. However enlightened the citizen may be about many things, his knowledge of mental illness remains quite primitive. Nothing can arouse such dread in the laiety as the strange remarks and behavior of psychotic people. To many the mentally ill are potentially violent and the mental hospital a place for the confinement of "depraved and maddened persons." It usually comes as a surprise to the laiety that a very small per cent of the mentally ill are actually dangerous to others. The belief that patients are responsible for many crimes when released into the community contrasts with the actual incidence of criminal behavior in the ex-patient population, which has been estimated as one fourteenth that in the population at large. Along with the widespread and largely unwarranted fear of sexual abnormality (see Chapter XXIII) is the mistaken belief that mental hospital patients are given to uncontrolled sexual behavior instead of the sexually inhibited behavior which is far and away more common.

That the public should have these misconceptions is perhaps not surprising in view of the preoccupation with security measures rather than with treatment, which prevails in many of our mental hospitals to this very day. However, more fundamental reasons operate, too, which have been referred to previously (Chapters X, XII, XXIII, etc.). The psychiatrist cannot lose sight of the fears of the laiety in his attempts to educate them. It is only by helping them to master their fears that the need for denial can be overcome. When misconceptions have been corrected, the public will be more ready to listen to facts. However, fantasies are surrendered piecemeal, and one who attempts to educate the public psychiatrically must expect them to persist in spite of frequent explanatory corrections. This is analogous to the process of "working through" in psychotherapy, a repetitive process whereby old prejudices are undermined and replaced by more realistically flexible attitudes.

What Should Be Taught?

A program of public education for mental health should seek to replace obsolete ideas involving shame, fear and superstition with up-to-date facts and scientific knowledge. There is a need to overcome the stigma of mental illness which causes people to delay seeking help and to create an awareness that in mental disease, as in all disease, prompt diagnosis and treatment greatly increase the chances for improvement and cure. It should help parents to understand the special importance of early childhood experiences in the emotional development of their children, and motivate them to provide a more wholesome home environment. By learning the emotional needs of the child at every stage of its development, parents, teachers, law-enforcement officers and others can be better equipped to meet those needs. The program should correct misconceptions which give rise to anxiety, guilt feelings, prejudices and various hostile and antisocial attitudes. These dysphoric states destroy family life and human relationships in general. It should promote an awareness that there is no sharp definition of "normal" and that there are deeper sources of motivation and purposeful behavior than usually appear on the surface. In the process a more charitable acceptance of deviant behavior in one's fellow man may be promoted. The program will also emphasize the right of every human being to develop his own individuality within rather wide limits and at the same time will insist on the need to respect the rights of others. At all times it will emphasize positive life values.

Accepting the fact that it is difficult for people to change and understanding the reasons for these difficulties, the mental health educator will also insist on the proposition that people can be reached with proper educational techniques and can be guided to a healthier emotional life.

The public education program can disseminate factual information about existing facilities for treatment, research and training. Such information would emphasize the need for financial support. It can also stimulate the application of psychiatric knowledge to specific social problems such as alcoholism, sexual offense, delinquency and crime, and in the process help promote more enlightened legislation and more effective methods of treatment.

Who Should Be Taught?

The educational program should seek to reach every individual in the community directly, from the youngest to the oldest. However, it should concentrate its efforts on key people in strategic positions for influencing attitudes and human relationships. These include expectant mothers and parents of school children, public health personnel, physicians, nurses and others who tend to the sick, probation officers and staffs of institutions for delinquency and dependency, vocational placement counselors and staffs of rehabilitation centers, the management staff in industry, the shop stewards in labor unions, lawyers, judges, clergy and religious educators, teachers, recreational and group workers, law-enforcement officers, and others in public service.

Who Should Teach?

The public's major source of information about psychiatry, particularly with respect to mental hospitals, are the daily newspapers. As a result of lurid headlines the criminal and sexual propensities of psychiatric patients have become grossly distorted in the public mind. Incidents involving the mistreatment of a patient are always widely publicized. Therapeutic advances, on the other hand, often go unnoticed. As a result, some mental hospitals are unjustifiably characterized as "snake-pits." This is not an abstract matter of inaccuracy and injustice to the professional staff, but it may hinder the mental health program of the area as well. A permanent mental hospital public relations committee with a full-time chairman who is suited for the job by inclination and training (see Chapter XXVII) can correct this situation. He accomplishes this not simply in the negative sense of protecting the public and the hospital against misinformation but by actively publicizing the constructive aspects of the hospital program. He is usually aided in this work by the local mental health associations affiliated with the National Association for Mental Health.

Hospital personnel represent the second most important source of public information about the activities in a mental hospital. This includes the volunteers as well as the paid staff. In informal social contacts they create public attitudes which can be a constructive or a destructive force in the mental hospital and the community. Careful preparation for this social responsibility should be an important part of the hospital training program.

Some mental hospitals maintain a speaker's bureau and arrange for various members of the staff to participate in community educational activities. These include psychiatrists, social workers, psychologists, chaplains, nurses, attendants, volunteer workers, dietitians, beauty parlor operators, special therapists, and others.

Finally, the patients themselves are playing a role of increasing importance in educating the public about mental health. In public appearances on radio and television they are tearing away the morbid veil of secrecy which has surrounded mental hospitals heretofore. (More of this later.)

How Should the Educational Program Be Conducted?

Just as every aspect of mental hospital life can be integrated into the treatment program of a truly therapeutic community, so can the program of public education be similarly integrated. That is, it should express itself in every contact with patients, relatives and visitors. Every employee is an ambassador to the surrounding community. A telephone conversation may be an opportunity to correct a prejudice. The use of bulletin boards and posters, the liberal distribution of mental hygiene literature (see references) represent simple devices readily available in all mental hospitals to raise the level of psychiatric understanding of every employee, patient and visitor. Such a global approach to public education cannot be carried out without the assistance of a public relations committee.

Open House is a custom which has been inaugurated in mental hospitals in which special days are set aside each year for visitors to tour the hospital. These days are invested with a festive quality; distinguished guests are invited to speak; refreshments are served; special literature is distributed; the art work of patients and products from occupational therapy are exhibited; patients put on entertainments; and all departments of the hospital are opened to inspection. Such occasions provide opportunities to acquaint the public with the treatment program and to dispel pessimistic prejudices about the hopelessness of mental disease. An honest display of shortcomings may impel visitors to participate in the volunteer program, or to make gifts of special equipment or money.

The Press. Releases to the press should feature volunteer activities, open house, special awards to hospital personnel, reports of scientific meetings and therapeutic innovations, donations, the vocational rehabilitation program, religious and educational activities, distinguished visitors and group tours. Whenever possible pictures should accompany articles. Stories involving matters of scientific fact should be cleared for accuracy by a responsible member of the professional staff.

Films. The use of films for educational and mental health purposes has been referred to in Chapter XXIX. Useful film catalogues are listed in the references for that chapter. It is important to stress that films should be used, ideally, as a springboard for discussion. Before the film is shown, the audience should be briefed on its main points. Very often mental health films shown to lay groups raise more questions and disturbed feelings than they settle. The animated discussions which invariably follow such showings provide the chief opportunity for public education. It is a serious error not to permit sufficient time for such discussions to develop fully.

Group discussions which may or may not accompany a film represent the most useful method of public instruction for mental health. An intimate spirit should be maintained by limiting the size of the groups. An ideal community plan is to follow a large-audience film showing by a number of small discussion groups, each with its own leader. In airing their problems, people are amazed to learn how much they have in common with their neighbors. This discovery relieves anxiety and feelings of guilt. In the course of the discussion they answer each other's questions and gain assurance concerning their ability to handle their problems. In short, all the constructive things that happen in group therapy can happen in a skillfully guided public discussion on mental health.

Television is one of the most powerful instruments of communication that has appeared in the history of mankind (see Chapter IV). The most effective use of this medium in the interests of mental health is still to be explored.

A rather large selection of mental health films are available for television showings. Television rights to most films are held by special distributors, listed in the more recent film catalogues and in a special listing distributed by the National Association for Mental Health (see references). In inquiries about television rental rates the date of the film showing should be specified as well as the location of the station. These factors play a role in the rental costs. Special consideration is usually given to educational organizations. As in the case of "live" showings, it is important to follow telecasts of films with a talk which deals with anticipated anxieties or misunderstandings that may be aroused by the film and which endeavors to involve the television audience in positive constructive action.

The National Association for Mental Health has suggested various ways in which television can be employed. It has been possible, for example, to arrange for interviews of various members of the hospital treatment team on women's programs. Panel discussions and forums have provided opportunities to discuss the need for research, the nature and extent of mental illness, the need for new treatment facilities, the relationship of psychiatry to religion, the relationship of international tensions to mental health, and many other provocative topics. News commentators will present mental hygiene items of special importance if called to their attention. Sports announcers are often glad to get material to use between rounds, innings, or halves or during intermissions. Clergymen will co-operate if provided with material for broadcasting.

Local dramatic groups can be enlisted to present mental health plays for television. For example, the National Institute of Mental Health has prepared a series of fifteen-minute sketches called "How's Your Mental Health?" which are available for local use. Subjects covered by these plays include attitudes toward mental illness, sibling rivalry, problems of aging, volunteers in mental hospitals, the role of the father in family life, the way in which a community meets its mental health needs, and so on. Another television series which is available for local use is called "Face to Face." This was presented as a thirteen-week television series on emotional health by the District of Columbia Department of Public Health and Station WTOP-TV. Scripts may be obtained free of charge by writing to The Program Development Specialist, Department of Public Health, Government of the District of Columbia, Washington, D.C. The scripts may be used entirely or in part, but credit must be given to the Department of Public Health, Station WTOP-TV and the author.

Radio remains an important channel for disseminating public information in spite of the greater impact of television. Many of the scripts and suggestions referred to in the discussion of television can be adapted for presentation on radio. A particularly impressive series of mental health radio broadcasts have been presented by the Canadian Broadcasting Company, covering the history of psychiatry, the psychopathology of everyday life, psychosomatic medicine, psychiatric aspects of normal human relationships, psychiatry and the law, and others. After each script has been broadcast, it remains the personal property of the author and can be used locally after informal arrangements with the author have been made. Information concerning current programs and the authors of scripts can be obtained by writing to the Canadian Broadcasting Company.

A device specifically characteristic of radio is the "spot announcement" which can be repeated several times a day for several days to publicize some special event, like Mental Health Week, for example.

Patients on Radio and Television. The appearance of mental patients (or ex-patients) on radio and television can be extremely effective and need cause no problems if handled without sensationalism. On one program a commentator interviewed two former patients, one who had received insulin therapy at a state hospital and one who had received psychotherapy at the psychiatric clinic of a local hospital. The patients were presented without masks. Following the interviews two psychiatrists presented medical and research points of view on treatment of mental illness and preventive measures. In another program television cameras went directly into a state hospital, showing ward scenes, a staff conference, a display of arts and crafts work, recreational therapy and a patients' dance. During the program various patients were interviewed (but not identified by name) to show different types of disorders and to illustrate various therapies. The main idea of the program was to erase the stigma and the mystery attached to mental illness and to show that a state hospital is not the "end of the road."

On October 31, 1954, the NBC-Television network broadcast a program (sponsored by the Smith, Kline and French Laboratories in cooperation with the American Medical Association) entitled "The Search for Sanity." It opened with a scene in the New York State Psychiatric Institute, showing the research activities in progress there. It then went on to the Hudson River State Hospital and showed admission procedures, psychiatric interviews, psychological testing, and various treatments. Perhaps the most dramatic point of the program occurred when the attractive young woman who served as the tour guide identified herself as a former patient treated for schizophrenia in that very hospital. This program is on film and will most likely be made available for repeat showings in local telecasts. Also excellent was a recent "Medic" telecast devoted to ECT.

Mental patients have been heard on radio on a number of occasions during the last few years, although their names have not been given. In West Virginia, a private hospital has been conducting a radio program on which ex-patients identify themselves. This is a regular series entitled "Hiways to Health." Programs are simple and informal; ex-patients talk about rehabilitation; music is supplied by the patients' chorus. Occasionally, medical staff members of the hospital talk about various kinds of therapy.

Another example of broadcasting with patients has been reported by a state hospital which produced a series of tape recordings telling the story of a hypothetical patient from the time of his admission to the hospital to his return home and subsequent adjustment in the community. As he would come in contact with each department of the hospital, the contribution of that department to his recovery would be highlighted. "On-the-spot" interviews with other patients were heard as counterpoint to the main story. Music was supplied by patients' musical groups. Another hospital made tape recordings of dramatized case histories, acted and produced entirely by patients.

The National Association for Mental Health

It is perhaps well to recall that a layman, a patient who recovered from a mental illness, first conceived the idea of recruiting the resources of the general community for the improvement of mental health. I refer, of course, to Clifford Beers who founded the National Committee for Mental Hygiene. Two other organizations, the National Mental Health Foundation and the Psychiatric Foundation, which were formed later, fused with the original organization in 1950 to form the National Association for Mental Health (NAMH), with George S. Stevenson as the Medical Director and International Consultant. The contribution of this compound group of lay people has been a substantial one. Through ceaseless public activities the NAMH has awakened the public consciousness to the need for improved psychiatric services. It demonstrated that these improvements were not only necessary but possible. It set up an organizing apparatus that created new psychiatric services in communities, expanded and improved others. It provided a liaison between governmental leaders and the professions in working out these improvements. It conducted surveys and studies for the collection of much needed knowledge and then made them available to the public in an impressive list of publications (see references). It sponsored and financed research. It can be credited with contributing to the construction of modern mental hospitals, the improvement of hospital conditions, the changing attitude toward mental illness and the mentally ill, the introduction of modern treatment methods, the organization of research on prevention and treatment, the development of clinics and other community services for the disturbed and maladjusted and the growth of education for mental health. It sponsors National Mental Health Week.

In addition to its work on a national level, it gives direction, audiovisual materials and other forms of assistance to the activities of state and local mental health associations which are affiliated with the national body. It has stimulated the formation of many new state and local groups. It sponsors and partially finances the Central Inspection Board of the American Psychiatric Association which inspects mental hospitals on invitation and issues public reports which serve as a springboard for state and local mental health association activity toward improving hospital conditions. It has made a particularly rich contribution in assisting communities to establish new outpatient psychiatric clinics (see Chapter XXXV).

Besides stimulating a nationwide interest in the recruiting and training of attendants, it sponsors the annual award for the psychiatric aide of the year. It also gives awards and Certificates of Achievement to many other attendants. It has involved thousands of citizens in volunteer activities and compiled their valuable experiences into a highly practical manual which is available through the NAMH office (see Chapter XIII). It has been a great source of public information about mental health and disease. It has worked at legislative changes for the improvement of admission procedures and has promoted rehabilitation projects for the mentally ill. It sponsored the road tour of a play called "My Name is Legion" in which Nora Stirling and Nina Ridenour adapted to the stage the autobiography of Clifford W. Beers. The play was enthusiastically received by large audiences in many cities and gained considerable publicity for the mental hygiene movement. This road tour was instrumental in bringing hundreds of influential people into the mental health movement.

The NAMH collected ancient metal restraints formerly used in hospitals to bind the mentally ill. From them they had made a 300 pound bell bearing the legend:

> Cast from Shackles Which Bound Them This Bell Shall Ring Out Hope for the Mentally Ill and Victory Over Mental Illness.

This bell is rung each year at the opening of Mental Health Week, calling upon the people across the nation to join in the fight against mental disease.

The following excerpts from the reports of several state and local mental health affiliated organizations illustrate some details and the scope of their activities:

> . . . held a series of seminars, including: (a) industrial personnel directors—subject: "Mental Health in Industry"; (b) teachers—subject: "Recognizing Emotional Problems in the Classroom; (c) clergy—subject: "Religion and Mental Health"; (d) health groups—subject: "Emotional Aspects of Illness"; (e) legal groups—subject: "Symptoms of Poor Mental Health Which a Lawyer needs to Recognize in Dealing with Clients."
>
> . . . distributed 20,000 copies of "Mental Health is . . . 1,2,3" (a leaflet) through three grade schools, one high school and five churches; distributed 500 copies of "Some Special Problems of Children" through PTA.
>
> . . . Sponsored a series of lectures by a leading psychiatrist on the subject, "Mental Health is a Family Affair."
>
> . . . Exhibited the "Mental Health is . . . 1,2,3" display at the state medical convention.
>
> . . . Gave three showings of the "Temperate Zone" dramatic sketch series and two each of "And You Never Knew" and "The Case of the Missing Handshake" at a series of meetings arranged for parents and teachers, jointly by the PTA, the YWCA, the Kiwanis Club, the Junior Chamber of Commerce, and a local branch of the Auto Workers Union.
>
> . . . conducted a mental health film forum one day each month

throughout the year. Four films were shown at each of these sessions, in which PTA, parent education, church and community leaders were invited.

. . . Carried on, for the sixth year, an extensive educational program in the state public school system to assist teachers in understanding the emotional needs of children. The program includes orientation workshops in the schools, courses in the principles of child development and behavior, a seminar in individual and group psychology, and an annual institute on mental health for educators.

. . . Arranged a discussion group for psychiatric students at the seminary and a pastoral internship program at a state hospital. College credits were given for both these programs.

. . . Conducted an institute for physicians on "The Physician Looks at Mental Health."

This prodigious contribution, it should be recalled, was made by an enlightened laity. When the psychiatrist seeks to expand his program of education for mental health into the community at large, it would seem logical to do this in conjunction with the local mental health organization affiliated with the NAMH. If no organization exists, then he should sponsor the formation of one as the first step in community action.

Other local organizations exist which can play a role in launching a community mental health program—the Red Cross, the American Association of University Women, the Lion's Clubs, the National Council of Jewish Women, and others. These organizations, too, should avail themselves of NAMH help in starting their local programs.

The National Mental Health Act

The National Mental Health Act has been referred to previously in these pages (Chapters XXIX, XXX and XXXV) in connection with research and training. The National Institute of Mental Health, which administers the provisions of this act, also maintains a Community Services Branch which seeks to improve the mental health of the nation by direct and immediate means. Some of the activities of this branch impinge upon the problem of public education for mental health.

During the first three years of the act, Congress appropriated a total of almost $10,000,000 to support mental health services in state and local communities. All states, territories, and the District of Columbia are eligible to receive federal funds. The amount each state can receive depends upon its financial need, population, extent of its mental health problem, and its ability to match each $2 of federal funds with $1 of State or local funds.

Except that the funds cannot be used to support any type of institutional care, wide latitude is given to states in the expenditure of these grants. The mental health resources of the states are surveyed by the State Mental Health Authority and a plan for improving them is submitted to the Public Health Service.

During the first year of the program, forty-three states, Alaska, Hawaii, and the District of Columbia participated; in the second year, three more states, Puerto Rico and the Virgin Islands joined in the program; and by the end of the third year, the entire Nation, with the exception of one state, was participating. In half of these areas, Federal aid made it possible to start a program where none had existed before. While people living in eastern and urban areas still have most of the mental health services, there is now at least a minimal type of services for people in many rural, southern, and western areas that formerly had no mental health facilities except institutions for the mentally ill and defective. During the first two years, 53 per cent of the Federal funds granted to states and territories were used for clinical services. As a result of this aid, 106 new clinics were started and 186 existing clinics were expanded.

Although many more clinics are needed for the early treatment of behavior disorders as well as for preventive work, the difficulty of obtaining clinic staffs is causing an increasing number of State Mental Health Authorities to explore additional ways of meeting mental health needs. As a consequence, there has been a tremendous growth of preclinical services. Several states, pooling a portion of their grant-in-aid funds, made possible the formation of the Mental Health Film Board, a private nonprofit organization which produces documentary films to provide mental health education for lay audiences. Among the first films produced by the Board for State Mental Health Authorities were films on child guidance, mental health of school children, adolescence, fears of children, mental health of the aging, and a general film on mental health. Other devices used for bringing mental health information to lay groups have included pamphlets, posters, and radio programs.

Because mental health education is most effective when provided through group activities and personal contacts, much emphasis has been placed on preparing public health personnel and other community leaders to handle study and discussion groups and to give mental health information in personal interviews with people who look to them for guidance. The short-term mental health institute or seminar has proved a most effective way of giving mental health orientation to these leaders. The seminars last from one to two weeks and consist of lectures, discussions, and clinical experience which give those who attend an understanding of the basic principles of personality growth and development, some experience in using mental health principles in their usual work, and a keener awareness of the effect of interpersonal relationships on mental and emotional health. More than 100 such seminars have been held for public health officers, public health nurses, general practitioners, teachers, ministers, and other special groups.

As a further means of strengthening community services, the states have almost tripled the number of mental health specialists employed outside of clinics. They provide consultation and other services to schools, courts, churches, industries, and other community organizations.

In 1948, a demonstration project was established by the National Institute of Mental Health, in co-operation with the Maryland State Health Department, in Prince George County, Md. Its purpose is to demonstrate the incorporation of mental health services in a local health department program. Only half of the staff's time is used in treatment of individual patients. The remainder is spent in providing consultation and services to the other divisions of the health department and to community agencies, and in mental health educational activities with health and welfare agencies and citizen groups.

In a sense, every one of the growing number of state and community mental health programs developing throughout the nation is, like the Prince George clinic, a demonstration. As time goes by and as ideas are exchanged between the states, those programs which have stood the test of time will undoubtedly be adopted by other states. Out of this process, we may hope that eventually there will develop protection against mental illness comparable to that against physical illness.

Such devices might include mass screening techniques which would detect mental illness at an early stage, when chances of cure are greatest, just as the mass X-ray program detects early tuberculosis. They might include environmental control measures—comparable to the swamp drainage and DDT spraying programs—which would remove community factors that contribute to mental illness. Inexpensive methods of building individual resistance to mental illness—just as vaccination immunizes the individual against smallpox—are also needed in a preventive program for mental health. Likewise, there must be devised treatment methods that are less costly and time-consuming than the methods that are now most effective.

Through the action programs of states and communities, as well as through research, answers are being sought to these as yet unsolved problems of preventing the onset and progress of disease. The National Advisory Mental Health Council and its Community Services Committee are co-operating with the states by reviewing and evaluating current mental health services and by suggesting further approaches that seem promising.

A Visitors' Check List

In the past, occasional irresponsible reporters visiting mental hospitals seized upon morbid details for sensational headlines and lurid stories. These stories sold newspapers but contributed little to the welfare of patients. As a result, medical directors came to resent publicity and suspected the intentions of a curious public. This is now changed. Hospital inspection by local groups of responsible citizens is highly welcomed by directors today, not only to show off the favorable aspects of the hospital but to compel them to see the hospital's limitations and to motivate them to volunteer their services for work with patients and to improve legislation.

It is suggested that visitors on tour of the hospital be provided with a mimeographed checklist which they can use in rating the hospital. Their findings can then be used in public-spirited discussions to promote constructive action in the patients' behalf. A useful example of such a checklist is that given by Edith M. Stern (see references).

SELECTED REFERENCES*

CANADIAN BROADCASTING CORPORATION: *Mental Health Broadcast*. Department of Health, Queen's Park, Toronto, Ontario.
  A folder listing a series of Monday evening radio broadcasts for 1954-1955, with a brief description of each script.
GROUP FOR THE ADVANCEMENT OF PSYCHIATRY: *The Psychiatrist in Mental Health Education*. G.A.P. Report No. 29, 1954.
  A brief summary of the goals of the psychiatrist in public education in mental health; the opportunities, difficulties, and methods.
NATIONAL ASSOCIATION FOR MENTAL HEALTH: *Annual Reports:* Second (1951-1952), Third (1952-1953), Fourth (1953-1954). National Association for Mental Health, 1790 Broadway, New York 19, N.Y.
  These reports provide a summary of the mental health activities currently in progress under the direction of the N.A.M.H. Useful for orienting the newcomer concerning the range of possible lay activities in this field.
—— *Mental Health Publications and Audio-Visual Aids.*
  A catalogue of the many highly useful publications brought out by this organization. As examples of brief, popularly written leaflets which have proven of great value mention may be made of "Mental Health is 1, 2, 3" and "What Every Child Needs for Mental Health."

* See also Chapter XXIX references for motion picture catalogue listings, and Chapter XXXIV for additional references.

PUBLIC HEALTH SERVICE: *Catalog of Mental Health Pamphlets and Reprints Available for Distribution in 1951.* Public Health Service Publication No. 19, U.S. Gov. Printing Office, Washington 25, D.C. (25¢).

A complete and standard reference guide to current mental health pamphlets. Content of the literature is not evaluated.

—— *National Institute of Mental Health.* Mental Health Series No. 4.

A description of the goal, history and organization, the research program, the training program, the community services and other activities of this great organization.

—— *The National Mental Health Act and Your Community.* Mental Health Series No. 3.

A description of the provisions of this act and its implication for the general public in simple, readable form.

—— *The Role of the Police in Mental Health.* Public Health Service Publication No. 360 (5¢).

—— *The Teacher and Mental Health.* Public Health Service Publication No. 385 (15¢).

These informative pamphlets are simply written, contain excellent reference lists for additional readings, and films useful for public education. These titles are mentioned as examples of the superb pamphlets which are available for public education in mental health.

ROONEY, H. L.: Cultivating Community Relationships in a Mental Health Program. *Public Health Reports,* 66:636, 1951.

Describes the role of the social worker in the community mental health program.

STERN, E. M.: The Mental Hospital—A Guide for the Citizen, 1947. National Association for Mental Health, 1790 Broadway, New York 19, N.Y.

A useful summary in popular language of the activities within a mental hospital. It contains a recently revised visitors' checklist.

Chapter XXXVIII

THE MENTAL HOSPITAL AND CIVIL EMERGENCIES

Are Psychiatric Casualties Inevitable?

Prior to World War II mental health authorities in Great Britain predicted that mental casualties in the civilian population would outnumber physical casualties three to one in the event of enemy attack. The actual figures were considerably lower. One factor which may have contributed to this unexpected result was the policy of voluntary evacuation, in accordance with which selective emigration could take place to eliminate the most unstable elements. There is no doubt, however, that the community adapted more successfully to the stress of the bombings than had been anticipated. The most important cause was the fact that human beings are not passively molded like lumps of clay by the pressure of external events, but are capable of active, constructive, mastering reactions if properly prepared for emergencies.

General Prophylactic Principles

Emotional preparation for civil emergencies cannot be separated from the need for education for the inevitable crises of everyday living. A community that observes good mental hygiene practices in the conduct of its schools, churches, and other institutions, that understands and supports its mental health facilities for children and adults, that seeks to increase the sense of fulfillment in the daily life of its citizens, that combats bigotry and endeavors to lessen social tensions, is better prepared to accept change and shock than the community that omits these measures. Thus, the development of a sound mental health program in the community (see Chapter XXXVII) is the first step in a program for civil defense. Preparation for the emotional crises attendant on pregnancy and childbirth, the first week of school, the dissolution of a family because of illness or divorce or economic factors, death of a loved one, adjustments to physical handicap, graduation from high school and college, employment experiences and other inevitable changes that human life is heir to, is preparation for community crisis.

The Role of Motivation

Positive motivation is essential for civilian morale. In a democratic society this is based on a reaffirmation of our basic beliefs in freedom of opportunity, freedom of speech, freedom of religion and freedom of conscience. Each citizen should have a large personal stake in the preservation and development of these principles and the deep conviction that the continuation of this way of life is worth great personal sacrifice.

On the other hand, creation of fear will never build a sound civilian defense. Without minimizing our dangers, our program should nevertheless emphasize positive values. Our strength lies in mutual love, trust, and devotion to the spiritual riches of our way of life, not in a fearfully paranoid search for exceptional malcontents in our midst. This is a matter of signal importance because of the current tendency to sacrifice more and more of our freedoms on the altar of our fears. In spite of a superficial logic to the principle of mutual surveillance, we lose more strength than we gain when we practice the very principles we abhor.

Specific Prophylactic Principles

The likelihood of panic in a civilian emergency will be less if people are well informed as to what to expect, if they have confidence in their leaders, and if they know what to do.

Dissemination of information calls for the full utilization of all communication devices (see Chapter XXXVII). The availability and relative simplicity of the mass techniques of radio and television should not lead to neglect of the most important device, which is the small discussion group, structured for group therapy and conducted by a competent discussion leader.

The importance of competent leadership in group morale was demonstarted repeatedly in the military experiences of World War II. Confidence in leaders must be earned. This calls for the scientific refinement and more widespread application of techniques for selecting people qualified to lead and for providing them with proper training.

During periods of crisis those with a mission to perform are more likely to survive emotionally, whereas those whose role is passive are more likely to collapse. Therefore, each should have an assignment and the know-how for carrying it out. The voluntary system has not succeded in creating a civilian defense force of sufficient size. General apathy has had a demoralizing effect on those already involved in civilian defense. A compulsory system of training may be the answer. Its use in Sweden, whose devotion to democratic ideals is respected in this country, should reassure those who have doubts on this score. In Sweden, enrollment is compulsory between sixteen and sixty-five, unless one is in the Armed Services. When a youth turns sixteen he is enrolled and given sixty hours of civil defense training in the first year. This is followed by twenty hours in the second and third years, and refresher training thereafter. As a result one out of eight Swedes is a civil defense worker today.

It is well to keep in mind that the principles involved in civil defense against enemy attack are equally applicable to community disasters of any origin, whether the result of flood, fires, tornadoes, earthquakes or other natural causes. It is not necessary, or desirable, to inculcate a chronic fear of nuclear attack to justify such training to the community.

The Emotional Needs of Children During Civil Emergencies

When the bombing of Britain began children were immediately evacuated to safer rural areas. It was soon discovered that this apparently logical step had important drawbacks. It was found, for example, that children exposed to direct enemy attack were not panicked if their elders were not. On the other hand, the emotional disorganization which sometimes resulted in child and mother alike from enforced separation more than offset the gain in physical safety. As a result of these experiences the following principles have been evolved:

1. There should be no evacuation of infants from emergency areas without their mothers.

2. Mothers with infants should be the last source of manpower for war.

3. If mothers with infants are employed in war work, provision should be made for substitute care in line with the best principles of mental hygiene.

4. Counseling service should be provided to help mothers understand their own and their baby's needs in wartime.

5. Honesty, never deception, should be employed in telling the child what is going to happen.

6. Give only as much information as the child can absorb or handle.

7. In the event of enforced separation frequent communication (visits, toys, letters) should occur between child and parents.

8. Expression rather than suppression of feelings about a traumatic experience should be encouraged.

9. Make the child part of a group of children his own age undergoing a similar experience. Group feeling should be fostered. Good leadership is vital.

10. Whenever feasible the child should be given an opportunity to make decisions, particularly as they concern the emergency experience.

The Initial Reaction to Disaster

When disaster first strikes a community, the initial reaction is one of stunned dismay. The full impact of the calamity cannot be encompassed all at once and the average individual retreats more or less into himself in a state of emotional shock. During this time he appears outwardly calm and he may wander about more or less aimlessly. After a variable number of minutes the complete realization of what happened dawns upon him. If he is away from home, his first impulse is to telephone. This results in a flood of calls that may tie up lines and seriously interfere with calls more urgently needed for civil defense. Almost every one with an automobile starts riding toward home or toward what he regards to be safety. The result is a traffic jam that interferes with movements more urgently needed for defense. More organized measures to protect one's self, loved ones and nearby casualties follow in the normal course of events. Disaster control training should include orders to postpone phone calls and automobile travel during this initial period until preliminary instructions have been received.

Pathological Reaction Types

Acute pathological reactions in time of disaster tend to fall into a few typical patterns: panic, retardation, overactivity, and somatic reactions.

Individual panic is characterized primarily by its quality of disorganization. It is totally nonadaptive and often results in the destruction of the victim as well as others who have the misfortune to be in his path, as for example when a terrified pasenger leaps into an already overcrowded lifeboat. In combat, men with this reaction will walk into enemy fire without attempt at self-protection. The major danger of this reaction is to be found in its contagiousness. One panic-stricken individual can precipitate a panic in hundreds of others, which may result in unnecessary deaths.

Retarded reactions sometimes occur as a continuation of the initial emotional shock from which the individual does not rally. In a sense, it represents the opposite pole to the panic reaction. These people seem indifferent and unconcerned. Typically, they are mute and immobile. If we think of the panic as a catatonic-like excitment, then we can think of the retarded reaction as a catatonic-like stupor.

Manic-like reactions are also seen in which the victim speaks rapidly, disjointedly, and jokes inappropriately. He is unable to sustain interest or maintain his attention at any one task long enough to contribute usefully to the general welfare. He may show some grandiosity in his verbal productions, the general pattern of which follows a tendency to deny disturbing realities. He tolerates the inevitable frustrations of such a situation very poorly and the manic-like reaction gives way very readily to paranoid ideation which may have just enough validity to demoralize those about him.

Some patients show primarily *somatic manifestations,* such as trembling, weeping, vomiting, sweating and other expressions of autonomic discharge. Others may show typical conversion hysteria with loss of motor power and sensation as their way of reacting to the acute emergency.

Each of these reaction patterns may be mixed with others. One pattern may give way to another. Each is a reaction to intolerable anxiety and represents an attempt to diminish its intensity. To this extent, each is an attempt at adaptation. The failure of these reactions to deal realistically with the danger is what marks them as pathological.

Prevention of Pathological Reactions

What underlies the pathological reaction is a feeling of utter helplessness. As previously indicated, this feeling is less likely to emerge in the emotionally mature and in those with specific assignments.

During the initial reaction of shock, people are inordinately suggestible. They react to the panic of others with panic of their own; but what is more important, they will accept constructive suggestions with equal readiness. If we can refer to the example provided by the panic-stricken person as negative leadership, then what the general population needs most during the initial shock reaction is strong positive leadership. The initial hypersuggestibility is expressive of a childlike regression in response to feelings of helplessness. In that state, people seek a strong parental figure. The sooner they can be exposed to positive leadership and assigned specific rescue tasks, the less likely are they to become psychiatric casualties. Training of leaders in Red Cross disaster teams and in civil defense programs is, therefore, a prophylactic measure of first-rate importance. Emotionally mature people who are able to assume a protective parental attitude will be, in general, the most successful leaders in times of disaster.

A potent source of fear in time of disaster is lack of information. Hence people should be kept currently informed. Information should be disseminated by radio and television, by public address systems in sound trucks and helicopters and by any other device that is available.

Treatment of Pathological Reactions

If the pathological reaction is understood as an expression of an infantile regression, then the role of the psychiatrist or whoever else is involved in administering psychiatric first aid should be that of a strong protecting parent. Hostile, punitive attitudes are useless. Gentle but firm leadership is required most of all. Assignment to tasks with others who are in better control will ease the terror and restore confidence. The very needs of others and the opportunities for fulfilling their needs is therapeutic for panic-stricken people.

Patients in severe panic or in deeply regressed mute states can often be hypnotized with surprising ease or influenced directly by suggestion. In spite of their superficial appearance of inaccessibility, they should be treated first by psychological techniques.

When a person is obviously terror-stricken, the natural impulse of the psychiatrist is to sedate him. This may have grave drawbacks in times of disaster. The quantity of sedative sufficient to control a panic reaction will also convert an ambulatory patient to a drowsy litter case, thereby severely impairing the ease with which he can be evacuated. If in spite of this disadvantage it is still deemed advisable to sedate him, then a tag should be attached to the patient's clothing stating clearly the type and quantity of sedation as well as the time that it was given. This will permit subsequent echelons of medical care to evaluate the clinical status of the patient more accurately.

The registration of names of all who are refugees or who are otherwise displaced from their homes should be carried out promptly. An official record of this kind helps re-establish a sense of personal identity and normal ego controls in bewildered and disorganized people. In addition, prompt availability of such listings facilitates the restoration of family units, a measure of profound psychological importance in its own right.

Countertransference

A common experience in disaster areas is fatigue and exhaustion in the psychiatrist himself or in other persons in positions of leadership. When this happens, emotional regression takes place which interferes with the proper discharge of leadership responsibilities. The person in question may become inordinately harsh or punitive in his dealings with disaster victims, or excessively soft in identifying with those whom he should lead, not emulate. Awareness of these reactions may help bring them under control. Otherwise, it may be necessary to relieve him of his duties until a period of rest has restored his emotional control.

Administrative Aspects of Disaster Control

In many areas the mental hospital psychiatrist and his staff will have the primary responsibility for the psychological aspects of disaster control. A first step should be the activation of a psychiatric advisory committee with representative sociologists, anthropologists, psychiatrists, psychologists, psychiatric social workers, the local medical school psychiatric faculty, child and family welfare agencies and mental hygiene societies as participating members. A roster of personnel who are available for consultation or assignment should be drawn up for the director of the civil defense program. This committee should collaborate in drawing up the mental hygiene aspects of the civilian training program, with particular emphasis on the problem of selecting and training leaders. The role of each specialist in the over-all program should be defined. Research should be carried out in the sources of tension in community groups and the means for relieving it.

The Mental Hospital in Civil Emergencies

Mental hospitals located in heavily populated areas should have a plan for civil emergencies. Each employee and staff member should know his assignment. Plans should include a procedure for evacuating patients who are helpless or uncontrollably disturbed.

In Great Britain mental hospitals played a very important role in World War II as emergency hospitals for short-term care of medical casualties. Mental hospital routines had to be modified to meet the needs of a general hospital, but the director of the hospital remained in full administrative control of the emergency hospital unit. The extent of the contribution to the nation's war effort can be measured by the fact that mental hospitals made available over 7,000 beds for the sick and wounded to which approximately 175,000 patients were admitted.

Conversely, general hospitals that are currently without psychiatric services should plan to establish emergency facilities.

The expansion of all extramural treatment facilities (see Chapters XXXV and XXXVI) will make more beds available and will give mental hospitals more flexible control of occupied beds for meeting community emergencies.

SELECTED REFERENCES

AMERICAN PSYCHIATRIC ASSOCIATION: *Psychological First Aid in Community Disasters.* Committee on Civil Defense of the APA, 1785 Massachusetts Ave., N.W., Washington 6, D.C.
   A practical manual that covers the topic well in highly readable language.
FREUD, A.; BURLINGHAM, D.: *War and Children.* New York: International Universities Press, 1943.
────── ──── *Infants Without Families: A Case for and against Residential Nurseries.* New York: International Universities Press, 1944.
   These are the now classical studies of the emotional disturbances of children during times of disaster.
GROUP FOR THE ADVANCEMENT OF PSYCHIATRY: *An Introduction to the Psychiatric Aspects of Civil Defense.* Committee on Cooperation with Governmental (Federal) Agencies, of the G.A.P., Report No. 19, 1951.
   A useful outline of the general principles governing prevention of disruptive group behavior, types of external stress that are to be expected, types of reaction that can be expected, control of disruptive group behavior, treatment of individual psychiatric casualties and the place of psychiatry in civil defense planning.
MEERLOO, J. A. M.: *Patterns of Panic.* New York: International Universities Press, 1950.
   Based on the author's experiences in Holland and England during World War II, the author analyzes the factors leading to panic and the means of preventing them; many concrete illustrations.
PUBLIC HEALTH SERVICE: *Mental Health Implications in Civilian Emergencies.* Public Health Service Publication No. 310, U.S. Gov. Printing Office, Washington 25, D.C. (15¢).
   This is the report of the Subcommittee on Civil Defense, Community Service Committee of the National Advisory Mental Health Council. In concise outline it covers basic principles, psychological implications in planning emergency care, psychological concepts pertinent to understanding civilian needs and leadership training. It is thoughtful and provocative, and contains an excellent bibliography. Highly recommended.
TYHURST, J. S.: *Psychological and Social Consequences of Disaster. What Should the Doctor Do?* Proceedings of the Second Annual Psychiatric Institute of the New Jersey Neuropsychiatric Institute, Skillman, New Jersey, September 1954.
When Disaster Strikes. American National Red Cross, Washington, D.C. 1948.
   A manual for disaster preparedness and relief based on the vast experience of the Red Cross. It deals with the non-psychiatric aspects of the problem.

APPENDICES

Appendix A

PRELIMINARY PSYCHIATRIC FORMULATION

1. *Present status:*
   a. neurotic and psychotic symptoms—duration
   b. character traits—duration
   c. somatic symptoms—duration.
2. *Historical development of character:*
   a. Important factors in birth and childhood, including family background and heredity.
   b. Early relationship with father and mother (oedipus conflict). How solved. Earliest experiences with mother and mother substitutes (preoedipal conflicts). How solved. Fixations, regressive tendencies. Sibling rivalry.
   c. Adolescence, education, work, army, sexual activity, marriage, parenthood, significant facts in relation to symptomatology, how derived from earlier personality factors.
3. *How does past history bear on:*
   a. Origin of symptom mechanism, defenses? What does symptom express (primary gain)? Sexual and aggressive components—can this be related to specific fantasies? On what evidence? Against what does symptom defend? Which defenses are predominant? Meaning of precipitating factors.
   b. Secondary gain—what purpose does the symptom serve, in the present life situation; how is it self-perpetuating? Against whom directed (present and past)?
   c. How is symptom development correlated with patient's character?
   d. How has the symptom influenced the patient's character since its beginning?
4. *Descriptive psychiatric diagnosis—reasons—correlation with somatic illness if present. Differential diagnosis.*
5. *What vital information is missing? Can it be obtained, and how?*
6. *Suggested plan of therapy and prognosis.*

Appendix B

READING MATERIALS USED IN GROUP BIBLIOTHERAPY PROGRAM V.A. HOSPITAL, NORTHPORT, NEW YORK*

Code: A—Admissions Ward; D—Acutely Disturbed Ward; G—Geriatrics Ward; H—Habit Training Ward; R—Reintegrative Service; S—Special Treatment Ward; T—Tuberculosis Ward; *—Books in large print.

FICTION

G	Adams, S. H. Banner by the wayside.* Random 1947
G	Aldrich, B. S. A white bird flying.* Appleton 1931
GTSA	Aymar, G. C. A treasury of sea stories. Barnes 1948
ADGHRTS	Best Sports Stories. Dutton 1945
G	Bristow, Gwen. The handsome road.* Crowell 1938
HR	Brown, M. W. Wonderful story book. Simon 1948
G	Cather, W. S. Death comes for the Archbishop.* Knopf 1929
G	Conrad, Joseph. Lord Jim.* Modern Lib. 1931
G	Davies, Valentine. Miracle on 34th Street. Harcourt 1947
RG	Disney, Walt. Bambi.* Simon 1941
TAG	Dumas, Alexandre. The Count of Monte Cristo.* McGraw 1946
ADGHRTS	Eaton, H. T., ed. Short stories. American Bk 1951
RA	Foley, Martha, ed. The best American short stories. Houghton 1953 (paperbound)
G	Forester, C. S. Lord Hornblower.* Little 1946
G	Guthrie, A. B. The way west.* Sloane 1949
G	Hewitt, E. R. Those were the days. Little 1943
RSHG	Hoffman, Gloria. Primitivo and his dog.* Dutton 1949
TRD	Kantor, MacKinlay. Pocket book of dog stories. (paperbound)
GHR	Leen, Nina. Lucky, the famous foundling. Wyn 1951
GHRS	Lin, Yu-t'ang. Famous Chinese short stories. Pocket Bks
G	Nordhoff, C. B. & Hall, J. N. Hurricane.* Little 1936
RGAST	O. Henry. The pocket book of O. Henry prize stories. Pocket Bks
SADGR	O. Henry. Stories. Random 1945
DG	Rawlings, Mrs. M. K. The yearling.* Scribner 1938

* By Roger C. Chaney and Gladys A. Ingalls. Reprinted from *The Bookmark* (New York State Library), June, 1954, pp. 211-214.

RGTA   Runyon, Damon. The best of Damon Runyon. Pocket Bks

GR   Spyri, Johanna. Heidi.* Random 1946

DGASR   Stevenson, R. L. The great short stories of Robert L. Stevenson. Pocket Bks

R   Thompson, R. P. Captain Salt in Oz.* Reilly 1936

HGDTR   Twain, Mark, *pseud.* Tom Sawyer (selected passages). Grosset 1946

SADGHRT   Wagenknecht, E. C., *ed.* Fireside book of Yuletide tales. Bobbs 1945

RG   Wilson, H. L. Ruggles of Red Gap (selected passages). Pocket Bks.

NONFICTION

HGRS   Adams, J. T. Album of American history. Scribner 1944

RD   Aiken, C. P., *ed.* Twentieth century American poetry. Modern Lib. 1944

GHR   Aistrop, J. B. Fun at the zoo. Roy 1951

GHS   Alexander, E. P. American locomotives. Norton 1950

GHS   Anderson, C. W. Horse show. Harper 1951

DRGH   Block, Irvin. Real book about explorers. Garden City 1952

RDGH   Block, Irvin. Real book about the Mounties. Garden City

RDGH   Block, Irvin. Real book about ships. Watts 1953

HG   Boni, M. B., *ed.* Fireside book of favorite American songs. Simon 1952

DRSGTA   Book of knowledge. Pocket Bks

TG   Botkin, B. A., *ed.* A treasury of American folk lore. Crown 1944

SRGH   Brown, Dee. Trail driving days. Scribner 1952

SADGHRT   Buchanan, Lamont. The world series, and highlights of baseball. Dutton 1951

RDGH   Burton, Hal. Real book about treasure hunting. Garden 1953

SRGH   Cairns, Huntington & Walker, John, *eds.,* Great paintings from the National gallery of art. Macmillan 1952

G   Carmer, C. L. Dark trees to the wind.* Sloane 1949

SADGHRT   Carnegie, Dale. Five-minute biographies (selected). Perma Bks.

GDSAH   Carnegie, Dale. Lincoln, the unknown. Pocket Bks.

DSR   Carson, R. L., The sea around us. Oxford 1951

GHSR   Chapman, F. M. Bird life. Oxford 1950

GHSR   Clymer, J. F. Treasury of early American automobiles. McGraw 1950

RGSA   Collier, John. The Indians of the Americas. Mentor

A   **Commager, H. S.,** *ed.,* America in perspective. Mentor

A   Conant, J. B. On understanding science. Mentor

GHR   Cook, G. E. American champions. Macmillan 1945

HGRS   Coplan, M. F. Pink lemonade. McGraw 1945

TGRD   Cowan, S. K. Sergeant York and his people. Funk 1922

SADGHRT   Danzig, Allison & Brandwein, Peter., *eds.,* Sport's golden age. Harper 1948

RDSGA   Daugherty, *Mrs.* S. M. Ten brave men. Lippincott 1951

SRGH   Davidson, M. B., *ed.,* Art treasures of the Metropolitan. Abrams 1952

ADG	Day, C. S. Life with father. Knopf 1935
HG	Dix, J. F., Flowers in color. Oxford 1948
DGAST	Douglas, W. O. Of men and mountains. Harper 1950
GHSR	Drury, John. Midwest heritage. Wyn 1948
SADGHRT	Durant, John & Bettmann, Otto. Pictorial history of American sports 1952
DGRH	Epstein, Samuel & Williams, Beryl. The real book of pirates. Garden City 1952
RG	Field, Eugene. Poems of childhood. Scribner 1904
SRGH	Ford, Alice, ed., Audubon's animals. Grosset 1951
SRGH	Foster, Harold & Trell, Max. Prince Valiant in the days of King Arthur. Hastings 1951
RADT	Franklin, Benjamin. Autobiography. Pocket Bks.
RG	Frost, Robert. Poems of Robert Frost. Holt 1949
DGASTH	Garst, D. S. Will Rogers, immortal cowboy. Messner 1950
DGT	Geagan, William. Nature I loved. Coward 1952
G	Gibbings, Robert. Lovely is the Lee.* Dent 1945
RGSA	Gilbreth, F. B. Jr. & Carey, Mrs. E. G. Belles on their toes. Crowell 1950 (Also Bantam Bks.)
GRTAD	Green, Abel and Laurie, Joe, Jr. Show biz. Holt 1951
SADGHRT	Grombach, J. V. The saga of sock. Barnes 1949
SRGH	Hager, Mrs. A. R. Washington, city of destiny. Macmillan 1949
GH	Hammond, C. S. & Co. Nature study atlas of America. Hammond 1952
SADGHRT	Hart, H. H., pseud. & Tolleris, Ralph. Big-time baseball. Holt 1950
SADGHRT	Henderson, J. Y. Circus doctor. Little 1950
SRGH	Henderson, L. T. Ships.* Donahue 1937
RGS	Henry, Mrs. Marguerite. Birds at home. Donahue 1942
GH	Herzberg, M. J. This is America. Pocket Bks.
DRASGT	Heyerdahl, Thor. Kon-Tiki. Rand 1950 (Also Permabooks)
GD	Hibben, F. C. Treasure in the dust. Lippincott 1951
HGR	Hogner, Mrs. D. C. & Hogner, Nils. Animal book. Oxford 1942
HGR	House, Bryant, ed. Book of kittens. Wyn 1951
DGHR	Judson, Mrs. C. I. Abraham Lincoln. Wilcox 1950
RDGT	Kenny, N. A. Day unto day, the best of Nick Kenny. Fell 1945
RG	Kipling, Rudyard. Poems. Doubleday 1946
GD	Lamb, Dana & Lamb, Ginger. Quest for the lost city. Harper 1951
RDGHAT	Leonard, T. B. Sixty snappy quizzes. Holt 1949
RGH	Life (periodical) Life's picture history of western man. Time 1951
GDRS	Longfellow, H. W. The poems of Henry W. Longfellow. Cerf 1932
SRGH	Look. (periodical) Look at America. Houghton 1951
RAS	Maas, Carl. How to know and enjoy New York. Mentor
R	McCoy, Paul. Ten ten-minute plays. Eldredge
SADGHRT	Mack, Connie. My 66 years in the big leagues. Winston 1950
G	Mauldin, W. H. Back home.* Sloane 1947 (Also Bantam Bks.)
GHS	Meredith, Roy. Mr. Lincoln's camera man. Scribner 1946

GHS	Milhollen, H. D. & Kaplan, Milton. Presidents on parade. Macmillan 1948
SADGHRT	Moore, C. C. 'Twas the night before Christmas. Simon
DGRS	Mott, F. L. Gallery of Americans. Mentor
DGRTAS	Neider, Charles, ed., Great shipwrecks and castaways. Harper 1951
DGRTA	Parker, E. M., ed., 100 story poems. Crowell 1951
GD	Pinkerton, Mrs. K. S. G. Wilderness wife. Carrick 1939
ASRGH	Popular Mechanics. Fifty years of Popular Mechanics. Simon 1951
SADGHRT	Powers, J. J. A. Baseball personalities. Fields 1949
GDH	Rasmussen, A. H. Sea fever. Crowell 1952
HRG	Roberts, C. M. Washington, past and present. Public Affairs Press 1949-50
SADGHRT	Robinson, Donald. The 100 most important people. Pocket Bks.
GHSR	Robinson, Gregory. Ships that have made history. Halcyon 1936
GHR	Rothe, Paul. Movie parade. Studio 1950
G	Russell, Harold, & Rosen, Victor. Victory in my hands.* Creative Age 1949
G	Saroyan, William. My name is Aram.* Harcourt 1940
GDRH	Service, R. W. Complete poems of Robert Service. Dodd 1945
SADGHRT	Smith, Ken. Baseball's hall of fame. Barnes 1947
SADGHRT	Spafford, Justin, & Esty, Lucien, comps. Ask me another. Blue Ribbon 1927
SADGHRT	Speare, M. E. Pocket book of verse. Pocket Bks.
GTSA	Stanley, Dave, ed., A treasury of sports humor. Lantern 1946
SADGHRT	Stefferud, Alfred, ed. The wonderful world of books. Mentor
SADGHRT	Stern, Bill. Favorite boxing stories. Blue Ribbon 1949
SADGHRT	Stern, Bill. Favorite baseball stories. Pocket Bks. 1949
SRGH	Stern, P. V. A pictorial history of the automobile. Viking 1953
SADGHRT	Thomas, Henry, pseud. & Thomas, D. L. 50 great Americans. Doubleday 1953
RS	Tousey, Sanford. Indians and cowboys.* Rand 1937
RTG	Tuttle, W. C. Bluffer's luck. Houghton 1937
RTG	Tuttle, W. C. The keeper of Red Horse Pass. Houghton 1937
RDT	Untermeyer, Louis, ed. The pocket book of American poems. Pocket Bks.
RD	Untermeyer, Louis, ed. A treasury of great poems. Simon 1942
SRGH	U. S. Camera. U. S. Camera Pub. Co.
ATR	U.S.A.F.I. Improving your reading. Ginn 1944
R	Victor, Jeffrey. The fix-it book. Roberts 1949
SADGHRT	Waldman, Frank. Famous American athletes of today. Page 1951
GDR	Whittier, J. G. Complete poetical works of John G. Whittier. Houghton 1904
RA	Whitman, Walt. Poems and prose of Walt Whitman. Viking 1953
HGR	Wilder, Mrs. L. B. The garden in color. Macmillan 1937
DR	Wordsworth, William. Poems of William Wordsworth. Macmillan 1947
SADGHRT	Year

PERIODICALS

RSGT	Argosy (selected articles)
SADGHRT	Civil Education Service, Inc. The American Observer (selected articles)
DRASGT	Collier's (selected articles)
R	N. Y. State Mental Health Assn. Blondie Comics
R	Classics Illustrated Comics:

                    Dumas, Alexandre. Three musketeers

                    Verne, Jules. Twenty thousand leagues beneath the sea

                    Twain, Mark. Prince and the pauper

                    Dana, R. H. Two years before the mast

                    Nordhoff and Hall. Men against the sea

                    London, Jack. Call of the wild

                    Melville, H. Moby Dick

RDAST	Coronet (selected articles)
DRASGT	Holiday (selected articles)
RGASD	National Geographic (selected articles)
RDASTG	Reader's Digest (selected articles)
DRTG	Saga (selected articles)
RASDT	Saturday Evening Post (selected articles)
SADGHRT	Sport (selected articles)
RAGT	Time (selected articles)

Appendix C

CHARACTEROLOGIC INVENTORY—A CHECK LIST

NAME OF PATIENT _____ CHART NO. _____

1. *Attitudes Toward:*
   a. Food
   b. Work
   c. Cleanliness, neatness, own body, clothes, looks, "self"
   d. Money, property
   e. Sex, masculinity and femininity, menstruation, pregnancy, menopause
   f. Family—parents, siblings, children, friends, authorities
   g. Ethical concepts—religion, duty, honesty, right, wrong
   h. Degree of conventionality, "practicality," ritualistic tendencies
   i. Idiosyncrasies of speech: characteristic cliches, humor, need to express self
   j. Time—punctuality, wasting time
   k. Attitude toward health and illness, doctors, symptoms. Behavior following operation and during previous hospitalization
   l. Obsessive need to be right, to deny mistakes, stubborness, alibis
   m. Feelings of inadequacy, self-consciousness
   n. Attitude toward unpleasant facts of life (tendency to forget, be unaware, deny, fantasy, blame someone else)

2. *Drive:*
   a. Does patient act in response to joyous positive attitudes, b. or to relieve anxiety, or with competitiveness, compulsiveness, need for superiority, prestige values, or as a reaction to failure

3. *Patterns in Interpersonal Relations:*
   a. Degree of maturity, capacity for love and interchange of feelings
   b. Active-Passive Tendencies:
      (1) Dependence—passivity, receptivity, demanding, willingness to accept favors, willingness to give praise
      (2) Domination—overt, sadistic, sacrificing, overgenerosity and sympathy, manipulative, self-inflating—pompous, demands respect from others
      (3) Tendency to withdraw, to be asocial

4. *Characteristic Manifestations of Failure to Adapt Emotionally:*
   a. Sensitivity
   b. Temper outbursts, irritability, intolerance

    c. Euphoric talkativeness
    d. Depression
    e. Boredom
    f. Sleepiness
    g. Worry
    h. Felt tension
    i. Physical symptoms
    j. Jealousy, suspicion

5. *Miscellaneous:*
    a. Persistence of an attitude or feeling
    b. Adaptability to change
    c. Reaction under alcohol
    d. Sleep habits, dreaming, recurrent dreams
    e. Earliest memories

Appendix D

A HOME TRAINING PROGRAM FOR
RETARDED CHILDREN*

TABLE 1

INSTRUCTIONS FOR SCHOOL PREPARATION

DEAR PARENT:

To train your child in the following tasks for school preparation, you must act the part of a teacher as well as a loving mother. Therefore, before starting your child on a task, get him to want to accomplish it. There is no set way to motivate a task. You must understand YOUR child and use a variety of devices, all of which must appear as a game or play. PRAISE and PRACTICE will speed your child's progress in the various areas of training. It is very important to be aware that these children have a very short attention span and that patience and persistence with this plan is of the essence.

CAUTION: Consult your pediatrician to see whether your child is physically, intellectually and emotionally ready to acquire the developmental abilities which arise from the tasks suggested.

Keep the appended record sheet as a chart. Bring it with you whenever you have an appointment with your pediatrician.

SUGGESTED ACTIVITIES	Attempts	Failures	Completion
1. Toilet training			
a. sitting on the seat properly (make sure that height and seat are correct—supply stool or step if necessary)			
b. standing proper distance from bowl			
c. raising and lowering seat cover (at beginning and end of toilet act)			
d. tearing one sheet of toilet tissue from a roll as practice (this should be done away from the toilet)			
e. tearing two sheets as practice			
f. tearing one sheet while sitting on the toilet seat, etc.			
g. wiping doll's behind (before child performs act on self)			
h. wiping self			

* By Margaret Joan Giannini, M.D., Elkan Snyder, Ph.D., Harold Michal-Smith, Ph.D., and Lawrence B. Slobody, M.D. Reprinted in part from *Pediatrics,* 13:279-281, 1954.

527

SUGGESTED ACTIVITIES	Attempts	Failures	Completion
i. schedules for training (same time daily), incentives but not bribes, associations for training (identification with parents performing same act)			
j. pulling up trousers (sharing this performance with mother)			
k. buttoning elsewhere fly or zippering (practice on separate piece of clothing)			
l. washing hands with soap before leaving bathroom (water play should be allowed with plain water or with soap and done with mother present with an approving attitude)			
m. drying hands with towel (grasp towel, wrap towel around hands then allow child to imitate)			
n. flushing bowl			
2. Care of person			
a. wiping nose with handkerchief—provide child with own and allow child to carry it on person. Have child practice with doll first. Suitable handkerchief with children's figures.			
b. brushing teeth (size appropriate—start with small one. Bathroom should have its own small medicine chest)			
c. combing hair (provide child with own comb and brush—colorful)			
d. tying shoe laces (practice on self or another shoe—play shoe)			
e. swallowing pills (practice with small candy bits)			
f. putting on outer clothes (practice on self)			
g. adjusting trousers or dress (practice on self)			
h. putting on galoshes or rubbers			
3. Following directions			
a. sitting, standing, jumping, clapping hands, waiting			
b. walk, skip, run			
c. bounce, throw, catch a large ball—use cotton ball first, then small rubber ball			
d. bend down, reach for something			
e. opening and closing door, drawer			
f. follow the leader			
g. sitting up tall, resting head on table, etc.			

Note: Make games out of the above. Teach and practice these directions with the child. Do one at a time and when a child has learned one direction, add another until the child has learned all directions and can follow instructions.

SUGGESTED ACTIVITIES	Attempts	Failures	Completion

4. Helping at home
  a. carrying a water glass to the table (plastic colored cups)
  b. carrying a small pitcher to the table (doll cups and saucers, pitchers)
  c. watering a plant—child's watering can
  d. washing fruit before eating
  e. carrying a tray with some dishes (plastic —then slow conversion to regular dishes)
  f. cleaning table with a spoon (if oilcloth or plastic)
  g. cleaning table of dishes (practice with one dish or cup at a time)
  h. folding paper napkins and placing them in position
  i. placing utensils in place
  j. dusting furniture
  k. picking up papers from floor
  l. drying silverware
  m. carrying wastepaper basket to incinerator (accompanied by parent)			

Note: When practicing those tasks involving dishes, try with larger, lighter objects first. Plastic or nonbreakable toy or real items should be the beginning. From there proceed to breakable things. Set a pattern or schedule and repeat this pattern. Other helping devices may be used in addition to this list. But this list should be a guide.

5. Traveling
  a. daily trip with parent when marketing is being done, allow to select products
  b. visit to relatives, friends, ring door bell
  c. experiences in restaurants with parents —allow to order, pay check, tip waiter
  d. always follow on separate bus or a few blocks behind on first trip			

Note: Give child these personal experiences. Try the child on simple short experiences until he has mastered them. Then add further experiences to the ones he has learned.

6. Shopping
  a. for candy, for simple items identify coin with buying object
  b. carrying notes to store
  c. carrying items home when you are shopping with him			

Note: Trust the child with memory experiences. First allow him to go to the store for a single item, then add more items. Make game situations and responsibilities out of this.

SUGGESTED ACTIVITIES	Attempts	Failures	Completion

7. Listening
  a. to stories (read to him and get him to listen to children's radio programs)
  b. to music (use children's records)
  c. to adults who are talking (try to bring him into the conversation by asking an occasional question)
  d. to comparisons—e.g., big, little, etc. Give him as much language experience as is possible for him to comprehend.			

Note: Remove all distracting stimuli from the child during the teaching of listening. Make the listening experience one of pleasure and privilege rather than a task. Repeat many of the stories and music so that the child gains recognition of them. Stories, rhythms, etc., are important parts of a child's world. Start with simple items and try to have the child repeat the story. Try, also, to have the child respond bodily to the rhythm. Recordings, such as "March of the Toy," will be extremely valuable in the development of these postural rhythms.

8. Playing
  a. At home: string beads, macaroni, finger painting, sailing boats, water play, building blocks, cutting with a blunted scissors (use wrapping paper or newspaper to start. Then try to have child follow a short line).
  b. The playground: swinging, playing ball, climbing the jungle bar, walking to and from playground (this should be a game) —stopping for lights, jumping back, skipping, etc., resting after active play (sitting on bench)
9. Language
  a. Teach words of description: raining, snowing, jumping, sitting, rocking, dirty, clean, white, sticky, etc.
  b. Teach words of direction
  c. Teach words of manners			

Note: These language activities should come out of play. The simpler the language the greater will be the child's understanding.

AXIOM: YOU CANNOT GO WRONG BY GIVING THE CHILD VERY SIMPLE TASKS AND THEN ADDING MORE DIFFICULT TASKS AS HE MASTERS THE SIMPLE ONES.

Appendix E

CLASSIFICATION OF MENTAL DISORDERS*

In order to provide mental hospitals with a scheme that permits detailed tabulation of diagnostic data as well as easy contraction of the detailed classification into summary form, a code suitable for machine tabulation has been devised for the titles in the Psychobiological Unit of the Standard Nomenclature. This is presented in detail at the end of this section. The inclusions for each category are cross-referenced with the appropriate International List and Standard Nomenclature numbers. This code consists of four digits in which the first represents the broad class of mental disorder; the second, major categories within each of these broad classes; the third, subdivisions within major categories; and the fourth, qualifying phrases where applicable.

The new nomenclature is somewhat of a departure from that being used currently in mental hospitals. The use of the terms acute and chronic brain syndromes is new, as well as the use of the qualifying phrases, *with psychotic reaction, with neurotic reaction* and *with behavioral reaction*. In addition, the categories dealing with psychoneuroses, psychophysiologic autonomic and visceral disorders and personality disorders are considerably expanded over what was included in the 1934 Classification of Mental Disorders. Because of these differences between the 1934 Classification of Mental Disorders and the present one, it is desirable for hospitals to classify diagnoses by both codes for at least a year in order to determine what differences the new classification will effect in their historical statistical series dealing with admissions, discharges and resident patients by diagnosis.

Below is a scheme for presenting tabulations of mental disorder. The arrangement follows essentially the underlying subdivisions of the new nomenclature.

I. *Acute Brain Syndromes Associated With:*
Epidemic encephalitis
Other intracranial infections
Systemic infections
Alcohol intoxication
Drug or poison intoxication, except alcohol
Trauma
Circulatory disturbance

* Reprinted from *Diagnostic and Statistical Manual: Mental Disorders.* Washington: American Psychiatric Association Mental Hospital Service, 1952, pp. 74-86.

Convulsive disorder
Disturbance of metabolism, growth or nutrition
New growth
Other diseases and conditions, NEC (not elsewhere classified), or unspecified disease or condition

II. *Chronic Brain Syndromes With Psychotic Reaction, Associated With:*
Conditions and diseases due to prenatal influence
Central nervous system syphilis
Epidemic encephalitis
Other intracranial infections, except syphilis
Alcohol intoxication
Drug or poison intoxication, except alcohol
Birth trauma
Other trauma
Cerebral arteriosclerosis
Circulatory disturbance other than cerebral arteriosclerosis
Convulsive disorder
Senile brain disease
All other disturbance of metabolism, growth or nutrition
New growth
Other diseases and conditions, NEC, or unspecified disease or condition

III. *Chronic Brain Syndromes With Neurotic Reaction, Associated With:*
Conditions and diseases due to prenatal influence
Central nervous system syphilis
Epidemic encephalitis
Other intracranial infections, except syphilis
Alcohol intoxication
Drug or poison intoxication, except alcohol
Birth trauma
Other trauma
Cerebral arteriosclerosis
Circulatory disturbance other than cerebral arteriosclerosis
Convulsive disorder
Senile brain disease
All other disturbance of metabolism, growth or nutrition
New growth
Other diseases and conditions, NEC, or unspecified disease or condition

IV. *Chronic Brain Syndromes With Behavioral Reactions Associated With:*
Conditions and diseases due to prenatal influence
Central nervous system syphilis
Epidemic encephalitis
Other intracranial infections, except syphilis
Alcohol intoxication
Drug or poison intoxication, except alcohol
Birth trauma
Other trauma
Cerebral arteriosclerosis

Circulatory disturbance other than cerebral arteriosclerosis
Convulsive disorder
Senile brain disease
All other disturbance of metabolism, growth or nutrition
New growth
Other diseases and conditions, NEC, or unspecified disease or condition

V. *Chronic Brain Syndrome Without Qualifying Phrase Associated With:*
Conditions and diseases due to prenatal influence
Central nervous system syphilis
Epidemic encephalitis
Other intracranial infections, except syphilis
Alcohol intoxication
Drug or poison intoxication, except alcohol
Birth trauma
Other trauma
Cerebral arteriosclerosis
Circulatory disturbance other than cerebral arteriosclerosis
Convulsive disorder
Senile brain disease
All other disturbance of metabolism, growth or nutrition
New growth
Other diseases and conditions, NEC, or unspecified disease or condition

VI. *Psychotic Disorders:*
Involutional psychotic reaction
Affective reactions
Schizophrenic reactions
Paranoid reactions
Psychotic reactions without clearly defined structural change other than above

VII. *Psychophysiologic Autonomic and Visceral Disorders*

VIII. *Psychoneurotic Disorders*

IX. *Personality Disorders*
Alcoholism (addiction)
Drug addiction
All other personality disorders

X. *Transient Situational Personality Disorders*

XI. *Mental Deficiency*

TABULATING SCHEME BASED ON STRUCTURE OF NEW NOMEN-
CLATURE WITH CORRESPONDING STANDARD NOMENCLATURE
AND INTERNATIONAL LIST NUMBERS

Code No.[1]	Disorder	Standard Nomenclature	Int'l List Nos.
01–09	ACUTE BRAIN DISORDERS		
01	ACUTE BRAIN SYNDROME ASSOCIATED WITH INFECTION		
01.0	Intracranial infection, except epidemic encephalitis	009–100	308.5 (pt [2])
01.1	Epidemic encephalitis	009–163	083.2 (pt)
01.2	With systemic infection, NEC	000–100	308.3
02	ACUTE BRAIN SYNDROME ASSOCIATED WITH INTOXICATION		
02.1	Alcohol intoxication	000–3312	307 (pt)
02.2	Drug or poison intoxication (except alcohol)	000–3..	308.5 (pt)
03	ACUTE BRAIN SYNDROME ASSOCIATED WITH TRAUMA	000–4..	308.2
04	ACUTE BRAIN SYNDROME ASSOCIATED WITH CIRCULATORY DISTURBANCE	000–5..	308.4
05	ACUTE BRAIN SYNDROME ASSOCIATED WITH CONVULSIVE DISORDER	000–550	308.1 (pt)
06	ACUTE BRAIN SYNDROME ASSOCIATED WITH METABOLIC DISTURBANCE	000–7..	308.5 (pt)

1 This code consists of four digits in which the first represents the broad class of mental disorder; the second, major categories within each of these broad classes; the third, subdivisions within these major categories; and the fourth, qualifying phrases where applicable. Where no subdivision exists within a major category the third digit should be punched with an "X" punch. Where no qualifying phrase is applicable the fourth digit should also be punched with an "X" punch, except in the Chronic Brain Syndromes where diagnoses without qualifying phrase are coded "0" in the fourth digit.

2 The abbreviation "pt" following an International List Number means that the Standard Nomenclature title is only one part of the titles included under the indicated International List Number. For example, International List No. 308.5 Acute Brain Syndrome Associated with Other Causes Not Elsewhere Classified includes the following Standard Nomenclature titles:

Acute Brain Syndrome associated with:
  (a) Intracranial infection, except encephalitis
  (b) Drug or poison intoxication, except alcohol
  (c) Metabolic disturbance
  (d) Diseases of unknown or uncertain cause.

Code No.	Disorder	Standard Nomenclature	Int'l List Nos.
07	ACUTE BRAIN SYNDROME ASSOCIATED WITH INTRACRANIAL NEOPLASM	000–08..	308.0
08	ACUTE BRAIN SYNDROME WITH DISEASE OF UNKNOWN OR UNCERTAIN CAUSE	000–900	308.5 (pt)
09	ACUTE BRAIN SYNDROME OF UNKNOWN CAUSE	000–xx0	309.1 (pt)

10–19 CHRONIC BRAIN DISORDERS

10 CHRONIC BRAIN SYNDROME ASSOCIATED WITH DISEASES AND CONDITIONS DUE TO PRENATAL (CONSTITUTIONAL) INFLUENCE

		Standard Nomenclature	Int'l List Nos.
10.0	With congenital cranial anomaly		
10.00	Without qualifying phrase	009–0..	328.0 (pt)
10.01	With psychotic reaction	009–0...x1	308.8 (pt)
10.02	With neurotic reaction	009–0...x2	319.0 (pt)
10.03	With behavioral reaction	009–0...x3	327.0 (pt)
10.1	With congenital spastic paraplegia		
10.10	Without qualifying phrase	009–016	328.0 (pt)
10.11	With psychotic reaction	009–016.x1	308.8 (pt)
10.12	With neurotic reaction	009–016.x2	319.0 (pt)
10.13	With behavioral reaction	009–016.x3	327.0 (pt)
10.2	With mongolism		
10.20	Without qualifying phrase	009–071	328.0 (pt)
10.21	With psychotic reaction	009–071.x1	308.8 (pt)
10.22	With neurotic reaction	009–071.x2	319.0 (pt)
10.23	With behavioral reaction	009–071.x3	327.0 (pt)
10.3	Due to prenatal maternal infectious diseases		
10.30	Without qualifying phrase	009–052	328.0 (pt)
10.31	With psychotic reaction	009–052.x1	308.8 (pt)
10.32	With neurotic reaction	009–052.x2	319.0 (pt)
10.33	With behavioral reaction	009–052.x3	327.0 (pt)

11 CHRONIC BRAIN SYNDROME ASSOCIATED WITH CENTRAL NERVOUS SYSTEM SYPHILIS

		Standard Nomenclature	Int'l List Nos.
11.0	Meningoencephalitic		
11.00	Without qualifying phrase	009–147.0	025.9
11.01	With psychotic reaction	009–147.0.x1	025.6
11.02	With neurotic reaction	009–147.0.x2	025.7
11.03	With behavioral reaction	009–147.0.x3	025.8
11.1	Meningovascular		
11.10	Without qualifying phrase	004–147.0	026.9 (pt)
11.11	With psychotic reaction	004–147.0.x1	026.6 (pt)
11.12	With neurotic reaction	004–147.0.x2	026.7 (pt)
11.13	With behavioral reaction	004–147.0.x3	026.8 (pt)
11.2	Other central nervous system syphilis		
11.20	Without qualifying phrase	0y0–147.0	026.9 (pt)

Code No.	Disorder	Standard Nomenclature	Int'l List Nos.
11.21	With psychotic reaction	0y0–147.0.x1	026.6 (pt)
11.22	With neurotic reaction	0y0–147.0.x2	026.7 (pt)
11.23	With behavioral reaction	0y0–147.0.x3	026.8 (pt)
12	CHRONIC BRAIN SYNDROME ASSOCIATED WITH INTRACRANIAL INFECTION OTHER THAN SYPHILIS		
12.0	Epidemic encephalitis		
12.00	Without qualifying phrase	009–163.0	083.9
12.01	With psychotic reaction	009–163.0.x1	083.2 (pt)
12.02	With neurotic reaction	009–163.0.x2	083.7
12.03	With behavioral reaction	009–163.0.x3	083.1
12.1	Other intracranial infections		
12.10	Without qualifying phrase	009–1...0	328.1
12.11	With psychotic reaction	009–1...0.x1	308.9 (pt)
12.12	With neurotic reaction	009–1...0.x2	319.1
12.13	With behavioral reaction	009–1...0.x3	327.1
13	CHRONIC BRAIN SYNDROME ASSOCIATED WITH INTOXICATION		
13.0	Alcohol intoxication		
13.00	Without qualifying phrase	009–3312	322.9
13.01	With psychotic reaction	009–3312.x1	307 (pt)
13.02	With neurotic reaction	009–3312.x2	322.7
13.03	With behavioral reaction	009–3312.x3	322.8
13.1	Drug or poison intoxication, except alcohol		
13.10	Without qualifying phrase	009–3..	328.2
13.11	With psychotic reaction	009–3...x1	308.6
13.12	With neurotic reaction	009–3...x2	319.2
13.13	With behavioral reaction	009–3...x3	327.2
14	CHRONIC BRAIN SYNDROME ASSOCIATED WITH TRAUMA		
14.0	Birth trauma		
14.00	Without qualifying phrase	009–050	328.3
14.01	With psychotic reaction	009–050.x1	308.8 (pt)
14.02	With neurotic reaction	009–050.x2	319.3
14.03	With behavioral reaction	009–050.x3	327.3
14.1	Brain trauma, gross force		
14.10	Without qualifying phrase	009–4..	328.4 (pt)
14.11	With psychotic reaction	009–4...x1	308.7 (pt)
14.12	With neurotic reaction	009–4...x2	319.4 (pt)
14.13	With behavioral reaction	009–4...x3	327.4 (pt)
14.2	Following brain operation		
14.20	Without qualifying phrase	009–415	328.4 (pt)
14.21	With psychotic reaction	009–415.x1	308.7 (pt)
14.22	With neurotic reaction	009–415.x2	319.4 (pt)
14.23	With behavioral reaction	009–415.x3	327.4 (pt)

Code No.	Disorder	Standard Nomenclature	Int'l List Nos.
14.3	Following electrical brain trauma		
14.30	Without qualifying phrase	009–462	328.4 (pt)
14.31	With psychotic reaction	009–462.x1	308.7 (pt)
14.32	With neurotic reaction	009–462.x2	319.4 (pt)
14.33	With behavioral reaction	009–462.x3	327.4 (pt)
14.4	Following irradiational brain trauma		
14.40	Without qualifying phrase	009–470	328.4 (pt)
14.41	With psychotic reaction	009–470.x1	308.7 (pt)
14.42	With neurotic reaction	009–470.x2	319.4 (pt)
14.43	With behavioral reaction	009–470.x3	327.4 (pt)
14.5	Following other trauma		
14.50	Without qualifying phrase	009–400	328.4 (pt)
14.51	With psychotic reaction	009–400.x1	308.7 (pt)
14.52	With neurotic reaction	009–400.x2	319.4 (pt)
14.53	With behavioral reaction	009–400.x3	327.4 (pt)
15	CHRONIC BRAIN SYNDROME ASSOCIATED WITH CIRCULATORY DISTURBANCE		
15.0	With cerebral arteriosclerosis		
15.00	Without qualifying phrase	009–516	328.5
15.01	With psychotic reaction	009–516.x1	306
15.02	With neurotic reaction	009–516.x2	319.5
15.03	With behavioral reaction	009–516.x3	327.5
15.1	With circulatory disturbance other than cerebral arteriosclerosis		
15.10	Without qualifying phrase	009–5..	328.6
15.11	With psychotic reaction	009–5...x1	308.9 (pt)
15.12	With neurotic reaction	009–5...x2	319.6
15.13	With behavioral reaction	009–5...x3	327.6
16	CHRONIC BRAIN SYNDROME ASSOCIATED WITH CONVULSIVE DISORDER		
16.00	Without qualifying phrase	009–550	353.9
16.01	With psychotic reaction	009–550.x1	308.1 (pt)
16.02	With neurotic reaction	009–550.x2	353.7
16.03	With behavioral reaction	009–550.x3	353.8
17	CHRONIC BRAIN SYNDROME ASSOCIATED WITH DISTURBANCE OF METABOLISM, GROWTH OR NUTRITION		
17.1	With senile brain disease		
17.10	Without qualifying phrase	009–79x	794.9
17.11	With psychotic reaction	009–79x.x1	304
17.12	With neurotic reaction	009–79x.x2	794.7
17.13	With behavioral reaction	009–79x.x3	794.8
17.2	Presenile brain disease		
17.20	Without qualifying phrase	009–700	328.7
17.21	With psychotic reaction	009–700.x1	305 (pt)

Code No.	Disorder	Standard Nomenclature	Int'l List Nos.
17.22	With neurotic reaction	009–700.x2	319.7
17.23	With behavioral reaction	009–700.x3	327.7
17.3	With other disturbance of metabolism, etc., except presenile brain disease		
17.30	Without qualifying phrase	009–700	328.8
17.31	With psychotic reaction	009–700.x1	308.9 (pt)
17.32	With neurotic reaction	009–700.x2	319.8
17.33	With behavioral reaction	009–700.x3	327.8
18	CHRONIC BRAIN SYNDROME ASSOCIATED WITH NEW GROWTH		
18.0	With intracranial neoplasm		
18.00	Without qualifying phrase	009–8..	328.9 (pt)
18.01	With psychotic reaction	009–8...x1	308.0 (pt)
18.02	With neurotic reaction	009–8...x2	319.9 (pt)
18.03	With behavioral reaction	009–8...x3	327.9 (pt)
19	CHRONIC BRAIN SYNDROME ASSOCIATED WITH DISEASES OF UNKNOWN OR UNCERTAIN CAUSE; CHRONIC BRAIN SYNDROME OF UNKNOWN OR UNSPECIFIED CAUSE		
19.0	Multiple sclerosis		
19.00	Without qualifying phrase	009–900	328.9 (pt)
19.01	With psychotic reaction	009–900.x1	308.9 (pt)
19.02	With neurotic reaction	009–900.x2	319.9 (pt)
19.03	With behavioral reaction	009–900.x3	327.9 (pt)
19.1	Huntington's chorea		
19.10	Without qualifying phrase	009–900	328.9 (pt)
19.11	With psychotic reaction	009–900.x1	308.9 (pt)
19.12	With neurotic reaction	009–900.x2	319.9 (pt)
19.13	With neurotic reaction	009–900.x3	327.9 (pt)
19.2	Pick's disease		
19.20	Without qualifying phrase	009–900	328.9 (pt)
19.21	With psychotic reaction	009–900.x1	305 (pt)
19.22	With neurotic reaction	009–900.x2	319.9 (pt)
19.23	With behavioral reaction	009–900.x3	327.9 (pt)
19.3	Other diseases of unknown or uncertain cause		
19.30	Without qualifying phrase	009–900	328.9 (pt)
19.31	With psychotic reaction	009–900.x1	308.9 (pt)
19.32	With neurotic reaction	009–900.x2	319.9 (pt)
19.33	With behavioral reaction	009–900.x3	327.9 (pt)
19.4	Chronic brain syndrome of unknown or unspecified cause		
19.40	Without qualifying phrase	009–xx0	328.9 (pt)
19.41	With psychotic reaction	009–xx0.x1	309.1 (pt)
19.42	With neurotic reaction	009–xx0.x2	319.9 (pt)

Code No.	Disorder	Standard Nomenclature	Int'l List Nos.
	19.43 With behavioral reaction	009–xx0.x3	327.9 (pt)

20–24 PSYCHOTIC DISORDERS

Code No.	Disorder	Standard Nomenclature	Int'l List Nos.
20	INVOLUTIONAL PSYCHOTIC REACTION	000–796	302
21	AFFECTIVE REACTIONS	000–x10	301,309.0
	21.0 Manic depressive reaction, manic type	000–x11	301.0
	21.1 Manic depressive reaction, depressed type	000–x12	301.1
	21.2 Manic depressive reaction, other	000–x13	301.2
	21.3 Psychotic depressive reaction	000–x14	309.0
22	SCHIZOPHRENIC REACTIONS	000–x20	300
	22.0 Schizophrenic reaction, simple type	000–x21	300.0
	22.1 Schizophrenic reaction, hebephrenic type	000–x22	300.1
	22.2 Schizophrenic reaction, catatonic type	000–x23	300.2
	22.3 Schizophrenic reaction, paranoid type	000–x24	300.3
	22.4 Schizophrenic reaction, acute undifferentiated type	000–x25	300.4
	22.5 Schizophrenic reaction, chronic undifferentiated type	000–x26	300.7 (pt)
	22.6 Schizophrenic reaction, schizoaffective type	000–x27	300.6
	22.7 Schizophrenic reaction, childhood type	000–x28	300.8
	22.8 Schizophrenic reaction, residual type	000–x29	300.5
	22.9 Other and unspecified	000–x20	300.7 (pt)
23	PARANOID REACTIONS	000–x30	303
	23.1 Paranoia	000–x31	303 (pt)
	23.2 Paranoid state	000–x32	303 (pt)
24	PSYCHOTIC REACTION WITHOUT CLEARLY DEFINED STRUCTURAL CHANGE OTHER THAN ABOVE	000–xy0	309.1 (pt)

30–39 PSYCHOPHYSIOLOGIC AUTONOMIC AND VISCERAL DISORDERS

Code No.	Disorder	Standard Nomenclature	Int'l List Nos.
30	PSYCHOPHYSIOLOGIC SKIN REACTION	001–580	317.3
31	PSYCHOPHYSIOLOGIC MUSCULOSKELETAL REACTION	002–580	317.4
32	PSYCHOPHYSIOLOGIC RESPIRATORY REACTION	003–580	317.0
33	PSYCHOPHYSIOLOGIC CARDIOVASCULAR REACTION	004–580	315.2

Code No.	Disorder	Standard Nomenclature	Int'l List Nos.
34	PSYCHOPHYSIOLOGIC HEMIC AND LYMPHATIC REACTION	005–580	317.5 (pt)
35	PSYCHOPHYSIOLOGIC GASTROINTESTINAL REACTION	006–580	316.3
36	PSYCHOPHYSIOLOGIC GENITO-URINARY REACTION	007–580	317.1
37	PSYCHOPHYSIOLOGIC ENDOCRINE REACTION	008–580	317.5 (pt)
38	PSYCHOPHYSIOLOGIC NERVOUS SYSTEM REACTION	009–580	318.3 (pt)
39	PSYCHOPHYSIOLOGIC REACTION OF ORGANS OF SPECIAL SENSE	00x–580	317.5 (pt)
40	**PSYCHONEUROTIC DISORDERS**		
40	PSYCHONEUROTIC REACTIONS	000–x00	318.5
40.0	Anxiety reaction	000–x01	310
40.1	Dissociative reaction	000–x02	311 (pt)
40.2	Conversion reaction	000–x03	311 (pt)
40.3	Phobic reaction	000–x04	312
40.4	Obsessive compulsive reaction	000–x05	313
40.5	Depressive reaction	000–x06	314
40.6	Psychoneurotic reaction, other	000–x0y	318.5
50–53	**PERSONALITY DISORDERS**		
50	PERSONALITY PATTERN DISTURBANCE		
50.0	Inadequate personality	000–x41	320.3
50.1	Schizoid personality	000–x42	320.0
50.2	Cyclothymic personality	000–x43	320.2
50.3	Paranoid personality	000–x44	320.1
50.4	Personality pattern disturbance, other	000–x40	320.7
51	PERSONALITY TRAIT DISTURBANCE		
51.0	Emotionally unstable personality	000–x51	321.0
51.1	Passive-aggressive personality	000–x52	321.1
51.2	Compulsive personality	000–x53	321.5 (pt)
51.3	Personality trait disturbance, other	000–x5y	321.5 (pt)
52	SOCIOPATHIC PERSONALITY DISTURBANCE		
52.0	Antisocial reaction	000–x61	320.4
52.1	Dyssocial reaction	000–x62	320.5
52.2	Sexual deviation	000–x63	320.6
52.3	Alcoholism (addiction)	000–x641	322.1
52.4	Drug addiction	000–x642	323
53	SPECIAL SYMPTOM REACTION		
53.0	Learning disturbance	000–x71	326.0
53.1	Speech disturbance	000–x72	326.2
53.2	Enuresis	000–x73	321.3
53.3	Somnambulism	000–x74	321.4 (pt)
53.4	Other	000–x7y	321.4 (pt)

Code No.	Disorder	Standard Nomenclature	Int'l List Nos.
54	TRANSIENT SITUATIONAL PERSONALITY DISORDERS		
54	TRANSIENT SITUATIONAL PERSONALITY DISTURBANCE		
54.0	Gross stress reaction	000–x81	326.3
54.1	Adult situational reaction	000–x82	326.6
54.2	Adjustment reaction of infancy	000–x83	324.0
54.3	Adjustment reaction of childhood	000–x84	324.1
54.4	Adjustment reaction of adolescence	000–x85	324.2
54.5	Adjustment reaction of late life	000–x86	326.5
54.6	Other transient situational personality disturbance	000–x80	326.4
60–62	MENTAL DEFICIENCIES		
60	MENTAL DEFICIENCY (FAMILIAL OR HEREDITARY)		
60.0	Mild	000–x901	325.3 (pt)
60.1	Moderate	000–x902	325.2 (pt)
60.2	Severe	000–x903	325.1 (pt)
60.3	Severity not specified	000–x90	325.5 (pt)
61	MENTAL DEFICIENCY, IDIOPATHIC		
61.0	Mild	000–y901	325.3 (pt)
61.1	Moderate	000–y902	325.2 (pt)
61.2	Severe	000–y903	325.1 (pt)
61.3	Severity not specified	000–y90	325.5 (pt)

The following codes are to be used as the qualifying phrase x4 and will be coded as separate diagnoses. They represent mental deficiency by grades of severity, associated with and as the major symptom in impairment of brain tissue function.

Code No.	Disorder		Int'l List Nos.
62	MENTAL DEFICIENCY (x4)		
62.0	Severe		325.6 *
62.1	Moderate		325.7
62.2	Mild		325.8
62.3	Severity not specified		325.9

* If Mongolism is specified, code 325.4

INDEX

Abortion
  as cause of mental illness, 294
  indications, 296
  therapeutic, general considerations, 294
Abrahams, J., 36, 460, 461
Abreaction, 104, 105
Abstinence syndrome
  electroconvulsive therapy in, 258
  in addiction, 255
  methadone withdrawal schedule, 257
Abt, L. E., 142
Accidents, 100, 344
Acetylcholine therapy, 52
Activities program, 226
  role of attendant, 152
Addicting drugs, 253
Addiction, 249
  abstinence syndrome, 255
  action of drugs on central nervous system, 253
  cultural factors, 252
  definition, 249
  diagnosis, 255
  group therapy, 261
  habituation compared, 250
  juvenile, 230, 233
  Nallorphine diagnosis, 256
  Narcotics Anonymous, 261
  orality in, 251
  popular misconceptions, 249
  psychological factors, 251
  social service, 231
  tolerance and physical dependence, 253
  treatment, 260
Adler, M. H., 306
Administration, see Administrative psychiatry
Administrative psychiatry
  budget planning, 372
  definition, 359
  group psychotherapy, 361
  lay board, 371
  letters to patient, 365
  medical executive committee, 372
  personnel director, 363
  principles, 362
  public relations, 372
  research, 370, 374
  therapeutic community, 373

  training, 373
Admission to hospital
  attendant's role, 148
  children, 225
  initial interview, 11
  letter of welcome, 11, 365
  social service role, 115
Adolescence, 216; see also Child
  behavior disturbances in, 220
  mental disease in, 220
  psychosomatic disorders in, 220
  relationship of mental disease to, 220
  sleep disturbance, 220
  symptom formation, 220
  transitory phobias, 220
Adoption proceedings, 298
Aftercare
  aged, 212
  clinic, 469, 470, 471
  social service role, 122
Aged (Geriatrics)
  aftercare, 212
  causes of mental illness, 201
  community centers, 207
  church as social center, 207
  civil defense role, 207
  day hospital, 207
  deterioration, 211
  dual leadership in group therapy, 212
  electroconvulsive therapy, 209
  electroencephalogram, 205
  foster home, 206
  group psychotherapy, 212
  medical procedures, 209
  memory impairment, 211
  nursing homes, 207
  physical restraints, 210
  prevention of mental illness, 206
  psychological studies, 207
  psychopathology, 203
  psychotherapy, 211
  public libraries as social centers, 207
  research, 213
  social service, 207
  somatotherapy, 209
  special housing, 206
  statistics, 201
  treatment, 207
  volunteer workers, 207

543

Aichhorn, A., 334
Alcohol, science and society, 247
Alcoholics Anonymous (A.A.), 28, 240, 247
Alcoholism, 235
  absenteeism caused by, 246
  acute, 238
  Alcoholics Anonymous, 28, 240, 247
  antabuse therapy, 242
  as disease, 236
  conditioned aversion therapy, 241
  Consolidated Edison Co. of N. Y., pro-
    gram for employees, 246
  countertransference in therapy of, 245
  disulfiram (antabuse), 242
  formulating case, 245
  lobotomy, 245
  orality, 246
  pathological intoxication, 238
  physical changes, 237
  psychological studies, 236
  psychosis, 246
  psychotherapy, 244
  research, 241, 246
  sex deviate, 313
  social factors, 237
  treatment, 239, 240
Alexander, F., 23, 334
Allen, E. B., 247
Allport, D. B., 174
Alpert, H. S., 346
Alvord, E. C., Jr., 291
Alzheimer's disease, 204
Ambivalence, 219
  in group psychotherapy, 33
American Association of University Wom-
    en, role in mental hygiene, 503
American Board of Psychiatry and Neu-
    rology
  certification by, 391
  examinations, 394
  fees, 394
  requirements for applicants, 391
American Psychiatric Association, 358,
    374, 515
Ames, F. R., 430 .
Amphetamine therapy, 51, 259
Amytal, 51; see also Sodium amytal
Amytal test, 53, 55
  for organic brain disease, 438
Anal phase of development, 217
Anderson, G. L., 142
Anderson, H. H., 142
Animal pets, in therapy, 489
Antabuse, see Disulfiram, 51

Architecture, see also Mental hospital and
    child, architectural problems in in-
    patient treatment
  of mental hospital, 208
  as therapy, 349
Arithmetic disability, 227
Arthur, J. K., 214
Ascending reticular activating system, of
    central nervous system, 56
Association of Casualty and Surety Com-
    panies, and epileptic employee, 285
Asylum, versus hospital in teaching at-
    tendants, 145
Atcheson, J. D., 321
Attendant
  activities program, 152
  anxiety in ward work, 154
  asylum versus hospital, 145
  charted record of emergency procedures,
    153
  disturbed behavior, and crowding, 150
  disturbed behavior at bedtime, 150
  emergency measures for violent patient,
    151
  empathy, 147
  group therapy, 155
  initial contact, 148
  meaning of symptoms, 146
  objectivity, 147
  prejudices, 145
  psychiatric aide, 144
  psychiatric nurse, 144
  psychiatric technician, 144
  recruiting, 143
  relationship to nurse, 163
  restraints, 152
  screening, 144
  sex of, 195
  teaching, 145, 153
  transference in realtionship to physi-
    cian, 154
  violent patient, 149
  ward management, 149
Audio-visual techniques, see also Motion
    Pictures, Television, Music
Axelrod, R. L., 38

Baer, W. H., 156
Baganz, C. N., 359, 361, 374
Bahn, A. K., 482
Barber shop, relation to treatment, 72
Barbiturism, 259
  electroconvulsive therapy, 360
  electroencephalogram, 259, 438
  nonprotein nitrogen, 260

Barhash, A. Z., 482
Barker, W., 290
Barrett, J. E., 82, 91
Barrier against stimuli, 56
Baskin, T. G., 307
Beauty parlor, relation to treatment, 72, 178
Beaver, N., 72
Beck, S. J., 142
Bedtime, disturbed behavior at, 150
Beers, C. M., 486, 501, 502
Behavior disturbances, 218
Bellak, L., 142
Bender, M. B., 107, 110
Bennett, A. E., 449
Bentley, M. C., 482
Berger, H., 279
Berkman, T. D., 127
Betz, B. J., 196, 200
Bible in bibliotherapy, 68
Bibliotherapy, 68
  reading materials in, 520
Bickford, J. A. B., 200
Bickford, R. G., 290
Bielinski, B., 246, 248
Bierer, J., 474, 482
Birthday celebrations, in treating child, 226
Black, K., 163
Blain, D., 72
Bleckwenn, W. J., 102
Blom, G. E., 233
Blum, M. L., 375
Bochner, R., 142
Bond, D. D., 306
Bonner, C. A., 346
Boone, J. T., 306
Bovet, L., 334
Bowlby, J., 232
Bozeman, M. F., 92
Brauer, P. H., 475
Brigg's Law, 329
Brill, N. Q., 449
Brody, E. B., 23
Bromidism, 259
Brosin, H. W., 418
Brown, F., 142
Broy, W. R., 247
Bruder, E. E., 173, 174
Bryan, W. A., 346, 365, 375
Budget planning, in administrative psychiatry, 372
Bunker, H. A., 440
Burchard, E., 36
Burling, T., 91

Burlingham, D., 515
Business manager, 360

Cafeteria service, therapeutic advantages, 97
Cameron, D. E., 214, 373, 472, 474, 482
Canadian Broadcasting Corporation, 506
Capa, C., 276
Carbon dioxide therapy, 52
Carmichael, D. M., 470
Case histories
  Fish, 327
  Heirens, 313
  Little Hans, 216
Caseworker, see Social service
Castration complex, 218
Central nervous system, activating system, 56, 57, 103
Chaplain, 165; see also Religion
  anxiety, 168
  miscellaneous duties, 173
  number required, 167
  place on therapeutic team, 167
  religious services, 171
  training, 167
  work with individual patients, 173
Characterologic inventory, check list (Appendix C), 525
Charge nurse, 448
Charted record of emergency procedures, 153
Child, 216
  aftercare, 226
  animal pets, 226
  architectural problems in inpatient treatment, 225
  athletic competitions, 226
  birthday celebrations, 226
  booklist for children's library, 234
  community relations, 228
  countertransference, 227
  dental supervision, 227
  disturbed behavior, control of, 229
  educational needs, 227
  ego weakness, 222
  emotional development, 216
  formulating case, 226
  gifts, 226
  holiday celebrations, 226
  infantile neurosis, 218
  intake problem, 225
  obesity, 227
  outpatient care, 222
  physical check-ups, 227
  plastic surgery, 227

Child (cont'd.)
  playground facilities, 226
  police, 228
  preparation for discharge, 229
  preparation for hospitalization, 226
  religious program, 227
  research, 221, 232
  residential treatment center list, 234
  rivalry between cottage parent and real parent, 227
  skin care, 227
  social service role, 222, 226, 229
  somatotherapy, 228
  special aspects of treatment, 226
  surgical procedures, 227
  swimming, 226
  therapeutic community, 224
  training personnel, 231
  underweight, 227
  volunteer worker's role, 228
  welfare worker, 113
Chlorpromazine (thorazine), 52, 210
Chronic patients, and research, 199
Church
  and mental hygiene, 459
  as social center for aged, 207
C.I.O., Annual (1953) Report of the Mental Hygiene Clinic of the Health Institute of the UAW-CIO, 91
Civil defense, role of aged, 207
Civil emergencies
  administrative aspects, 514
  countertransference in leaders, 514
  emotional needs of children, 510
  initial reaction to disaster, 511
  leadership, 509
  manic-like reactions, 512
  mental hospital, 508, 514
  panic reaction, 511
  pathological reaction types, 511
  prevention of pathological reactions, 512
  prophylactic principles, 508, 509
  psychiatric casualties, 508
  retarded reactions, 512
  role of motivation in adaptation, 509
  treatment of pathological reactions, 513
Clancy, J., 200
Classification of mental disorders (Appendix E), 531
Cleckley, H., 313
Clinical director, 360
Cobb, D., 276
Cobb, S., 419
Cocaine, 259

Coffin, T. E., 334
Cohen, J., 449
Cohen, L. H., 334
Coleman, L., 232
Coleman, M. L., 408
Coles, R., 449
Coma
  acute alcoholic intoxication as cause, 239
  blood transfusions in irreversible insulin coma, 436
Commitment proceedings, forensic psychiatry, 422
Community centers, for aged, 207
Community organization, branch of social service, 114
Community relations, social service role, 126
Competence of witness, psychiatrically considered, 427
Conant, J. B., 414
Conception, prevention of, in mental illness, 297
Conditional discharge, 384; see also Trial visit
Conditioned aversion therapy, in alcoholism, 241
Conference on Psychosurgery of the National Institute of Mental Health, 59
Conferences of Mental Hospital Administrators and Statisticians, 375, 388, 449, 482, 507, 515
Conscious awareness, 56
Consciousness, 54
Consolidated Edison Company of N. Y., program for mentally ill worker, 90
Constant, G. A., 247
Consultants, for mental hospitals, 342
"Continued Treatment Building," 198
Contraception, in mental illness, 297
Controlling influences, need for in therapy, 221
Convalescent care, 384; see also Trial visit
Convalescent status, 384; see also Trial visit
Cooking classes, as therapy, 99
Coroner, notifying, 345
Cote, F., 461
Cottage plan, in child care, 225
Council of State Governments, 408, 419
Council on Pharmacy and Chemistry Report, 261
Counseling residents, as training device, 397

Countertransference, 8, 10, 27, 81, 162, 445
  in child care, 227
  with schizophrenics, 197
Cramer, J. B., 37
Credibility of testimony, psychiatrically considered, 428
Cretinism, 268
Criminal
  acts, by patients on trial visit, 333
  appraisal of treatment, 322
  examination, 328
  formulating case, 331
  legal responsibility, 324
  parole, 332
  psychosis, 323
  psychotherapy, 331
  sociologic aspects, 324
  theory of, behavior, 329
Crowding, and disturbed behavior, 150
Crutcher, H. B., 126, 127
Cruvant, B. A., 36, 370
Cummings, R., 490, 492
Cummins, J. F., 247
Custodial care, see "Continued Treatment Building"

Daly, D., 290
Dance therapy, 67
Dancey, T. E., 461
Davidson, H. A., 299, 321, 426, 430, 472
Day hospital, 373, 472
  aged, 207
  Cameron report, 472
  children, 224
  Menninger Foundation, 474
  New Jersey State Hospital in Trenton, 474
Day, M., 37
Day nursery, 224
Deactivating impulses, in the central nervous system, 56, 57, 103
Defense mechanisms, 21, 58
Definition of terms, in psychiatric statistics, 383
Déjà vu, 205
Delinquency
  comics and television, role, 221
  mental deficiency in, 273
  relation to mental illness, 230
  therapy, 230
  training schools, 230
Denial, as defense mechanism, 54, 55, 57, 493

Dental department, in mental hospital, 343
Depression
  as defense, 55
  electroconvulsive therapy, 41
  involutional, 386
  postpartum, 293
  psychotherapy, 15, 293
Deterioration
  aged, 211
  meaning, 463
  social psychology, 191
Deutsch, A., 185, 421, 430
Deutsch, H., 232
Dewitt, H. B., 128, 492
Diagnosis, see Addiction, Aged, Alcoholism, Child, Criminal, Depression, Epilepsy, Formulating case, Group psychotherapy, Mental deficiency, Pregnant patient, Psychotherapy, Recreational therapy, Religion, Schizophrenia, Sex deviate, Somatotherapy, Tuberculosis, Veteran
Dibenamine therapy, 52
Dietitian
  family care, 99
  member of the treatment team, 99
Disaster, psychiatric first aid, see Civil emergencies
Disturbed behavior
  control of, in child, 229
  crowding, 150
  oral tensions, 98
Disulfiram (Antabuse)
  chlorpromazine therapy in, 243
  contraindications, 243
  therapy, 243
Divorce, mental illness as basis for, 426
Double simultaneous stimulation (DSS), 107
Doyle, K., 457, 461
Dream, 13
  associations, 14
  day residue, 14
  early in therapy, 13
  interpretation, 14
  latent content, 14
  manifest, 14
  oedipal, 21
  suggested, 19, 54
  wish fulfillment, 13
  work, 14
Dribben, I. S., 306
Drinker, C. K., 419
Drugs, habituating, 259

Dual leadership, in group therapy of aged, 212
Dundan, H. D., 186
Duval, A., 375

Eating, psychopathology of, 95
Ebaugh, F. G., 395, 449
ECT, see Electroconvulsive therapy
Educating the public
  audience, 495
  content of program, 494
  group discussions, 498
  mechanism of denial, an obstacle to, 493
  motion pictures, 497
  National Association for Mental Health, 500
  National Mental Health Act, 503
  open house, 497
  patients on radio and television, 499
  press, 497
  radio, 499
  teachers, 496
  technique, 497
  television, 498
  visitors' check list, 506
  working-through process, 494
EEG, see Electroencephalography, 437
Ego, 219
  boundary, 94, 96
  weakness of, 221
Eisenman, A. J., 261
Eissler, K. R., 334
Electrocardiography, in mental hospital, 436
Electroconvulsive therapy (ECT), 41, 57, 109
  aged, 209
  APA standards, 44
  barbiturates in, 43
  curare-like agents in, 43
  in abstinence syndrome, 258
  in barbiturism, 260
  in epilepsy, 282, 287
  indications, 41
  mental deficiency, 273
  music in, 70
  outpatient, 43, 476
  varieties of electrical stimuli, 44
Electroencephalography (EEG), 53, 57, 437
  aging process, 205
  in epilepsy, 281, 290
  provocative measures in, 440
  research, 439, 440
Elliott, M. E., 334

Elliott, S. A., 233
Emotional development
  of child, 216
  oral phase, 94
  role of early feeding experiences, 93
Emotional stress, and life transitions, 165
Empathy, need for, 147
Employment service for patients, 83
Endicott-Johnson Company, and mentally ill worker, 90
Engle, B. S., 449
Epilepsy, 278
  amphetamine sulfate, 283
  Babinski, 281
  bromides, 282
  childbearing, 289
  definition, 279
  diagnosis, 282
  dilantin, 282
  effect of emotions, 279
  electroconvulsive therapy, 287
  electroencephalogram, 281, 290
  focal, 282
  formulating case, 284
  group psychotherapy, 286
  heredity, 288
  intramural care, 286
  Jacksonian, 283
  lobotomy, 287
  marriage, 289
  medicolegal aspects, 289
  mesantoin, 282
  motion pictures, 286
  paradione, 284
  petit mal, 281
  phenobarbital, 282
  phenurone, 282, 288
  psychiatric aspects, 284, 287
  psychological studies, 284
  psychomotor, 281
  social service, 284, 285
  status epilepticus, 281
  symptomatic, 279
  traveling clinics, 286
  treatment, 282
  tridione, 282
  work, 285
Epilepsy Association of New York, 285
Erickson, T. C., 438
Ether therapy, 52
Ethics
  for attendants, 150
  for volunteers, 184
  in mental hygiene, 166
  in religion, 166

Expert witness, 328

Face-hand test, 53, 55, 107, 438
Fainting, relation to defense mechanisms, 57
Fallacy of partial insanity, 298, 326, 424, 427
Family care, 475, 485
 community type, 486
 Gheel Colony, 484
 growth of, 486
 individual type, 486
 instructions to foster families, 488
 patient returns from, 490
 popular misconceptions, 491
 purpose, 484
 results, 490
 school type, 487
 selection of foster families, 487
 social service in, 123, 487
 therapeutic advantages, 489
 transition to unsupervised care, 492
 types, 486
Family caseworker, 113
Family doctor, and mental hospital patient, 459
Fechner, A. H., 186
Federal Security Association, Public Health Service, 408
Feeding mental hospital patients, 97
Feldman, D. J., 247
Feldman, P. E., 346
Felix, R. H., 388
Fenichel, O., 101
Ferraro, A., 440
Fidler, G. S., 81, 91
Fidler, J. W., 81, 91
Field, M., 124
Films, see Motion pictures
Fish, A., case history, 327
Fisher, C., 19, 23
Fisher, T. M., 36, 37, 88
Fitzsimmons, L. W., 375
Flechsig, C., 433
Folin, O., 433
Food
 handlers, 344
 refusal, 99
 therapy, 93
Ford Motor Company, and epileptic worker, 285
Forel, A., 433
Forensic psychiatry
 commitment proceedings, 422
 legal transactions involving mental patients, 423
 loss of personal liberty, 420
 psychosurgery, 429
Forepleasure, relation to deviant sexuality, 309
Formulating case, 4, 130, 207, 223, 454, 519
 aftercare clinic, 471
 child patient, 226
 criminal behavior, 331
 epilepsy, 284
 mental deficiency, 266
 psychological tests in, 4
 social service in, 4, 117
 sodium amytal in, 104
 value of, in treating schizophrenia, 196
Fort, J. P., Jr., 261
Foster home, 229; see also Family care
 for aged, 206
 in mental deficiency, 271
Foulkes, S. H., 37
Fountain House Foundation, Inc., 124
Fox, R., 244
Fraiberg, S. H., 128, 233
Frank, B., 334
Frank, J. D., 32, 37
Frank, M., 176
Frank, M. H., 186
Fraser, H. F., 261
Freeman, R. V., 186
Freeman, W., 49
Freiman, G. V., 215
French, T. M., 23
Freud, A., 233, 515
Freud, S., 16, 19, 23, 25, 190, 205, 216, 233, 309, 321, 433, 434
Fried, D. G., 247
Friedlander, K., 334
Froehlich's syndrome, 268
Fromm-Reichmann, F., 22, 23
Fuller, R. G., 375
Funkenstein, D. H., 109, 110

Garrett, A. M., 128
Gasser, H. S., 419
Gates, P. H., 306
Gavrin, J. B., 233
General hospital, psychiatric service, 305, 441, 443
General paresis, 204, 380, 381
Genes in mental deficiency
 dominant, 267
 multiple, 266
 recessive, 267
Geoghegan, J. J., 59, 476, 483

Geriatric unit, in mental hospital, 208;
    see also Aged
Gheel Colony, 484
Gianini, M. J., 269, 277
Gilbertson, R. J. L., 233
Gill, M., 23
Ginsburg, S. W., 306
Ginzberg, E., 306
Ginzberg, R., 214
Glueck, B. C., Jr., 321
Glutamic acid therapy, 52
Goal in treatment, in treating schizo-
    phrenia, 196
Goodale, E., 128, 461
Gould, S. E., 346
Gray, J., 186
"Great Books" program, 68, 72
Greenbaum, H., 247
Greenblatt, M., 110, 164
Greenstein, L., 439, 440
"Gripe sessions," in group therapy, 28
Group activities, types, 27
Group for the Advancement of Psychiatry,
    128, 164, 214, 233, 321, 334, 346, 388,
    430, 506, 515
Group formation, psychoanalytic theory,
    24
Group ideal, definition, 25
Group psychotherapy, 24
    advantages of, 26
    ambivalence, 33
    as administrative technique, 361
    contraindications, 35
    countertransference, 32
    hostility in, 31, 35
    insight type, 28
    integrated with individual psychother-
        apy, 31
    monopoly of attention, as resistence, 30
    new patient in, 31
    outpatient, 29, 468, 471
    psychoneurosis, 29
    public education for mental health, 498
    replacement of group leader, 31
    research, 36
    schizophrenia, 32
    sex deviate, 320
    sexual acting out in, 35
    silences, 30, 34
    supportive, 28
    with aged, 212
    with attendants, 155
Group worker, social, 114
Gruber, T. R. K., 346
Guilt feelings, 16, 219, 222

Gursi, J., 37
Guttmacher, A. F., 299
Guttmacher, M. S., 317, 320, 321, 329, 430

Habituating drugs, 259
Haddock, J. N., 186
Hadley, R. V., 346
Hagan, H. R., 234
Halfway house, 229, 489, 491
Hall, B. H., 156
Halpern, F., 142
Hamburg, D. A., 307
Hamilton, G., 128
Hamilton, S. W., 462
Hannigan, M. C., 72
Hargrove, E. A., 449
Haun, P., 101, 350, 353, 356, 358, 361, 441,
    448, 449
Health insurance, and mental illness, 447
Hecker, A. O., 346
Heirens, W., case history, 313
Heldt, T. J., 442
Heppenstall, M. E., 290
Herman, J. L., 306
Hill, D., 290
Hilliard, R. M., 214
Hippocrates, 286
Histamine therapy, 52
Hoch, A., 433
Hoch, P. H., 44, 50, 58, 110, 290, 299, 321
Hoffman, P., 271
Hollis, F., 128
Home for the aged, 206
Homicide, and sex deviate, 313
Hormone therapy, 52
Hospital administrator, patient relation-
    ships, 365
Houliston, M., 164
House-Tree-Person Test (HTP), 137
Howe, H. S., 249, 258, 261
Huie, W. B., 334
Hyde, R. W., 37
Hydrotherapy, 71
Hypnotism, 513
Hypochondriasis, 5

Id, 218
Identification, 20, 218
Immunizations, in mental hospital, 343
Indefinite leave, 384; see also Trial visit
Individual psychotherapy, see Psycho-
    therapy, individual
Infantile fixation, 310
Infantile neurosis, 218
Infirmary in mental hospital, 341

Initial contact with patient, 148
Initial interview, 11
Injury, as cause of mental illness, 426
Insight psychotherapy, 8
Insulin coma therapy (ICT), 47
  complications, 48
  indication, 47
  modifications, 49
  technique, 47
Insurance policies, for mental illness, 447
Intake problem, and inpatient treatment
  of child, 225
International Business Machines, use in
  psychiatric statistics, 285
Involutional psychosis, 386; see also De-
  pression
Inwood, E. R., 460, 461
Isbell, H., 261
Isolation, as defense mechanism, 57
Isoniazid therapy, 52

Jasper, H., 58
Jenkins, R. L., 50, 233
Jervis, G. A., 277
Jessner, L., 233
Jetter, W. W. E., 346
Jones, M., xix, 37, 78

Kahn, R. L., 59, 110, 156, 400, 449
Kalinowsky, L. B., 44, 50, 58, 110, 290,
  299, 321
Kanner, L., 233, 265, 277
Karpman, B., 321
Kasius, C., 128
Kaufman, M. R., 440, 449
Keith, H. M., 290
Keith-Lucas, A., 233
Kelley, D. M., 430
Kemp, C., 174
Kirkpatrick, M. E., 482
Klapman, J. W., 37
Kleptomania, 313, 330
Kline, N. S., 145, 157, 178, 181, 182, 186,
  199, 200
Kohl, R. N., 375
Kraepelin, E., 189
Kramer, M., 378, 384, 387, 388
Kris, E., 60, 72
Kubie, S. H., 214
Kugelmass, I. N., 277
Kurland, A. A., 37

Laboratory, in mental hospital, 432
Lactic acid therapy, 52
Landau, G., 214

Latency period, 219
  delinquency in, 219
  neurosis in, 219
  psychosis in, 219
Laughlin, H. P., 375
Lawton, G., 214
Legal responsibility, and criminal be-
  havior, 324
Lehrman, S. R., 346
Leighton, A. H., 408
Lennox, W. G., 278, 286, 290
Letters to patient, 365
Level of general awareness, 54, 55
Levine, M., 23
Levy, S., 210, 214
Lewis, N. D. C., 233
Liberson, W. T., 58
Lidz, T., 408
Lie detector, 428
Linden, M. E., 36, 212, 214
Lindsley, D. B., 59
Ling, T. M., 482
Linn, L., 59, 110, 449
Linton, D., 164
Lion's Clubs, role in mental hygiene, 503
Listening, technique, 12
"Little Hans," case history, 216
Lobotomy
  medial, 50
  precoronal, 50
  transorbital, 50
  unilateral, 50
Location, of mental hospital, 350
Lolli, G., 247
Lourie, N. V., 233
Lowry, F., 128

MacDonald, J. H., 430
MacLean, R. R., 214
MacMurchy, H., 262, 277
McBee, M., 186
McCarthy, R. G., 37, 247
McConnell, G. F., 72
McKerracher, D. G., 144, 157
McNaghten Rule, 326

Magoun, H. W., 56, 59
Mail, of mental patients, 425
Malamud, W., 419
Malononitrile therapy, 52
Malpractice suit, 426
Malzberg, B., 200, 379, 380
Manic reaction, 55
  electroconvulsive therapy in, 41
Marihuana, 259

Marimoto, F. R., 164
Marshall, D., 449
Martensen-Larsen, O., 247
Martin, D. W., 72
Massage as therapy, 72
Masturbation, 19-21, 218, 219
Matlin, M., 335
Maves, P. B., 174
Mealtime, disturbed behavior at, 96
Medical procedures, for the aged, 209
Medical examiner, notifying the, 345
Medical Executive Committee, and administrative psychiatry, 372
Medical services, in mental hospital, 343
Medical social worker, 114
Meduna, L. J., 41, 287
Meerloo, J. A. M., 515
Meislin, J., 91
Memory impairment, in the aged, 211
Menninger, K. A., 23
Mental deficiency, 70, 262
  absolute retardation, 265
  colony plan in treatment, 271
  contraception, 297
  definition, 263
  delinquency, 265
  diagnosis and classification, 263
  electroconvulsive therapy, 273
  endocrinology, 268
  formulating case, 266
  foster home care, 271
  "four pillars of care," 273
  genes, dominant, as cause, 267
    multiple, as cause, 266
    recessive, as cause, 267
  glutamic acid in treatment of, 273
  high grade, 265
  idiot, 264
  imbecile, 264
  infections as cause, 267
  institutional care, 272
  low grade, 264
  medicolegal aspects, 275
  middle grade, 264
  mongolism, 268
  moron, 265
  outpatient treatment, 268
  prevention, 274
  pseudo retardation, 265
  psychological testing, 263
  relative retardation, 265
  seizures, 270
  sex deviate, 312
  sexual drive, 265
  sheltered workshop, 270

  social service, 266, 268, 271
  somatic factors, 266
  somatotherapy, 273
  sterilization, 273
  thyroid in treatment, 273
  toxic factors as cause, 268
  training and research, 274
  trauma as cause, 267
  vocational guidance, 269
Mental Health Film Board, 408, 504
Mental Hospital
  aesthetic considerations, 353, 354, 357
  architecture, 208
  as "big business," 377
  building arrangement, 356
  civil emergencies, 508, 514
  consultants, 342
  dental department, 343
  electrocardiography, 436
  food handlers, 344
  geriatric unit, 208
  immunizations in, 343
  infirmary, 341
  laboratory, 432
  location, 350
  medical care, 356
  medical services, 343
  miscellaneous considerations in construction, 357
  pastoral psychiatry, 166
  pathology laboratory, 432
  personnel, 208
  physical illness, 336
  public health measures in, 344
  research in pathology, 434-436
  research in psychosomatic medicine, 341
  sexes, segregation, 354
  size, 351
  structure, 352
  training and research facilities, 357
  traumatic effect, 441
  tuberculosis, 337
  X-ray, 437
Mental Hospital Institute, 388
Mental hygiene, ethics, 166
Mental illness
  basis for divorce, 426
  injury as cause, 426
Merrill, B. R., 358
Merritt, H., 282, 439
Methadone Withdrawal Schedule, in treatment of abstinence syndrome, 257
Methylguanidine therapy, 52
Metropolitan Life Insurance Company, 215

Meyer, A., 216, 433, 434
Meynert, T., 433
Mezer, R. R., 482
Middelton, J., 157
Milieu of therapeutic optimism, 194
Milieu therapy, *see* Therapeutic community, Day hospital
Miller, A., 72
Miller, D. H., 200
Miller, T. K., 358
Miller, V., 101
Minister, and mental hospital patient, 459
Monakow, C., 433
Money, as work incentive, 85
Mongolism, 268
Moniz, E., 49
Moran, M. L., 128
Moravia, A., 234
Morris, L. S., 249, 258, 261
Motion pictures, 66
Motion picture catalogues, 66
Motivation, 39; *see also* Psychodynamics
and employability, 84
and military service, 306
money as work incentive, 85
Murphy, B. W., 200
Music as therapy, 70
Myanesin therapy, 52

Nace, F. D., 215
Nallorphine, in diagnosis of addiction, 256
Narcoanalysis, 428
Narcotic addiction, *see* Addiction
National Association for Mental Health, 388, 408, 461, 482, 506
public education, 500
National Council of Jewish Women, role in mental hygiene, 465, 503
National Epilepsy League, Inc., 285
National Institute of Mental Health, 430
National Mental Health Act
application for training benefits, 407
eligibility for training, 405, 406
grants to institutions, 404
outpatient care, 464
psychiatric nursing, training opportunity, 406
psychiatry, training opportunities, 405
psychology, training opportunities, 406
public education, 503
public health mental health training opportunities, 406
research opportunities, 414-417

responsibilities of traineeship recipients, 407
social service training opportunities, 126, 406
traineeships, 405
Negation, as defense mechanism, 19
Negativism, 103
Neher, J., 461
Newman, R., 23
New York State Department of Mental Hygiene, 430
Nichtenhauser, A., 408
Nicolson, G. T., 200
Nightmare, 14
Nomenclature
new, 382, 531
standard, 531
statistics, 381
Nomenclature and Statistics Committee of the American Psychiatric Association, 387
Nonverbal means of expression, 62
Note taking, 11
Nurse, *see also* Attendant
administrative duties, 162
duties, 158
relationship to attendant, 163
team concept, 163
Nursing homes, for aged, 207
Nutritional requirements, 100

Objectives, or goals of treatment, 5
Objectivity, need for, in work with patients, 147
Occupational therapy (O.T.), 74, 177
bridge between recreation and work, 78
countertransference in, 81
formulating case, 80
functions, 80
prescribing, 81
records, 79, 83
specific characterisitcs, 79
suicide in, 82
therapeutic role, 80
training, 82
transference, 81
volunteers, 82
Oedipus complex, 218
Old age assistance benefits, 206
Oral phase of development, 94, 217
Oral tensions, and disturbed behavior, 97, 98, 344
"Orality," 94
in addiction, 251

Organic brain disease, sodium amytal test for, 106
Osborne, L. A., 449
Ostow, M., 288, 290, 439, 440
Outpatient care
aftercare clinic, 469
for children and adolescents, 222, 467
day hospital, 472
economics of, 464
electroconvulsive therapy in, 476
fees, 467
group formation, 466
importance, 463
National Council of Jewish Women, role in, 465
National Mental Health Act, 464
Netherlands' Plan, 475
night clinics, 468
organizational problems, 465
psychologist, role in, 468
referral of patients, 467
social service, role in, 468
statistical problems, 477
traveling clinics, 468
Outpatient statistical problems, 477
collecting uniform data, 480
types of clinic data, 477
Overholser, W., 322, 431

Pacella, B. L., 233
Paranoid reactions, 54, 55
Paraphasic naming, 53
Parent-Teacher Associations, and mental hygiene, 459
Parke, J. H., 186
Parole and probation
of criminal, 332
social service in, 114, 332, 333
Pastoral psychiatry, in mental hospital, see Chaplain, Religion
Pathological excited states, and hidden staff disagreements, 197
Pathology laboratory, in mental hospital, 432
Patient
as employee, 84
on trial visit, criminal acts by, 333
self-government, 28, 226
Pavlov, I., 103
Peabody, F., 390
Peck, H. B., 37
Peck, S. M., 440
Peffer, P. A., 85, 91
Pellagra, 100
Penfield, W. G., 284, 288, 291, 419, 438

Perkins, C. T., 375
Perkins, G. L., 409
Personality, see Ego
Personnel, of mental hospital, 208
Pfeffer, A. S., 37
Phallic phase of development, 218
Phobias, 218
Physical illness, 194, 336
and patient's family, 345
Pick's Disease, 204
Play, see also Recreation
theory of, 60
Play therapy, 223
Pleasure, H., 246
Podolsky, E., 73
Polatin, P., 49, 50
Polch, J., 419
Pollock, H. M., 492
Postpartum, depression, 293; see also Pregnant patient
Potter, H. W., 215
Powdermaker, F. B., 32, 37
Powell, J. W., 68, 73
Pratt, D., 461
Precipitating factor in mental illness, 4
Preconvalescent period, social service in, 121
Pregenital phase of development, 217
Pregnancy fantasies, 96
Pregnant patient, 292; see also Abortion, Contraception
electroconvulsive therapy, 296
insulin coma therapy, 297
psychological aspects, 292
somatotherapy, 296
treatment, 296
Prejudices of attendants, 145
Preliminary psychiatric formulation (Appendix A), 519
Preparation of food, accidents in, 100
Prevention of mental illness, in the aged, 206
Preverbal phase of development, 218
"Primary process," 190
Privileged communications, 429
Projection, as defense mechanism, 190
Projective tests, 132
Prout, C. T., 247
Pseudo-neurotic schizophrenia, 40
Psychiatric aide
handbook, 156
relation to attendant, 144
Psychiatric nurse, 163; see also Attendant
as a career, 164
educational program, 161

Psychiatric nurse (*cont'd.*)
  federal funds for training, 161
  personnel shortage, 160
  relation to attendant, 144
  requirements, 159
Psychiatric nursing, personnel, 164
Psychiatric social worker, 114; *see also*
  Social service
Psychiatric technician, relation to attendant, 144
Psychiatrist
  as witness, 424
  psychological testing by, 137
Psychiatry and religion, 169
Psychoanalysis
  of sex deviate, 320
  training in, 10
Psychoanalytic theory of group formation,
  24
Psychodrama, 28, 177, 226
Psychodynamics, 39, 102
Psychogenic concept in medicine, 434
Psychologist
  aged patient, 207
  criminal patients, 332
  deterioration, estimation of, 131
  diagnostic aid, 131
  formulating case, 130
  prognosis, estimation of, 131
  psychodynamics, elucidation of, 131
  report, 139
  request for studies, 130
  research role, 141
  retesting patients, 131
  selection of patients for testing, 139
  sex deviate, 318
  therapist role, 141
Psychoneurosis
  after abortion, 290
  as defense, 364
  hypochondriasis, 5
  in adolescence, 220
  in child, 218
  psychotherapy, 294
Psychoneurotic reactions, and sex deviate,
  312
Psychopathic personality, and sex deviate,
  313
Psychopathology
  aging, 203
  eating, 95
  everyday life, 205
Psychosis
  alcoholism, 246
  depressive, 15, 41, 55, 293, 386

general paresis, 304, 380, 381
  involutional, 386
  manic, 41, 55
  paranoid, 54, 55
  schizophrenic, 189-193, 196, 197, 463
  senile, 286
  sex deviate, 312
Psychosurgery, 49; *see also* Lobotomy
  forensic psychiatry, relationship to, 429
  future of, 51
Psychotherapist, qualities of, 196
Psychotherapy, group, 24; *see also* Group
  psychotherapy
Psychotherapy, individual, 3; *see also*
  Formulating case
  aged, 211
  criminal, 331
  dosage in, 18
  dreams in, 13
  effect of somatotherapy on, 58
  end of treatment, 15
  goal, or objective, 6, 196
  in outpatient clinic, 471
  insight type, 8
  magical expectations in, 15
  reality testing in, 14
  research in, 22
  resistance in, 18
  role of dreams, 13
  schizophrenia, 196
  supportive type, 5
  termination of, 21
  tuberculosis, 340
  working-through process, 15
Public Assistance Agency, and social service, 114
Public health measures, in mental hospital, 344
Public libraries, as social centers for aged,
  207
Public relations, and administrative psychiatry, 372
Putnam, T. J., 282, 283, 291, 439
Pyromania, 313

Rabinovitch, R. D., 37
Rackower, L. W., 91
Randall, G. C., 37, 291
Ransohoff, J., 431
Rauwolfia serpentina (reserpine), 52
Ray, I., 324
Reach, C. F., 375
Reading disability, 227
Reading materials in Bibliotherapy
  (Appendix B), 520

Reality needs of patients, 190, 193, 221
Reality testing, 8
Recreational therapist, 63
Recreational therapy, 60
  prescribing, 62
  records, 65
  social service, 62
  training, 64
  volunteers, 65, 177
Redlich, F. C., 23
Reformatory, 230; see also Training school
  for delinquent children
Refrigeration therapy, 52
Regression
  as defense mechanism, 60, 61, 62, 162
    165, 192, 310, 513
  in service of ego, 60
Rehabilitation of mentally ill, see also
  Work
  family objections, 198
  foster home placement, 199
  inertia of staff, 198
  of chronic patients, 199
  sheltered residences, 199
  social service role, 198
  work, 199
Reid, J. H., 234
Reiser, M. F., 409
Relatives of patients
  anxiety, 454
  average family, 456
  defense mechanisms, 455
  do's and don't's, 457
  guilt, 455
  hostile family, 460
  positive program for, 458
  psychiatrist's hostility to, 453
"Release" effect, of sodium amytal, 102
Religion
  ceremonials, 165
  ethics, 166
  power of, 170
  psychiatry, relationship to, 169
  psychology of, 165
  services for patients, 171
  symbolism as therapeutic device, 172
Remedial arithmetic, 227
Remedial reading, 227
Rennie, T. A. C., 76, 84, 88, 91
Repression, 218
Research
  administrative aspects, 370, 410
  aged, 213
  alcoholism, 241, 246
  child psychiatry, 232

  chronic patients, 199
  Council of State Governments Report,
    174, 200
  difficulties in psychiatry, 411
  electroencephalography in, 439, 440
  individual psychotherapy, 22
  mental hospital pathology, and, 434-436
  National Mental Health Act, 414-417
  psychologist in, 141
  psychosomatic medicine in mental hos-
    pital, 341
  selection of projects for investigation,
    413
  social service in, 125
  tradition in mental hospital, role of,
    410
  veterans, 303
Reserpine, 52
Restraints, 152, 210
Retarded children, see also Mental de-
  ficiency
  home training program (Appendix D),
    527
Retarded Children, Inc., 269
  sheltered workshop, 271
Reynolds, Q., 335
Ridenour, N., 502
Rinker, C. D., 375
Rioch, D. M., 291
Robertson, J., 232
Rogers, W. C., 37, 291
Rond, P. C., 482
Rooney, H. L., 507
Rorschach test, 134
Rosemeier, M. R., 101
Rosen, E., 73
Rosen, H., 299
Rosen, J. N., 22, 23, 140
Rosen, V., 5
Rosenbaum, M., 409
Rosenbluth, D., 232
Rothenberg, S. F., 283, 291
Ruhe, D. S., 408
Russell, W. L., 375

Saint Dymphne, 485
Sakel, M., 47
Sanders, H. A., 482
Sargent, W., 59, 290
Saucier, J., 461
Schafer, R., 142
Schizophrenia
  deterioration in, 191, 463
  psychology of, 189
  psychotherapy in, 196

Schizophrenia (cont'd.)
  qualities of good psychotherapist for, 196
  realities of hospital, 190
  results of treatment, 197
  treatment, 189-193
School social worker, 114
Schrager, J., 234
Schroeder, S. F., 121, 128
Schulman, R., 233
Schwartz, A., 186
Schwartz, C. G., 128
Schwartz, M. S., 157, 191, 200
Schwing, G., 23
Screening, personnel, 144, 180, 390
Scully, A. W., 174
Sechehaye, M. A., 22
"Secondary process," 190
Seefeldt, C. J., 129
Selective service, role of psychiatry, 305
Self-determination, see Patient self-government
Selinger, R. V., 247
Sellin, T., 335
Selwyn, A., 462
Semrad, E. V., 37
Senile psychosis, 386; see also Aged
Serpasil, 52
Sex deviate
  and alcoholism, 313
  classification, 312
  clinical manifestations, 310
  counterseductive attitude of child, 17
  effect on victim, 315
  examination, 315
  formulating case, 312
  group psychotherapy, 320
  homicide, 313
  mental deficiency, 312
  popular dread of, 308
  psychoanalysis of, 320
  psychological studies, 310, 312
  psychoneurotic reactions, 312
  psychopathic personality, 313
  psychosis, 312
  report on, 322
  social service in treatment, 312
  sociological classification, 314
  somatotherapy, 320
  supportive therapy, 312
  theory, 309
  treatment, 320
Sexes, segregation of, in mental hospitals, 354
Sheffel, I., 375

Sheltered residence, 229
  social service in, 123
Sheltered workshop, 206, 471
  for mental defectives, 89, 270
Shupel, L. M., 248
Silberman, M., 431
Silver, A., 37
Size, of mental hospital, 351
Slater, E., 59
Slavson, S. R., 37
Smith, L. H., 483
Social casework, see Social service
Social group worker, 114
Social security, 206
Social service, 51, 63, 90
  aftercare, 122
  aftercare clinic, 470, 471
  aged, 207
  children's services, 226
  chronic patient, 197
  community relations, 126
  criminal rehabilitation, 114, 332, 333
  economics of, 124
  epilepsy, 284, 285
  family care, 123, 487, 492
  family of patient, 454
  formulating case, 117
  group psychotherapy, role in, 466
  history taking, 117
  intake, 115
  juvenile narcotic addiction, 231
  mental deficiency, 268, 271
  outpatient care, 222, 476
  period of active treatment, 119
  preconvalescent period, 121
  pregnant patient, 297
  preparation for discharge of child, 229
  public assistance agency, 114
  qualifications, 126
  reception, 115
  research, 125
  sex deviate, 312, 317
  sheltered homes, 123
  subprofessional groups, 127
  symposium, 129
  technician, 127
  training program, 126
  veteran, 303, 305
  vocational rehabilitation, 88
Social service aide, see Social service technician
Social Service Exchange, 116
Social work, see Social service

Social worker
  definition of, 113
  technicians, 127
Sodium amytal
  diagnositc value, 103
  in formulating case, 104
  prognostic value, 102
  "release" effect, 102, 104
  test for organic brain disease, 106
Solomon, H. C., 37, 110, 482
Solow, R. A., 84, 195, 200
Somatic factors, in mental deficiency, 266
Somatotherapy, 39; see also Therapy
  aged, 209
  child, 228
  chronic patient, 197
  pregnant patient, 296
  sex deviate, 320
  theory of, 52
  tuberculosis, 339
Special housing, for aged, 206
Sperber, I. J., 346
Spiegel, E. A., 50
Staff, see also Treatment team, Thera-
    peutic community
Staff conferences, 363
Stainbrook, E. J., 191, 200
Standish, C. T., 37
Stanton, A. H., 157, 191, 200
State Rehabilitation Bureau, 86
Statistics
  budget, 379
  collecting data, 378, 387
  construction planning, 379
  definitions, Cohort, 384
    discharge, 384
    family care, 384
    first admission, 383
    readmission, 383
    temporary visit, 384
    transfer, 384
    trial visit, 384
  difficulties, in mental hospital, 380
  evaluation of treatment methods, 380
  importance, 376
  involutional psychoses, 386
  nomenclature, relation to, 381
  outpatient psychiatric clinics, 387
  reporting system, 384
  schizophrenia, 386
  senile disorders, 386
Staub, H., 334
Sterilization
  of mental defectives, 273
  of mentally ill, 297
Stern, E. H., 462, 507

Sterne, M., 157
Stetson, E. R., 186
Stevenson, G. H., 59, 476, 483
Stevenson, G. S., 375
Stevenson, I., 36, 37, 88
Stewart, K. K., 38
Stewart, M. S., 214
Stieglitz, E. J., 205, 215
Stirling, N., 502
Stockton State Hospital Experiment, 193
Strauss, H., 439, 440
Strecker, E. A., 419
Stringham, J. A., 198, 200
Structure of mental hospital, 352
Structured versus unstructured psycho-
    logical test situations, 132
Sublimation, 219, 222
Success, those destroyed by, 16
Sugarman, L. A., 110
Sullivan, H. S., 23
Superego, 218
Sutton, H., 233
Swimming, as therapy, 71
Symbols, in religious services, 172
Symptoms, meaning of, 146, 168, 364

Talbot, B., 245
Tanner, J. M., 419
Taylor, L. E., 346
Teamster's Union, program for mentally
    ill, 90
Technician, social worker, 127
Television, 66, 67
Temporal lobe surgery, 50
Tenney, A. M., 200
Testimonial capacity, 427
Thalamotomy, 50
Thematic Apperception Test (T.A.T.),
    136
Theory, importance of, xxi
Therapeutic community, 66, 142, 150, 225
  administrative psychiatry, 373
  child intramural care, 224
  volunteer worker in, 175
Therapeutic milieu, see Therapeutic com-
    munity
Therapy, see also Addiction, Aged, Alco-
    holism, Child, Criminal, Depression,
    Epilepsy, Group psychotherapy, Men-
    tal deficiency, Pregnant patient, Psy-
    chotherapy, Recreational therapy,
    Religion, Schizophrenia, Sex deviate,
    Somatotherapy, Tuberculosis, Veteran
  abstinence syndrome, 257
  acetylcholine, 52
  amphetamine, 51, 259

Therapy (*cont'd.*)
  beauty parlor and barber shop, 72, 178
  carbon dioxide, 52
  children, 226
  chlorpromazine, 52, 210
  conditioned aversion for alcoholism, 241
  cooking, 99
  dibenamine, 52
  disulfiram (antabuse), for alcoholism, 242
  electroconvulsive, *see* Electroconvulsive therapy
  ether, 52
  glutamic acid, 52
  goals of, 29
  histamine, 52
  hormones, 52
  hydro, 71
  insulin, 47-49
  isoniazid, 52
  lactic acid, 52
  malonitrile, 52
  massage, 72
  methylguanidine, 52
  music, 70
  myanesin, 52
  occupation, 74
  of mental deficiency, 268-273
  play, 223
  recreational, 60
  refrigeration, 52
  religion, 165-170
  reserpine, 52
  sex deviate, 320
  swimming, 71
  ultraviolet, 72
  vocational, 74
Thomas, G. W., 38
Thompson, G. N., 246, 248
Thorazine (Chlorpromazine), 52, 210
Tompkins, H. J., 307
Topectomy, 50
Training
  administrative aspects, 370, 403
  background of resident, 390
  Council of State Governments Report, 174, 200
  counseling residents, 397
  facilities for, 357
  for child psychiatry, 231
  leadership for civil emergencies, 513
  lectures versus seminars, 402
  mental defectives, care of, 274
  nonprofessional staff, 389, 403
  opportunities, *see* National Mental Health Act

  program for residents, 395
  psychoanalytic, 10, 399
  psychological problems of residents, 398
  senior staff, 400
  motion pictures in, 402
  week-end seminars as teaching device, 400
Training school for delinquent children, 230
Transference, 9, 25, 35, 81, 162, 223, 445
  of attendants in relationship to physician, 154
Transitions of life, and emotional stress, 165
Treatment team, 99, 111
True-False Test for volunteers, 182
"Truth Serum," 105, 428
Tuberculin skin testing, 338
Tuberculosis
  BCG vaccine, 338
  case finding in mental hospital, 338
  control of, in mental hospitals, 338
  electroconvulsive therapy in, 339
  incidence, in mental hospitals, 337
  psychotherapy in, 340
  rehabilitation of mental patients with, 341
  segregation, 338
  somatotherapy in, 339
  treatment in mental hospital, 339
Tucker, A. C., 307
Tupper, W. E., 247
Tureen, L. L., 90, 248
Tyhurst, J. S., 515
Types of therapeutic group activities, 27

Ultraviolet therapy, 72
Unconscious (ucs), 4, 192, 218
Unconscious wishes, 6, 7
United Auto Workers Union, program for mentally ill, 90
Unstructured psychological test situation versus structured, 132

Van de Wall, W., 73
Varon, E., 36, 461
Veteran, 300
  contact representative, 301
  fact sheets, 307
  history of military service, 302, 304
  outpatient facilities, 304
  rights, 300
  social service, 303, 304
  special problems in psychotherapy, 304
Veterans Hospitals, and other mental hospitals, liaison between, 305

"Violent" patient, 149-151
Vocation, see Work
Vocational counselor, 83
Vocational rehabilitation, 99; see also Work
Vocational rehabilitation services
  counseling, 86
  governmental assistance, 86
  job finding and placement, 87
  restoration services, 87
  State Rehabilitation Bureau, 87
  training, 86
Vocational therapy, 74, 83; see also Work
Voluntary health insurance for mental illness, 447
Volunteer worker, 83, 175, 305
  "Adopt a Patient" program, 178
  "Adopt a Ward" program, 178
  aged, 207
  application form, 181
  barrier of language, 178
  child, 228
  college students as, 185
  ethics of, 184
  hospital co-operation with, 178
  hospital's responsibilities to, 179
  initiating program, 180
  occupational therapy, 82
  recruiting, 180
  relatives of patients as, 459
  screening, 180, 182
  selection, 180
  specific contribution, 175
  therapeutic community, 175
  training, 183
  "True-False Test," 182
  varieties of activities, 177
  ward work, 183
Vosburgh, P., 72

Waldfogel, S., 233
Walkiewicz, S. T., 85, 129
Ward management, 149
Ward procedures, 102
Watts, J., 49
Wechsler Bellevue Intelligence Scale, 133
Wechsler, D., 142, 264, 277
Wechsler, I. S., 291
Weihofen, H., 321, 430
Weinroth, L., 80
Weinstein, E. A., 54, 59, 106, 110, 291, 449
Wender, L., 38
Wernicke, C., 433
White, R. R., 129
Whitehorn, J. C., 196, 200, 409, 419

Wikler, A., 261
William Hodson Community Center, 207
Williams, D. C., 321
Willis, T., 279
Wish
  childhood, 39
  to be well, 54
  unconscious, 6
Witness
  as to fact, 425
  competence of, psychiatrically considered, 427
  expert, 425
  psychiatrist as, 424
  testimonial capacity, 427
Wolberg, L. R., 23
Woodward, L. I., 91
Word Association Test, 136
Work
  Barden-LaFollette Amendment (Public Law 113), in rehabilitating mentally ill, 86
  defensive functions of, 76
  epileptic as employee, 285
  industry and unions, programs for mentally ill, 90
  mental defective as employee, 269
  money as incentive, 85
  occupational history, 76, 83
  psychodrama in preparation for, 88
  rehabilitation program, 177
  role of motivation, 84
  selective placement, 86
  social service in rehabilitation, 88
  state rehabilitation laws for mentally ill, 86
  strength of ego and specific skills, 74
  therapeutic value, 195
  as sublimation, 75
  theory of, 74
  transition to extramural work, 86
  vocational counselor as therapist, 87
World Health Organization, Expert Committee on Mental Health, 358, 482
Writ of Habeas Corpus, in mental hospital, 425

X-ray, in mental hospital, 437

Yahraes, H., 291

Zehnder, J., 277
Zeman, F. D., 215
Zilboorg, G., 335
Zucker, H. D., 247